SYSTEMATIC EMBRYOLOGY
OF THE ANGIOSPERMS

SYSTEMATIC
EMBRYOLOGY
OF THE
ANGIOSPERMS

GWENDA L. DAVIS

DEPARTMENT OF BOTANY
UNIVERSITY OF NEW ENGLAND
ARMIDALE. N.S.W. AUSTRALIA

JOHN WILEY & SONS, INC.

NEW YORK · LONDON · SYDNEY

Library of Congress Catalog Card Number: 66-26739
Printed in the United States of America

ACKNOWLEDGMENTS

The preparation of a work such as this is a formidable task for a nonlinguist, but one which was eased considerably by the assistance of Professor N. C. W. Beadle of the Department of Botany, University of New England, in German translation and in checking the German titles in the bibliography. Nevertheless, he cannot be held responsible for errors which may have insinuated themselves during the final stages. I would like to thank Professor Beadle, also, for his interest in the project throughout and for reading the text. I am very grateful to the late Professor P. Maheshwari of the Department of Botany, University of Delhi, for his constructive criticism of the introductory section and for having sent me a photostat copy of Schnarf's classic work "Vergleichende Embryologie der Angiospermen." My thanks are also due to Mrs. Margaret Myers of the Botany Department, University of New England, for her assistance in checking the typescript.

Obtaining large numbers of microfilms and photocopies of articles in journals held elsewhere in Australia, as well as abroad, was made possible by a research grant from the University of New England.

Finally, I am indebted to the staff of the Dixon Library for arranging innumerable Inter-Library-Loans of periodicals and to Mrs. N. Pulle of the Central Embryological Library, Utrecht, for assistance in tracing some of the literature not available in Australia.

CONTENTS

SYSTEMATIC EMBRYOLOGY
OF THE ANGIOSPERMS

INTRODUCTION

To assess the relative merits of publications in angiosperm embryology is a difficult task, but special mention must be made of the works of Souèges, Schnarf, Maheshwari and Johansen, whose important contributions have stimulated interest in all processes relating to embryo formation.

Although the pursuit of any branch of knowledge should not require justification, that of angiosperm embryology has a special claim to attention in connection with the breeding and cultivation of crop and pasture plants. Breeding programs in most countries are almost exclusively cytology-centered, but it must be emphasized that unless a parallel embryological study is carried out on each species and hybrid in question, the problems involved are understood only in part. The somewhat facile assumption that all plants reproduce sexually is a rule-of-thumb approach and, although this may be true for the majority, the incidence of apomixis is probably higher than the records suggest. Selection for apomixis has practical possibilities as a means of obtaining true-breeding hybrids, but detailed embryological studies must accompany such work. Similarly, the possibility of adventive embryony must always be excluded in work on hybridization, for pollination may supply no more than the stimulus required to initiate nucellar budding and the origin of the functional embryo should not merely be assumed.

Far from the descriptive phase of angiosperm embryology being over, it is hardly begun and much that is published is too superficial to be of value. In the Compositae, for example, although there are over 300 publications, these concern species in only 15% of the genera, and most records cover only one aspect of embryology. In the Rosaceae, work has been directed almost entirely to embryo sac formation in hybrids and in cultivated species with a long history of selective breeding, and there is virtually no basis of comparison with their naturally occurring relatives. Finally, in 80 of the 411 families recognized by Hutchinson (1959), no information was traced on any embryological structure or process.

Ideally, plant breeders should familiarize themselves with all details involved in embryo formation in the plants they handle. In some countries this is routine procedure but in most it is regarded as an "old-fashioned" approach, since obtaining the information requires the use of techniques evolved during the preceding century.

Chiefly through the work of Indian and Russian botanists, the literature is growing rapidly but in a somewhat unbalanced manner, for some families attract many workers and others remain embryologically unknown. This state of affairs is self-perpetuating owing to the understandable tendency of workers to concentrate on families for which a bibliography can be assembled readily from previous work. The alternative to this approach is to incur the risk of the species having been investigated already, but the results published under a generalized title. After some personal experiences of this nature, this writer set out to compile an index of all published work on angiosperm embryology, and it is this index that forms the basis of the present book. The task has been of a greater magnitude than anticipated, and inevitably some papers will have been overlooked.

The term *embryology* is used in its broad sense, following Cave (1948), Maheshwari (1950d), and Schnarf (1929b). In justification, Cave's statement is sufficient that "in angiosperms, three generations, the old sporophyte, the gametophyte and the new sporophyte are concerned and these are so intimately involved in the origin and development of the embryo, that all three should be considered in any comprehensive study. Consequently, plant embryology in its widest sense, has to do with the development of the entire ovule and anther, including micro- and megasporogenesis, gametophytes, gametogenesis and growth of the embryo, endosperm, nucellus and integuments."

Because the present work is intended as a guide to future workers, the families are listed alphabetically, and are those recognized by Hutchinson (1959). No opinions are expressed on affinities between families or on the validity of the families themselves. The short factual description of embryological characters which accompanies each family is not intended as a review of previous work, and, in some cases, interesting controversial aspects have been excluded for brevity.

The aspect of embryology which has been most neglected covers events taking place in the anther and which are dismissed frequently, if they are mentioned at all, with the comment "the formation of pollen is normal"—whatever that may mean. Development of the anther wall is seldom described in detail, owing to the general impression that the same sequence of events occurs in all angiosperms and, with few exceptions, it is only certain of the Indian botanists who record the formation and fate of the wall layers as standard procedure. It is for this reason that what may be regarded as disproportionate emphasis has been placed on the processes leading up to pollen formation.

In describing embryo sac development, the terminology of Maheshwari (1948, 1950) has been followed and that of Johansen (1950) for embryogeny. The classification of embryo types put forward by Souèges (1934–51) and ably summarized by Crété (1963a) is more flexible in expressing relationships, but for the present purpose that of Johansen has the merit of expediency. Little attention has been devoted to embryogeny, since no compromise seems possible between that approach and the exhaustive treatment which merits a book in itself.

As the development and structure of the endosperm has been reviewed recently by Chopra and Sachar (1963), Swamy and Parameswaran (1963), and Wunderlich (1959), its treatment in the present work is brief. Information on the presence or absence of endosperm in the mature seed is available in texts on taxonomy, although it must be pointed out that in these the term *exalbuminous* is applied to instances where no endosperm is formed (Podostemaceae, Trapaceae, and most Orchidaceae), to those in which it is all digested during embryo growth, and finally even to those seeds where a single layer of endosperm cells persists (Compositae and others). Taxonomic conclusions based on the exalbuminous nature of the seed, therefore, have little or no value unless they are supported by a detailed study of the formation and fate of this tissue.

No reference is made to the development and structure of the seed coat, since this constitutes a special aspect.

The terms used for embryological processes, unless otherwise stated, are those adopted and described by Maheshwari (1950).

The references listed under each family are an indication of relevant published work, but not all of these have been available to the present author. To avoid considerable repetition, publications of a general nature and those concerned with the discussion of data rather than original reports are listed only in the bibliography and should be consulted in connection with all families. Titles enclosed in brackets are translations from the language of publication, which is usually Russian, Ukrainian, or Japanese. A supplementary list of references is included as an Appendix, but it has not been possible to incorporate the subject matter of these references in the text.

SYSTEMATIC AND TAXONOMIC CHARACTERS

All plants can be regarded as accumulations of characters, and those which vary discontinuously in their expression are the tools of classification. The practice of grouping like with like in a hierarchical system is *systematics*, but when an attempt is made for the system to express phylogeny as well as morphological agreement, the discipline is referred to as *taxonomy*. The title of this book, therefore, refers to *systematic* embryology, in that its aim is to list the embryological characteristics of families, although the families themselves are those recognized in the latest taxonomic system of classification.

Both systematic and taxonomic characters are those which enable the breaking-up of a vast array of forms into conveniently sized units, but whereas the first take no cognizance of convergent evolution, the second are intended to arrive at groups or taxons, the components of which are more closely related to each other than they are to members of other such groups. Because all such characters are determined genetically, all should indicate affinity, but in practice evolution does not proceed at the same rate in all parts of a plant and those characters which have survival value tend to be influenced by selection in such a manner that their basic expressions of affinity are obscured. For this reason, the most reliable characters on which to base a "natural" classification are those which appear to possess the least survival value, the assumption being that these characters will resemble most closely the basic form of any particular line of descent. The classification put forward by Hutchinson (1959), and followed in the present work, is based on this argument. In themselves, however, such characters are not absolute and their value must be reassessed for each taxon. For example, in one genus a species may be distinguished by the nature of the fruits, whereas in another these may be identical, but certain floral or vegetative features may show the discontinuous variation required to define the component species. In other words, *the nature of taxonomic characters varies with the taxon*.

Although taxonomic characters are traditionally and conveniently morphological, in those plants where developmental processes vary discontinuously, the processes themselves may be regarded as legitimate taxonomic characters, even though the results of the different processes are apparently morphologically identical. For this reason, every detail of embryology is of potential taxonomic value, but its actual value in this respect can only be established after routine examination of the same process in all apparently related species. It would be informative if such studies included plants grown under a variety of environmental conditions.

Cave (1959), B. M. Johri (1963b), P. Maheshwari (1950c,d, 1954b, 1958, 1959, 1963c, 1964), and Subramanyam (1962) have emphasized the importance of embryological characters in relation to particular cases, but until considerably more evidence is available this valuable source of information will remain largely unexploited.

TAXONOMIC EVALUATION OF EMBRYOLOGICAL CHARACTERS

Embryological characters, in the present context, refer to all processes and structures associated with sporogenesis, gametogenesis, and embryogeny. Because no such characters are consistently expressed throughout the angiosperms, their discontinuities are of interest insofar as the groups of individuals they demarcate may be compared with taxons based on gross morphology. Ideally, these should correspond, but the significance of any departure cannot be assessed until many more embryological data have been accumulated and the basis of embryological variation more throughly understood.

Hutchinson (1959) recognizes 411 families, of which 342 (83.2%) are dicotyledonous. At the outset, then, there is a dicotyledon to monocotyledon ratio of 5 to 1, so that any character which occurs in five times as many dicotyledonous as compared to monocotyledonous families has an equal frequency in the two groups. In view of the comparatively small number of families in which information is available for any embryological character, it is remarkable that this ratio is almost always so closely approximated. The fact that this does occur, however, supports the opinion of various authors that there is no embryological distinction between dicotyledons and monocotyledons.

In order to avoid generalities, an attempt is made to examine objectively all such characters which show discontinuous variation, and as far as possible to evaluate their importance as taxonomic characters. These will be discussed under appropriate headings, but in all cases the insufficiency of data makes any conclusions purely tentative.

ANTHER

Microsporangium. Information on the number of microsporangia comprising the anther is available in 218 families, of which 181 (83%) are dicotyledonous. The tetrasporangiate condition is commonest, occurring exclusively and constituting a family character in 190 families, of which 159 (83.6%) are dicotyledonous. The bisporangiate condition is characteristic of only 9 families, 2 of which are monocotyledonous, and the anthers of the Bixaceae are unique in being composed of 8 sporangia.

For a character so easily determined, it is surprising that information should be obtainable from the literature for only little over half the number of families. Probably one reason is the assumption that anthers are invariably tetrasporangiate, but another is the loose usage of the term *loculus*, which may refer either to the number of sporangia or to the cavities in the anther immediately prior to dehiscence. Accordingly, both bi- and tetrasporangiate anthers may be described as bilocular if in the latter the intersporangial septa break down before dehiscence. Unless a text figure clarifies matters, there is no means of deciding which condition pertains.

The number of microsporangia is consistent, and consequently represents a family character, in 199 families, but there are 18 families in which both sporangial types occur and in these this character is of generic significance. In *Persea gratissima*, however, both bi- and tetrasporangiate anthers alternate in the flower, and both types occur in the same flower in *Cucumis sativus* and *Echinocystis lobata*. In the Balsaminaceae it is only the cleistogamous flowers of *Impatiens fulva* which possess bisporangiate anthers. In the Adoxaceae the bisporangiate condition is more apparent than real, since it results from splitting of staminal primordia, and in the Moringaceae, according to Puri (1941), it is secondarily acquired by the two adaxial sporangia of each anther failing to develop. A reverse tendency has been reported in *Najas flexilis* (Campbell, 1897) and *Vallisneria spiralis* (Witmer, 1937), where the tetrasporangiate condition is attributed to subdivision by sterilization of groups of potentially sporogenous cells. Further investigations are required on the origins of both bi- and tetrasporangiate conditions before this character can be fully exploited taxonomically.

Anther wall formation. The fully formed anther wall has a dual ontogeny in that the region external to each microsporangium is derived from the primary parietal cells, whereas the tapetum and endothecium adjacent to the connective originate from specialization of pre-existing connective cells. The following discussion is concerned only with that portion of the anther wall that owes its formation to the activity of the primary parietal cells and their descendants.

Information is available for only 87 (21.1%) families, of which 77 (88.5%) are dictyledonous. Few authors have described the sequence of cell divisions involved in wall formation, but in some instances it has been possible to trace events from accurate text figures. The tendency is strong, however, to draw cells of adjacent parietal layers with the same arrangement as bricks in a wall, and such figures are virtually meaningless.

The origin of the anther wall in the Ericaceae and Gramineae has been discussed by Batygina, Teriokhin, Alimova, and Yakovlev (1963), but otherwise the significance of its method of formation has been overlooked.

The primary parietal layer originates by periclinal division of the archesporial cells, and in all angiosperms it undergoes a further periclinal division to form the two secondary parietal layers, which intervene between the epidermis and the sporogenous tissue. Discontinuous variation, however, is apparent in the behavior of the secondary parietal layers and, although the final product is an anther wall, it is achieved by a precise series of periclinal cell divisions. In almost all instances families have been found to be consistent in this respect, and because it is a character of no apparent survival value, the method of wall formation constitutes a taxonomic character at the family level.

It is on the behavior of the secondary parietal layers that the following four types of anther wall formation are based.

1. BASIC TYPE. On the assumption that both daughter cells of each primary parietal cell possess equal potentialities, those instances in which both cells undergo a periclinal division are more primitive than those in which such a division of one or the other cell is suppressed. This type, in which both secondary parietal layers divide periclinally, is regarded as that from which the other three types are derived, and is named accordingly (Fig. 1a). The resulting four cell layers usually differentiate as the endothecium, two middle layers, and tapetum, but because the potentiality to divide periclinally is a primitive features, those instances where one or both middle layers undergo further such divisions to form a wall of more than four cell layers in thickness are to be regarded as exhibiting an archaic feature.

The Basic type of wall formation has been described exclusively only in the Anacardiaceae, Elatinaceae, Ficoidaceae, Lecythidaceae, Nyctaginaceae, Rhamnaceae, Tiliaceae, Vitaceae, and Winteraceae.

2. DICOTYLEDONOUS TYPE. This is derived from the Basic type by suppression of periclinal division in the inner secondary parietal layer, which develops directly into the tapetum. The outer secondary parietal layer, however, gives rise to two layers, the outermost forming the endothecium and the inner the single middle layer (Fig. 1b). By this method three wall layers are formed, but it is not unusual for at least some cells of the middle layer to divide again.

This type of wall formation is the most common and is characteristic of 43 families, or half of those investigated. Its name is suggested by the preponderance of dicotyledonous families, the Taccaceae being the only monocotyledonous representative. The families in which the Dicotyledonous type of wall formation is the only one described are: Acanthaceae, Annonaceae, Aristolochiaceae, Asclepiadaceae, Bignoniaceae, Boraginaceae, Campanulaceae, Caprifoliaceae, Circaeasteraceae, Compositae, Convolvulaceae, Cuscutaceae, Dipsacaceae, Dipterocarpaceae, Ehretiaceae, Gentianaceae, Gesneriaceae, Illecebraceae,

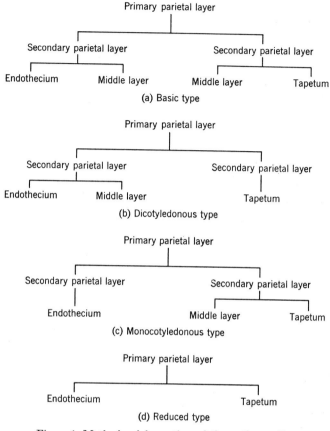

Figure 1. Methods of formation of the anther wall.

Labiateae, Lobeliaceae, Lythraceae, Malvaceae, Menispermaceae, Opiliaceae, Orobanchaceae, Papilionaceae, Pedaliaceae, Periplocaceae, Polemoniaceae, Polygalaceae, Ranunculaceae, Rubiaceae, Santalaceae, Schisandraceae, Scrophulariaceae, Solanaceae, Sonneratiaceae, Stylidiaceae, Styracaceae, Taccaceae, Umbelliferae, Vacciniaceae, Valerianaceae.

3. MONOCOTYLEDONOUS TYPE. This is a parallel type to the preceding one in that the secondary parietal layers show reverse behavior. In this case it is the outer secondary parietal layer in which periclinal division is suppressed and it develops directly into the endothecium, while its inner counterpart forms the middle layer and the tapetum (Fig. 1c). This type of wall formation is characteristic of the Agavaceae, Alismataceae, Amarantaceae, Aponogetonaceae, Balanitaceae, Butomaceae, Chenopodiaceae, Cruciferae, Cyperaceae, Dioscoreaceae,

Droseraceae, Fumariaceae, Gramineae, Halorrhagaceae, Hydrocharitaceae, Liliaceae, Linaceae, Loranthaceae, Molluginaceae, Moraceae, Orchidaceae, Petiveriaceae, Piperaceae, Polygonaceae, Portulacaceae, Salicaceae.

Although in actual numbers the dicotyledonous families predominate, this type is conformed to by 10 out of the 13 monocotyledonous families for which details of anther wall development are available, which suggested the name.

4. REDUCED TYPE. This is the most advanced method of wall formation. Its essential feature is the suppression of all periclinal divisions in the secondary parietal cells, each layer developing directly into a mature tissue (Fig. 1d). No middle layers are formed, and the fully developed anther wall is composed only of two subepidermal cell layers, the endothecium and the tapetum. This type occurs in all species examined of the Lemnaceae and Najadaceae, and some association with habitat might be suspected, if it were not for Chou's (1952) description of this type in *Gaultheria*. Unfortunately, wall formation has not been traced in any other members of the Ericaceae.

5. FAMILIES WITH MIXED TYPES OF ANTHER WALL FORMATION. In 6 dicotyledonous families, two types of wall formation have been reported among the component species. In the Thymelaeaceae, *Lasiosiphon eriocephalus* conforms to the Monocotyledonous type, but *Wikstroemia canescens* to the Basic type, as does *Pterospermum sterculia*, although other members of the Sterculiaceae follow the Dicotyledonous type. Similarly, the Combretaceae is characterized by the Basic type, except for *Guiera senegalensis*, where only a single middle layer is formed, although its origin was not traced. In the Euphorbiaceae, the Monocotyledonous type is represented by *Acalypha* and *Phyllanthus*, but the Dicotyledonous type by *Euphorbia*. An interesting condition occurs in the Caryophyllaceae where, in *Stellaria media*, P. C. Joshi (1936a) and N. Pal (1952) have described respectively the Dicotyledonous and the Monocotyledonous types of wall formation. This is the only example in which this character has not been consistent, at least at the generic level, and consequently requires further investigation.

Constituents of the anther wall. ENDOTHECIUM. Except in anthers with pore dehiscence, the outermost parietal layer develops characteristic ("fibrous") thickenings, whose variation in form was reviewed by Kuhn (1908). These thickenings are apparently associated with the mechanics of anther dehiscence and are not present on the endothecial cells at the dehiscence points. In some instances (*Agave, Amyema, Argemone, Crinum, Olax, Oxychloe*, and the Zingiberaceae generally), one or more of the underlying middle layers may develop similar thickenings, whereas in the Orobanchaceae and Zingiberaceae some epidermal cells may become similarly differentiated.

Although the endothecium is usually a single cell layer, periclinal divisions sometimes occur soon after its formation. In *Juncus effusus*, *J. prismatocarpus, Strombosia*, and several members of the Schisandraceae, it becomes irregularly 2-layered, but in the Eucommiaceae there are 2 complete layers and in *Chelone glabra* the 4 to 8 fibrous layers are of endothecial origin.

The endothecium itself appears to have no taxonomic value, but a detailed study of the types of thickenings might yield interesting information.

MIDDLE LAYERS. The initial number of middle layers formed in any anther depends on the type of wall formation, 2 such layers being formed in the Basic type, a single layer in both Dicotyledonous and Monocotyledonous types, and none in the Reduced type. In 190 families for which information is available, a single middle layer is characteristic of only 67 families, whereas more than one such layer is found in 113 families, and in 10 families the condition is variable. For example, in the Anacardiaceae, Combretaceae, and Meliaceae usually 2 or 3 middle layers are formed, but in *Rhus mysurensis, Guiera senegalensis* and *Cipadessa baccifera* only a single layer is present, and in the Cruciferae 1, 2, or 3 middle layers are characteristic of particular species. In the Melastomataceae, Scrophulariaceae, and Verbenaceae, although a single middle layer is usual, certain exceptions have been described. *Melastoma malabathricum*, for example, has a thick anther wall which includes up to 7 middle layers, of which the outer 2 or 3 layers are persistent, whereas in *Chelone glabra* and *Avicennia officinalis* 2 or 3 middle layers are invariably formed. Development of the 10 to 12 parietal layers in *Agave* and *Doryanthes* has not been traced, although their origin is of particular interest taxonomically.

Cells of the middle layers lack the ability to divide anticlinally; therefore because the tissue cannot adjust itself to the multiplying and expanding sporogeneous cells within each sporangium, it is crushed against the relatively unyielding endothecium. For this reason, the middle layers almost invariably degenerate early and their formation is regarded as a relic feature. Only those cells which possess some special means of mechanical thickening persist until anther dehiscence.

TAPETUM. This is a highly specialized wall layer whose development is, to some extent, controlled by events taking place in the adjacent sporogenous tissue and which, in turn, appears to play a part in the nutrition of the pollen grains. This tissue has not received the attention it deserves and information on its nature is available only in 231 families, of which 79.6% are dicotyledonous. Two main types of tapetum are recognized, the glandular, or secretory, and the amoeboid, but the relationship between them and the nature of subtypes is not clear.

A glandular tapetum is characteristic of 181 families, of which 87% are dicotyledonous, and an exclusively amoeboid tapetum has been described in 29 families, 11 being dicotyledonous, and both tapetal types have been reported in the remaining 21 families. Although the records are insufficient for generalizations, a glandular tapetum appears to predominate slightly in the dicotyledons and an amoeboid one in the monocotyledons. In 210 families the nature of the tapetum is a family character, but the 21 families in which both types have been reported require further investigation. If this information is confirmed, the character would then assume generic or specific status. Greater use should be made of crushes and dissections in studying the tapetum, preferably by using living material because poor fixation may distort the cells. Moreover, conclusions based entirely on a few sections can be very misleading. Nuclear divisions and fusions are a common feature of tapetal cells, and the suggestion that their mitotic activity is a "sympathetic" reaction to the onset of meiosis in the adjacent microspore mother cells has been put forward by G. L. Davis (1961a).

Although the tapetum consists fundamentally of a single cell layer, there are reports of occasional periclinal divisions which result in its becoming irregularly 2-layered. This is not a consistent character in any taxon, and it appears to be the expression of a latent potentiality to periclinal division which is possessed by all parietal cells. In the Asclepiadaceae, a 2- or 3-layered tapetum occurs in several genera, and in *Calotropis* it becomes multilayered. A connection between the Dicotyledonous type of wall formation and periclinal divisions in the tapetum is worth investigation, since in this type, although the inner secondary parietal layer develops directly into the tapetum, differentiation is not completed until the endothecium and middle layer have formed. In other words, during the time lag while its sister layer is dividing periclinally, some cells of the future tapetum may behave in a similar manner. In other instances, it is possible that when the spindle of a tapetal mitosis is orientated anticlinally, the formation of a cell plate across its equator may be followed by periclinal cell division.

The origin and function of the Ubisch granules is obscure, but they have been reported only in association with a glandular tapetum. There are insufficient records to assess the taxonomic value of these granules, which have been recorded in the Acanthaceae, Amarantaceae, Amaryllidaceae, Aristolochiaceae, Bixaceae, Bombacaceae, Cuscutaceae, Cyclanthaceae, Cyperaceae, Euphorbiaceae, Gentianaceae, Linaceae, Molluginaceae, Moringaceae, Olacaceae, Pedaliaceae, Portulacaceae, Rhamnaceae and Verbenaceae.

Sporogenous tissue. The number of premeiotic mitoses intervening between the formation of archesporial cells and microspore mother cells is so seldom recorded that no analysis was attempted. There is some evidence to suggest that the number of such divisions may be constant, at least at the generic level.

Microsporogenesis. Because details of cytokinesis in the microspore mother cells in relation to meiosis is a well-known taxonomic character, it is surprising that information has been traced for only 234 families. Simultaneous cytokinesis is characteristic of 186 families, of which 176 (94.6%) are dicotyledonous, whereas the successive type alone is found in 40 families, 35 being monocotyledonous. On the other hand, both types have been reported in the Agavaceae, Annonaceae, Apocynaceae, Aponogetonaceae, Aristolochiaceae, Asclepiadaceae, Liliaceae, and Palmaceae. That the successive method is the more primitive is suggested by reports in several families of ephemeral cell plate formation across the heterotypic spindle preceding simultaneous cytokinesis.

The arrangement of microspores in the tetrads is determined by the orientation of the homotypic spindles and is commonly tetrahedral, isobilateral, or decussate. T-shaped and linear tetrads are of occasional occurrence intermixed with other types in the sporangium, but linear tetrads alone are characteristic of the Asclepiadaceae.

Microspores are usually liberated from the tetrads, and the pollen is shed as single grains, but in the Hydrostachyaceae, Nepenthaceae, Periplocaceae, and Winteraceae they invariably remain together as permanent tetrads. In other families (Annonaceae, Apocynaceae, Droseraceae, Empetraceae, Epacridaceae, Ericaceae, Goodeniaceae, and Juncaceae) the formation of permanent tetrads is exhibited only by certain genera, whereas in the Podostemaceae pollen is shed as single grains, tetrads, and dyads. The liberation of either single grains or tetrads is a generic character in the Mimosaceae and Orchidaceae, although in the former certain genera are characterized by polyads and in the latter by tetrads, massulae, and pollinia, and in the Asclepiadaceae the formation of pollinia is general. The pollen grains of the Cyperaceae are unique and described either as cryptotetrads or pseudomonads.

Male gametophyte. Information is available for 243 families, of which 81.8% are dicotyledonous. The number of cells comprising the male gametophyte when the pollen is shed is constant in 192 families, 137 being characterized by the 2-celled condition, and of these 115 are dicotyledonous, whereas the 3-celled condition is present in 55 families, including 41 dicotyledonous families. In the remaining 51 families this character is variable, occasionally within the same species.

OVULE

Ovule morphology. Excluding the Balanophoraceae and Lorantha-ceae, where ovules as such are not formed, information has been derived from 315 families, 266 (84%) being dicotyledonous. Ovule morphology is constant in 248 families, of which 204 are characterized by the anatropous form, and among these 84.6% are dicotyledonous. Ortho-tropous ovules are typical of 20 families, 14 being dicotyledonous, and hemianatropous ovules occur exclusively in 13 families. In the Phytolaccaceae the ovules are invariably anacampylotropous, and the campylotropous form represents a family character in the Capparida-ceae, Chenopodiaceae, Petiveriaceae, Philesiaceae, and Ruppiaceae. Amphitropous ovules are characteristic of the Cneoraceae, Crossosoma-taceae, Cynocrambaceae, and Leitneriaceae, but the Cactaceae is the only family in which the ovules are invariably circinotropous. In the remaining 67 families ovule form is a generic character, two or more types occurring within each family. The most variable family in this respect is the Papilionaceae where, according to the genus, ovules are anatropous, hemianatropous, amphitropous, or campylotropous.

Integuments. Among the 319 families from which data were derived, 82.7% are dicotyledonous. The bitegmic condition characterizes 208 families, of which 155 are dicotyledonous as are also the 90 families whose ovules are exclusively unitegmic. However, in 15 families, 2 of which are monocotyledonous, the number of integuments is either a generic or a specific character and in the Olacaceae those of *Liriosma, Olax imbricata,* and *Ptychopetalum* are ategmic. In the Myzodendraceae although a nucellar papilla forms, no integuments are differentiated. Aril development and its occurrence in angiosperms have been discussed by Corner (1949, 1953), who has also reported the postfertilization formation of a fourth integument in some members of the Annonaceae. The number of integuments, as such, is of doubtful value as a taxonomic character unless supported by developmental studies, because both conditions may be more apparent than real. In *Lannea* and *Rhus* the single integumentary initial splits and consequently the ovules are secondarily bitegmic, whereas it has been pointed out by Maheshwari (1950) that unitegmic ovules may result from the suppression of one integument or the early fusion of integumentary primordia.

Micropyle. In bitegmic ovules the number and nature of integuments which form the micropyle is a taxonomic character. Information has been drawn from 189 families, of which 143 are dicotyledonous, and in 88 of these the micropyle is formed by the inner integument. In 74 families both integuments are involved, and in only 4 families is the micropyle composed of the outer integument. In the remaining families, the components of the micropyle are constant only within genera. In the Trapaceae and certain members of the Commelinaceae and Euphorbiaceae, micropyle formation is prevented by the presence of a long nucellar beak, whereas in *Macadamia* the growth of the integuments is so slow that they do not enclose the nucellus until after fertilization.

Endothelium. In 57 families the innermost layer of the integument usually differentiates as an endothelium when it comes in contact with the embryo sac after degeneration of the intervening nucellar cells. However, in the Acanthaceae and Loganiaceae, where this contact is always achieved, an endothelium is formed only in certain members, and it has not been reported in the Diapensiaceae although the nucellus breaks down early. The formation of an endothelium is mainly a character of tenuinucellate ovules, and its presence is a taxonomic character at the family level in 54 instances.

A false endothelium is characteristic of the Begoniaceae and Droseraceae, where persisting lateral nucellar cells elongate radially and form a jacket around the embryo sac.

Obturator. Any structure which appears to be associated with directing the growing pollen tube toward the micropyle is referred to as an obturator, but its taxonomic value, if any, is not clear. The commonest type is the funicular obturator, which is a local swelling of the funicle, and has been reported in the Acanthaceae, Alstroemeriaceae, Anacardiaceae, Boraginaceae, Cyperaceae, Labiateae, Linaceae, Magnoliaceae, Rubiaceae, and Tecophilaeaceae. A variation of this form is seen in *Crinum* where the funicle becomes knee-shaped, and in the Combretaceae long papillate cells extend from the funicle to the micropyle. A placental obturator occurs in the Cuscutaceae and Euphorbiaceae, but in the Meliaceae it is composed of placental hairs. In the Garryaceae and Molluginaceae both funicular and placental obturators are represented, but elongate cells which extend from the base of the style to the micropyle have been reported only in the Thymelaeaceae. The reverse arrangement of cells at the lip of the inner integument forming long hairs which reach the stylar canal has been described in *Leucosyke* and *Myriocarpa*.

Nucellus. Loose usage of the terms *crassinucellar* and *tenuinucellar* has resulted in some confusion in the literature. In the present work, *crassinucellar* is restricted to those ovules in which the archesporial cell cuts off a primary parietal cell, whether this cell undergoes division or not, and a *tenuinucellar* ovule is one in which the archesporial cell develops directly into the megaspore mother cell. A new term, *pseudocrassinucellar*, is now introduced to describe those ovules in which no primary parietal cell is formed, but in which the apical cells of the nucellar epidermis divide periclinally and give rise to a nucellar cap. In such instances although the megaspore mother cell may be deeply buried, the overlying cells are epidermal derivatives and are arranged in radiating rows. No special term is employed for crassinucellar ovules which develop a nucellar cap, but this occurrence is noted under the families concerned.

Nucellar details are available for 314 families, 260 (82.8%) of which are dicotyledonous. The crassinucellar condition is characteristic of 179 families, 143 of which are dicotyledonous, whereas tenuinucellar ovules occur in 105 families, 94 of these being dicotyledonous. The possession of pseudocrassinucellar ovules characterizes 11 families, 4 of which are dicotyledonous. The nature of the nucellus constitutes a generic or specific character in the Aquifoliaceae, Boraginaceae, Caprifoliaceae, Celastraceae, Convolvulaceae, Cornaceae, Cruciferae, Droseraceae, Ehretiaceae, Escalloniaceae, Gramineae, Icacinaceae, Liliaceae, Linaceae, Olacaceae, Ranunculaceae, Saururaceae, Ulmaceae, Umbelliferae.

Megasporogenesis. Data have been obtained for 292 families, 82.8% of which are dicotyledonous. In 221 families cytokinesis is successive, each meiotic division being followed by wall formation and resulting in a tetrad of megaspores. In most cases the spindles of both divisions are parallel to the long axis of the megaspore mother cell and the tetrad is linear, but it is not unusual for the homotypic spindle in the micropylar dyad cell to form at right angles to that in the dyad cell and give rise to a T-shaped tetrad. This arrangement of mega-spores is usually quite fortuitous and has no taxonomic significance except in *Rheum* and *Rumex* where it constitutes a generic character. In the Crassulaceae, Hydrocharitaceae, and Musaceae there have been reports of the occasional occurrence of isobilateral, tetrahedral and ⊥-shaped tetrads respectively.

Although each megaspore has equal potentialities, it is usually the chalazal which gives rise to the embryo sac, and the remaining three degenerate. However, in *Asarum canadense, Furcraea andina*, the Balanophoraceae, the Onagraceae, and the tribe Calenduleae (Compositae), the micropylar megaspore is functional. In *Schizomeria serrata* the functioning of the subchalazal megaspore is a specific character and, although this is usually the case in *Aristotelia manqui, A. racemosa*, and *Weinmannia fraxinea*, it is not invariable. In *Rubus* any megaspore may give rise to an embryo sac, but in *Rosa* the micropylar is usually functional.

Suppression of cytokinesis in the micropylar dyad cell after the homotypic nuclear division results in the formation of a row of 3 cells ("triad"), consisting of two basal megaspores and an upper 1- or 2-nucleate dyad cell. This behavior is characteristic of the Connaraceae, although it is of occasional occurrence in 23 other families. Singh (1954) has reported an unusual condition in *Hedera nepalensis* where, usually, only the micropylar dyad cell undergoes cytokinesis and the upper megaspore forms the monosporic embryo sac.

When the homotypic division is not followed by cytokinesis in either dyad cell, a bisporic embryo sac develops usually from the chalazal cell. In *Ammobium alatum, Cassiope mertensiana*, and *Tridax trilobata*, however, both meiotic divisions are completed before wall formation and in the first two examples the "coenomegaspore" becomes divided into a pair of 2-nucleate cells. In *Tridax*, however, the arrangement of megaspore nuclei is such that cytokinesis usually results in a row of 3 cells and Hjelmqvist (1951) describes the bisporic embryo sac developing from the central 2-nucleate cell. With the elimination of cytokinesis in relation to meiosis, the four megaspore nuclei remain in the common cytoplasm of the megaspore mother cell and the "coenomegaspore" develops into a tetrasporic embryo sac.

The formation of aggressive haustoria from all megaspores of a tetrad has been described in *Galium lucidum, Putoria calabrica, Rosularia pallida*, and *Sedum sempervivoides*.

Female gametophyte formation. Information is available for 295 families, of which 245 (83%) are dicotyledonous. The Polygonum type is characteristic of 239 families, 207 of these being dicotyledonous. The Allium type of embryo sac development represents a family character in the Alismataceae, Datiscaceae, Malpighiaceae, and Theaceae whereas, among tetrasporic embryo sacs, the Adoxa type characterizes the Adoxaceae, the Drusa type appears to be invariable in the Limnanthaceae and in the Penaeaceae and Onagraceae embryo sac formation follows the Penaea and Oenothora types respectively.

In 48 families two or more types of development have been reported, the commonest combination being the Polygonum and Allium types, which occurs in 23 families. The Caprifoliaceae, Caryophyllaceae, Commelinaceae, Orchidaceae, Solanaceae, and Trilliaceae all contain members with Polygonum, Allium, or Adoxa types of embryo sac development, but other combinations of two or more types are found in several families. The Compositae, Euphorbiaceae, and Liliaceae exhibit the greatest variation in this character. In the Euphorbiaceae, the Polygonum, Allium, Adoxa, Drusa, Fritillaria and Penaea types occur, and in the Compositae and Liliaceae embryo sac development may follow the Polygonum, Allium, Scilla, Adoxa, Drusa and Fritillaria types.

The formation of different types of embryo sacs within the same species, and even by the same individual, has been reviewed by Hjelmqvist (1964), and the same occurrence within the Composite capitulum is described in detail by Harling (1950, 1951a,b).

In examining the variation in female gametophyte formation within families, the suspicion arises that a relationship may exist between the extent of this variation and the number of embryological investigations. Although this may be true for certain families, it is reassuring that in the Gramineae, apart from apomixis, only the Polygonum type has been reported in nearly 280 records.

Mature embryo sacs, including those of apomictic origin, are remarkably similar in their organization and it is seldom possible to deduce their origin by inspection of the fully developed structure. The expression "a normal 8-nucleate embryo sac" is meaningless, for if its development has been traced it should be referred to a specific type and if not the assumption of normality, whatever that may be, is of questionable value.

Embryo sac components. SYNERGIDS. Before the taxonomic value of synergid morphology can be assessed, authors must provide more accurate information than is customary. The statement "synergids sometimes hooked" suggests that this is a variable character within the species, but, although this may be true in certain cases, the so-called hooks are really folds of the wall which develop as the cell ages. For observations to be of value and to avoid comparisons between developmental stages, the form of the synergids should always be recorded in embryo sacs awaiting fertilization. Similarly, the filiform apparatus is seen to advantage only in mature cells, and careful staining may be required to demonstrate it.

Among the 295 families in which information is available, 59 contain members with hooked synergids, in 20 the filiform apparatus has been reported, and in a further 56 families both characters occur, although not necessarily in the same species. In no family is either character invariably exhibited, which suggests that their taxonomic value may lie at the generic or specific level. The possession of apical caps on the synergids appears to be consistent in the Grossulariaceae, but elsewhere these have been reported only in *Helianthemum vulgare* and *Sedum ternatum,* and those of *Pahira rosea* are bordered by a frilled rim.

Enlarged synergids occur in the Hydrocharitaceae, Juncaceae, Martyniaceae, Stylidiaceae, and Styracaceae, and in *Ceropegia, Corchorus, Sparrmania, Spiranthes,* and *Triumfetta* they are considerably elongated and occupy one-third to one-half the length of the embryo sac.

Usually the synergids are wholly enclosed within the embryo sac but instances where their tips enter the micropyle occur in the Brunoniaceae, Clethraceae, and Compositae. In some species of Compositae and Ericaceae they penetrate the micropyle deeply, and in the Gesneriaceae they extend throughout its whole length.

Haustorial synergids have been reported in *Ursinia, Calendula,* and *Cotula,* but their most elaborate development is in *Quinchamalium chilense* where their apices elongate as tubular outgrowths which penetrate the style for one-third of its length.

POLAR NUCLEI. Three types of behavior of the polar nuclei are known. In the first their fusion occurs prior to fertilization and, after the resulting secondary nucleus is fertilized, it forms the primary endosperm nucleus. In the second type the polar nuclei remain distinct although closely associated, and fusion occurs only after one has been fertilized. In this, as well as in the succeeding type, the primary endosperm nucleus forms without the intervention of a secondary nucleus. The third type of behavior is the true "triple fusion," where the polar nuclei and the male gamete fuse simultaneously.

There is little exact information in the literature on the behavior of the polar nuclei and the statement that they fuse "at fertilization" is not sufficiently specific to be of value. Since in each case the final product is the primary endosperm nucleus, the method by which this is achieved is a possible taxonomic character. In the Penaea, Peperomia, and Plumbago types of embryo sacs where more than 2 polar nuclei are formed, their fusion seems to be completed before the entry of the male gamete.

The region of the embryo sac in which the polar nuclei become closely associated does not appear to be of taxonomic significance except for the connection between the chalazal position of the secondary nucleus and the formation of Helobial endosperm (Schnarf and Wunderlich, 1939).

ANTIPODALS. In the undifferentiated 8-nucleate embryo sac, irrespective of the number of megaspores involved in its formation, cytokinesis is initiated at the chalazal pole and usually proceeds in an orderly manner toward the micropyle. In the Cyclanthaceae, Cannaceae, Hydnoraceae, Hydrostachyaceae, Sapotaceae, Scheuchzeriaceae, and Thismiaceae, however, the 3 antipodal nuclei are not enclosed in cells and soon degenerate. This feature is of occasional occurrence and appears to represent a generic character in certain members of the Araliaceae, Hydrophyllaceae, Illecebraceae, Lauraceae, Liliaceae, Linaceae, Marcgraviaceae, Menyanthaceae, Musaceae, Myrtaceae, Orchidaceae, Palmaceae, Pontederiaceae, Verbenaceae, and Xyridaceae.

In most instances, however, the antipodal nuclei are enclosed in 3, 2, or, rarely, 1 cell, which may degenerate at once or persist into postfertilization stages. The commonest condition is when the antipodal cells commence degeneration just before or soon after fertilization, without any appreciable alteration in size. However, the cells become enlarged in certain members of the Aristolochiaceae, Asclepiadaceae, Capparidaceae, Commelinaceae, Compositae, Ericaceae, Fumariaceae, Globulariaceae, Gramineae, Icacinaceae, Lentibulariaceae, Papaveraceae, Podophyllaceae, Primulaceae, Rhamnaceae, and Xanthorrhoeaceae, whereas those of *Ceropegia, Cynanchum, Fumaria, Lysimachia,* and *Rudbeckia,* in particular, bear a resemblance to the egg apparatus. In *Gaultheria, Maerua,* and some of the Helleboraceae and Ranunculaceae the antipodals occupy at least half the embryo sac. Degeneration of the two lower antipodal cells, and enlargement of the upper almost to the center of the embryo sac, is seen in *Pinguicula vulgaris* and occasionally in *Utricularia flexuosa.*

Nuclear division results in coenocytic antipodal cells in certain members of the Compositae, Hydrangeaceae, Marantaceae, Palmaceae, Polygalaceae, Polygonaceae, Ranunculaceae, and Stackhousiaceae. Although usually the cells become 2- or 3-nucleate, up to 12 nuclei have been reported in those of *Hepatica acutiloba* and *Polygala sibirica*, and this number is also approached in some of the Compositae.

In 49 families nuclear division in the antipodals is accompanied commonly by cell division. The extent of this secondary multiplication varies from the formation of 4 to 6 cells to the extreme instances of 100 cells in *Piper nigrum*, 150 in *Sparganium simplex*, and the record number of at least 300 in *Sasa paniculata*.

Haustorial activity has been attributed to the antipodal cells of *Aristolochia clematitis*, *Asarum* spp., *Areca catechu*, and those members of the Compositae in which the antipodals persist in an apparently healthy condition during early embryogeny. Aggressive haustorial activity has been reported in *Artemisia arborescens*, *A. triternata*, *Bidens pilosa*, *Coreopsis tinctoria*, *Cosmos sulphureus*, *Grindelia squarrosa*, *Gutierrezia*, *Haplopappus ciliatus*, and *Othonna carnosa* where at least the lowest antipodal cell penetrates deeply into the chalaza, sometimes reaching the loculus in *A. triternata*. Such records, however, should be accepted with caution in view of the remarkable resemblance in the supporting figures between the supposedly haustorial cell and an embryo sac developing by somatic apospory in the chalaza.

Phenomenon of "strike." Whereas secondary multiplication of antipodals increases the number of cells in the embryo sac, "strike" (Harling, 1951a) has the reverse effect as certain nuclei of the developing embryo sac fail to undergo some or all of the postmeiotic mitoses. Only the chalazal nuclei are affected and "strike" may express itself at any point in embryo sac development. In the tetrasporic Drusa type of embryo sac the theoretical complement of 16 nuclei is seldom attained because of one or more chalazal nuclei failing to divide or, in other words, exhibiting "strike," and the number of antipodal cells is reduced accordingly. The 6- and 5-nucleate embryo sacs which occur in the Alismataceae, Butomaceae, and Orchidaceae have originated in this manner, and in all instances where less than 8 nuclei are formed, it is some or all of the antipodal cells that are not represented in the mature embryo sac.

The ultimate expression of strike is shown in certain members of the Compositae, Cornaceae, Limnanthaceae, and Scrophulariaceae where, although embryo sac development is tetrasporic, the 3 lower megaspore nuclei degenerate soon after completion of meiosis. In such embryo sacs their components are all derived from a single megaspore nucleus and for this reason they may be referred to as pseudomono-sporic. A similar condition occurs in the Podostemaceae where only the upper of the 2 megaspore nuclei in the functional dyad cell under-goes the postmeiotic mitoses and the lower degenerates. The resulting embryo sac is also pseudomonosporic but is commonly spoken of as a reduced Allium type.

The taxonomic significance of strike is not clear. It appears to occur in relatively few families but it may be more general than the records indicate. It is of occasional occurrence in the Adoxaceae, where the basal megaspore nucleus fails to divide and the 7-nucleate embryo sac contains only 2 antipodal cells, but varying degrees of strike are particularly associated with the Drusa type of embryo sac development.

Apomixis. In view of the recent review by Battaglia (1963) it is not proposed to discuss this process in any detail. Once regarded as an abnormality, it is now known to be the usual method of repro-duction in some species, and it occurs occasionally in others. Battag-lia's definition of the process, which excludes adventive embryony, as well as his terminology, have been accepted in the present work.

It seems unlikely that apomixis has any value as a taxonomic char-acter, since the concept of the species as an evolutionary unit is based on the assumption that each is made up of a series of potentially interbreeding populations. Obligate apomicts represent an evolution-ary dead end and, although selection for apomixis could be a valuable method of producing true-breeding hybrids, the process itself is merely a sophisticated form of vegetative reproduction.

Although there is evidence in the Gramineae that apomixis is geneti-cally controlled, according to Hjelmqvist and Grazi (1964) the inci-dence of apomictic embryo sacs in *Limonium transwallianum* increases in plants grown in a warm glasshouse as compared to those grown under cool conditions or outside.

Of the two major types of apomixis, gonial (generative) apospory has been reported in the Amarantaceae, Amaryllidaceae, Balanophora-ceae, Burmanniaceae, Compositae, Gramineae, Plumbaginaceae, Rosa-ceae, and Urticaceae, whereas somatic apospory occurs in the Com-positae, Globulariaceae, Gramineae, Papilionaceae, and Rosaceae.

Endosperm. Of the 288 families for which information is available, 82.6% are dicotyledonous. The unsatisfactory nature of many records of endosperm formation is particularly apparent in the Nuclear type, which requires careful observation at the earliest stages in order to distinguish it from the Helobial type with a very small primary chal-

azal chamber. Such a structure is overlooked easily and the free-nuclear divisions in the large primary micropylar chamber would then
be interpreted as indicating Nuclear endosperm. Schnarf and Wunderlich (1939) have drawn attention to a relationship between the chalazal position of the secondary nucleus or of the closely associated
polar nuclei and the formation of Helobial endosperm. Although this
may not hold for all cases, it is a valuable guide and particular
attention should be paid to any such species where the endosperm
appears to be Nuclear.

As the records stand, the possession of Nuclear endosperm is a
consistent character of 161 families, 83% of which are dicotyledonous,
and the Helobial type is characteristic of 17 families, 14 of which
are monocotyledonous. In families with only one type of endosperm
formation, the Nuclear type occurs with equal frequency in both dicotyledons and monocotyledons, whereas the Helobial predominates sub-
stantially in monocotyledons. On the other hand, the invariable formation of *ab initio* Cellular endosperm is found in 79 families, all being
dicotyledonous except the Araceae and the Lemnaceae. In each of
29 families, however, 2 or 3 endosperm types are represented. The
Nuclear and Cellular combination is the most frequent and occurs
in the Alangiaceae, Asclepiadaceae, Buxaceae, Compositae, Gentianaceae, Halorrhagaceae, Hydrophyllaceae, Lauraceae, Nymphaceae,
Philadelphaceae, Piperaceae, Rubiaceae, Vacciniaceae, and Winteraceae. Both Nuclear and Helobial endosperm are reported in the
Agavaceae, Alismataceae, Amaryllidaceae, Hypoxidaceae, Linaceae,
Spigeliaceae, and Trilliaceae where some records of the Nuclear type
are doubtful. In the Olacaceae, Santalaceae, and Thismiaceae, both
Cellular and Helobial types occur, and all three endosperm types
are found in the Boraginaceae and Solanaceae. Finally, in the Podostemaceae, Trapaceae, and commonly in the Orchidaceae, no endosperm
is formed.

ENDOSPERM HAUSTORIA. In 23 families characterized by Nuclear endosperm, the embryo sac undergoes postfertilization elongation and
usually its base invades the chalaza, but a lateral diverticulum is
formed in certain of the Limnanthaceae and Papilionaceae. In the
Caryophyllaceae 1 or 2 diverticula arise from the side or extremities
of the embryo sac during postfertilization stages. In the Droseraceae,
Solanaceae, and Tecophilaeaceae the base of the embryo sac is either
nonaggressive or only weakly haustorial, but otherwise it forms a
haustorial tube which becomes considerably elongated in the Rosaceae.
The longest such haustoria are found in the Euphorbiaceae and Cucur-

bitaceae, those of *Croton klotzschianus* and *C. sparsiflorus* reaching
1000μ, and in *Cucurbita ficifolia* the record length of 12000μ is attained. After a period of free-nuclear division the endosperm proper
becomes cellular, but wall formation does not occur in any but the
short haustoria.

In species with *ab initio* Cellular or Helobial endosperm, the haustoria are more varied in their origin and form than those associated
with Nuclear endosperm. The Fouquieriaceae is characterized by a
lateral haustorium which arises from the primary chalazal endosperm
chamber, and in the Pontederiaceae the 2 lateral haustorial arms
originate from the primary micropylar chamber. In 32 families of
dicotyledons, both micropylar and chalazal haustoria are developed,
but included in these are the Acanthaceae and Epacridaceae in which
certain members possess only a micropylar haustorium, and the Bignoniaceae where just a chalazal haustorium is the usual condition.
A further 18 families, 5 of which are monocotyledonous, are characterized by the possession of only a chalazal haustorium, but in the
Araceae, Hydrophyllaceae, and Icacinaceae, certain of the genera
show no haustorial development of any type. Only a micropylar haustorium is formed in the Boraginaceae, Marcgraviaceae, and Philadelphaceae. The Scrophulariaceae is the most variable family in this
respect, for although both terminal haustoria are usually formed, only
the chalazal is present in *Chaenorrhinum minus* and *Linaria genistaefolia*, and certain other genera show no haustorial development.

The presence of endosperm haustoria, as such, is probably an expression of convergent evolution and, consequently, has little or no
taxonomic significance. On the other hand, details of the origin and
formation of haustoria are probably consistent within taxa. Further
information which is based on dissections is required before the taxonomic potential of haustoria can be assessed.

Embryogeny. Information has been obtained from 216 families,
179 (82.8%) of which are dicotyledonous, and among these the distribution of the 6 major types (Johansen, 1950) is as follows:

	Dicotyledons	Monocotyledons	Total
Asterad	39	10	49
Onagrad	42	3	45
Solanad	40	–	40
Caryophyllad	16	13	29
Chenopodiad	5	1	6
Piperad	4	–	4

In addition, the Paeoniaceae has a unique method of embryogeny, and in the Burmanniaceae, Caricaceae, Dipterocarpaceae, Leitneriaceae, Orchidaceae, Pandanaceae, and Santalaceae either the cleavages are very irregular or they are arrested so early that it is not possible to assign the embryos to a type.

In a further 35 families, the genera conform to 2 or more embryo types, the greatest variation being exhibited by the Liliaceae where the Onagrad, Asterad, Caryophyllad, and Chenopodiad types have been reported.

It is beyond the scope of the present work to examine the nature and extent of variation within types, which appears to be considerable. A great amount of descriptive work still remains to be carried out before it is known whether these variations are sufficiently consistent to be of taxonomic importance. It is regrettable that so few accounts of proembryonic development have been based on whole mounts of the developmental stages, which are much more reliable than serial sections.

Adventive embryony. The formation of adventitious embryos by nucellar budding into the cavity of the embryo sac is invariable in the Calycanthaceae, and common in the Anacardiaceae, Myrtaceae, Orchidaceae, Rutaceae, and Trilliaceae, and it is of occasional occurrence in the Capparidaceae, Cucurbitaceae, Euphorbiaceae, Malpighiaceae, Symplocaceae, Tecophilaeaceae, and Urticaceae.

The occurrence of adventive embryony is not of taxonomic significance, and the formation of embryos by this means can be detected only by a detailed study of embryogeny. In *Eugenia jambos* adventive embryos are initiated prior to pollination, but in several other members of the Myrtaceae nucellar budding is stimulated by fertilization, although the zygotic embryo seldom completes its development.

Polyembryony. An analysis of the incidence of polyembryony was unrewarding for, although it is of common occurrence, the origin of the supernumerary embryos is usually in doubt. An additional embryo at the micropylar end of the embryo sac is commonly attributed to budding from the zygotic embryo or to its early cleavage into two halves. Serial sections, however, can be deceptive and superimposed embryos may appear to be organically connected. Fertilization of a synergid is often suggested by the position of the extra embryo, but unless the synergid is egglike or otherwise atypical, this would first involve complex dedifferentiation of a relatively specialized cell. Before fertilization of an antipodal cell is suggested as the origin of an embryo at the base of an embryo sac, adjacent sections should be examined for an aposporic embryo sac close to the base of the sexual structure. Parthenogenetic development of the unreduced egg, accompanied by degeneration of the intervening nucellar cells, may result in what appears to be an antipodal embryo within the sexual embryo sac. In somatic apospory generally, it is common for several apomictic embryo sacs to be closely associated, and, as their boundaries may be indistinct, a false impression of polyembryony may arise when an embryo develops in each of the multiple embryo sacs. Although adventive embryony usually initiates the formation of several embryos, it is seldom that more than one completes development.

Polyembryony, in the present work, is used in its strict sense and refers to the formation of more than one embryo in the embryo sac, as distinct from *false polyembryony* which follows multiple embryo sac formation within an ovule. In the family descriptions of the following section it has not been possible always to distinguish between these two types.

The incidence of polyembryony among angiosperms has been reviewed by Robyns and Louis (1942) and its significance in plant breeding has been discussed by Maheshwari and Sachar (1963).

DESCRIPTIONS
OF THE
FAMILIES

ACANTHACEAE

The anther is tetrasporangiate and its wall development conforms to the Dicotyledonous type. The epidermis is commonly cutinized and in *Elytraria acaulis* its cells become papillate and contain starch grains. The cells of the endothecium enlarge radially and usually develop fibrous thickenings, although these are absent in *Barleria prionitis*, *Justicia betonica*, and *Ruellia tuberosa*. The middle layer is ephemeral and the cells of the glandular tapetum become 2–4-nucleate, with frequent nuclear fusions. A dimorphic tapetum occurs in *Justicia*, and Ubisch granules are present on the inner tapetal walls in *Elytraria acaulis*. Simultaneous cytokinesis in the microspore mother cells follows meiosis and the microspore tetrads are tetrahedral, decussate, or isobilateral. Pollen grains are 2-celled when shed and starch grains are present in those of *Dipteracanthus patulus*, *Elytraria acaulis*, and *Justicia simplex*. Pollen dimorphism occurs in several genera and in *Diclipta javanica* 8 pollen types have been reported in a single anther.

The ovule is anatropous, amphitropous, or campylotropous, unitegmic, and tenuinucellar. The archesporial cell functions directly as the megaspore mother cell in which cytokinesis accompanies meiosis and the chalazal megaspore of a linear tetrad develops into a Polygonum type embryo sac. Although the embryo sac is in contact with the inner epidermis of the integument, an endothelium is differentiated only in *Elytraria acaulis*, *Nelsonia campestris*, and *Tubiflora acaulis*. The mature embryo sac is curved and a chalazal caecum may develop which, in *Andrographis serpyllifolia*, is subterminal in origin and results in bifurcation of the base of the embryo sac. During maturation the embryo sac in *Dipteracanthus patulus* penetrates the micropyle and in *Justicia simplex* it extends further and reaches a schizogenous cavity in the funicle. An extreme condition occurs in *Nelsonia campestris* where the apex of the embryo sac passes through the micropyle, over the surface of the funicle, and finally penetrates the placenta. The synergids are pyriform, and the polar nuclei remain closely associated until one fuses with the male gamete, after which the second polar nucleus unites with the fusion nucleus to form the primary endosperm nucleus. The 3 antipodal cells are small and usually ephemeral,

31

but in *Aphelandra aurantiaca* and *Barleria cristata* they undergo secondary multiplication to form a group of 4 or 5 cells, and in *B. prionitis* 8–13 antipodal cells are found. Starch grains have been reported in the embryo sacs of *Adhatoda vasica* and *Blepharis maderaspatensis*. A funicular obturator has been described in *Elytraria* and *Nelsonia*, and a jaculator, with varying degrees of development, is of general occurrence.

Endosperm formation is *ab initio* Cellular, with the development of terminal hasutoria, except in *Blepharis* and *Thunbergia* where a chalazal haustorium is absent. The central cell of the initial row of 3 cells gives rise to the endosperm proper and either wall formation follows all nuclear divisions or a free-nuclear zone remains at its base which ultimately becomes cellular, except in *Asteracantha* where the free-nucleate condition is retained. Both haustoria remain 1-cellular but become 2- or 4-nucleate. The micropylar haustorium is usually the more aggressive and persistent of the two, and in *Hemigraphis primulaefolia* and *Thunbergia alata* it branches profusely around the vascular strand of the funicle. Secondary haustoria develop from peripheral cells of the endosperm proper and, in *Andrographis, Elytraria, Haplanthus,* and *Nelsonia,* these invade the integument and result in the formation of ruminate endosperm.

Embryogeny conforms either to the Onagrad type (*Asteracantha, Elytraria, Nelsonia*) or the Solonod type (*Acanthus, Adhatoda, Andrographis, Dipteracanthus, Justicia*). The suspensor varies from the short 3-celled structure of *Elytraria acaulis* to that of *Ecbolium* where it reaches a length of 60–70 cells. Large coenocytic suspensor cells have been reported only in *Andrographis serpyllifolia*, but suspensor haustoria occur in *Eranthemum albo-maculata* and *Ruellia rosea*. Polyembryony in *Barleria cristata* and *Dipteracanthus patulus* has been attributed to budding from the suspensor, but additional embryos have been reported also in *Acanthus*.

Bhaduri, 1944 • Bremekamp, 1938, 1942, 1944, 1953 • Chatin, 1870 • Crété, 1951 • Gigante, 1929 • Hartman, 1923 • Hofmeister, 1858b, 1859 • B. M. Johri, and Singh, 1956, 1959 • Juel, 1915 • Karsten, 1891 • P. Maheshwari, and Negi, 1955 • Mauritzon, 1934g • Mohan Ram, 1956, 1959a,b, 1960a,b, 1961, 1962 • Mohan Ram and Masand, 1962, 1963 • Mohan Ram and Sehgal, 1958 • Mohan Ram and Wadhi, 1964, 1965 • Narayanan, 1956 • Phatak and Ambegaokar, 1955, 1956, 1957, 1961a,b, 1963 • Rangasamy, 1941a • V. S. Rao, 1953 • Schürhoff, 1926b • Strasburger, 1882 • Tieghem, 1908a • Vesque, 1878.

ACERACEAE

The anther is tetrasporangiate with a persistent epidermis. The endothecium develops fibrous thickenings and the 1–3 middle layers are usually ephermeral, although those of *Acer pseudoplatanus* are reported to persist. The cells of the glandular tapetum become multinucleate. Simultaneous cytokinesis in the microspore mother cells follows meiosis and the microspore tetrads are tetrahedral or isobilateral. Pollen grains are 2-celled when shed.

The ovule is anatropous to hemianatropous, bitegmic, and crassinucellar, with the micropyle formed by the inner integument. The archesporial cell cuts off a primary parietal cell which gives rise to several parietal layers, and the apical cells of the nucellar epidermis divide periclinally to form a nucellar cap 8–10 cells in thickness. Cytokinesis in the microspore mother cell accompanies meiosis and the chalazal megaspore of a linear tetrad or "triad" develops into a Polygonum type embryo sac. The synergids of *A. oblongum* are hooked, the polar nuclei fuse before fertilization, and the 3 antipodal cells are ephemeral. Starch grains are present in the embryo sac of *A. oblongum*.

Endosperm formation is Nuclear and the tissue does not become cellular at a later stage. Embryogeny, according to Johansen (1950), probably conforms to the Onagrad type. Polyembryony by suspensor budding has been reported in *A. platanoides*.

Cardiff, 1906 • Dahlgren, 1915a • Darling, 1909 • Guérin, 1909 • Hofmeister, 1958 • Johansen, 1950 • Khushalani, 1963b • Mottier, 1893b • Prozina, 1953 • Rossler, 1911 • Strasburger, 1880b, 1884b • Taylor, 1920.

ACHARIACEAE

Embryologically unknown.

ACHATOCARPACEAE

Embryologically unknown.

ACTINIDIACEAE

The development of the anther and pollen grains has not been described.

The ovule is anatropous, unitegmic, and tenuinucellar, with a small nucellus and long micropyle. The origin of the embryo sac has not been investigated but in *Actinidia* the synergids are elongated, the polar nuclei fuse before fertilization, and the three antipodal cells are ephemeral. An endothelium encloses the embryo sac and a hypostase is differentiated.

Endosperm formation is *ab initio* Cellular.

Embryogeny follows the Solanad type and a filament of 3–7 cells is formed before vertical divisions occur. A second embryo is sometimes formed by budding from the suspensor in *A. chinensis*.

Crété, 1944 • Schnarf, 1924 • Mottier, 1914 • Souèges, 1943d • Tieghem, 1899.

ADOXACEAE

Because each staminal pair results from the splitting of a single primordium, each "anther" is bisporangiate. The endothecium develops fibrous thickenings, the middle layer is ephemeral, and the cells of the amoeboid tapetum become 2-nucleate. Simultaneous cytokinesis in the microspore mother cells follows meiosis and the microspore tetrads are tetrahedral. Pollen grains are 3-celled when shed.

The ovule is anatropous, unitegmic, and tenuinucellar. The archesporial cell functions directly as the megaspore mother cell in which meiosis is not accompanied by cytokinesis and the embryo sac is of the tetrasporic Adoxa type. Occasionally, one of the chalazal megaspore nuclei fails to divide and a 7-nucleate embryo sac results in which only 2 antipodal cells are differentiated. The synergids are pyriform, the polar nuclei fuse only in association with a male gamete, and 1 of the 3 antipodal cells is commonly larger than the others.

Endosperm formation is *ab initio* Cellular. The primary endosperm cell undergoes several longitudinal divisions to form tubelike cells, which then divide transversely.

Embryogeny conforms to the Asterad type and polyembryony has been reported in *Adoxa moschatellina*.

Eichinger, 1907 • Fagerlind, 1938c • Hegelmaier, 1886 • Jönsson, 1897–1880 • Lagerberg, 1909 • T. A. Sprague, 1926 • Sturm, 1910.

AEGICERATACEAE

Development of the anther and pollen grains has not been investigated, but according to Karsten, the anthers are septate.

The ovule of *Aegiceras majus* is anatropous, unitegmic, and crassinucellar, with a parietal tissue of about 6 cell layers which are derived, presumably, from a primary parietal cell. Embryo sac development has not been described but the mature structure is 8-nucleate, although there is no information on its components.

Endosperm formation is Nuclear, but the tissue later becomes cellular following centripetal wall formation. The outermost 6 or 7 layers of endosperm cells become meristematic and secondary endosperm tissue is formed whose haustorial lobes invade the integument and the funicle.

Embryogeny is unknown.

Carey and Fraser, 1932 • Dahlgren, 1916 • Haberlandt, 1895 • Karsten, 1891.

AEXTOXICACEAE

Development of the anther and pollen grains has not been described. The ovule is bitegmic and crassinucellar, and the micropyle is formed by the inner integument, which in *Aextoxicon punctatum* projects considerably beyond the outer integument. Mauritzon's figure (1936) shows a massive nucellar beak and numerous parietal layers are indicated. Embryo sac development, endosperm formation, and embryogeny have not been described.

Mauritzon, 1936d.

AGAVACEAE

The anther is tetrasporangiate and in *Sanserviera* its three parietal layers develop according to the Monocotyledonous type. In *Agave* and *Doranthes*, the origin of the 10–12 wall layers has not been traced. The endothecium develops fibrous thickenings and in *Agave* it is multilayered. The tapetum is glandular and the report of an amoeboid tapetum in *A. lechuguilla* (Grove, 1941) requires confirmation. The tapetal cells become 2–4-nucleate and nuclear fusions occur in *Polianthes*. Usually, successive cytokinesis in the microspore mother cells accompanies meiosis, but the simultaneous type occurs in *Doryanthes* and *Phormium*. The microspore tetrads are tetrahedral, isobilateral, or linear and the pollen grains are 2-celled when shed.

The ovule is anatropous, bitegmic, and crassinucellar, with the micropyle formed by the inner integument. The archesporial cell usually cuts off a primary parietal cell which gives rise to 1 or 2 parietal layers, but in *Phormium* it functions directly as the megaspore mother call, and periclinal divisions of the apical nucellar epidermal cells form a nucellar cap 3 or 4 cells in thickness. Cave (1955) considers that the massive parietal tissue of *Doryanthes* is probably epidermal in origin and that the formation of an initial primary parietal cell is doubtful. In *Yucca* the lateral and basal nucellar cells divide actively both before and after fertilization, and persist as the perisperm of the seed. Cytokinesis in the megaspore mother cell accompanies meiosis, and usually the chalazal megaspore of a linear or T-shaped tetrad develops into a Polygonum type embryo sac. In *Furcraea*, however, it is invariably the micropylar megaspore which is functional. The report by Gioelli (1930) of the Adoxa type embryo sac in four species of *Aloe* requires further investigation in view of the occurrence of the Polygonum type in *A. vera* (Joshi, 1937). According to the genus, the mature embryo sac either is ovate or its chalazal extremity forms a tubelike structure which exhibits some slight haustorial activity. The synergids are pyriform and in *Doryanthes, Phormium,* and *Yucca* they show the filiform apparatus; the polar nuclei fuse before fertilization and the secondary nucleus migrates to the basal portion of the embryo sac. Secondary multiplication of the 3 antipodal cells occurs only in *Doryanthes* where up to 5 cells are formed, and starch grains have been reported in the embryo sacs of *Agave*. A hypotase is commonly present.

Endosperm formation is Helobial and records of the Nuclear type have probably overlooked the formation of the small primary chalazal chamber.

Embryogeny in *Yucca glauca* conforms to the Caryophyllad type.

Arnott, 1959a,b, 1961, 1962 • Cappelletti, 1927 • Catalano, 1928, 1929, 1930, 1931 • Cave, 1953, 1955 • Ernst, 1918 • Folsom, 1916 • Gioelli, 1930, 1933 • Goebel, 1887 • Grove, 1941 • Guérin, 1927 • L. Guignard, 1882b • Guzowska, 1960 • Habermann, 1906 • Hérail, 1889 • Hubert, 1896 • A. C. Joshi, 1937c • A. C. Joshi, and Pantulu, 1941 • Koerniche, 1901 • Lary de Latour, 1908 • Nevins, 1927 • Newman, 1928, 1929 • Osterhout, 1902 • B. Palm, 1920 • H. S. Reed, 1903 • Regen, 1941 • Schlimback, 1924 • Schnarf, 1931a • Stenar, 1942 • Vesque, 1879b • Vignoli, 1936, 1937b • Watkins, 1937 • J. M. Webber, 1953 • Went and Blaauw, 1906 • Wolf, 1940 • Wòycicki, 1911a • Wunderlich, 1938, 1950.

AGDESTIDACEAE

Embryologically unknown.

AKANIACEAE

The development of the anther and pollen grains has not been described.

The ovule of *Akania hillii* is hemianatropous, bitegmic, and crassinucellar, with the micropyle formed by both integuments. Development and structure of the embryo sac are unknown.

Endosperm formation and embryogeny have not been investigated.

Mauritzon, 1936d.

ALANGIACEAE

The anther is tetrasporangiate. The endothecium develops fibrous thickenings, the middle layer is ephemeral, and the cells of the glandular (?) tapetum become 2-nucleate. Cytokinesis in the microspore mother cells has not been described, but the microspore tetrads are isobilateral. According to Gopinath (1945) the pollen grains are uninucleate when shed, but possibly those observed were immature.

The ovule is anatropous, unitegmic, and crassinucellar. The archesporial cell cuts off a primary parietal cell which gives rise to 1–2 parietal layers, and periclinal divisions of the apical nucellar epidermal cells form a nucellar cap 2 or 3 cells in thickness. Cytokinesis in the megaspore mother cell accompanies meiosis and the chalazal megaspore of a linear tetrad develops into a Polygonum type embryo sac. The synergids are broadly pyriform but although the polar nuclei become closely associated soon after their formation, their fusion does not occur until fertilization. The three antipodal nuclei may degenerate before becoming enclosed in cells, but occasionally they undergo secondary multiplication and form a group of 12 or more cells. An endothelium is differentiated and a hypostase is present in the mature ovule.

Endosperm formation is Nuclear in *Alangium lamarckii* but *ab initio* Cellular in *A. chinense*.

Embryogeny is unknown.

Gopinath, 1943b, 1945 • Horne, 1914 • Mitra and Dutta, 1949 • Schnarf, 1922b.

ALISMATACEAE

The anther is tetrasporangiate and its wall development conforms to the Monocotyledonous type. The endothecium develops fibrous thickenings, the middle layer is ephemeral, and the cells of the amoeboid tapetum remain 1-nucleate. Successive cytokinesis in the microspore mother cells accompanies meiosis and the microspore tetrads are isobilateral. Pollen grains are 3-celled when shed.

The ovule is anatropous, bitegmic, and weakly pseudocrassinucellar, with the micropyle formed by the inner integument. The archesporial cell functions directly as the megaspore mother cell and the nucellar epidermis becomes irregularly 2-layered through periclinal divisions of its apical cells. Cytokinesis in the megaspore mother cell accompanies only the heterotypic nuclear division and the micropylar dyad cell usually degenerates soon after its formation, while the chalazal dyad cell develops into an Allium type embryo sac. During embryo sac formation the two chalazal nuclei usually do not undergo the final postmeiotic mitosis and the mature structure is consequently 6-nucleate, but occasionally one or both of these nuclei divide and a 7- or 8-nucleate embryo sac results. In *Echinodorus ranunculoides* Dahlgren (1928a) reported the formation of a 5-nucleate embryo sac through failure of division ("strike") of the primary chalazal nucleus, which is, in fact, the lower megaspore nucleus. The synergids are usually hooked and exhibit the filiform apparatus, the polar nuclei fuse before fertilization, and the secondary nucleus moves toward the antipodal region. In the 6-nucleate embryo sac, only 1 antipodal nucleus is present and this either remains free or is enclosed in a cell. An endothelium is differentiated in *Alisma* and *Damasonium*.

Endosperm formation is Helobial. The small chalazal chamber degenerates early, although one or two nuclear divisions may occur, but in the large micropylar chamber many free nuclei are formed before the tissue becomes cellular. Wall formation is centripetal but does not extend to the center, and the developing embryo is surrounded by free-nuclear endosperm. Nuclear endosperm has been reported in *Damasonium alisma*, *Elisma natans*, and *Machaerocarpus californicus* but these records require confirmation because the small ephemeral chalazal chamber may have been overlooked.

Embryogeny conforms to the Caryophyllad type and the basal suspensor cell is large and vesicular. Johri (1936a) has reported the occurrence in *Sagittaria graminea* of three 2-celled proembryos in one embryo sac.

Bessey, 1898 • Buchenau, 1857, 1869, 1882 • Claussen, 1927 • M. T. Cook, 1907c • Dahlgren, 1927d, 1928a, 1934a • Elfving, 1879 • Famintzin, 1879 • A. Fischer, 1880 • Hofmeister, 1858, 1861 • B. M. Johri, 1933, 1934a,b, 1935b,c,e, 1936a • Kudryashov and Savich, 1963 • Lemesle, 1929b • P. Maheshwari and Singh, 1943 • Nagl, 1962 • S. K. N. Murthy, 1933a,b, 1935b • Nitzschke, 1914 • Raciborski, 1893 • J. H. Schaffner, 1896, 1897a • Schürhoff, 1919, 1926b • Soltwedel, 1882 • Souèges, 1917a,b, 1931b • Stenar, 1925b • Sykes, 1909 • Tischler, 1915 • Ward, 1880b.

ALSTROEMERIACEAE

The development and structure of the anther has not been investigated except for the report (Stenar, 1925b) that in *Alstroemeria pulchella* the cells of the glandular tapetum become 2-nucleate. Successive cytokinesis in the microspore mother cells accompanies meiosis, but pollen grain formation has not been described.

The ovule is anatropous, bitegmic, and tenuinucellar, with the micropyle formed by the inner integument. The archesporial cell functions directly as the megaspore mother cell, in which cytokinesis accompanies meiosis and the chalazal megaspore of a linear or T-shaped tetrad develops into a Polygonum type embryo sac. The synergids are beaked, the polar nuclei fuse before fertilization, the 3 antipodal cells are 1-nucleate, and starch grains are present in the embryo sac. A weak endothelium is differentiated and a funicular obturator is developed.

Endosperm formation is Nuclear, but embryogeny is unknown.

L. Guignard, 1884, 1889 • Stenar, 1925b, 1951b.

AMARANTACEAE

The anther is bisporangiate in *Alternanthera sessilis* but otherwise tetrasporangiate, and its wall development follows the Monocotyledonous type. The endothecium develops fibrous thickenings except in *Achyranthes aspera*, the middle layer is ephermeral, and cells of the glandular tapetum become at least 2-nucleate, while Ubisch granules are present on their inner walls. Simultaneous cytokinesis in the microspore mother cells follows meiosis and the microspore tetrads are tetrahedral, isobilateral, or decussate. Pollen grains are 3-celled when shed, except in *Digera arvensis* where the 2-celled condition is usual. In *Alternanthera* starch grains are present in the mature pollen grains.

The ovule is anacampylotropous, campylotropous, or circinotropous, bitegmic, and crassinucellar. The micropyle is formed only by the inner integument except in *Gomphrena celosioides* where both integuments are involved. Except in *Digera arvensis* an air space develops between the bases of the integuments early in ovule development. A multicellular archesporium is common, but only one cell is functional and cuts off a primary parietal cell which gives rise to a parietal tissue of up to 5 cell layers. The apical cells of the nucellar epidermis may also undergo a few periclinal divisions and form a nucellar cap. Cytokinesis in the megaspore mother cell accompanies meiosis and a linear tetrad of megaspores is formed, but the suppression of the homotypic division in the micropylar dyad cell is not uncommon and results in the formation of a row of 3 cells. The chalazal megaspore develops into a Polygonum type embryo sac in which the synergids are hooked, and a filiform apparatus occurs in *Achyranthes aspera*. The polar nuclei fuse before fertilization and the 3 antipodal cells

are short-lived, except in *Pupalia lappacea* where secondary multiplication results in the formation of 30–40 small nonvacuolate cells.
In *Aerva tomentosa* the megaspore mother cell develops directly into
an unreduced embryo sac (gonial apospory) in which the synergids
are ephemeral and the 3 antipodal cells persist. Sachar and Murgai
(1958, 1959) estimated that nearly 20% of the ovules of *A. tomentosa*
abort following degeneration of the egg. The embryo sac undergoes
postfertilization elongation by the growth of a chalazal caecum, and
becomes horseshoe-shaped, but the antipodal cells remain *in situ*.
Starch grains occur in the mature embryo sacs of *Allmania nodiflora*,
Amarantus viridis, and *Cyathula tomentosa*. In *Psilostachys sericea*
the pollen tube persists in the ovule as a dead structure into early
embryogeny.

Endosperm formation is Nuclear, but later the tissue becomes cellular. Walls are initiated first at the micropylar pole and extend
throughout the embryo sac, except in *Alternanthera sessilis* where
the endosperm remains free-nuclear at the chalazal extremity. Curvature of the embryo sac encloses the central portion of the nucellus,
which persists as the perisperm.

Embryogeny follows either the Chenopodiad or the Solanad type,
and in *Aerva tomentosa* the unreduced egg develops parthenogeneti-
cally, undergoing the cleavages characteristic of the former type. In
Allmania and *Aerva* the suspensor is uniseriate, but otherwise it is
multiseriate and rather massive proximally. Polyembryony has been
reported in *Celosia cristata* and *Gomphrena decumbens*.

Bakshi, 1952 • Braun, 1860 • Dahlgren, 1916 • Dambroise, 1947 • A. Fischer,
1880 • L. Guignard, 1882b • Hofmeister, 1859 • A. C. Joshi, 1936b • A. C.
Joshi, and Kajale, 1937 • A. C. Joshi and Venkata Rao, 1934 • Kajale, 1935,
1937b,c, 1940a • P. Maheshwari, 1941b • Naithani, 1933 • Padhye, 1962b • Puri
and Singh, 1935 • Sachar and Murgai, 1958, 1959 • Souèges, 1937c,g • A. Winkler,
1882 • Woodcock, 1931.

AMARYLLIDACEAE

The anther is tetrasporangiate with a persistent epidermis and a
well-developed endothecium which becomes fibrous at maturity. In
Crinum defixum four middle layers are formed, of which the outermost
layer becomes fibrous and persists. The tapetum is glandular and
its cells become binucleate, but Pankow (1958) has reported an amoeboid tapetum in *Galanthus*. Ubisch granules occur in *Crinum* on the
inner tapetal walls. Successive cytokinesis in the microspore mother
cells accompanies meiosis and the microspore tetrads are tetrahedral,
isobilateral, or decussate. Pollen grains are 2-celled when shed.

AMARYLLIDACEAE 41

The ovules are anatropous to hemianatropous, uni- or bitegmic, and pseudocrassinucellar. In *Crinum* a definite integument is not differentiated, and in *Zephyranthes* the micropyle is formed by the inner integument. Periclinal divisions of the apical cells of the nucellar epidermis give rise to a nucellar cap several cells in thickness. In *Pancratium maritimum* the archesporial cell cuts off a primary parietal cell which divides only anticlinally, but otherwise it functions directly as the megaspore mother cell. In most cases, cytokinesis in the megaspore mother cell follows only the first meiotic division and the chalazal dyad cell develops into an Allium type embryo sac, although the Polygonum type occurs in *Allium mutabile, Crinum* spp., *Nothoscordum fragrans, N. striatum*, and *Pancratium maritimum*. The synergids are hooked and exhibit the filiform apparatus, the polar nuclei fuse before fertilization and the 3 antipodal cells often persist into early embryogeny. A limited degree of secondary multiplication of antipodals has been reported in *Nothoscordum*, and in *Allium odorum* and *A. paniculatum* a chalazal caecum forms by embryo sac elongation. Gonial apospory has been reported in *Allium* and *Zephyranthes*, which also exhibit a hypostase, and in *Crinum asiaticum* and *C. defixum* a knee-shaped bend of the funicle forms an obturator.

Endosperm formation is Helobial in *Brodiaea, Clivea, Cooperia, Haemanthus, Hippeastrum, Ixiolirion, Nothoscordum, Vallota*, and *Zephyranthes*. The small coenocytic chalazal chamber usually degenerates when the micropylar chamber becomes cellular and its formation may have been overlooked in some of the reported occurrences of Nuclear endosperm (*Allium, Amaryllis, Calostemma, Cooperia, Crinum, Cyrtanthus, Galanthus, Hymenocallis, Leucojum, Narcissus, Nerine, Phaedranassa, Spreklia*, and *Zephyranthes*). In *Crinum defixum* the peripheral endosperm cells behave as a phellogen and a few layers of cork are formed.

Embryogeny conforms either to the Asterad or the Onagrad type, and polyembryony is common.

F. d' Amato, 1948–1949 • Baranov and Poddubnaja, 1925 • Battaglia, 1958b • Braun, 1860 • W. V. Brown, 1951 • Cappelletti, 1931 • Cave, 1939, 1942a, 1953 • Church, 1916 • G. E. Coe, 1953 • Dahlgren, 1915a • B. S. M. Dutt, 1957a,b, 1959, 1962, 1964 • Eckles, 1941 • Elfving, 1879 • Elmore, 1898 • Ernst, 1918 • Farrell, 1914 • A. Fischer, 1880 • L. H. Flint, and Moreland, 1943 • Geitler, 1955 • Goebel, 1880 • L. Guignard, 1882b, 1900b • Gustafsson, 1946 • Guttenberg, Heydel, and Pankow, 1954 • Gvaladze, 1961 • Haberlandt, 1922b, 1923a,b, 1925 • Håkansson, 1951, 1953b, 1957a • Hegelmaier, 1897 • Hoffman, 1933 • Höfmeister, 1858, 1861 • Johnston, 1941 • H. A. Jones and Emsweller, 1936 • Kapinos, 1960, 1964 • Kapoor and Tandon, 1963a,b, 1964 • Koshimizu, 1930 • Kosmath, 1927 • Kostriukova, 1939a • Kostriukova and Benetskaia, 1939 • Levan, 1936, 1940 • Mellink, 1880 • Merry, 1937 • Messeri, 1931 • Modilewski,

1925, 1928a, 1930, 1931 • Murphy, 1946 • Nakajima, 1928 • Pace, 1913 • B. Palm, 1920 • Pankow, 1958 • Petit-Thouars, 1808 • Porter, 1936 • Preda, 1897 • L. C. Richard, 1808 • D. Sato, 1938 • Schlimbach, 1924 • Schnarf, 1929a, 1931a • Schniewind, 1901 • Schürhoff, 1922c, 1926b • Shadowsky, 1925 • Soltwedel, 1882 • Souèges, 1926b, 1931a, 1952b • Stauffacher, 1911 • Stenar, 1924b, 1925b, 1932b, 1933, 1937b, 1949, 1951a,b, • Stiffler, 1925 • Strasburger, 1877, 1878, 1879, 1880, 1882b • Suita, 1937a, 1938 • Sundar Rao, 1940b • Swamy, 1946b,e • Tandon and Kapoor, 1962a,b • Taylor, 1921 • Tomita, 1931 • Trankowsky, 1930 • Tretjakow, 1895 • Treub and Mellink, 1880 • Troll, 1928 • Tulasne, 1855 • Ustinova, 1944 • Vesque, 1879 • N. Weaver, 1943 • Weber, 1929 • Whitehead and Brown, 1940 • Wóycicki, 1926, 1929, 1931 • Wunderlich, 1936.

ANACARDIACEAE

The anther is tetrasporangiate and in *Lannea coromandelica* the development of its wall follows the Basic type. The epidermis persists at maturity and the endothecium develops fibrous thickenings. Usually, 2 ephemeral middle layers are formed, but in *Rhus mysurensis* only a single layer is found and in *Pistacia chinensis* and *Toxicodendron diversifolia* there are 3 such layers. The tapetum is glandular and its cells become 2-nucleate. Simultaneous cytokinesis in the microspore mother cells follows meiosis and the microspore tetrads are tetrahedral. The pollen grains are 2-celled when shed. In *Rhus, Schinus,* and *Toxicodendron* the female flowers contain stamens whose development proceeds normally up to the formation of microspore mother cells, which then collapse without undergoing meiosis.

The ovule is anatropous, uni- or bitegmic, and crassinucellar. The single integument of *Pistacia* and *Anacardium* is considered by Copeland (1955, 1961) to be a fusion structure, whereas according to Kelkar (1958a,b) the bitegmic condition of *Lannea* and *Rhus* results from the splitting of a single integumentary initial. In *Schinus* the micropyle is formed by both integuments, but in *Toxicodendron* only the inner one is involved. The archesporial cell cuts off a primary parietal cell from which is derived the massive parietal tissue of up to 10 cell layers and in *Anacardium occidentale* a nucellar cap is also present. Cytokinesis accompanies meiosis in the megaspore mother cell, and the chalazal megaspore of the linear tetrad develops into a Polygonum type embryo sac. The synergids are hooked, the polar nuclei fuse before fertilization close to the egg, and the 3 antipodal cells persist only until fertilization. A hypostase occurs in *Schinus* and a funicular obturator has been reported in *Lannea, Pistacia, Rhus,* and *Toxicodendron.*

Endosperm formation is Nuclear, but walls are initiated later at the micropylar pole and the tissue becomes cellular throughout. In the Indian mango, Sen and Mallik (1940) found that the chalazal endosperm remained free-nuclear for a considerable time, but ultimately became cellular, whereas in *Anacardium occidentale* Copeland (1961) reported that this region was permanently free-nuclear.

Embryogeny conforms to the Onagrad type in *Lannea, Rhus,* and *Semecarpus* but to the Asterad type in *Anacardium,* and usually no definite suspensor is formed. Adventive embryony and polyembryony are of general occurence in *Mangifera,* and in the Carabao or Pico variety Mendiola (1926) found up to 30 seedlings developing from one seed. Polyembryony is also of occasional occurrence in *Lannea coromandelica.*

Arndt, 1935 • Belling, 1908 • Braun, 1960 • M. T. Cook, 1907d • Copeland, 1955, 1959, 1961 • Copeland and Doyel, 1940 • Engler, 1900 • Gaértner, 1791 • Grimm, 1912 • Gurbel, 1952 • Horn, 1943 • Juliano, 1932, 1934c, 1937 • Juliano and Cuevas, 1932 • Kelkar, 1958a,b, 1961 • Kennard, 1955 • Longo, 1910b • P. Maheshwari, 1934b • P. Maheshwari, Sachar, and Chopra, 1955 • Mendiola, 1926 • Moquin-Tandon, 1841 • Raineri, 1952 • Reinwardt, 1824 • Sachar and Chopra, 1957 • Schacht, 1859 • Sen and Mallik, 1940 • U. R. Singh, 1962 • Srinivasachar, 1940a • Strasburger, 1878 • H. J. Webber, 1931.

ANCISTROCLADACEAE

Embryologically unknown.

ANNONACEAE

The anther is tetrasporangiate and its wall development conforms to the Dicotyledonous type. The endothecium develops fibrous thickenings, the 2–4 middle layers are ephemeral, and the cells of the glandular tapetum become 2–4 nucleate. In *Artabotrys* and *Miliusa* the sporogenous tissue is massive but in *Annona, Asimina, Canangium, Monodora,* and *Xylopia* it is uniseriate and certain of the cells form sterile partitions which subdivide the loculus and resemble tapetal cells. The earlier reports of a tapetal periplasmodium were probably based on observations of these sterile sporogenous cells. In the microspore mother cells of *Annona* and *Cananga* both simultaneous and successive cytokinesis have been described. The microspore tetrads are tetrahedral, isobilateral, or decussate and in *Annona* they remain together as permanent units. The individual pollen grains are 3-celled when shed.

The ovule is anatropous, bitegmic, and crassinucellar, with the micropyle formed by the inner integument and in *Canangium, Mezzettia,* and *Xylopia* a middle integument develops during postfertilization stages. The archesporial cell cuts off a primary parietal cell which gives rise to up to 5 parietal layers and the reports of a subhypodermal archesporial cell appear to be based on material in which the primary parietal cell was already formed. Cytokinesis in the megaspore mother cell accompanies meiosis and the chalazal megaspore of a linear tetrad develops into a Polygonum type embryo sac. The synergids are pyriform, the polar nuclei fuse just before or at fertilization, and the 3 antipodal cells are ephemeral. Starch grains occur in the embryo sacs of *Annona cherimolia* and *Cananga odorata* and the deeply cup-shaped hypostase of *Asimina triloba* encloses the base of the embryo sac.

Endosperm formation is *ab initio* Cellular and it becomes ruminate in the seed. In *Anaxagorea, Desmos,* and *Miliusa* the outermost layer of the nucellus is persistent whereas in *Cananga* and *Miliusa* postfertilization periclinal divisions of this layer and the functioning of a perichalazal meristem lead to the formation of secondary nucellus.

Embryogeny follows the Onagrad type.

Adatia, 1946 • Asana and Adatia, 1947 • Corner, 1949 • Dahlgren, 1927c, 1939a • Erdtman, 1945, 1957 • Herms, 1907 • Juliano, 1935b • Lampton, 1957 • Lecomte, 1896 • Locke, 1936 • Nicolosi-Roncati, 1903, 1905a,b • Oes, 1914 • Periasamy, 1954, 1961, 1962b • Periasamy and Swamy, 1956, 1959, 1961 • Samuelsson, 1914 • Sastri, 1955a, 1957b,c • Schnarf, 1931a • Subramanyam, 1962 • Vesque, 1879b • Voigt, 1888.

ANTONIACEAE

Embryologically unknown.

APOCYNACEAE

The anther is tetrasporangiate. In *Cerbera* and *Vallaris* the endothecium is not well defined, 1 or 2 middle layers are formed, and the cells of the glandular tapetum remain 1-nucleate. Simultaneous cytokinesis in the microspore mother cells follows meiosis in *Ackocanthera spectabilis, Cerbera odollam, Vallaris heyneii,* and *Vinca rosea,* but successive cytokinesis occurs in *Apocynum androsaemifolium* and both types have been reported in *Rauwolfia canescens.* The microspore tetrads are tetahedral, isobilateral, or decussate and pollen grains are 3-celled when shed.

The ovule is anatropous, unitegmic, and tenuinucellar. The archesporial cell functions directly as the megaspore mother cell in which cytokinesis accompanies meiosis and the chalazal megaspore of a linear tetrad develops into a Polygonum type embryo sac. The synergids are pyriform and in *Carissa carandas* and *Vallaris heyneii* they reach almost to the middle of the embryo sac. The polar nuclei fuse before fertilization, the 3 antipodal cells are ephemeral, and starch grains occur in the embryo sacs of *Apocynum* and *Strophanthus*. An endothelium is usually differentiated. In *Ervatamia heyneana* an aril develops from a funicular outgrowth which in *Voacanga grandifolia* forms a common fleshy mass around the seeds, and in both species considerable chalazal growth follows fertilization.

Endosperm formation is Nuclear, but although centripetal wall formation is initiated early, during embryogeny a central cavity free of endosperm may persist.

Embryogeny conforms to the Caryophyllad type, but cleavage of the zygote is delayed until a large number of free endosperm nuclei have formed. Polyembryony has been reported in *Kopsia longifolia*.

Andersson, 1931 • Benetskaia, 1939 • F. H. Billings, 1901 • Finn, 1928b • Frye and Blodgett, 1905 • Guignard, 1917a,b • Helm, 1895 • Hofmeister, 1858 • Léger, 1913 • Mahlberg, 1959, 1960, 1961 • S. Meyer, 1938 • Pannocchia, 1938 • Periasamy, 1962b, 1963 • V. S. Rao and Ganguli, 1963 • Rau, 1940a • Schürhoff and Müller, 1937 • Strasburger, 1884b • Täckholm and Söderberg, 1918 • Vesque, 1878, 1879b.

APONOGETONACEAE

The anther is tetrasporangiate and its wall development conforms to the Monocotyledonous type. The endothecium develops fibrous thickenings, the middle layer is ephemeral, and the cells of the amoeboid tapetum remain 1-nucleate. Simultaneous cytokinesis in the microspore mother cells follows meiosis in *Aponogeton crispum, A. monostachyon*, and *A. ulvaceus*, but in *A. abyssinicus* cytokinesis is successive, and both types have been reported in *A. distachys*. The microspore tetrads and tetrahedral or decussate and pollen grains are 3-celled when shed.

The ovule is anatropous, bitegmic, and crassinucellar, with the micropyle formed by the inner integument. In *A. crispus* and *A. quadrangularis* the integuments are partly fused but in the other species they are free of each other and of the nucellus. The archesporial cell cuts off a primary parietal cell which forms 2 or 3 parietal layers, and the apical cells of the nucellar epidermis undergo a few periclinal divisions. Cytokinesis in the megaspore mother cell accompanies meiosis and the chalazal megaspore of a linear tetrad develops into a

Polygonum type embryo sac. The synergids are pyriform, the polar nuclei fuse before fertilization, and the secondary nucleus migrates close to the 3 antipodal cells which persist into early embryogeny.

Endosperm formation is Helobial. The nucleus of the small chalazal chamber increases in size but seldom divides and in the large micropylar chamber the thin layer of free-nuclear endosperm is digested by the embryo.

Embryogeny follows the Caryophyllad type and *cb* forms a large vesicular suspensor cell.

Afzelius, 1920 • P. Claussen, 1927 • Palm, 1915 • Sâné, 1939 • Serguéeff, 1907 • Stenar, 1925b • Süssenguth, 1919, 1921a • Tischler, 1915.

APOSTASIACEAE

Embryologically unknown.

APTANDRACEAE

Embryologically unknown.

AQUIFOLIACEAE

The anther is tetrasporangiate but no satisfactory account exists of the development or structure of its wall. According to Copeland (1963) the endothecium of *Ilex cornuti* is "ribbed" (fibrous ?) and the tapetum, whose cells become 2-nucleate, is "not strictly a single layer." As no reference is made to the formation of a periplasmodium, the tapetum is probably glandular. Microsporogenesis has not been described but the pollen grains are 2-celled when shed.

The ovule is anatropous, unitegmic, and usually crassinucellar although the tenuinucellar condition has been reported in *I. decidua* and *I. vomitoria*. In *I. aquifolium* and *I. cornuti* the archesporial cells cuts off a primary parietal cell which forms 1 or 2 parietal layers and the report of Herr (1959b) that the crassinucellar condition in 6 species of *Ilex* is due entirely to periclinal divisions of the nucellar epidermis is not supported by his figures. Cytokinesis in the megaspore mother cell accompanies meiosis and the chalazal megaspore of a linear tetrad develops into a Polygonum type embryo sac. The synergids are pyriform, the polar nuclei fuse before fertilization, and the remains of the 3 small antipodal cells may persist during early post-fertilization stages. The embryo sac is enclosed by an endothelium and a hypostase is differentiated.

Endosperm formation is *ab initio* Cellular, and embryogeny probably conforms to the Caryophyllad type.

Copeland, 1963 • Herr, 1959a,b,c, 1961 • Mauritzon, 1936d • Schürhoff, 1921a.

AQUILARIACEAE

Embryologically unknown.

ARACEAE

The anther is bisporangiate (*Arisaema, Dieffenbachia*) or tetrasporangiate (*Calla, Peltandra, Spathyema*), with a persistent epidermis. The endothecium develops fibrous thickenings and, although a single ephemeral middle layer is present in *Theriophonum*, 2 or more such layers are formed in *Arisaema* and *Peltandra*. The tapetum is amoeboid and may become 2–4-layered. Successive cytokinesis in the microspore mother cells accompanies meiosis and the microspore tetrads are tetrahedral, isobilateral, or decussate. Pollen grains are 2-celled when shed in *Arisaema, Dieffenbachia, Spathyema, Symplocarpus*, and *Theriophonum*, but 3-celled in *Aglaonema, Arum, Peltandra* and *Zantedeschia*, and both conditions occur in *Calla* and *Pothos*. Dimorphic pollen grains have been reported in *Colocasia antiquorum* and those of *Peltandra virginica* contain starch grains.

The ovule is orthotropous in *Arisaema* but in the other representatives it is anatropous to hemianatropous, bitegmic, and pseudocrassinucellar, with the micropyle formed by the inner integument except in *D. seguine*, where both integuments are involved. The apical cells of the nucellar epidermis divide periclinally to form a nucellar cap 2–6 cells in thickness, and this tissue has sometimes been considered as presumptive evidence for the formation of a primary parietal cell. The archesporial cell functions directly as the megaspore mother cell in which cytokinesis accompanies meiosis and the chalazal megaspore of a linear tetrad develops into a Polygonum type embryo sac. According to S. C. Maheshwari (1955) and S. C. Maheshwari and Khanna (1956), the reports of bisporic and tetrasporic embryo sacs are either erroneous or very doubtful. The synergids are pyriform and in *Arisaema wallichianum* are nonvacuolate, the polar nuclei fuse before fertilization, and the secondary nucleus sometimes migrates to the chalazal pole. The 3 antipodal cells are usually ephemeral, but in *Arum orientale* and *Symplocarpus foetidus* they enlarge considerably and some secondary multiplication has been reported in *Aglaonema,*

Lysichiton, and *Xanthosma.* Starch grains are commonly present in the embryo sac, an endothelium is differentiated, and a hypostase is present in *Acorus gramineus* and *Theriophonum.*

Endosperm formation is *ab initio* Cellular and Wunderlich (1959) considers that the reports of Nuclear and Helobial endosperm require reinvestigation. Following division of the primary endosperm nucleus a transverse wall is formed and although the chalazal chamber remains 1-nucleate it may increase considerably in size and show haustorial activity. The endosperm proper is derived from the primary micropylar chamber.

Embryogeny appears to follow the Caryophyllad type although in *Pistia stratioides* both *ca* and *cb* divide vertically. Polyembryony has been reported in *Spathiphyllum floribundum* and *S. patinii.*

Atkinson, 1899 • Banerji, 1934, 1937, 1947 • Boodle and Hill, 1929 • M. F. Buell, 1935, 1938 • Campbell, 1899d, 1900, 1903, 1905, 1912 • Claussen, 1927 • Dahlgren, 1923 • Dudley, 1937 • Duggar, 1900 • T. I. Edwards, 1934 • Elfving, 1879 • Engler, 1877, 1884 • Gatin, 1921 • Goldberg, 1941 • Gow, 1907, 1908a,b, 1913 • J.-L. Guignard, 1963c • Guttenberg, 1960 • Hanstein, 1870 • Hegelmaier, 1874 • Hofmeister, 1858, 1861 • Jacobson-Paley, 1920a,b,c, • Jönsson, 1879–1880 • Juel, 1915 • Jüssen, 1928 • Koschnikoff, 1877 • Kubin, 1878 • S. C. Maheshwari, 1955 • S. C. Maheshwari, and Khanna, 1956 • Mascré, 1928 • Meada, 1932 • Mellink, 1880 • Mitchell, 1916 • Mottier, 1892 • Mücke, 1908 • B. Palm, 1920 • Parameswaran, 1959 • Pickett, 1913, 1915, 1916 • Rosendahl, 1906, 1909 • Rowlee, 1896 • Schürhoff and Jüssen, 1925 • Shadowsky, 1931 • Stenar, 1925b • Strasburger, 1879, 1882a, 1884b • Süssenguth, 1919 • Svedelius, 1910 • Tieghem, 1907a • Tulasne, 1855 • Vesque, 1879 • Wunderlich, 1959.

ARALIACEAE

The anther is tetrasporangiate. The endothecium develops fibrous thickenings, the 1 or 2 middle layers are ephemeral, and the cells of the glandular tapetum become multinucleate, but finally 1-nucleate by fusion. Simultaneous cytokinesis in the microspore mother cells follows meiosis and the microspore tetrads are tetrahedral or isobilateral. Pollen grains are 2-celled when shed in *Nothopanax arborea,* but otherwise they are 3-celled.

The ovule is anatropous, unitegmic, and usually crassinucellar. The archesporial cell cuts off a primary parietal cell which either degenerates or gives rise to parietal tissue but, occasionally, it may function directly as the megaspore mother cell and the ovule is then tenuinucellar. Cytokinesis in the megaspore mother cell accompanies meiosis and the chalazal megaspore of a linear tetrad develops into a Polygonum type embryo sac. Suppression of the homotypic division in the nucleus of one dyad cell is common and this results in a row of 3 cells ("triad"), of which only 2 are megaspores. In *Hedera nepalensis* Singh (1954) reported that it is usually the micropylar dyad cell which undergoes the second meiotic division and that the uppermost megaspore forms the embryo sac. The synergids are pyriform, the polar nuclei fuse just before fertilization, and the 3 ephemeral antipodal nuclei either remain free or are enclosed in separate cells. An endothelium is differentiated and a hypostase is commonly present. A funicular obturator has been reported in *Hedera australiana*, *Nothopanax arborea*, *Panax fruticosa*, and *Polyscias pinnata*.

Endosperm formation is Nuclear but finally the tissue becomes cellular. Ruminate endosperm occurs in *Arthrophyllum diversifolium* and *Hedera helix*.

Embryogeny has not been traced in detail.

Cammerloher, 1910 • Ducamp, 1901, 1902 • Faure, 1911 • Gopinath, 1943a, 1944 • Hegelmaier, 1886 • Horne, 1914 • Jönsson, 1879–1880, 1881 • Periasamy, 1962b • Pigott, 1915 • Schürhoff, 1929 • D. Singh, 1954.

ARISTOLOCHIACEAE

The anther is tetrasporangiate with a persistent epidermis and its wall development conforms to the Dicotyledonous type. The endothecium develops fibrous thickenings, and in *Aristolochia bracteata* it may become irregularly 2-layered. The 2 or 3 middle layers are ephemeral but in *Aristolochia* they degenerate only after the anther reaches maturity. The tapetum is glandular and becomes irregularly 2-layered and Ubisch granules are present on its inner surface. Simultaneous cytokinesis in the microspore mother cells follows meiosis in *Aristolochia bracteata*, *Asarum europaeum*, and *Bragantia wallichii*, but the successive type occurs in *Aristolochia clematitis*, *A. elegans*, and *A. sipho*. The microspore tetrads are tetrahedral, isobilateral, decussate, or, rarely, T-shaped. Pollen grains are 2-celled when shed, and those of *Aristolochia* contain starch grains, while in *A. elegans* some have been found to germinate *in situ*.

The ovule is circinotropous in *Bragantia*, but otherwise anatropous, bitegmic, and crassinucellar, with the micropyle formed by the inner integument. The archesporial cell cuts off a primary parietal cell which forms at least 3 parietal layers, and the apical cells of the nucellar epidermis may also divide periclinally. Cytokinesis in the megaspore mother cell accompanies meiosis and the chalazal megaspore of a linear or T-shaped tetrad develops into a Polygonum type embryo sac. According to Wyatt (1955) the micropylar megaspore is functional in *Asarum canadense*. The synergids are pyriform and frequently degenerate before fertilization, the polar nuclei fuse early, and considerable variation has been reported in the behavior of the 3 antipodal cells. In *Bragantia* they are ephemeral, but in the species of *Aristolochia* investigated by Johri and Bhatnagar (1955) they survive until after fertilization, and in *A. clematitis* and *Asarum* spp. they are large and exhibit haustorial activity. A hypostase is of general occurrence in the mature ovule.

Endosperm formation is *ab initio* Cellular and a row of up to eight cells forms before longitudinal divisions occur. Ruminate endosperm is found in *Apama siliquosa*.

Embryogeny is little known but the early cleavages in *Aristolochia bracteata* suggest the Solanad type, and in this species polyembryony is of occasional occurrence.

Chakravarty, 1944 • Dahlgren, 1915a • Hegelmaier, 1886 • Hofmeister, 1858b, 1859 • Jacobsson-Stiasny, 1918 • B. M. Johri and Bhatnagar, 1955 • Jönsson, 1881 • Kratzer, 1918 • Leemann, 1927 • Nair and Narayanan, 1961 • Periasamy, 1962b • Samuelsson, 1914 • Täckholm and Söderberg, 1918 • Venugopalan, 1949 • Warming, 1878 • Westermaier, 1897 • Wyatt, 1955.

ASCLEPIADACEAE

The anther is tetrasporangiate in *Secamone*, but otherwise bisporangiate. In *Asclepias mexicana* wall development follows the Dicotyledonous type except that the hypodermal and subhypodermal layers undergo several periclinal divisions. A thick undifferentiated anther wall is common, and a fibrous endothecium has been reported only in *Ceropegia elegans* and *Vincetoxicum nigrum*. The tendency towards periclinal divisions of the wall cells is expressed also in the glandular tapetum, which is 2- or 3-layered in *Cynanchum, Pergularia,* and *Tylophora*, and multilayered in *Calotropis*. Usually, simultaneous cytokinesis in the microspore mother cells follows meiosis but the successive type is characteristic of the Cynanchoideae. The microspore tetrads are linear and the pollen grains are 3-celled when shed. The contents of the pollen sacs are liberated as pollinia.

The ovule is anatropous, unitegmic, and pseudocrassinucellar. The archesporial cell functions directly as the megaspore mother cell and is deeply embedded below the thick nucellar cap derived from periclinal divisions of the apical nucellar epidermal cells. Cytokinesis in the megaspore mother cell accompanies meiosis and the chalazal megaspore of a linear or T-shaped tetrad develops into a Polygonum type embryo sac. The synergids are pyriform and those of *Daemia extensa* exhibit the filiform apparatus, while in *Ceropegia* the egg apparatus occupies nearly half the embryo sac. The polar nuclei fuse just before fertilization and the 3 antipodal cells are ephemeral except in *Ceropegia* and *Cynanchum* where they simulate the egg apparatus. Starch grains are commonly present in the embryo sac.

Endosperm formation is Nuclear, but after the formation of 8, 16, or 32 nuclei, centripetal walls develop and the tissue becomes cellular throughout. According to Sabet (1931) *ab initio* Cellular endosperm is of occasional occurrence in *Calotropis procera*.

Embryogeny follows the Solanad type and polyembryony is common in *Vincetoxicum*.

Baillon, 1882 • Baum, 1848b • Benetskaia, 1939 • Billings, 1901 • Biswas, 1955, 1957 • Braun, 1860 • Chatin, 1870 • Chauveaud, 1892a,b, 1902 • Corry, 1883, 1884 • Dahlgren, 1923, 1927c • Deshpande and Joneja, 1962 • Dop, 1902, 1903 • Finn, 1921, 1925, 1926 • Francini, 1927a,b, • Frye, 1901, 1902 • Gager, 1902 • L. Guignard, 1903a, 1917a,b, 1921, 1922 • Hofmeister, 1858b • Hubert, 1896 • Kordyum, 1961b,c • Léger, 1913 • Maheswari Devi, 1964 • Mirbel, 1815 • Nirula, 1945a,b • Pardi, 1933b • Richharia, 1934 • Sabet, 1931 • Safwat, 1962 • Schacht, 1853b • Schleiden, 1837, 1839a • Seefeldner, 1912 • W. C. Stevens, 1898 • Strasburger, 1889, 1901 • Venkata Rao and S. R. Rao, 1954 • Vesque, 1878, 1879b • Wefelscheid, 1911 • Wille, 1886.

AUSTROBAILEYACEAE

Embryologically unknown.

AVERRHOACEAE

The number of microsporangia comprising the anther has not been recorded. The endothecium develops fibrous thickenings, the 2 middle layers are ephemeral, and the cells of the glandular tapetum become 2-4-nucleate. Simultaneous cytokinesis in the microspore mother cells follows meiosis, but microspore tetrads have not been described. Pollen grains are 2-celled when shed.

The ovule of *Averrhoa bilimbi* and *A. carambola* is anatropous, bitegmic, and crassinucellar. The archesporial cell cuts off a primary parietal cell which undergoes a single periclinal division and both daughter cells soon degenerate. Cytokinesis in the megaspore mother cell accompanies meiosis and the chalazal megaspore of a linear tetrad develops into a Polygonum type embryo sac. The synergids are pyriform, the polar nuclei fuse close to the egg, and the 3 small antipodal cells degenerate soon after fertilization.

Endosperm formation is Nuclear and the tissue becomes cellular after 32 nuclei have formed.

Embryogeny follows the Asterad type.

Thathachar, 1942a.

BALANITACEAE

The anther is tetrasporangiate in *Balanites roxburghii* and its wall development follows the Monocotyledonous type. The endothecium develops fibrous thickenings and the 2 or 3 middle layers persist until anther maturity, some cells becoming fibrous. The tapetum is glandular and its cells become 2-nucleate. The microspore mother cells undergo simultaneous cytokinesis and the microspore tetrads are tetrahedral or decussate. Pollen grains are 2- or 3-celled when shed.

The ovule is hemianatropous, bitegmic, and crassinucellar, with the zig-zag micropyle formed by both integuments. The archesporium consists of 1–4 cells, only one of which usually cuts off a primary parietal cell and this gives rise to 3 or 4 parietal layers. Although an occasional nucellar epidermal cell may divide periclinally, a nucellar cap is not formed. Cytokinesis in the megaspore mother cell accompanies meiosis and the chalazal megaspore of a linear tetrad gives rise to a Polygonum type embryo sac. The synergids are hooked and the nucleus of each cell occupies a basal position, while the apices are vacuolate. The chalazal polar nucleus is larger than the micropylar one and although they become associated in the center of the embryo sac, fusion occurs close to the egg at fertilization. The 3 antipodal cells are ephemeral. An endothelium encloses the embryo sac and its cells become 2–4-nucleate.

Endosperm formation is Nuclear but the tissue finally becomes cellular.

Embryogeny has not been described in detail but the zygote divides after about 20 endosperm nuclei have formed.

Nair and Jain, 1956 • Narayana, 1957a.

BALANOPHORACEAE

The anther is tetrasporangiate with a persistent epidermis and its wall development in *Balanophora elongata* conforms to the Dicotyledonous type. The 2 subepidermal cell layers are ephemeral with no differentiation of an endothecium, and the tapetum is probably glandular. Development of the pollen grains has not been described but they are 3-celled when shed.

The ovule is ategmic and the megaspore mother cell is enclosed within tissue which is extended into a long beak and interpreted either as nucellus or as a much reduced and modified carpel. Cytokinesis in the megaspore mother cell accompanies meiosis and the micropylar megaspore develops into a Polygonum type embryo sac in *Balanophora dioica, B. elongata*, and *Langsdorffia hypogaea*. However, a bisporic Allium type embryo sac has been described in *Ditepalanthus afzelli* and *Helosis cayannensis*, and apomixis (gonial apospory) occurs in many species of *Balanophora*. In *Helosis* two of the nuclei from the chalazal quartet in the undifferentiated embryo sac fuse with the upper polar nucleus and the remaining two chalazal nuclei are enclosed in 1 or 2 antipodal cells. In *Balanophora* and *Langsdorffia* embryo sac development involves a regular reversal of polarity, because at the 2- or 4-nucleate stage, a caecum develops either from the base or toward the apex of the embryo sac and the chalazal nuclei migrate into it as it elongates and finally extends beyond the original apex. The remaining postmeiotic mitoses then take place and the egg apparatus and single polar nucleus differentiate at the tip of the caecum, while the 4 nuclei in what is morphologically the micropylar pole of the embryo sac fuse into a lobed nucleus which degenerates.

Endosperm formation is *ab initio* Cellular, and in *Balanophora* the first wall cuts off a large haustorial basal cell which remains uninucleate and is finally crushed by the developing endosperm proper which is derived from the upper cell.

Embryogeny in *Balanophora* follows the Piperad type because at least the first two divisions are longitudinal, but development does not proceed beyond the 12-celled stage until after germination of the seed. Polyembryony has been reported in *Balanophora globosa* and *Helosis guianensis*.

Bernard, 1903 • Chodat and Bernard, 1900 • Ekambarum and Panje, 1935 • Ernst, 1913, 1914, 1918 • Fagerlind, 1938b,d, 1945a,b,c • Hofmeister, 1858b, 1959 • Juel, 1902, 1910 • Kuwada, 1928 • Lotsy, 1899, 1901 • Rosenberg, 1930 • Schnarf, 1929 • Steindl, 1945 • Tieghem, 1896a, 1907 • Treub, 1898 • Umiker, 1920 • Zweifel, 1939.

BALANOPSIDACEAE

Embryologically unknown.

BALSAMINACEAE

The anther is tetrasporangiate except in the cleistogamous flowers of *Impatiens fulva*, where only two sporangia are formed. The epidermis is persistent and in *I. fulva* its cells become vesicular. The endothecium develops fibrous thickenings, the 2 or 3 middle layers are ephemeral, and the cells of the glandular tapetum become 2–4-nucleate. Trabeculae separate the sporogenous cells into groups and in *Hydrocera* they are considered to be of tapetal origin, although similar partitions in *Impatiens* arise from the sporogenous tissue itself. Simultaneous cytokinesis in the microspore mother cells follows meiosis and the microspore tetrads are tetrahedral or isobilateral. Pollen grains are 2-celled when shed and those of the cleistogamous flowers of *I. fulva* germinate *in situ*.

The ovule is anatropous, bitegmic, and tenuinucellar, with the micropyle formed by the inner integument. The archesporial cell functions directly as the megaspore mother cell in which cytokinesis usually accompanies each meiotic division. The chalazal megaspore of a linear tetrad develops into a Polygonum type embryo sac in *I. balsamina*, *I. fulva*, *I. inconspicua*, *I. levengi*, *I. pallida*, *I. radiata*, *I. tennella*, and *I. tripetala*, but sometimes cytokinesis is suppressed after the homotypic division and the chalazal dyad cell develops into an Allium type embryo sac as in *I. leschenaultii*, *I. roylei*, *I. sultani*, and *Hydrocera triflora*. The synergids are elongated and pyriform, the polar nuclei fuse before fertilization, and the 3 antipodal cells are ephemeral. Starch grains occur in the embryo sacs of *I. arguta*, *I. balsamina*, and *I. tripetala*. An endothelium is differentiated and a hypostase has been described in *H. triflora* and *I. fulva*.

Endosperm formation is *ab initio* Cellular, with the formation of terminal haustoria. Branches of the aggressive micropylar haustorium may reach the placenta but the large basal endosperm cell is only weakly haustorial.

Embryogeny conforms to the Asterad type.

Brandza, 1891 • Brunotte, 1900 • Caroll, 1919 • Dahlgren, 1927a, 1933, 1934b, 1939a • L. Guignard, 1893a,b • Heinricher, 1888 • Jönsson, 1879–1880, 1881 • Lebon, 1929 • Longo, 1907, 1910a • L. L. Narayana, 1963b • L. L. Narayana, and Sayeeduddin, 1959 • Ottley, 1918 • Phouphas, 1951 • Raghaven et al., 1939 • Riatt, 1916 • Richter-Landmann, 1959 • Schnarf, 1931a • Schürhoff, 1931 • Souèges, 1945b • Steffen, 1946, 1948, 1951, 1952 • Steffen and Landmann, 1958 • Venkateswarlu and Narayana, 1955, 1957 • Wulff, 1934.

BARBEUIACEAE

Embryologically unknown.

BARBEYACEAE

Embryologically unknown.

BASELLACEAE

The anther is tetrasporangiate. Its wall is composed of two sub-epidermal cell layers and a glandular tapetum whose cells become multinucleate. Simultaneous cytokinesis in the microspore mother cells follows meiosis but the microspore tetrads have not been described. Pollen grains are 3-celled when shed.

The ovule is anatropous to anacampylotropous, bitegmic, and crassinucellar, with the micropyle formed by the inner integument. The archesporial cell cuts off a primary parietal cell which gives rise to several parietal layers, and periclinal divisions of the apical cells of the nucellar epidermis form a nucellar cap. Cytokinesis in the megaspore mother cell accompanies meiosis and the chalazal megaspore of a linear tetrad develops into a Polygonum type embryo sac. The synergids are pyriform, the polar nuclei fuse before fertilization, and the 3 small antipodal cells are ephemeral, sometimes degenerating before the formation of the secondary nucleus. Starch grains occur in the embryo sacs of *Basella alba* and *Ullucus tuberosus*.

Endosperm formation is Nuclear, but the tissue later becomes cellular.

Embryogeny has not been investigated.

Dahlgren, 1916 • Dambroise, 1947 • Knuth, 1898 • B. Palm, 1915 • Rocén, 1927.

BATIDACEAE

The anther is tetrasporangiate. The endothecium develops fibrous thickenings and Johnson's figure (1935) of *Batis maritima* shows 2 or 3 persistent middle layers and 2-nucleate tapetal cells. Microsporogenesis has not been investigated, but the pollen grains are 2-celled when shed.

The ovule morphology, embryo sac formation, and postfertilization developments are undescribed

D. S. Johnson, 1935.

BAUERACEAE

Development and structure of the anther and pollen grains have not been investigated.

The ovule of *Bauera rubioides* is anatropous, bitegmic, and crassinucellar, with the zigzag micropyle formed by both integuments. The archesporial cell cuts off a primary parietal cell which gives rise to 3 or 4 parietal layers. Cytokinesis in the megaspore mother cell accompanies meiosis, and the chalazal megaspore of a linear tetrad develops into a Polygonum type embryo sac. The synergids are pyriform, the polar nuclei fuse before fertilization, and the 3 antipodal cells are ephemeral.

Endosperm formation is Nuclear, but the tissue later becomes cellular.

Embryogeny is unknown.

Mauritzon, 1933a, 1939c.

BEGONIACEAE

The anther is tetrasporangiate with a persistent epidermis. The endothecium develops fibrous thickenings, the ephemeral middle layer may become irregularly 2-layered, and cells of the glandular tapetum become 2-nucleate. Simultaneous cytokinesis in the microspore mother cells follows meiosis and the microspore tetrads are tetrahedral. Pollen grains are 2-celled when shed.

The ovule is anatropous, bitegmic, and crassinucellar, with the micropyle formed by both integuments. The archesporial cell cuts off a primary parietal cell which divides once anticlinally and both cells soon degenerate. Cytokinesis in the megaspore mother cell accompanies meiosis and the chalazal megaspore of a linear tetrad develops into a Polygonum type embryo sac. The synergids are pyriform, the polar nuclei fuse before fertilization, and the 3 antipodal cells are ephemeral. The lateral nucellar cells elongate radially and simulate an endothelium.

Endosperm formation is Nuclear but the tissue becomes cellular following centripetal wall formation and the outermost layer of its cells persists in the seed as an aleurone layer. Endosperm commonly fails to develop in Begonia froebeli.

Embryogeny conforms to the Onagrad type.

Elfving, 1879 · Goebel, 1886 · Hofmeister, 1849 · Jönsson, 1879–1880 · Madhulata, 1956 · Mauritzon, 1936b · Meremiński, 1936 · K. Müller, 1847 · Pastrana, 1932 · Sandt, 1921 · Soltwedel, 1882 · Souèges, 1939b · Swamy and Parameswaran 1960 · Warming, 1878 · Wille, 1886.

BERBERIDACEAE

The anther is tetrasporangiate. The endothecium develops fibrous thickenings, the 2 or 3 middle layers are ephemeral, and the cells of the glandular tapetum become multinucleate. Simultaneous cytokinesis follows meiosis and the microspore tetrads are tetrahedral or isobilateral. Pollen grains are 2-celled when shed.

The ovule is anatropous, bitegmic, and crassinucellar, with the micropyle formed by both integuments. Although a group of archesporial cells is common, only one is functional and cuts off a primary parietal cell. Several parietal layers are formed which, together with the nucellar cap derived from periclinal divisions of the apical epidermal cells, form a tissue of 6–8 layers above the megaspore mother cell. In *Berberis nepalensis* the megaspore mother cell occasionally develops directly from an archesporial cell, and no parietal tissue is formed. Cytokinesis in the megaspore mother cell accompanies meiosis and the chalazal megaspore of a linear tetrad develops into a Polygonum type embyro sac. The synergids are pyriform, the polar nuclei fuse before fertilization, and the 3 antipodal cells are large and highly vacuolate.

Endosperm formation is Nuclear.

Embryogeny conforms to the Onagrad type and polyembryony has been reported in *Berberis vulgaris*.

Braun, 1859 • Dahlgren, 1915 • Erdtman, 1945 • L. Guignard, 1882b • Hofmeister, 1858 • Huss, 1906 • B. M. Johri, 1935d • Jönsson, 1879–1880, 1881 • Langlet, 1928 • Mauritzon, 1936f • F. E. Rudenko, 1961 • Sastri, 1956a • Schnarf, 1931a • Subramanyam, 1962 • Tischler, 1903b • Vesque, 1879b.

BETULACEAE

The anther is tetrasporangiate but neither its development nor that of the pollen grains has been described. According to Woodworth (1929, 1930) only 2–3% of the pollen of *Alnus rugosa* is normal.

The ovule is anatropous, unitegmic, and crassinucellar. The archesporial cell cuts off a primary parietal cell which gives rise to 1–4 parietal layers, although Nawaschin (1894) considered the tissue above the megaspore mother cell of *Betula alba* to be epidermal in origin. Cytokinesis in the megaspore mother cell accompanies meiosis and the chalazal megaspore of a linear tetrad develops into a Polygonum type embryo sac. In *A. rugosa* meiosis is suppressed and 1–4 embryo sacs develop apomictically (gonial apospory) from a multicellular archesporium. The synergids are pyriform, the polar nuclei fuse before fertilization, and the 3 antipodal cells of *B. verrucosa* are ephemeral, although those of *A. glutinosa* are longer lived. Fertilization is chalazogamous and in *B. alba* more than 4 weeks intervene between pollination and fertilization.

Endosperm formation is Nuclear, but later the tissue becomes cellular.

Embryogeny in *A. glutinosa* conforms to the Asterad type, and polyembryony has been reported in several species of *Alnus*.

Benson, 1894 • Chamberlain, 1898 • Dahlgren, 1915a • Hofmeister, 1858 • Mestre, 1964b • Nawaschin, 1892, 1894a,b, 1895, 1899 • Nawaschin and Finn, 1913 • Wolpert, 1910 • Woodworth, 1929a,b,c, 1930a,b.

BIGNONIACEAE

The anther is tetrasporangiate in *Bignonia* but in *Dolichandrone* and *Parmentiera* only two microsporangia are formed and these are each subdivided by a tapetal ingrowth. The epidermal cells become much enlarged radially and are cutinized on the outer surface. In *Bignonia* the anther wall develops according to the Dicotyledonous type although the endothecium does not develop fibrous thickenings. In *Oroxylum* at least 9 wall layers are formed and the fibrous endothecium is multilayered. The tapetum is amoeboid and its cells become multinucleate but finally 2-nucleate following nuclear fusions. Simultaneous cytokinesis in the microspore mother cells follow meiosis, and the microspore tetrads are tetrahedral. Pollen grains are 2-celled when shed.

The ovule is anatropous to hemianatropous, unitegmic, and tenuinucellar. The archesporial cell develops directly into the megaspore mother cell in which cytokinesis accompanies meiosis and the chalazal megaspore of a linear tetrad develops into a Polygonum type embryo sac. The synergids are large and hooked, the polar nuclei fuse before fertilization, and the three antipodal cells either persist into the early stages of endosperm formation (*Jacaranda, Parmentiera, Tecoma*) or are very ephemeral. An endothelium is formed and a hypostase is usually present.

Endosperm formation is *ab initio* Cellular, and an aggressive 2- or 4-celled chalazal haustorium develops, and in *Bignonia* and *Oroxylum* a micropylar haustorium is also formed. Embryogeny follows the Onagrad type.

Crété, 1942, 1951d, 1952e, 1955f • Duggar, 1899 • Ghatak, 1956 • Govindu, 1950 • L. Guignard, 1882 • B. J. Harris and Baker, 1959 • Hofmeister, 1858b, 1859 • Mauritzon, 1935d • Raghavan and Venkatasubban, 1940 • Samuelsson, 1913 • Souèges, 1940a • Swamy, 1941a • Venkatasubban, 1945.

BIXACEAE

The anther is octosporangiate with a papillate epidermis, and those endothecial cells which are close to the dehiscence slits develop thickenings. The 1 or 2 middle layers are ephemeral and Ubisch granules are present on the inner tangential and radial walls of the glandular tapetum. Simultaneous cytokinesis in the microspore mother cells follows meiosis and the microspore tetrads are tetrahedral or, occasionally, decussate. The pollen grains are 2- or 3-celled when shed.

The ovule of *Bixa orellana* is anatropous, bitegmic, and crassinucellar, with the micropyle formed by both integuments. The archesporial cell cuts off a primary parietal cell which gives rise to 4–6 parietal layers, and a nucellar cap up to 6 cells in thickness is formed by periclinal divisions of the apical nucellar epidermal cells. Cytokinesis in the megaspore mother cell accompanies meiosis and the chalazal megaspore of a linear tetrad develops into a Polygonum type embryo sac. The synergids are hooked, the polar nuclei fuse before fertilization, and the 3 antipodal cells are ephemeral. A weak hypostase is formed.

Endosperm formation is Nuclear but later the tissue becomes cellular throughout.

Embryogeny has not been described.

Chopra and Kaur, 1965 • Mauritzon, 1936b • Venkatesh, 1956e.

BOMBACACEAE

The number of sporangia comprising the anther has not been reported but the epidermis is persistent and its cells become filled with tannin. The endothecium develops fibrous thickenings and 3 or 4 middle layers are formed. The cells of the glandular tapetum become multinucleate but finally each contains a single lobed fusion nucleus and Ubisch granules occur on its inner walls in *Ochroma lagopus*. Many microspore mother cells degenerate but in the functional ones simultaneous cytokinesis follows meiosis and the microspore tetrads are tetrahedral. Pollen grains are 2-celled when shed.

The ovule is anatropous, bitegmic, and crassinucellar, with the zig-zag micropyle formed by both integuments. An air space is present between the integuments. The archesporial cell cuts off a primary parietal cell which gives rise to 8–12 parietal layers and, in addition, a nucellar cap 8 cells in thickness is formed by periclinal divisions of the apical nucellar epidermal cells. Cytokinesis in the deeply buried megaspore mother cell accompanies meiosis and the chalazal megaspore of a linear or T-shaped tetrad develops into a Polygonum type embryo sac. The synergids are hooked and in *Ochroma* a filiform apparatus is present, while in *Pachira rosea* the apex of each synergid bears a round area with a frilled rim. The polar nuclei fuse before fertilization and the 3 antipodal cells are ephemeral, except in *Ochroma* where they persist until just after fertilization.

Endosperm formation is Nuclear but later the tissue becomes cellular. In *Eriodendron anfractuosum* the chalazal end of the embryo sac becomes haustorial after fertilization and penetrates into the nucellus.

Embryogeny conforms to the Asterad type and in *Pachira oleaginea* adventive polyembryony occurs.

Baker, 1959, 1960 • Banerji, 1942b • Decaisne, 1880 • Doumet, 1866 • Lynch, 1880 • A. N. Rao, 1964d • Thirumalachar and Khan, 1941 • Venkata Rao, 1954a.

BONNETIACEAE

Embryologically unknown.

BORAGINACEAE

The anther is tetrasporangiate with a persistent epidermis and its wall development conforms to the Dicotyledonous type. The endothecium usually develops fibrous thickenings but in *Cynoglossum* only the inner and radial cell walls are thickened. The middle layer is ephemeral and the cells of the glandular tapetum become multinucleate in *Anchusa*, *Echium*, *Lycopsis*, and *Trichodesma* but they remain 1 or 2-nucleate in *Cynoglossum* and *Heliotropium*. Simultaneous cytokinesis in the microspore mother cells follows meiosis, and the microspore tetrads are tetrahedral or isobilateral. Pollen grains are 3-celled when shed except in *Heliotropium* and *Trichodesma* where they are 2-celled, and starch grains are usually present.

The ovule is anatropous to hemianatropous, unitegmic, and tenuinucellar, except in *Heliotropium* where a periclinal division of the apical nucellar epidermal cells results in the pseudocrassinucellar condition. The archesporial cell functions directly as the megaspore mother cell in which cytokinesis usually accompanies meiosis and the chalazal megaspore of a linear tetrad develops into a Polygonum type embryo sac. However, suppression of cytokinesis after the homotypic division and the development of the chalazal dyad cell into an Allium type embryo sac has been reported by Svensson (1922, 1925) in *Anchusa officinalis* and *Lycopsis arvensis*, and found by Millsaps (1940) to be of occasional occurrence in *Cynoglossum amabile*. The synergids are pyriform and sometimes hooked and the polar nuclei fuse at, or just before, fertilization. The 3 antipodal cells are usually ephemeral but in *H. curassavicum* they persist into early postfertilization stages and in *H. europeum* 6 cells are formed by secondary multiplication. An endothelium is differentiated in *Heliotropium* and an obturator is present in *Trichodesma*.

Endosperm formation varies from Nuclear to *ab initio* Cellular, with intermediate forms, and Svensson (1925) recognized 5 different endosperm types. A short micropylar haustorium is formed in *Heliotropium*.

Embryogeny usually follows the Chenopodiad type but in *Cynoglossum, Lycopsis,* and *Trichodesma* it conforms to the Asterad type.

Chatin, 1874 • Crété, 1950f, 1953a, 1955d, 1959b,c • Dahlgren 1915a, 1922 • L. Guignard, 1882b, 1893b • Hegelmaier, 1886 • Hofmeister, 1858b • Jönsson, 1879–1880 • Junell, 1938 • Khanna, 1964b • Lötscher, 1905 • Mascré, 1922 • Millsaps, 1940 • Ramamurti, 1958 • Rosanoff, 1866 • Schnarf, 1931a • Souèges, 1921d,e 1923g, 1938e,f, 1941a, 1943f • Strasburger, 1884b, 1889 • Svensson, 1922, 1923a,b,c, 1925 • Tieghem, 1906 • Venkateswarlu and Atchutaramamurti, 1955a • Vesque, 1878, 1879, 1885 • Warming, 1873, 1878 • Went, 1887b • Wille, 1882b.

BROMELIACEAE

Anther development has not been traced but a fibrous endothecium is formed and the tapetum is glandular. Successive cytokinesis in the microspore mother cells accompanies meiosis and the pollen grains are 2-celled when shed.

The ovule is anatropous, bitegmic, and crassinucellar, with the micropyle formed by the inner integument. The archesporial cell cuts off a primary parietal cell and in *Tillandsia usneoides* about 6 cell layers are present above the mature embryo sac but some may be epidermal derivatives. Cytokinesis in the megaspore mother cell accompanies meiosis and the chalazal megaspore of a linear tetrad develops into a Polygonum type embryo sac. The synergids are pyriform and the polar nuclei fuse before fertilization close to the 3 small antipodal cells.

Endosperm formation is Helobial. Nuclear divisions are accompanied by wall formation in the small chalazal chamber but the large micropylar chamber becomes multinucleate before it gives rise to the cellular endosperm proper.

Embryogeny conforms to the Asterad type and polyembryony has been reported in *T. juncea*.

Billings, 1904 • Birge, 1911 • Guignard, L., 1882b • Hofmeister, 1858b, 1861 • Jönsson, 1881 • Palm, B., 1920 • Schürhoff, 1926b • Süssenguth, 1919, 1921a • Tischler, 1912, 1915.

BRUNELLIACEAE

Embryologically unknown.

BRUNIACEAE

Development and structure of the anther and pollen grains have not been investigated.

The ovule is anatropous, unitegmic, and crassinucellar, with a long micropyle and small nucellus. Saxton's (1910) figures of *Audouinia*, *Berzelia*, *Brunia*, and *Staavia* ovules show a single layer of cells between the nucellar epidermis and the megaspore mother cell which may have been derived either from a primary parietal cell or by periclinal division of apical nucellar epidermal cells. Cytokinesis in the megaspore mother cell accompanies meiosis and the chalazal megaspore of a linear tetrad develops into a Polygonum type embryo sac. The synergids are pyriform, the polar nuclei fuse before fertilization, and the 3 antipodal cells are ephemeral. Starch grains occur in the embryo sacs of *Berzelia* and *Brunia*.

Endosperm formation and embryogeny have not been described.

Mauritzon, 1939c • Saxton, 1910.

BRUNONIACEAE

The development and structure of the anther and pollen grains have not been investigated.

The ovule is anatropous, unitegmic, and tenuinucellar. The archesporial cell functions directly as the megaspore mother cell, in which cytokinesis accompanies meiosis and the chalazal megaspore of a linear tetrad develops into a Polygonum type embryo sac. The synergids are elongated and their tips enter the micropyle, the polar nuclei fuse before fertilization, and the 3 antipodal cells are ephemeral. An endothelium is differentiated.

Endosperm formation and embryogeny have not been described, but in *Brunonia australis* a multinucleate suspensor haustorium has been reported in the micropyle.

Rosén, 1946.

BUDDLEIACEAE

The anther is tetrasporangiate but there is no information on its development and structure or that of the pollen grains.

The ovule is hemianatropous, unitegmic, and tenuinucellar. The archesporial cell functions directly as the megaspore mother cell, in which cytokinesis accompanies meiosis and the chalazal megaspore of a linear tetrad develops into a Polygonum type embryo sac. The synergids are pyriform, the polar nuclei fuse before fertilization, and the 3 antipodal cells persist into early endosperm formation. An endothelium is differentiated in all species of *Buddleia* except *B. lindbergiana*, and a hypostase is formed.

Endosperm formation in *Buddleia* is *ab initio* Cellular, with the development of a much-branched 2-celled micropylar haustorium and a 2- or 4-celled chalazal haustorium.

Embryogeny conforms to the Onagrad type.

Crété, 1942, 1951d • Dahlgren, 1922, 1923 • Dop, 1913 • Souèges, 1940c.

BURMANNIACEAE

Development and structure of the anther have not been described but the pollen grains of *Burmannia candida* are 2-celled when shed and those of *B. disticha* are 3-celled. In cleistogamous flowers the pollen grains germinate *in situ*.

The ovule is anatropous, bitegmic, and tenuinucellar. The archesporial cell functions directly as the megaspore mother cell in which cytokinesis accompanies meiosis in *Apteria setacea* and *Gymnosiphon trinitatis* and the chalazal megaspore of a linear tetrad develops into a Polygonum type embryo sac. In *Burmannia candida*, however, cytokinesis is suppressed after the homotypic division and the chalazal dyad cell develops into an Allium type embryo sac, while in *B. coelestis* meiosis does not occur and the megaspore mother cell develops into an unreduced embryo sac by gonial apospory. The synergids are pyriform and the polar nuclei fuse before fertilization in the center of the embryo sac or toward the 3 small antipodal cells.

Endosperm formation is Helobial with a small haustorial chalazal chamber and a large micropylar chamber which becomes free-nucleate and finally cellular at the time of zygote division.

Embryogeny is arrested at the 4-celled stages in *Apteria setacea, Burmannia javanica,* and *B. maburnia,* but reaches the 10-celled condition in *Gymnosiphon trinitatis*. Further development takes place after the seed is shed. Polyembryony occurs in *B. coelestis*.

Bernard and Ernst, 1914 • Dahlgren, 1927a • Ernst, 1909 • Ernst and Bernard, 1912a,b • Johow, 1885, 1889 • Miers, 1881 • Schoch, 1920 • Treub, 1883c,d.

BURSERACEAE

The anther is tetrasporangiate with a persistent epidermis. The endothecium develops fibrous thickenings, the 1 or 2 middle layers are ephemeral, and the cells of the glandular tapetum become 2-nucleate. Simultaneous cytokinesis in the microspore mother cells follows meiosis, and the microspore tetrads are tetrahedral except in *Balsamodendron mukul* and *Bursera serrata* where the microspore mother cells all degenerate. Pollen grains are 2-celled when shed.

The ovule is hemianatropous, bitegmic, and crassinucellar, with the micropyle formed by the inner integument. The single integument of *Commiphora, Santiria,* and two species of *Canarium* is considered by Narayana (1960) to be a fusion structure. The archesporial cell cuts off a primary parietal cell which forms up to 14 parietal layers and a nucellar cap about 6 cells in thickness results from periclinal divisions of the apical nucellar epidermal cells. Cytokinesis in the deeply buried megaspore mother cell accompanies meiosis and the chalazal megaspore of a linear tetrad develops into a Polygonum type embryo sac. The synergids are hooked and exhibit the filiform apparatus, the polar nuclei fuse before fertilization, and the 3 small antipodal cells are ephemeral.

Endosperm formation is Nuclear but embryogeny has not been investigated.

Mauritzon, 1935e · L. L. Narayana, 1957b, 1959, 1960c,d · Shukla, 1954 · Wiger, 1935, 1936.

BUTOMACEAE

The anther is tetrasporangiate with a persistent epidermis and its wall development follows the Monocotyledonous type. The endothecium develops fibrous thickenings, the middle layer is ephemeral, and the tapetum is amoeboid. Successive cytokinesis in the microspore mother cells accompanies meiosis and the microspore tetrads are tetrahedral, isobilateral, T-shaped, or linear. Pollen grains are 3-celled when shed.

The ovule is anatropous, bitegmic, and pseudocrassinucellar, with the micropyle formed by the inner integument. The apical cells of the nucellar epidermis undergo a single periclinal division and form a nucellar cap 2 cells in thickness. The archesporial cell functions directly as the megaspore mother cell in which usually cytokinesis follows only the first meiotic division and in *Butomopsis, Hydrocleys,* and *Limnocharis* the large chalazal dyad cell develops into an Allium type embryo sac. In *Butomus umbellatus,* however, a linear tetrad of megaspores is formed and the embryo sac is of the Polygonum type. During embryo sac development, one or more of the chalazal nuclei may fail to undergo division ("strike"), and consequently the mature structure may contain only 6 or 5 nuclei. The synergids are hooked and exhibit the filiform apparatus, the polar nuclei fuse before fertilization, and the number of antipodal cells varies from 3–0, according to the number of nuclei in the unorganized embryo sac.

Endosperm formation is Helobial. The small chalazal chamber usually remains uninucleate and later degenerates while the large micropylar chamber becomes multinucleate and forms the endosperm proper.

Embryogeny conforms to the Caryophyllad type and polyembryony has been reported in *L. emarginata.*

Buchenau, 1857, 1882 • Claussen, 1927 • Elfving, 1879 • Hall, 1902 • Herrig, 1919 • Holmgren, 1913 • B. M. Johri, 1935a, 1936b, 1938a,b • B. M. Johri, and Bhatnagar, 1957 • P. Maheshwari, 1943 • Nitzschke, 1914 • B. Palm, 1915, 1920 • Roper, 1952 • Sahni and Johri, 1936 • Strasburger, 1884b • Süssenguth, 1921a • Tischler, 1915 • Vesque, 1878, 1879 • Ward, 1880b.

BUXACEAE

The anther is tetrasporangiate with a persistent epidermis. The endothecium develops fibrous thickenings, the 1–3 middle layers are ephemeral, and the cells of the glandular tapetum become 2-nucleate. Simultaneous cytokinesis in the microspore mother cells follows meiosis and the microspore tetrads are tetrahedral or isobilateral. Pollen grains are 2-celled when shed.

The ovule is anatropous, bitegmic, and crassinucellar, with the micropyle formed by the inner integument. The archesporial cell cuts off a primary parietal cell which gives rise to a parietal tissue varying from 2 layers in *Simmondsia* to 15 or more in *Buxus,* and the apical nucellar epidermal cells divide at least once periclinally to form a nucellar cap. Cytokinesis in the megaspore mother cell accompanies meiosis and the chalazal megaspore of a linear tetrad develops into a Polygonum type embryo sac. The synergids are pyriform and exhibit the filiform apparatus, the polar nuclei fuse before fertilization, and the 3 antipodal cells persist into early postfertilization stages. In *Buxus microphylla* and *Pachysandra terminalis* Wiger (1935) has reported a small degree of secondary multiplication of antipodals.

Endosperm formation is *ab initio* Cellular in *Buxus* and *Pachysandra,* but Nuclear in *Sarcococca and Simmondsia.*

Embryogeny conforms to the Onagrad type. In *Sarcococca* polyembryony has been reported in several species and in *S. prunifolia* the egg apparatus degenerates and at least one embryo develops by adventive embryony.

Dahlgren, 1915a • Jönsson, 1879–1880, 1881 • Mauritzon, 1935e • Orr, 1923 • Samuelsson, 1913 • Schnarf, 1929b • Wiger, 1930, 1935, 1936.

BYBLIDACEAE

The anther is tetrasporangiate. The endothecium differentiates as a distinct layer only at the apex of the anther where its outer cell walls become considerably thickened. The remaining wall layers and development of the pollen grains have not been described.

The ovule of *Byblis gigantea* is anatropous, bitegmic, and tenuinucellar, with the micropyle formed by the inner integument. The archesporial cell functions directly as the megaspore mother cell, but development of the embryo sac has not been investigated, although the mature structure contains numerous starch grains and is enclosed by an endothelium.

Endosperm formation is probably *ab initio* Cellular and multicellular terminal haustoria are formed.

Embryogeny is unknown.

Lang, 1901.

CABOMBACEAE

The anther is tetrasporangiate but its structure and the development of the pollen grains have not been described.

The ovule is anatropous, bitegmic, and crassinucellar, with the micropyle formed by the inner integument. The behavior of the archesporial cell and development of the embryo sac have not been investigated but starch grains are present in the mature structure of *Brasenia purpurea* and *Cabomba piauhiensis*.

Endosperm formation is Helobial, and the small uninucleate chalazal chamber becomes haustorial.

Embryogeny is undescribed.

M. T. Cook, 1906, 1909a • Dahlgren, 1927c • Melikyan, 1964 • Nitzschke, 1914 • Raciborsky, 1894.

CACTACEAE

The anther is tetrasporangiate and its persistent epidermis becomes slightly lignified. The endothecium develops fibrous thickenings and the middle layer is ephemeral while the cells of the glandular tapetum become multinucleate and nuclear fusions occur. Simultaneous cytokinesis in the microspore mother cells follows meiosis and the microspore tetrads are tetrahedral. Pollen grains are 3-celled when shed.

The ovule is circinotropous, bitegmic, and crassinucellar, with the micropyle formed only by the swollen tip of the inner integument. The archesporial cells cuts off a primary parietal cell which forms 1 or 2 parietal layers, and either the apical cells of the nucellar epidermis undergo radial elongation (*Opuntia, Pereskia, Rhipsalis*) or they divide periclinally and form a nucellar cap (*Astrophytum, Thelocactus, Toumeya*). Cytokinesis in the megaspore mother cell accompanies meiosis and the chalazal megaspore of a linear tetrad develops into a Polygonum type embryo sac. Suppression of the homotypic meiotic division in the micropylar dyad cell is common and results in a row of three cells. The synergids are hooked and in *O. dillenii* a filiform apparatus is present. The polar nuclei fuse before fertilization and the 3 antipodals are ephemeral. Starch grains are formed in the embryo sac and at ovule maturity an air space occurs basally between the integuments.

Endosperm formation is Nuclear and in *Astrophytum, Thelocactus,* and *Toumeya* wall formation is initiated around the embryo at the fifth day of development and proceeds centrifugally. In *Opuntia,* however, it is doubtful that the endosperm becomes cellular before it is digested by the embryo.

No satisfactory account exists of normal embryogeny, and in *Opuntia* adventive embryony follows early degeneration of the egg. In *O. dillenii* Maheshwari and Chopra (1955) found that the majority of the seeds were empty and that 2–3% of the fertile ones contained more than one embryo, whereas in *O. vulgaris* Ganong (1898b) reported polyembryony in 50% of seeds.

Archibald, 1939 • Braun, 1860 • Buxbaum, 1948, 1955, 1956, 1958 • Chopra, 1957 • Engleman, 1960 • Ganong, 1898a,b • L. Guignard, 1886a,b • Hofmeister, 1858 • Huber, 1929, 1937 • Hubert, 1896 • Hull, 1915 • T. Ishii, 1929 • D. S. Johnson, 1918 • Jönsson, 1879–1880, 1881 • P. Maheshwari, 1936 • P. Maheshwari, and Chopra, 1954, 1955 • Mauritzon, 1934b • Montemartini, 1899 • M. Neumann, 1935 • Schnarf, 1929b • Schumann, 1898 • Strasburger, 1884b, 1908 • Tiagi, 1954a,b, 1956, 1957.

CAESALPINACEAE

The anther is tetrasporangiate with a persistent epidermis whose cells contain tannin in *Parkinsonia*. The endothecium develops fibrous thickenings, and in *Cassia* subg. *Senna* its cells become variously sclerified, whereas in *Cassia* subg. *Lasiorhegma* it is unthickened and becomes crushed during anther maturation. Three ephemeral middle layers are usually formed, although in *Cassia* sgg. *Fistulosa* and *Senna* 6–8 layers are present. The tapetum is usually glandular and its cells become multinucleate but nuclear fusions may restore the 1-nucleate condition. In *Cassia absus*, *C. kleinii* and *C. mimosoides* Venkatesh (1956b) has reported the formation of a tapetal periplasmodium. Simultaneous cytokinesis in the microspore mother cells follows meiosis and microspore tetrads are tetrahedral or occasionally decussate, isobilateral, or T-shaped. No archesporium is differentiated in the staminodes of *Cassia*. Pollen grains are 2-celled when shed.

The ovule is anatropous to campylotropous, bitegmic, and crassinucellar, with the zig-zag micropyle formed by both integuments except in *Cassia tora* where only the outer integument is involved. The archesporial cell cuts off a primary parietal cell very early and a thick parietal tissue is formed. In *Parkinsonia aculeata* the apical cells of the nucellar epidermis divide periclinally and form a nucellar cap 2–4 cells in thickness, but the degree of activity of the nucellar epidermis in other members is not clear. Cytokinesis in the megaspore mother cell accompanies meiosis and the chalazal or subchalazal megaspore of a linear tetrad develops into a Polygonum type embryo sac. The synergids are hooked and the filiform apparatus is exhibited in *Cassia*. The polar nuclei fuse before fertilization and the 3 antipodal cells are ephemeral in *Parkinsonia* but otherwise they persist until soon after fertilization.

Endosperm formation is Nuclear but later the tissue becomes cellular at the micropylar end of the embryo sac, while the chalazal region remains free-nuclear and forms an aggressive haustorium. In *Delonix* the endosperm haustorium is broad and saclike but in *Cassia* it forms a narrow tube with a vesicular tip.

Embryogeny is undescribed but polyembryony has been reported in *Cassia tora*.

Braun, 1860 • Chatin, 1870 • R. M. Datta, 1934 • Dnyansagar, 1956 • Francini, 1951 • Ghose and Alagh, 1933 • L. Guignard, 1881a,b • Hérail, 1889 • Hubert, 1896 • B. M. Johri, and Garg, 1959 • List, 1963 • S. K. Mukherjee, 1952 • Moore and Behney, 1908 • Nair and Kakate, 1961 • Pantulu, 1945, 1951 • Paul, 1937 • Pellegrini, 1954 • M. A. Rau, 1950a,b, 1951g, 1954a • Saxton, 1907 • Sethi, 1930 • Tischler, 1903, 1925 • Venkatesh, 1956c,d, 1957.

CALLITRICHACEAE

The number of sporangia comprising the anther has not been recorded. Prior to dehiscence its wall is composed of epidermis and fibrous endothecium but with the latter layer undifferentiated in *Callitriche autumnalis* and the entirely submerged forms. The tapetum is glandular and its cells become multinucleate. Simultaneous cytokinesis in the microspore mother cells follows meiosis and the pollen grains are 3-celled when shed.

The ovule is anatropous, unitegmic, and tenuinucellar. The archesporial cell functions directly as the megaspore mother cell in which cytokinesis accompanies meiosis and the chalazal megaspore of a linear tetrad develops into a Polygonum type embryo sac. The synergids are pyriform, the polar nuclei fuse before fertilization, and the 3 small antipodal cells are ephemeral. A well-developed endothelium is differentiated.

Endosperm formation is *ab initio* Cellular with the development of terminal haustoria. The aggressive micropylar haustorium is formed of 2 or 4 long, twisted cells which penetrate the micropyle and pass through the integument to the funicle. The chalazal haustorium is considerably smaller and its four cells form a short hook at the base of the endosperm proper.

Embryogeny follows the Onagrad type and a long filamentous suspensor is developed.

Baillon, 1858b • B. Clarke, 1865 • Hegelmaier, 1864, 1867 • Jørgensen, 1923, 1925 • Samuelsson, 1913 • Schürhoff, 1924b, 1926a • Souèges, 1952d • Strasburger, 1884b • Winge, 1917.

CALYCANTHACEAE

The anther is tetrasporangiate, but apart from the presence of a glandular tapetum, its structure has not been described. Simultaneous cytokinesis in the microspore mother cells follows meiosis and the microspore tetrads are tetrahedral or isobilateral. Developmental abnormalities result in the formation of double or distorted pollen grains, and although some reach the 2-celled condition degeneration follows and no fertile pollen is produced by either *Calycanthus* or *Chimonanthus*.

The ovule is anatropous, bitegmic, and pseudocrassinucellar, with the micropyle formed by the inner integument. A multiple archesporium of up to 10 cells differentiates and according to Peter (1920) and Schürhoff (1922c) each cell functions directly as a megaspore mother cell, with the overlying 5 or 6 cell layers being derived from periclinal divisions of the nucellar epidermis. Earlier workers, however, described the formation of a primary parietal cell. Cytokinesis in the megaspore mother cell accompanies meiosis and although sev-

eral linear tetrads of megaspores are formed, only one chalazal megaspore develops into the Polygonum type embryo sac. Fusion of polar
nuclei does not occur and one commonly degenerates together with
the egg apparatus and the 3 small antipodal nuclei.

Endosperm formation is *ab initio* Cellular and develops autonomously from the surviving polar nucleus.

Adventive embryony is the rule and the embryo develops from
a nucellar cell which protrudes into the embryo sac. Polyembryony
has been reported in *Calycanthus occidentalis*.

Braun, 1960 • Brofferio, 1930 • Erdtman, 1945, 1952 • Jönsson, 1879–1880 •
Longo, 1898, 1900 • Peter, 1920 • Schnarf, 1931a • Schürhoff, 1923 • Subramanyam,
1962 • Y. D. Tiagi, 1963.

CALYCERACEAE

Development of the anther and pollen grains has not been traced,
but at maturity the anther wall is composed only of the fibrous endothecium. The tapetum is glandular in *Acicarpha* and the pollen grains
are 2-celled when shed.

The ovule is anatropous, unitegmic, and tenuinucellar. The archesporial cell functions directly as the megaspore mother cell in which
cytokinesis accompanies meiosis and the chalazal megaspore of the
linear tetrad develops into a Polygonum type embryo sac. The synergids are elongated with slender beaks, the polar nuclei fuse before
fertilization, and the 3 antipodal cells are very ephemeral.

Endosperm formation is *ab initio* Cellular in *Acicarpha* and
Calycera where a row of 4 cells is formed before longitudinal divisions
occur.

Embryogeny has not been traced apart from the report that early
cleavages are transverse and the proembryo passes through a linear
tetrad stage.

Dahlgren, 1915b, 1923 • Doll, 1927 • Juel, 1915 • Warming, 1913.

CAMPANULACEAE

The anther is tetrasporangiate and its wall development follows
the Dicotyledonous type. The endothecium develops fibrous thickenings, a single ephemeral middle layer is usual but 2 such layers are
formed in *Pentaphragma horsfieldii*, and the cells of the glandular
tapetum become 2-nucleate. Simultaneous cytokinesis in the microspore mother cells follows meiosis, and the microspore tetrads are

tetrahedral or isobilateral. Pollen grains are 2-celled when shed in *Campanula americana* and *Wahlenbergia bicolor* but in other members, including *W. gracilis*, they are 3-celled, and those of *Cephalostigma schimperi* contain starch grains. Polymorphic pollen grains have been reported in *Phyteuma limonifolium*.

The ovule is anatropous, unitegmic, and tenuinucellar. The archesporial cell functions directly as the megaspore mother cell in which cytokinesis accompanies meiosis and the chalazal megaspore of a linear tetrad develops into a Polygonum type embryo sac. In *Pentaphragma horsfieldii* the micropylar portion of the embryo sac becomes extra-ovular at the 4-nucleate stage. The synergids are hooked in *Pentaphragma* and *Wahlenbergia* and Barnes (1885) shows the filiform apparatus in his figure of *Campanula americana*. The polar nuclei fuse before fertilization and the 3 antipodal cells are ephemeral, and starch grains are present in the embryo sacs of *Campanula*, *Cephalostigma*, and *Wahlenbergia*. An endothelium is differentiated which in *Campanula* does not enclose the extremities of the embryo sac.

Endosperm formation is *ab initio* Cellular and Rosén (1949) recognized three types of development in the family. Both micropylar and chalazal haustoria are 1-, 2- or 4-celled.

Embryogeny conforms to the Solanad type and polyembryony has been reported in *Jasione* and *Wahlenbergia*.

Armand, 1921 • Balicka-Iwanowska, 1899 • Barnes, 1885 • Crété, 1948c, 1951d, 1956e • Elfving, 1879 • L. Guignard, 1882b • Habermann, 1906 • Hegelmaier, 1886 • Hofmeister, 1858, 1859 • Hubert, 1896 • Jönsson, 1881 • Juel, 1915 • Kapil and Vijayaraghavan, 1962, 1965 • Kausik and Subramanyam, 1946c, 1947a • Poddubnaja-Arnoldi, 1933c • Radlkofer, 1856 • Rosén, 1932, 1949 • K. Y. Rudenko, 1961a • Safijowska, 1935a,b • Samuelsson, 1913 • Souèges, 1936d, 1938a • Strasburger, 1884, 1889 • Subramanyam, 1947, 1948b, 1950c, 1951b, 1953 • Sukacĕv, 1940 • Swamy and Padmanabhan, 1961c • Telesca, 1962 • Vesque, 1878, 1879a • Want, 1963 • Warming, 1873 • A. Winkler, 1882 • Yamaha, 1926.

CANELLACEAE

The number of sporangia composing the anther has not been recorded but the epidermis is persistent. The endothecium develops fibrous thickenings, 3 ephemeral middle layers are formed and the cells of the glandular tapetum become multinucleate but finally 1-nucleate by fusion. Ubisch granules occur on the inner tangential walls of the tapetal cells. Simultaneous cytokinesis in the microspore mother cells follows meiosis and the microspore tetrads are tetrahedral. Pollen grains are 2-celled when shed.

The ovule of *Canella alba* and *Warburgia stuhlmannii* is hemia-natropous, bitegmic, and crassinucellar, with the zigzag micropyle formed by both integuments. The archesporial cell cuts off a primary parietal cell which gives rise to an extensive parietal tissue. Cytokinesis in the megaspore mother cell accompanies meiosis and the chalazal megaspore of a linear tetrad develops into a Polygonum type embryo sac. The synergids are pyriform and the nucleus is situated in the broad basal end and a small vacuole occupies the apex, which exhibits the filiform apparatus. The polar nuclei fuse before fertilization and 3 small antipodal cells are present.

Endosperm formation has not been described but the tissue becomes ruminate in the seed.

Embryogeny is unknown.

Parameswaran, 1961, 1962.

CANNABIACEAE

The anther is tetrasporangiate with a cutinized epidermis. In *Cannabis sativa* the endothecial cells become filled with resin, the 2 or 3 middle layers are ephemeral, and the cells of the glandular tapetum become 2-nucleate. Simultaneous cytokinesis in the microspore mother cells follows meiosis and the microspore tetrads are tetrahedral. Pollen grains are 2-celled when shed.

The ovule is anatropous, bitegmic, and crassinucellar, with the micropyle formed by the inner integument. The archesporial cell cuts off a primary parietal cell which gives rise to up to 7 parietal layers, and the apical cells of the nucellar epidermis divide periclinally to form a nucellar cap 2 cells in thickness. Cytokinesis in the megaspore mother cell accompanies meiosis and the chalazal megaspore of a linear tetrad develops into a Polygonum type embryo sac. The synergids are shortly pyriform, the polar nuclei fuse before fertilization, and the 3 antipodal cells are ephemeral. Apomixis has been suspected in *C. sativa* and *Humulus lupulus* (Strasburger, 1909a; Wettstein, 1935).

Endosperm formation is Nuclear and during early postfertilization stages the base of the embryo sac elongates in a curved manner and becomes haustorial. Wall formation is initiated around the globular embryo and the endosperm becomes cellular except for the chalazal haustorium, which remains coenocytic until its collapse.

Embryogeny is of the Onagrad type and in *C. sativa* the suspensor is 2-celled. Polyembryony is of occasional occurrence in *Cannabis*.

Briosi and Tongnini, 1894 • Elfving, 1879 • MacPhee, 1924 • Mladentseva, 1960, 1963 • J. Modilewski, 1908b • Mohan Ram and Nath, 1964 • Ram, 1960 • Ranquini, 1928 • Savelli, 1928 • Strasburger, 1909a • Tournois, 1911, 1914 • Wettstein, 1924, 1925 • Winge, 1914b • Zinger, 1898.

CANNACEAE

Development of the anther of *Canna indica* is undescribed but the tapetum is amoeboid and multilayered. According to Kracauer the microspore mother cells undergo simultaneous cytokinesis but Täckholm and Söderberg consider the division to be successive. The pollen grains are 3-celled when shed.

The ovule is anatropous, bitegmic, and crassinucellar, with the micropyle formed by the inner integument. The archesporial cell cuts off a primary parietal cell which forms a single parietal layer and the apical cells of the nucellar epidermis divide periclinally to form a nucellar cap 2 cells in thickness. Cytokinesis in the megaspore mother cell accompanies meiosis and the chalazal megaspore of a linear tetrad develops into a Polygonum type embryo sac. The synergids are pyriform and the polar nuclei fuse close to the 3 antipodal nuclei before fertilization. A hypostase is differentiated.

Endosperm formation is Nuclear but later the tissue becomes cellular. In view of the basal position of the secondary nucleus it is possible that the chalazal chamber of Helobial endosperm has been overlooked.

Embryogeny is unknown.

Arcangeli, 1897 • Gatin, 1908 • L. Guignard, 1882b • Hegelmaier, 1874 • Hofmeister, 1849, 1858b, 1861 • J. E. Humphrey, 1896 • Jönsson, 1879–1880; Kracauer, 1930 • Mauritzon, 1936e • Radlkofer, 1856 • Schacht, 1850 • Täckholm and Söderberg, 1918 • Wiegand, 1900.

CAPPARIDACEAE

The anther is tetrasporangiate and the persistent epidermal cells become radially elongated. The endothecium develops fibrous thickenings, the 2–5 middle layers are ephemeral, and the cells of the glandular tapetum become multinucleate but nuclear fusions are common. Simultaneous cytokinesis in the microspore mother cells follows meiosis and microspore tetrads are tetrahedral or decussate. Pollen grains are 2-celled when shed but in *Crataeva* they are occasionally 3-celled and in *Capparis decidua* they may germinate *in situ*.

The ovule is campylotropous, bitegmic, and crassinucellar, with a zigzag micropyle formed by both integuments except in *Capparis*, where only the inner integument is involved. A multicellular archesporium is common and although each cell may cut off a primary parietal cell only one megaspore mother cell develops further. A parietal tissue of 3–7 cell layers is formed and in *Cleome chelidonii* and *Maerua arenaria* this is supplemented by a nucellar cap 2 cells in thickness derived from a periclinal division of the apical nucellar epidermal cells. Cytokinesis in the megaspore mother cell accompanies meiosis and the chalazal megaspore of a linear tetrad develops into a Polygonum type embryo sac. The synergids are hooked in *Capparis frondosa, Crataeva religiosa,* and *Gynandropsis pentaphylla* whereas in *Cleome chelidonni* their tips diverge in a hooklike manner and in *Isomeris arborea* they are ephemeral. A filiform apparatus is differentiated in *Cadaba, Capparis, Crataeva,* and *Maerua.* The polar nuclei fuse just before fertilization and the 3 antipodal cells are small and ephemeral except in *Maerua* where they become much enlarged and occupy the lower half of the embryo sac. Starch grains are present in the embryo sacs of *Capparis frondosa, C. rupestris,* and *Gynandropsis pentaphylla.*

Endosperm formation is Nuclear but the tissue becomes cellular at the globular stage of the embryo, although in *Isomeris* wall formation is delayed until late in embryogeny.

Embryogeny conforms usually to the Onagrad type but in *Cadaba indica* the resemblance is to the Caryophyllad type. The "endosperm nodules" of Billings (1937) and later authors have been shown by Maheshwari and Sachar (1955) and Sachar (1956b) to be coils of the long uniseriate suspensor whose cells become enlarged and coenocytic. The development of adventitious embryos from the nucellus has been reported in *Capparis frondosa.*

Baillon, 1867–1895 • Billings, 1937 • L. Guignard, 1893a,b • Hedayetullah, 1935a • R. Khan, 1950 • P. Maheshwari and Khan, 1953 • P. Maheshwari and Sachar, 1954a, 1955 • Mauritzon, 1934f • H. S. Narayana, 1962b, 1965 • Orr, 1921a,b,c,d • Raghavan, 1937, 1938 • Raghavan and Venkatasubban, 1941b • Rai, 1939 • V. S. Rao, 1936a,c, 1938a • Sachar, 1956b • Tiwary, 1936 • Vaidya, 1961a.

CAPRIFOLIACEAE

The anther is tetrasporangiate and its wall development follows the Dicotyledonous type. The endothecium develops fibrous thickenings and the middle layer is ephemeral. The tapetum is glandular in *Sambucus* and *Viburnum* but amoeboid in *Lonicera* and *Symphoricarpus* and the cells commonly become at least 2-nucleate. Simultaneous cytokinesis in the microspore mother cells follows meiosis and the microspore tetrads are tetrahedral. Pollen grains are 3-celled when shed.

The ovule is anatropous, unitegmic, and usually tenuinucellar, but crassinucellar in *Viburnum* where the archesporial cell cuts off a primary parietal cell which forms a single parietal layer. In *Linnaea, Lonicera, Sambucus,* and *Symphoricarpus* the archesporial cell develops directly into the megaspore mother cell in which, in *Linnaea, Lonicera, Symphoricarpus,* and *Viburnum,* cytokinesis accompanies meiosis and the chalazal megaspore of a linear tetrad develops into a Polygonum type embryo sac. Sunesson (1933), however, reported the Allium type of embryo sac development in *V. acerifolium, V. dentatum,* and *V. lantana* whereas the tetrasporic Adoxa type is characteristic of *Sambucus nigra* and *S. racemosa.* The synergids are pyriform, the polar nuclei fuse before fertilization, and the 3 antipodal cells are ephemeral. Small starch grains occur in the embryo sac of *S. nigra.*

Endosperm formation is *ab initio* Cellular and the early records of Nuclear endosperm are erroneous. Ruminate endosperm occurs in *V. foetens.*

Embryogeny in *Lonicera* is somewhat irregular and conforms best to the Asterad type, but otherwise is little known.

Asplund, 1920 • Billings, 1901 • Crété, 1954d • Dahlgren, 1927a • Eichinger, 1907 • Elfving, 1879 • Familler, 1896 • Feng, 1934 • Giger, 1913 • L. Guignard, 1882b, 1893 • Halsted, 1887 • Hegelmaier, 1885, 1886 • Horne, 1909, 1914 • Jönsson, 1879–1880, 1881 • Juel, 1915 • Lagerberg, 1909 • Moissl, 1841 • Periasamy, 1962b • Schnarf, 1929 • Schürhoff, 1921b, 1924a • Souèges, 1945g • Strasburger, 1889 • Sunesson, 1933 • Tieghem, 1908b • Vesque, 1878, 1879b • Went, 1887b • Wille, 1886 • Wunderlich, 1959 • Yamaha, 1926.

CAPUSIACEAE

Embryologically unknown.

CARDIOPTERIDACEAE

Embryologically unknown.

CARICACEAE

The anther is tetrasporangiate with a persistent epidermis. The endothecium develops fibrous thickenings, the middle layer is ephemeral, and the tapetum is glandular (?). Simultaneous cytokinesis in the microspore mother cells follows meiosis and the microspore tetrads are tetrahedral. Pollen grains are 2-celled when shed.

The ovule is anatropous, bitegmic, and crassinucellar, with the micropyle formed by both integuments. The archesporial cell cuts off a primary parietal cell which forms at least 8 parietal layers, and a nucellar cap 4 cells in thickness originates from periclinal divisions of the apical nucellar epidermal cells. Cytokinesis in the megaspore mother cell accompanies meiosis and the chalazal megaspore of a linear tetrad develops into a Polygonum type embryo sac. Occasionally, the micropylar megaspore is functional. The synergids are broad apically and exhibit the filiform apparatus, the polar nuclei become closely associated near the egg, and the 3 antipodals are very ephemeral. The broad pollen tube persists in the micropyle for some weeks after fertilization and a haustorial function has been suggested.

Endosperm formation in Nuclear and in *Carica papaya* Singh (1961a) described the formation of nucleated cytoplasmic nodules from the peripheral cytoplasm which ultimately fills the central vacule. According to Foster (1943) cell formation is initiated at the micropylar pole 79 days after pollination and proceeds throughout the embryo sac.

Embryogeny does not conform to any definite type owing to the irregular early cleavages. Parthenocarpic development is common.

Allan, 1963a,b • Asana and Sutaria, 1929 • L. T. Foster, 1943 • Heilborn, 1921, 1928 • Kratzer, 1918 • Schacht, 1858 • D. Singh, 1961a • Tieghem, 1903a • Traub and O'Rork, 1936, 1939 • Usteri, 1907 • Vasil, 1962.

CARTONEMATACEAE

Embryologically unknown.

CARYOCARACEAE

Embryologically unknown.

CARYOPHYLLACEAE

The anther is tetrasporangiate and its wall formation has been followed only in *Stellaria media* where, according to Joshi (1936a), it conforms to the Monocotyledonous type, but the sequence of events described by Pal (1952) is that of the Dicotyledonous type. The endothecium develops fibrous thickenings, the middle layer is ephemeral, and the cells of the glandular tapetum become at least 2-nucleate. Simultaneous cytokinesis in the microspore mother cells follows meiosis and the microspore tetrads are tetrahedral or decussate. Pollen grains are 3-celled when shed and those of *Stellaria* contain starch grains. Joshi (1936b) reported that less than 10% of *Thylacospermum* pollen was normal and some grains germinated *in situ*.

The ovule is hemianatropous to campylotropous, bitegmic, and crassinucellar, with the micropyle formed by the inner integument. Although a multicellular archesporium is common, only one cell cuts off a primary parietal cell and continues development. In *Stellaria* a single parietal layer is formed but in the other genera investigated the secondary nucellus appears to consist of parietal layers supplemented by derivatives of the nucellar epidermis. Cytokinesis in the megaspore mother cell accompanies meiosis and the chalazal megaspore of a linear tetrad develops into a Polygonum type embryo sac. Reports of an Allium type embryo sac in *Sabulina longifolia* and an Adoxa type in *Stellaria media* are doubtful. The synergids are hooked in *Spergula* and *Thylacospermum*, the polar nuclei fuse before fertilization, and the 3 antipodal cells are ephemeral. Starch grains have been reported in the embryo sacs of *Dianthus sinensis* and *Silene*. During early postfertilization stages 1–2 diverticula arise from the side and/or extremities of the embryo sac, and Rocén (1927) arranged the genera into 4 types according to the number and position of these processes.

Endosperm formation is Nuclear but the extent of wall development is variable in that cellular endosperm may finally occupy the entire embryo sac, it may be confined to the micropylar pole, or it may be limited to a single layer of cells around the hypocotyl of the embryo. These variations were recognized by Rocén (1927) as the Silene, Melandrium, and Heliosperma endosperm types respectively.

Embryogeny conforms to the Caryophyllad type in which *cb* or its derivatives give rise to a bladderlike and possibly haustorial suspensor.

Breslavetz, 1929 • K. M. Buell, 1952a,b • Cappelletti, 1927 • Compton, 1912 • M. T. Cook, 1903b, 1909c • Creasy, 1961 • Dahlgren, 1916 • Dambroise, 1947 • Devine, 1950 • Elfving, 1879 • A. Fischer, 1880 • Gaertner, 1849 • Gibbs, 1907 • J.-L. Guignard, 1963d, 1965 • L. Guignard, 1882b • Hegelmaier, 1885 • Hofmeister, 1849, 1858 • P. C. Joshi, 1936a,b • Kraft, 1917 • Kshirsagar, 1960 • Meier, 1962 • Nagl, 1962 • Němec, 1910b • N. Pal, 1952 • Perotti, 1913 • Pobedimova, 1929 • H. N. Pritchard, 1964 • V. S. Rao, 1940 • Rocén, 1926, 1927 • Safijowska, 1939 • Schürhoff, 1919a, 1921b, 1925b • Souèges, 1922d, 1924g, 1945f • Strasburger, 1877, 1884, 1910b • Tohda, 1960 • Tulasne, 1855 • Vesque, 1878 • Warming, 1878 • Woodcock, 1926b, 1928.

CASUARINACEAE

The number of sporangia comprising the anther has not been reported but its wall consists of epidermis, fibrous endothecium, middle layers, and tapetum of unspecified type. Microsporogenesis has not been described but the microspore tetrads are tetrahedral and the pollen grains are 2-celled when shed.

The ovule is orthotropous, bitegmic, and crassinucellar with the micropyle formed by the inner integument. Each cell of the multicellular archesporium cuts off a primary parietal cell in which periclinal divisions occur and a thick parietal tissue is formed. Meiosis accompanies cytokinesis in all megaspore mother cells and the chalazal megaspore of each linear tetrad is capable of development into a Polygonum type embryo sac, although only 2–12 usually do so. During their development the embryo sacs become much elongated and intertwined, extending into the chalaza and even the funicle. The polar nuclei fuse only in association with a male gamete and the 3 antipodal cells are ephemeral. Fertilization is chalazogamous and occurs in the embryo sac closest to the micropyle. Apomixis has been suspected in *Casuarina nana*.

Endosperm formation is Nuclear but after walls are initiated at the micropylar pole, the tissue becomes cellular throughout.

Embryogeny is uncertain and Johansen (1950) considers that in *C. equisetifolia* it probably follows the Onagrad type.

Barlow, 1958 • Chamberlain, 1896 • Frye, 1903 • Johansen, 1950 • Juel, 1903 • Kauffmann, 1869 • Porsch, 1904 • Swamy, 1944c, 1948d • Treub, 1891.

CELASTRACEAE

The anther is tetrasporangiate, except in *Celastrus paniculata* where it is bisporangiate, and its epidermis persists in a flattened condition. The endothecium develops fibrous thickenings, 2 or 3 ephemeral middle layers are formed, and cells of the glandular tapetum become multinucleate. Simultaneous cytokinesis in the microspore mother cells follows meiosis and the microspore tetrads are tetrahedral or decussate. The pollen grains are 2-celled when shed and those of *Gymnosporia rothiana* sometimes germinate *in situ*.

The ovule is anatropous, bitegmic, and either crassinucellar (*Celastrus, Elaeodendron*) or tenuinucellar (*Euonymus, Gymnosporia*), with the micropyle formed by both integuments. In the crassinucellar species the archesporial cell cuts off a primary parietal cell which gives rise to 1–4 parietal layers, but in the tenuinucellar representatives it functions directly as the megaspore mother cell. Cytokinesis in the megaspore mother cell accompanies meiosis and the chalazal megaspore of a linear or T-shaped tetrad develops into a Polygonum type embryo sac. The synergids are pyriform and bear hooks in several species. The polar nuclei fuse before fertilization and the 3 antipodal cells are usually ephemeral, but in *Gymnosporia spinosa* they persist until fertilization. An endothelium is present and an aril develops from the base of the outer integument.

Endosperm formation is Nuclear but walls develop centripetally after about 200 free nuclei have formed, and the tissue becomes cellular throughout.

Embryogeny follows the Solanad type in *Celastrus paniculata* and *Gymnosporia spinosa*, but the Caryophyllad type has been described in *Celastrus scandens* and *Euonymus europaeus*. Polyembryony has been reported in *Celastrus* and *Euonymus*.

Adatia and Gavde, 1962 • Andersson, 1931 • Bally, 1916 • Braun, 1860 • Brizicky, 1964 • Dahlgren, 1938 • Grebel, 1820 • Herr, 1959 • Hofmeister, 1858 • Jaeger, 1814 • Jönsson, 1879–1880, 1881 • Petit-Thouars, 1808 • Strasburger, 1878 • Treviranus, 1838.

CENTROLEPIDACEAE

Development of the anther and pollen grains has not been investigated.

The ovule is orthotropous, bitegmic, and tenuinucellar. In *Centrolepis tenuior* the archesporial cell functions directly as the megaspore mother cell in which cytokinesis accompanies meiosis and a linear tetrad of megaspores is formed. Development of the embryo sac and postfertilization events have not been described.

Hieronymus, 1873 • Jönsson, 1879–1880.

CEPHALOTACEAE

The development and structure of the anther and the pollen grains have not been investigated.

The ovule is anatropous, bitegmic, and crassinucellar. An endothelium is differentiated but embryo sac development and postfertilization events are both undescribed.

Schweiger, 1909.

CERATOPHYLLACEAE

The structure of the anther has not been described in detail but 4 parietal layers are formed and the innermost develops into the amoeboid tapetum. Successive cytokinesis in the microspore mother cells accompanies meiosis but the type of microspore tetrads has not been recorded. Pollen grains are 2-celled when shed.

The ovule is orthotropous, unitegmic, and crassinucellar. The archesporial cell cuts off a primary parietal cell which forms several parietal layers below the nucellar epidermis. Cytokinesis in the megaspore mother cell accompanies meiosis and the chalazal megaspore of a linear or T-shaped tetrad develops into a Polygonum type embryo sac. The synergids are pyriform, the polar nuclei fuse before fertilization, and the 3 antipodal cells are small. Starch grains occur in the mature embryo sac of *Ceratophyllum demersum*.

Endosperm formation is *ab initio* Cellular and the chalazal cells may be enlarged.

Embryogeny conforms to the Asterad type but no suspensor is formed.

Hofmeister, 1858, 1859 • Klercker, 1885 • Sastri, 1955c • Schnarf, 1931a • Strasburger, 1902 • Subramanyam, 1962.

CERCIDIPHYLLACEAE

The anther of *Cercidiphyllum* is tetrasporangiate but its development and structure have not been described except for the report of a glandular tapetum whose cells become 2-nucleate. Simultaneous cytokinesis in the microspore mother cells follows meiosis and the pollen grains are 2-celled when shed.

The ovule is anatropous, bitegmic, and crassinucellar, with the micropyle formed by both integuments. The archesporial cell cuts off a primary parietal cell which gives rise to 4 or 5 parietal layers, and a nucellar cap 2 or 3 cells in thickness is formed by periclinal divisions of the apical cells of the nucellar epidermis. Cytokinesis in the megaspore mother cell accompanies meiosis and the chalazal megaspore of a linear tetrad develops into a Polygonum type embryo sac. The synergids are pyriform, the polar nuclei fuse before fertilization, and the 3 antipodal cells are small.

Endosperm formation is *ab initio* Cellular and about 12 cells form a linear series before longitudinal divisions occur.

Embryogeny conforms to the Caryophyllad type.

Harms, 1916, 1918 • Subramanyam, 1962 • Swamy and Bailey, 1949.

CHAILLETIACEAE

Embryologically unknown.

CHENOPODIACEAE

The anther is tetrasporangiate and its wall development follows the Monocotyledonous type. The endothecium develops fibrous thickenings and the 1 or 2 middle layers are ephemeral. The tapetum is glandular, except in *Chenopodium album* where a periplasmodium has been reported, and the nuclei undergo several divisions and fusions. Simultaneous cytokinesis in the microspore mother cells follows meiosis and the microspore tetrads are tetrahedral, isobilateral, or decussate. Pollen grains are 3-celled when shed and in *Beta vulgaris* a Gigas type has been reported which results from failure of cytokinesis in the microspore mother cells so that each pollen grain contains 4 vegetative nuclei and 8 male gametes.

The ovule is campylotropous, bitegmic, and crassinucellar, with the micropyle formed by the inner integument. Sometimes an air space is present between the integuments in the chalazal region. The archesporial cell cuts off a primary parietal cell which forms 1–3 parietal layers, and a nucellar cap 2–4 cells in thickness is formed by periclinal divisions of the apical cells of the nucellar epidermis. Cytokinesis in the megaspore mother cell usually accompanies meiosis and the chalazal megaspore of a linear tetrad develops into a Polygonum type embryo sac. In *Suaeda fruticosa*, however, cytokinesis is suppressed after the homotypic division and the chalazal dyad cell forms an Allium type embryo sac. Hooked synergids occur in *Arthrocnemum indicum, Chenopodium album, C. ambrosioides, Kochia scoparia,* and *S. fruticosa.* The polar nuclei usually fuse before fertilization and the 3 antipodal cells are ephemeral except in *Beta vulgaris* where a small amount of secondary multiplication occurs. The chalazal end of the embryo sac in *Beta* and *Kochia* elongates and becomes haustorial but the antipodals remain *in situ.*

Endosperm formation is Nuclear, but after walls are initiated at the micropylar pole, the tissue becomes cellular throughout.

Embryogeny conforms to the Chenopodiad type and the suspensor is massive except in *Arthrocnemum* and *Kochia* where it is uniseriate with an enlarged basal cell. Polyembryony occurs in *Beta rubra* and *B. vulgaris.*

Artschwager, 1927a,b, 1946, 1947 • Artschwager and Starrett, 1933 • Bhargava, 1936 • Billings, 1934 • Bocanzeva, 1944 • Cohn, 1914 • Cole, 1895 • G. O.

Cooper, 1935 • Dahlgren, 1916 • Dambroise, 1914 • Favorsky, 1928 • A. Fischer, 1880 • H. E. Fischer, 1962 • Heel, 1925 • Hegelmaier, 1885 • Hindmarsh, 1965 • Konycheva, 1962 • Mahabale and Solanky, 1953a,b, 1954a,b,c • Matthysen, 1912 • H. A. Miller and Kline, 1959 • Oksijuk, 1927, 1928 • Rocén, 1927 • Romell, 1919 • Souèges, 1920c,d • Stomps, 1911 • Tuschnjakowa, 1929b • Warming, 1878 • M. E. Williams, 1932 • Witkus, 1945.

CHLOANTHACEAE

Apart from the report that the anther wall is composed of 4 cell layers and that the tapetal cells are usually 2-nucleate, there is no information on events taking place in the anther.

The ovule is hemianatropous, unitegmic, and tenuinucellar. The archesporial cell functions directly as the megaspore mother cell which, in *Pityrodia barlingii*, becomes much elongated. The origin of the embryo sac has not been described but the synergids are hooked, the polar nuclei do not fuse before fertilization, the antipodals degenerate early, and starch grains are present.

Endosperm formation and embryogeny have not been investigated.

Junell, 1934.

CHLORANTHACEAE

The anther is tetrasporangiate in *Ascarina*, *Hedyosmum*, and *Sarcandra* but in *Chloranthus* the androecium is a 3-lobed structure whose median lobe is tetrasporangiate and is flanked by bisporangiate laterals. The epidermis is persistent, the endothecium develops fibrous thickenings, and the 2 or 3 middle layers are not destroyed during another maturation. The tapetum is glandular and its cells become 2-nucleate. Simultaneous cytokinesis in the microspore mother cells follows meiosis and the microspore tetrads are tetrahedral or isobilateral. Pollen grains are 2-celled when shed.

The ovule is orthotropous, bitegmic, and crassinucellar, with the micropyle formed by the inner integument except in *Sarcandra irvingbaileyi* where both integuments are involved. The archesporial cell cuts off a primary parietal cell which forms 3–6 parietal layers, and in *Chloranthus* the apical cells of the nucellar epidermis may undergo a single periclinal division. Cytokinesis in the megaspore mother cell accompanies meiosis and the chalazal megaspore of a linear tetrad develops into a Polygonum type embryo sac. The synergids are pyriform and the polar nuclei fuse before or at fertilization. The 3 antipodal cells undergo secondary multiplication to form about 24 cells in *Sarcandra glabra* and at least 40 cells in *Chloranthus japonicus* but otherwise they remain unchanged.

Endosperm formation is *ab initio* Cellular.

Embryogeny is of the Chenopodiad type in *Hedyosmum*, but in *Sarcandra* and *Chloranthus* it conforms to the Onagrad type. In *Chloranthus* spp. the embryo is still very immature with undifferentiated cotyledons when the fruit is shed, and in *Sarcandra glabra* development of the embryo is completed only after the fruits are liberated.

H. Armour, 1906 • B. Clark, 1958 • J. G. Edwards, 1920 • D. S. Johnson, 1905 • Swamy, 1953b • M. R. Vijayaraghavan, 1964 • Yoshida, 1957, 1959a,b.

CIRCAEASTERACEAE

The anther is bisporangiate in *Circaeaster agrestis* and its wall development appears to follow the Dicotyledonous type. The endothecium has not been described but the middle layer is ephemeral and the cells of the glandular tapetum remain 1-nucleate. Simultaneous cytokinesis in the microspore mother cells follows meiosis and the microspore tetrads are tetrahedral. Pollen grains are 2-celled when shed.

The ovule is orthotropous, unitegmic, and tenuinucellar. The archesporial cell functions directly as the megaspore mother cell in which cytokinesis accompanies meiosis and the chalazal megaspore of a linear or T-shaped tetrad develops into a Polygonum type embryo sac. The synergids are pyriform, the polar nuclei fuse before fertilization, and 2 or 3 antipodal cells are formed.

Endosperm formation is *ab initio* Cellular and embryogeny conforms to the Chenopodiad type.

Junell, 1930.

CISTACEAE

The anther is tetrasporangiate with a persistent epidermis. The endothecium develops fibrous thickenings, the middle layer is ephemeral, and the cells of the glandular tapetum become 2–4 nucleate. Snoad (1954) has reported plasmodial microspore mother cells in two garden varieties of *Helianthemum*, but in *H. vulgare* they undergo simultaneous cytokinesis and the microspore tetrads are isobilateral, decussate, or tetrahedral. Pollen grains are 2-celled when shed.

The ovule is orthotropous, bitegmic, and crassinucellar, with the micropyle formed by both integuments. A multicellular archesporium is common and each cell cuts off a primary parietal cell which gives rise to 1–3 parietal layers. In *Cistus laurifolia* and *H. vulgare* the apical cells of the nucellar epidermis divide periclinally and form a shallow nucellar cap. Cytokinesis in the functional megaspore mother cell accompanies meiosis, although it may be suppressed in the micropylar dyad cell, and the chalazal megaspore of a linear tetrad or "triad" develops into a Polygonum type embryo sac. In *H. vulgare* all the megaspore mother cells undergo meiosis and several linear tetrads are formed but only one embryo sac reaches maturity, although several may start development. The synergids exhibit the filiform apparatus and are commonly hooked although those of *H. vulgare* bear prominent apical caps. The polar nuclei fuse before fertilization and the 3 antipodal cells commence degeneration at maturity of the embryo sac.

Endosperm formation is Nuclear but later the tissue becomes cellular throughout.

Embryogeny conforms to the Solanad type with a uniseriate suspensor 8–12 cells in length.

Boursnell, 1950 • Braun, 1860 • Brongniart, 1831 • Chiarugi, 1924, 1925 • Elfving, 1879 • A. Fischer, 1880 • L. Guignard, 1886 • Kapil and R. Maheshwari, 1964 • Snoad, 1954 • Souèges, 1937i • Strasburger, 1879 • Tulasne, 1855 • Warming, 1878.

CLETHRACEAE

The anther is tetrasporangiate and its epidermal cells contain tannin. The endothecium develops fibrous thickenings, the 2 middle layers are ephemeral, and the cells of the glandular tapetum become binucleate. Simultaneous cytokinesis in the microspore mother cells follows meiosis and the microspore tetrads are tetrahedral. Pollen grains are 2-celled when shed.

The ovule is anatropous, unitegmic, and tenuinucellar. The archesporial cell functions directly as the megaspore mother cell in which cytokinesis accompanies meiosis and the chalazal megaspore of a linear tetrad develops into a Polygonum type embryo sac. The synergids are pyriform and in *Clethra alnifolia* the egg apparatus extends into the micropyle. The polar nuclei fuse before fertilization and 3 antipodal cells are formed. An endothelium is differentiated around the lower two-thirds of the embryo sac.

Endosperm formation is *ab initio* Cellular with weak terminal haustoria.

Embryogeny follows the Asterad type and in *Clethra* the uniseriate suspensor is composed of at least 10 cells.

Artopoeus, 1903 • Copeland, 1933, 1938b • Crété, 1951d • Hagerup, 1928 • Kavaljian, 1952 • Lechner, 1914 • Peltrisot, 1904 • Samuelsson, 1913 • Veillet-Bartoszewska, 1960d.

CLUSIACEAE

The development of the anther and pollen grains has not been investigated.

The ovule is anatropous to hemianatropous, bitegmic, and tenuinucellar, with the micropyle formed by the outer integument. The archesporial cell functions directly as the megaspore mother cell in which cytokinesis accompanies meiosis and the chalazal megaspore of a linear or, occasionally, T-shaped tetrad develops into a Polygonum type embryo sac. The synergids may be hooked and Treub's figures (1911) of *Garcinia kydii* and *G. treubii* show the filiform apparatus. The 3 antipodals are very ephemeral and degenerate soon after their formation.

Endosperm formation is Nuclear and embryogeny conforms to the Onagrad type. Adventive embryony has been reported in *Garcinia mangostana* and polyembryony may occur in *Clusia* and *Garcinia*.

Goebel, 1900 • Horn, 1940 • Puri, 1939b • Sprecher, 1919 • Treub, 1911a,b.

CNEORACEAE

The pollen grains are 3-celled when shed but their development and that of the anther has not been described.

The ovule is amphitropous and bitegmic. The behavior of the archesporial cell has not been reported but cytokinesis in the megaspore mother cell accompanies meiosis and the chalazal megaspore of a linear tetrad develops into a Polygonum type embryo sac. The synergids are pyriform, the polar nuclei fuse before fertilization, and the secondary nucleus moves close to the 3 antipodal cells.

Endosperm formation is Nuclear and the embryogeny of *Cneorum tricoccum* conforms to the Asterad type.

M. A. Rau, 1962 • Schürhoff, 1924b • Souèges, 1955d.

COBAEACEAE

The number of sporangia comprising the anther of *Cobaea* has not been reported but the endothecium develops fibrous thickenings, the middle layer persists, and the tapetum is amoeboid. Simultaneous cytokinesis in the microspore mother cells follows meiosis and the microspore tetrads are tetrahedral. Pollen grains are 2-celled when shed.

The ovule is anatropous, unitegmic, and pseudocrassinucellar. The archesporial cell apparently gives rise directly to the megaspore mother cell and in *Cobaea scandens*, at least, the apical cells of the nucellar epidermis undergo a single periclinal division. Cytokinesis in the megaspore mother cell accompanies meiosis and the chalazal megaspore of a linear tetrad develops into a Polygonum type embryo sac whose structure has not been described.

Endosperm formation is Nuclear but embryogeny is unknown.

Bonnet, 1912 • Dahlgren, 1927a • W. K. Farr, 1920 • Juel, 1915 • Lawson, 1898 • Strasburger, 1882a, 1889.

COCHLOSPERMACEAE

Development of the anther and pollen grains has not been described.

The ovule of *Cochlospermum orinoccense* is anatropous, bitegmic, and crassinucellar, with a zigzag micropyle formed by both integuments. The apical cells of the nucellar epidermis divide periclinally and form a nucellar cap below which some parietal layers are present. The origin and structure of the embryo sac is not known.

Endosperm formation is Nuclear but embryogeny has not been investigated.

Mauritzon, 1936b • Schnarf, 1931b.

COLUMELLIACEAE

Embryologically unknown.

COMBRETACEAE

The anther is tetrasporangiate and its wall formation follows the Basic type except in *Guiera senegalensis* where only one middle layer is formed. The endothecium develops fibrous thickenings, usually 2 or 3 ephemeral middle layers are present, and the cells of the glandular tapetum become 2-nucleate. In *Poivrea coccinea* the tapetum may be irregularly 2-layered. Simultaneous cytokinesis in the microspore mother cells follows meiosis and the microspore tetrads are tetrahedral or isobilateral. The pollen grains are 2-celled when shed in *Guiera* and *Poivrea* but 3-celled in *Terminalia*.

The ovule is anatropous, bitegmic, and crassinucellar, with the zig-zag micropyle formed by both integuments. Although commonly several archesporial cells differentiate, only one cuts off a primary parietal cell and this gives rise to a parietal tissue of up to 12 cell layers. In addition, the apical cells of the nucellar epidermis divide periclinally and form a nucellar cap which, in *Quisqualis indica*, is 8 cells in thickness. Cytokinesis in the megaspore mother cell usually accompanies meiosis and the chalazal megaspore of a linear tetrad develops into a Polygonum type embryo sac. In *Combretum paniculatum* and *C. pincianum* Mauritzon (1939) reported the suppression of meiosis and the formation of a tetrasporic embryo sac of the Penaea type. The synergids are hooked and in *Poivrea* and *Guiera* they exhibit the filiform apparatus. The polar nuclei fuse before fertilization and the 3 antipodal cells are ephemeral in *Poivrea* and *Terminalia*, but in *Guiera* they may undergo some secondary multiplication and persist into early embryogeny. In *Combretum*, *Poivrea*, and *Quisqualis* an elaborate obturator is formed by growth of long papillate cells from the funicle.

Endosperm formation is Nuclear but later the tissue becomes cellular throughout.

Embryogeny follows the Asterad type.

Fagerlind, 1941a • Karsten, 1891 • Mauritzon, 1939c • Nagaraj, 1955 • N. Pal, 1951a • P. S. P. Rao, 1963 • Venkateswarlu, 1952.

COMMELINACEAE

The anther is tetrasporangiate with a persistent epidermis. The endothecium develops fibrous thickenings, the middle layer is ephemeral, and the amoeboid tapetum forms a periplasmodium. Successive cytokinesis in the microspore mother cells accompanies meiosis and the microspore tetrads are isobilateral or decussate. The pollen grains are 2-celled when shed except in *Floscopa scandens* where they are 3-celled, and in *Commelina subulata* starch grains are present. Dimorphic pollen has been reported in *Tripogandra grandiflora*.

The ovule is orthotropous to hemianatropous, bitegmic, and crassinucellar. The micropyle is formed of both integuments in *Cyanotis axillaris* and *Pollia sorzogonensis* but usually the outer integument is shorter than the inner and in *Aneilema*, *Commelina*, *Floscopa*, and *Murdannia* the apex of the nucellus is exposed. The archesporial cell cuts off a primary parietal cell which either divides only anticlinally or degenerates soon after its formation and may have been overlooked in those species in which the megaspore mother cell is reported to function directly as the archesporial cell (*Aneilema paniculata, Commelina stricta, Cyanotis axillaris, C. cristata, Tradescantia paludosa*). The apical cells of the nucellar epidermis usually divide periclinally to form a nucellar cap 2 or 3 cells in thickness, but in *Murdannia simplex* they undergo radial elongation. In the majority of species cytokinesis in the megaspore mother cell accompanies meiosis and the chalazal megaspore of a linear or T-shaped tetrad develops into a Polygonum type embryo sac. However, the Allium type of development has been described in *Commelina stricta, Rhoeo discolor,* and *Tradescantia paludosa* and the Adoxa type in *Commelina angustifolia*. Hooked synergids have been reported only in *Commelina benghalensis*, the polar nuclei fuse before fertilization, and the 3 antipodal cells are ephemeral except in *Tinantia fugax* where they are rather large and persistent. Starch grains occur in the embryo sac of *Commelina subulata*.

Endosperm formation is Nuclear, but after the initiation of walls at the micropylar pole, the tissue becomes cellular except in *M. simplex* where the chalazal pole remains coenocytic. An early aggregation of nuclei at the chalazal end of the embryo sac is common but haustorial activity has been reported only in *Cyanotis axillaris, C. cristata,* and *Commelina forskalaei*.

Embryogeny conforms to the Asterad type.

E. Anderson and Sax, 1934 • Baranetzky, 1880 • J. W. Beatty and A. V. Beatty, 1953 • J. B. Bishop and McGowan, 1953 • Chikkannaiah, 1961, 1962, 1963, 1964, 1965a,b • J. Clark, 1904 • Clausen, 1927 • Coulter and Rose, 1886 • Elfving, 1879 • Friemann, 1910 • J.-L. Guignard, 1962 • L. Guignard, 1882b • Hance, 1915 • Hofmeister, 1848, 1858, 1861 • Jönsson, 1879–1880 • Lakshmanan, 1962 • R. E. Lee, 1961 • P. Maheshwari and J. K. Maheshwari, 1955 • P. Maheshwari and Singh, 1934 • S. C. Maheshwari and Baldev, 1958 • Mascré, 1925a,b • McCollum, 1939 • K. L. Murthy, 1934, 1938 • B. Palm, 1920 • Parks, 1935 • N. S. Rau, 1930 • Said, 1960 • K. Sax and Edmonds, 1933 • Solms-Laubach, 1878 • Souèges, 1958a,b • Stenar, 1925b • Strasburger, 1879, 1884 • Süssenguth, 1919, 1921a • Täckholm and Söderberg, 1918 • Tischler, 1915 • Trochain, 1932 • Tschermak-Woess, 1947 • Uphof, 1934 • Walker, 1938 • Yasui and Suita, 1939.

COMPOSITAE

The anther is usually tetrasporangiate but the bisporangiate condition occurs in *Calotis hispidula, C. squamigera* and *Cotula* spp. Its wall develops according to the Dicotyledonous type and the epidermis is much stretched but persists at maturity. The endothecium develops fibrous thickenings, the middle layer is ephemeral, and the cells of

the amoeboid tapetum become multinucleate but fusions usually restore the 1-nucleate condition. A glandular tapetum has been reported
in *Ainsliaea aptera* (Kapil and Sethi, 1962). Simultaneous cytokinesis
in the microspore mother cells follows meiosis and the microspore
tetrads are tetrahedral, decussate, or isobilateral. The pollen grains
are 3-celled when shed and they may be dimorphic in *Wedelia*,
whereas in *Polymnia laevigata* 4 pollen types have been described.
In apomictic species plasmodial microspore mother cells or abortive
pollen grains are usual.

The ovule is anatropous, unitegmic, and tenuinucellar. A single
archesporial cell which functions directly as the megaspore mother
cell is usual but in *Achillea*, *Chrysanthemum*, and *Erigeron* the archesporium is multicellular and more than one cell commonly undergoes
meiosis. In the majority of species cytokinesis in the megaspore mother
cell accompanies meiosis and the chalazal megaspore of a linear tetrad
develops into a Polygonum type embryo sac, although in the Calenduleae it is the micropylar megaspore which is functional. An Allium
type embryo sac has been reported in *Ammobium alatum*, *Chrysanthemum* spp., *Erigeron* spp., and *Tridax trilobata* and three variations
of tetrasporic development have been described. The Adoxa type is
found only in *Rudbeckia hirta* but the Fritillaria type occurs in
Ratibida columnifera, *R. pinnata*, *Rudbeckia bicolor*, and *R. missouriensis*. The Drusa type is represented in *Chrysanthemum* spp.,
Erigeron spp., *Helichrysum bracteatum*, *Matricaria maritima*, *M.
oreades*, and *Minuria denticulata*, where seldom is the full component
of sixteen nuclei formed. Usually some degree of "strike" is exhibited
by the chalazal nuclei of the developing embryo sac. This condition
is shown in its extreme form in *Anthemis tinctoria*, *Chrysanthemum
balsamita*, and *Pyrethrum balsaminatum*, where the three chalazal
megaspore nuclei fail to divide and may even degenerate. An embryo
sac with such an origin is referred to either as tetrasporic, because
the megaspore mother cell remains undivided, or pseudomonosporic
in that its functional nuclei are derived from a single megaspore nucleus. That little taxonomic significance can be attached to the method
of embryo sac formation in this family is shown by the occurrence
of both Polygonum and Adoxa types in *Leontodon hispidus*, whereas
in *Erigeron frigidus*, although the Drusa type is usual, either Allium
or Scilla development also takes place. The occurrence of both mono-
and bisporic embryo sacs, even in the same capitulum, has been reported in *Minuria cunninghamii*, *Sanvitalia procumbens*, and *Tridax
trilobata* while in *Erigeron* spp. and *Tridax glabellus* tetrasporic embryo sacs may also occur. Embryo sac formation by gonial apospory

has been described in *Antennaria porsildii, Arnica alpina, Brachycome ciliaris, Erigeron annuus, E. karwinskianus, E. strigosum,* and others, while in the polyploid species of *Taraxacum* an unreduced embryo sac develops from the chalazal dyad cell containing a restitution nucleus. Somatic apospory has been reported in *Artemisia nitida, Crepis* spp., *Leontodon hispidus, Minuria integerrima, Picris hieracioides,* and others, where one or more nucellar cells enlarge and develop into embryo sacs. Hooked synergids occur in *Acanthospermum, Ammobium, Caesulia, Enhydra, Gerbera,* and *Grangea,* and a filiform apparatus has been described in *Erechtites* and *Helianthus.* Frequently, the apices of the synergids extend into the micropyle but their haustorial activity has only been recorded in *Calendula, Cotula,* and *Ursinea.* The polar nuclei become closely associated near the egg and they fuse prior to fertilization. In some apomictic species, however, the formation of a secondary nucleus does not occur and the polar nuclei function independently as the first two endosperm nuclei. On differentiation of the embryo sac, the 3 antipodal nuclei are enclosed in 2 or 3 cells and may remain in that condition until their degeneration. In some species, however, the cells become multinucleate and in others secondary multiplication occurs and may continue after fertilization until up to 60 cells occupy the narrow chalazal extremity of the embryo sac. Although some haustorial activity is associated with secondary multiplication of antipodals, the reports of aggressive haustoria are usually in genera characterized by only 2 antipodal cells. In *Aster, Bidens,* and *Othonna* at least one of the cells becomes aggressive and in *Grindelia, Gutierrezia,* and *Haplopappus* one or both cells grow laterally into the integument and reach almost to the surface of the ovule. In *Artemisia* the lowest of the 4–6 antipodals becomes haustorial and in *A. tridentata* (Diettert, 1938) penetration of the chalaza sometimes occurs and the haustorium reaches the cavity of the ovary. It is probable, however, that reinvestigation will show that reports of aggressively haustorial antipodal cells are based on misinterpretation of somatic aposporic embryo sacs which, through lack of accommodation, expand laterally in the chalaza. An endothelium differentiates early in embryo sac development.

Endosperm is usually *ab initio* Cellular but, in some species, wall formation does not occur in association with the earliest nuclear divisions. Nuclear endosperm was first reported by Hofmeister (1858) in *Aster* and *Grindelia* but it has been described since in *Antennaria alpina, A. porsildii, Barkhausia foetida, Bidens biternata, Centaurea napifolia, Chrysanthemum indicum, Eupatorium glandulosum, Galin-*

soga ciliata, Gerbera jamesonii, Glossocardia bosvallia, Hieracium aurantiacum, Volutarella ramosa.

Embryogeny conforms to the Asterad type and polyembryony has been reported in *Andryala, Erigeron, Helianthus, Hieracium, Minuria,* and *Taraxacum.*

Afzelius, 1924, 1936 • Annen, 1945 • Anzalone, 1949 • Arnoldi and Dianova, 1934 • Avanzi, 1948 • Ayres, 1915 • Babcock and Stebbins, 1938 • Banchetti, 1961 • Banerji, 1940b,c,d, 1942a • Banerji and Pal, 1959 • Battaglia, 1940, 1945a,b, 1946a,b,c,d, 1947b,c,d,e,f,g, 1948a,b, 1949, 1950, 1951b,c, 1952a,b, 1955c, 1956 • Beaudry, 1959 • C. A. Berger, Feeley and Witkus, 1956 • Bergman, 1932, 1935a,b,c, 1937, 1941, 1942, 1944, 1950, 1951 • Beruti, 1961 • H. R. Bhargava, 1935, • D. E. Bianchi, Schwemmin and Wagner, 1959 • Bijok, 1960 • Billings, 1901 • Böös, 1917, 1920, 1924 • Borthwick and Robbins, 1928 • Briquet, 1916 • W. H. Brown and Sharp, 1911 • Buchenau, 1872 • Carano, 1913, 1914a, 1915a,c, 1918, 1919a,b, 1920a, 1921a, 1924 • Catelani, 1950–1951 • Cesca, 1961b • Chamberlain, 1895, 1918 • Chatin, 1870 • Chiappini, 1954 • Chiarugi, 1926a,b, 1927b,c, • Christoff, 1940 • D. C. Cooper and Brink, 1949 • G. O. Cooper, 1936 • Crété, 1955b • Czapik, 1954 • Dahlgren, 1920, 1924 • G. L. Davis, 1961a,b,c,d, 1962a,b, 1963a,b, 1964a,b,c,d • P. K. Deshpande, 1960a,b, 1961, 1962a,b,c,d, 1964a,b • Desole, 1951 • Dianova, Sosnovitz, and Steshina, 1934, 1935, 1938–1939 • Diettert, 1938 • Digby, 1914 • Doll, 1927 • Dutta, 1939 • Dzyubenko, 1959 • K. Eichler, 1906 • Elfving, 1879 • Erickson and Benedict, 1947 • Esau, 1944, 1946 • Fagerlind, 1939c, 1941b, 1946a, 1947d,f,g • C. H. Farr, 1916 • Ferri, 1961 • J. R. Fisher and Wells, 1962 • Gates, 1920 • Gates and Rees, 1921 • Gelin, 1934, 1936 • Gentscheff, 1937 • Gerassimova, 1933 • Gerassimova-Navashina, 1947a,b,c • Gerdts, 1905 • R. B. Ghosh, 1962b • Giroux, 1930, 1933 • Goldfus, 1898–1899 • Greene, 1898 • L. Guignard, 1882b, 1893 • Gustafsson, 1932, 1933a,b, 1942 • Gustafsson and Nygren, 1946 • Haberlandt, 1921b, 1922a, 1923a, 1938b • Haenlein, 1874 • Harling, 1950, 1951a,b, 1954, 1960 • C. J. Harris, 1935 • Hegelmaier, 1889 • Heitz, 1951 • Hjelmqvist, 1951, 1964 • Hjelmqvist and Holmberg, 1961 • Hofmeister, 1849, 1858b • Holmgren, 1915, 1916, 1919 • Howe, 1922, 1926, 1959, 1964 • Hubert, 1896 • Ikeno, 1910 • Jacobsson-Paley, 1918 • H. A. Jones, 1927a,b, 1929 • Jönsson, 1879–1880 • A. C. Joshi, 1939 • Juel, 1898, 1900a, 1904, 1906, 1915 • Kapil and Sethi, 1962a,b • Katz, 1943 • Kerner, 1876 • Kirchner, 1904 • J. E. Kirkwood, 1910 • Kordyum and Boiko, 1962 • Kostryukova, 1961 • Land, 1900 • Langlet, 1925 • Lavaille, 1911, 1912, 1921, 1922 • Leavitt and Spalding, 1905 • Lundegårdh, 1909 • P. Maheshwari and Hague, 1948 • P. Maheshwari and Roy, 1952 • P. Maheshwari and Srinivasan, 1944 • Maheswari Devi, 1957, 1963 • Malecka, 1961 • Manum, 1955 • G. W. Martin, 1892 • R. W. Martin and Smith, 1955 • Martinoli, 1939, 1940a, 1942, 1943 • Martinoli and Angiolini di Moisè, 1963 • Maugini, 1962 • McDonald, 1927 • Merrell, 1900 • Mestre, 1957a,b, 1958, 1964a • K. Meyer, 1925a • S. Misra, 1957, 1964, 1965 • Mitra, 1947 • Montgomery and Yang, 1960 • Mottier, 1893 • Movsesyan, 1963, 1964 • Murbeck, 1901, 1904 • Nawaschin, 1900a, 1909 • Negodi, 1936a,b • Norris, 1892 • Nygren, 1950c • Okabe, 1932 • Opperman, 1904 • Osawa, 1913b • Ostenfeld, 1904a,b, 1910 • Padmanabhan, 1962c • Paizieva, 1962 • B. Palm, 1914a,b, 1915, 1922b, 1925, 1934 • B. T. Palm, 1931 • Poddubnaja-Arnoldi,

1927, 1931, 1933a,b, 1939a,b • Poddubnaja-Arnoldi and Dianova, 1934 • Poddub-naja-Arnoldi, Steschina and Sosnovetz, 1935 • Popham, 1938 • Portheim, 1901 • Powers, 1945 • Raghavan and Venkatasubban, 1941a • Renzoni-Cela, 1963 • Rodolico, 1930, 1933 • Rosén, 1944 • Rosenberg, 1906, 1907, 1909b, 1912, 1917, 1930 • F. E. Rudenko, 1962 • Ruth, 1943 • Schiller, 1907 • Schkorbatow, 1910, 1912 • Schnarf, 1919, 1923 • Schürhoff, 1920a, 1924a, 1926c • Schwere, 1896 • Sears, 1917, 1922 • Shimotomai, 1937 • Skawińska, 1962 • F. H. Smith, 1943 • R. W. Smith, 1911 • Snoad, 1954 • Söderberg, 1929 • Souèges, 1920h,i • Stebbins 1932a,b • Stebbins and Jenkins, 1939 • Stork, 1920 • Strasburger, 1879, 1882a, 1884, 1889 • Täckholm, 1916 • Tahara, 1915a,b, 1921 • Tateishi, 1929 • Tiagi and Taimni, 1960, 1963 • Tongiorgi, 1936, 1942 • Tulasne, 1849 • G. and B. Turesson, 1960 • Urbańska, 1956 • Urbańska-Woytkiewicz, 1961, 1962 • Ustinova, 1964 • Vaidya, 1961b • Vandeveldé, 1896–1905 • Venkateswarlu, 1941a,b, 1959 • Venkateswarlu and Maheswari Devi, 1955a,b • Vernin, 1952a,b • Vesque, 1878, 1879 • R. I. Walker, 1944 • Ward, 1880b • Warming, 1878 • Warmke, 1943 • Weislo, 1951 • Weinedel-Lieban, 1928 • Westermaier, 1890 • Wille, 1886 • Winge, 1914a • A. Winkler, 1882 • Wunderlich, 1959 • Yamaha, 1926.

CONNARACEAE

Development and structure of the anther and pollen grains have not been described.

The ovule is hemianatropous, bitegmic, and crassinucellar, with the micropyle formed by both integuments. The archesporial cell cuts off a primary parietal cell which divides periclinally at least once. In *Connarus luccus* cytokinesis in the megaspore mother cell accompanies meiosis, except that the micropylar dyad cell remains undivided and sometimes the homotypic division of its nucleus is suppressed. The chalazal megaspore of the linear "triad" develops into a Polygonum type embryo sac in which the polar nuclei fuse in the center of the embryo sac and the secondary nucleus moves towards the 3 antipodal cells.

Endosperm formation is Nuclear and the tissue becomes cellular only after several thousand free nuclei have formed.

Embryogeny has not been described.

Mauritzon, 1939c.

CONVOLVULACEAE

The anther is tetrasporangiate and its wall develops according to the Dicotyledonous type although the middle layer commonly undergoes at least one periclinal division. The tapetum is glandular and its cells become multinucleate. In *Quamoclit* the vertical series of sporogenous cells may be interrupted in one or two places by a cell which does not develop further. Simultaneous cytokinesis in the micro-

spore mother cells follows meiosis and the microspore tetrads are tetrahedral or decussate. The pollen grains are 2-celled when shed, although
an occasional 3-celled grain may occur in *Ipomoea*.

The ovule is anatropous, bitegmic, and either crassinucellar or
tenuinucellar. The archesporial cell cuts off a primary parietal cell
which gives rise to up to 6 parietal layers in *Convolvulus arvensis,
C. sepium, Ipomoea horsfalliae, I. learii, I. obscura, I. pulchella, I.
sepiaria, Jacquemontia violacea*, and *Operculina turpethum*, but in
Evolvulus alsinoides, Ipomoea aquatica, I. batatus, I. pes-tigridis,
and *I. staphylina* it functions directly as the megaspore mother cell.
Cytokinesis in the megaspore mother cell accompanies meiosis and
the chalazal megaspore of a linear tetrad develops into a Polygonum
type embryo sac. The synergids are slender and elongated except in
I. arborea where they are small, nonvacuolate, and ephemeral. The
polar nuclei become closely associated immediately below the egg
but do not fuse until entry of the pollen tube and possibly only in
association with a male gamete. The 3 antipodal cells are usually
ephemeral, although in *Evolvulus alsinoides* they become prominent
and may persist until after fertilization. Starch grains are present
in the embryo sac of *C. tricolor*.

Endosperm formation is Nuclear but the tissue later becomes cellular throughout.

Embryogeny conforms to the Caryophyllad type in *I. aquatica* and
I. pes-tigridis. A very large suspensor occurs in *C. sepium* while in
I. learii it becomes haustorial and penetrates the micropyle. Synergid
polyembryony has been reported in *C. sepium*.

Baranetzky, 1880 • Beer, 1911 • Billings, 1937 • Bobde, 1963 • Dahlgren, 1922,
1927a,c • Fedortschuk, 1932 • K. Ishii, 1964 • B. M. Johri and Nand, 1934
• Jos, 1963 • Juliano, 1935a • Kenyan, 1929 • Macpherson, 1921 • P. Maheshwari,
1943b • P. Maheshwari and Sachar, 1954a • Mathur, 1934 • K. Peters, 1908
• K. V. R. Rao, 1940 • V. S. Rao, 1944 • Schacht, 1850 • Souèges, 1937f •
Strasburger, 1884, 1889 • Svensson, 1925 • Tiwary and Rao, 1936 • Wimmel,
1850 • Woodcock, 1943 • Yamaha, 1926.

CORIARIACEAE

The development and structure of the anther and pollen grains
have not been described.

The ovule of *Coriaria myrtifolia* and *C. terminalis* is anatropous,
bitegmic, and crassinucellar, with the micropyle formed by the inner
integument. The outer integument arises almost at the apex of the
inner one and is very short. The archesporial cell cuts off a primary

parietal cell which gives rise to at least 12 parietal layers and periclinal divisions of the apical nucellar epidermal cells form a nucellar cap. Cytokinesis in the megaspore mother cell accompanies meiosis and the chalazal megaspore of a linear tetrad develops into a Polygonum type embryo sac. The synergids are pyriform, the polar nuclei fuse at fertilization, and the 3 antipodal cells are uninucleate.

Endosperm formation is Nuclear but the embryogeny is unknown.

Grimm, 1912 • Mauritzon, 1936d.

CORNACEAE

The anther is tetrasporangiate but its wall structure has not been described. In *Cornus mas* simultaneous cytokinesis in the microspore mother cells follows meiosis and the microspore tetrads are tetrahedral, isobilateral, or decussate. Pollen grains are 2-celled when shed.

The ovule is anatropous, unitegmic, and usually crassinucellar. A multicellular archesporium occurs in *Benthamia* but otherwise it is unicellular and cuts off a primary parietal cell which gives rise to 3–7 parietal layers. In *C. mas,* however, the archesporial cell sometimes functions directly as the megaspore mother cell. The apical cells of the nucellar epidermis undergo at least one periclinal division and form a nucellar cap. In *Aucuba japonica, Cornus alba,* and *C. svecica* cytokinesis in the megaspore mother cell accompanies meiosis and the chalazal megaspore of a linear tetrad develops into a Polygonum type embryo sac. In *C. mas,* however, a Fritillaria type embryo sac has been reported and in *C. florida* Morse (1907) described a tetrasporic ("pseudomonosporic") embryo sac developing from only one megaspore nucleus, the other three degenerating. The synergids are pyriform, the polar nuclei fuse before fertilization, and the 3 antipodal cells are ephemeral. An endothelium is differentiated and in *C. mas* a hypostase develops.

Endosperm formation is *ab initio* Cellular but embryogeny is unknown.

Amato, 1946a • A. W. Eichler, 1878 • Fagerlind, 1939a • Håkansson, 1923 • Horne, 1914 • Jönsson, 1881 • Lombard-Dumas, 1904 • Moore and Behney, 1908 • Morse, 1907 • B. Palm and Rutgers, 1917 • Vesque, 1879 • Warming, 1877, 1913 • Winkler, 1908.

CORSIACEAE

Embryologically unknown.

CORYNOCARPACEAE 95

CORYLACEAE

Development and structure of the anther and pollen grains have not been described, but the tapetum is glandular and the microspore mother cells undergo simultaneous cytokinesis.

The ovule is anatropous, unitegmic (*Corylus*) or bitegmic (*Carpinus*), and crassinucellar, with the micropyle in *Carpinus* formed by the inner integument. The archesporium is multicellular, each cell cutting off a primary parietal cell, and 3 or 4 parietal layers are formed. In *Corylus* the apical cells of the nucellar epidermis undergo a single periclinal division and form a shallow nucellar cap. Meiosis, accompanied by cytokinesis, may take place in several megaspore mother cells and the chalazal megaspore of each linear tetrad starts development into a Polygonum type embryo sac. Only one embryo sac reaches maturity and a long chalazal caecum is formed which invades the nucellus. The egg apparatus is poorly differentiated and the 3 antipodal cells disorganize *in situ*, but the polar nuclei pass into the caecum and fusion takes place just before fertilization. Fertilization is chalazogamous and Benson (1894) attributes the weak development of the synergids to this occurrence.

Endosperm formation is Nuclear but embryogeny is unknown. Polyembryony has been reported in *Carpinus viminea*.

Abbe, 1935 · Baillon, 1875 · Benson, 1894 · Benson, Sanday, and Berridge, 1906 · Braun, 1959 · Chamberlain, 1898 · Dahlgren, 1915a · Finn, 1936 · Hagerup, 1942 · Hofmeister, 1858 · Luersson, 1869 · Moore and Behney, 1908 · Nawaschin, 1895b, 1899b · Treviranus, 1838 · Woodworth, 1929a,b, 1930a.

CORYNOCARPACEAE

Development and structure of the anther and pollen grains have not been investigated.

The ovule of *Corynocarpus laevigata* is anatropous, bitegmic, and crassinucellar, with the micropyle formed by the inner integument. The presence of 3 parietal layers presupposes the formation of a primary parietal cell and, in addition, there is a nucellar cap 3 or 4 cells in thickness which is epidermal in origin. The development of the embryo sac is not clear from Pigott's description, but in the mature structure the polar nuclei fuse in the center before fertilization and the 3 antipodal cells undergo secondary multiplication to form up to 8 cells. Fertilization takes place several weeks after pollination.

Endosperm formation is Nuclear and although the tissue later becomes cellular around the periphery of the embryo sac, it remains free-nuclear at the center.

Embryogeny probably follows the Caryophyllad type.

Pigott, 1927.

CRASSULACEAE

The anther is tetrasporangiate with a persistent epidermis. The endothecium develops fibrous thickenings, 2 ephemeral middle layers are formed in *Sedum ternatum,* and the cells of the glandular tapetum remain 1-nucleate. Simultaneous cytokinesis in the microspore mother cells follows meiosis and the microspore tetrads are tetrahedral. Pollen grains are 2-celled when shed and sometimes contain starch grains.

The ovule is anatropous, bitegmic, and crassinucellar. In *Bryophyllum crenatum* and *Sedum ternatum* both integuments form the micropyle, but in *Cotyledon gibbiflora* the outer one is much reduced and in *Sedum acre* both integuments unite into a single structure early in their development. The archesporial cell cuts off a primary parietal cell which gives rise to one or more parietal layers and the nucellar epidermis does not divide periclinally. Cytokinesis in the megaspore mother cell usually accompanies meiosis and the chalazal megaspore of a linear, T-shaped, or isobilateral tetrad develops into a Polygonum type embryo sac. In *Sedum fabaria* and *S. populifolia,* however, cytokinesis does not follow the homotypic nuclear division and an Allium type embryo sac develops from the chalazal dyad cell. In *Rosularia pallida* and *Sedum sempervivoides* haustoria are given off from the megaspores and pass through the nucellus into the integuments. The synergids are pyriform with well-developed apical caps in *S. ternatum,* the polar nuclei fuse before fertilization, and the 3 small antipodal cells disorganize soon after maturity. Starch grains are of general occurrence in the embryo sac. Just before or at fertilization in *S. ternatum,* the chalazal end of the embryo sac elongates into a tubular structure which penetrates the chalaza.

Endosperm formation is *ab initio* Cellular with the formation of a chalazal haustorium which, in *Sedum ternatum,* remains 1-nucleate.

Embryogeny conforms to the Caryophyllad type. In the 2-celled proembryo *cb* becomes much enlarged and gives off haustorial processes which invade the micropyle and adjacent integumentary tissue.

Crété, 1946c,d • Dahlgren, 1923, 1927c, 1939a • Elfving, 1879 • Herrig, 1919 • Hubert, 1896 • Jacobsson-Stiasny, 1913 • Johnston, 1941 • Koch, 1877b, 1879

Mauritzon, 1930, 1933a, 1939 • Rocén, 1928 • Rombach, 1911 • Souèges, 1925d, 1927e, 1936f,g • Subramanyam, 1962, 1963.

CROSSOSOMATACEAE

Development and structure of the anther and pollen grains have not been described.

The ovule of *Crossosoma* is amphitropous and bitegmic but there is no information on the formation and structure of the embryo sac.

Endosperm formation is Nuclear (?) and embryogeny has not been investigated.

Cave, Arnott, and Cook, 1961 • Mauritzon, 1939c.

CRUCIFERAE

The anther is tetrasporangiate with a persistent epidermis and its wall development conforms to the Monocotyledonous type. The endothecium develops fibrous thickenings, the middle layer is ephemeral but in *Brassica juncea* its cells divide periclinally to form 2 or 3 such layers, and the cells of the glandular tapetum usually become 2-nucleate. Simultaneous cytokinesis in the microspore mother cells follows meiosis and the microspore tetrads are tetrahedral, isobilateral, or decussate. The pollen grains are 3-celled when shed except in *Cardamine chenopodifolia* where they are 2-celled.

The ovule is anatropous, bitegmic, and either tenuinucellar or crassinucellar, with the micropyle formed by both integuments. A multicellular archesporium is common but only one cell undergoes further development. In *Arabidopsis thalianum*, *Brassica oleracea*, and *Erophila verna* the archesporial cell functions directly as the megaspore mother cell, but in *Brassica juncea*, *Cardamine chenopodifolia* and others, a primary parietal cell is cut off, and either condition may occur in *B. oleracea*. Cytokinesis in the megaspore mother cell accompanies meiosis and the chalazal megaspore of a linear tetrad develops into a Polygonum type embryo sac. The synergids are hooked, and in *Brassica* spp. they show the filiform apparatus, the polar nuclei fuse before fertilization, and the 3 antipodal cells are ephemeral.

Endosperm formation is Nuclear and in *Capsella bursa-pastoris* the nuclei tend to aggregate in small groups and, with their associated cytoplasm, form "nodules" which disappear when the endosperm becomes cellular.

Embryogeny follows the Onagrad type and the terminal cell of the slender suspensor is usually vesicular. Polyembryony has been reported in *Cheiranthus cheiri, Erysinum odoratum, Lepidium sativum,* and *Raphanus sativus.*

Ahuja, 1955 • Ahuja and Bhaduri, 1956 • Bannier, 1923 • Baranetzky, 1880 • Baur, 1912 • Belyaeva, 1964 • Bijok, 1962 • Böcher, 1951 • Braun, 1860 • Byelyayeva, 1963 • A. P. de Candolle, 1827 • Corti, 1930b • Coulter and Chamberlain, 1903 • Elfving, 1879 • Famintzin, 1879 • Farr, 1922b • Gorczyński, 1930, 1935 • Griesinger, 1935 • L. Guignard, 1881a,b, 1902b • Håkansson, 1956 • Hanstein, 1870 • Hofmeister, 1858b • Homedes, 1928 • Hubert, 1896 • Il'ina, 1962b • Jaretzky, 1928 • Lebèque, 1948b • Lloyd, 1902 • Lötscher, 1905 • Lotsy, 1926 • P. Maheshwari and Sachar, 1954b • Masters, 1869 • Misra, 1962 • Moquin-Tandon, 1841 • Noguchi, 1928 • O. H. Pearson, 1933 • Radlkofer, 1856 • Riddle, 1898 • A. N. Rao, 1957a • Rosell, 1936 • Schacht, 1858 • M. Schaffner, 1906 • Schwarzenbach, 1922 • Souèges, 1914b,c, 1916, 1919d • Stokes, 1955 • Strasburger, 1877, 1884b • Sulbha, 1957 • Sutaria, 1930 • Tarasevich, 1963 • R. C. Thompson, 1933 • Tjutajuk, 1939 • Tulasne, 1849 • Turpin, 1837 • Vandendries, 1909, 1912 • Vesque, 1879 • Warming, 1873 • Westermaier, 1876 • Wille, 1886 • A. Winkler, 1874 • Yamaha, 1926.

CRYPTERONIACEAE

Embryologically unknown.

CTENOLOPHONACEAE

Embryologically unknown.

CUCURBITACEAE

The anthers are bi- or tetrasporangiate and in *Cucumis sativus* and *Echinocystis lobata* both conditions occur in the same flower. The endothecium develops fibrous thickenings, the 1–3 middle layers are ephemeral, and the cells of the glandular tapetum become 2 or 3 nucleate. Simultaneous cytokinesis in the microspore mother cells follows meiosis and the microspore tetrads are tetrahedral. The pollen grains are 2-celled when shed.

The ovules are anatropous, bitegmic, and crassinucellar, with the micropyle formed by the inner integument. The archesporial cell cuts off a primary parietal cell that forms several parietal layers which, together with derivatives of the nucellar epidermis, give rise to a narrow nucellar beak extending in *Bryonia, Cucurbita, Cyclanthera, Ecballium,* and *Sicyos* through the micropyle. Cytokinesis in the megaspore mother cell accompanies meiosis and the chalazal megaspore of a linear tetrad develops into a Polygonum type embryo sac. In *Benincasa cerifera,* however, the micropylar dyad cell is small and degenerates without undergoing the homotypic division, and the chalazal dyad cell develops into an Allium type embryo sac. The synergids are hooked, the polar nuclei fuse at fertilization, the 3 antipodal cells are ephemeral, and starch grains are commonly present. The broad persistent pollen tube is dilated at the base of the micropyle and in *Cucurbita pepo* it gives off haustorial branches which penetrate the nucellus and inner integument. A hypostase is present in *Citrullus* and *Melothria.*

Endosperm formation is Nuclear and the upper portion of the embryo sac becomes swollen while the remainder usually forms an aggressive chalazal haustorium which varies in length from 270 μ in *Benincasa cerifera* to 12,000 μ in *Cucurbita ficifolia.* In *Melothria heterophylla* the haustorium is reduced to a short protuberance but in *Corallocarpus conocarpus* and *Ctenolepis garcini* it is absent. Cell formation is initiated at the micropylar end of the embryo sac and proceeds to the chalazal pole but the haustorium often remains coenocytic. The chalazal haustorium remains active up to the heart-shaped stage of the embryo and additional absorbing organs are the protruding cells from the lower part of the endosperm proper. In *Luffa acutangulata* and *L. graveolens* these cells divide and form short cellular secondary haustoria.

Embryogeny conforms to the Onagrad type and in *Sicyos angulata* the embryo sometimes develops adventitiously. Polyembryony has been reported in *Hodgsonia heteroclita.*

Asana and Sutaria, 1932 • Banerji and Das, 1937 • K. G. Barber, 1909 • Bitter, 1906 • Castetter, 1926 • Chakravarty and Sensarma, 1960 • Chakravorti, 1947 • Chopra, 1953a,b, 1954, 1955 • Chopra and Agarwal, 1958, 1960 • Crété, 1958a,c, 1960c • Dzevaltors'kyi, 1961, 1963a,b • Elfving, 1879 • Facchini, 1884 • Fickel, 1876 • Guliayev, 1961, 1963 • Hagedoorn, 1924 • Heimlich, 1927a,b, 1929 • Hofmeister, 1849 • Höhnel, 1876 • B. M. Johri and Chowdhury, 1957 • Juel, 1915 • Kirchner, 1904 • J. E. Kirkwood, 1904, 1907 • Kratzer, 1918 • Lloyd, 1904 • Longo, 1901, 1903a,b, 1904, 1907 • Luerssen, 1869 • L. E. Mann and Robinson, 1950 • Mellink, 1880 • W. L. Miller, 1929 • Mirbel, 1829, 1835 • Montanelli, 1907 • Mühlethaler, 1933 • Nägeli, 1842 • Paliwal, 1950 • Passmore, 1930 • Reiche, 1921 • Schacht, 1850 • Schagen, 1956 • Schloms, 1958 • F. M. Scott, 1953 • B. Singh, 1952b, 1953 • D. Singh, 1955a,b, 1956a, 1957, 1961a,b, 1963a, 1964a,b • S. N. Singh, 1958 • Souèges, 1939a • Strasburger, 1875, 1882, 1884 • Sykes, 1909 • Traub and O'Rork, 1939 • Vasil, 1960, 1962 • Warming, 1873, 1913 • Wefelscheid, 1911 • Weiling and Schagen, 1955 • Wimmel, 1850 • Yamaha, 1926 • Yasuda, Inaba, and Takakashi, 1935 • Zahur, 1962.

CUNONIACEAE

Development and structure of the anther and the pollen grains have not been described but, according to Mauritzon (1939), tannin accumulates in the endothecium and simultaneous cytokinesis in the microspore mother cells follows meiosis.

The ovules are anatropous to hemianatropous, bitegmic, and crassinucellar, with a zigzag micropyle formed by both of the integuments. A multicellular archesporium is usually differentiated and each cell cuts off a primary parietal cell from which several parietal layers are derived. In *Callicoma serratifolia* and *Cunonia capensis* the apical cells of the nucellar epidermis divide periclinally to form a nucellar cap 2 cells in thickness. Only one of the megaspore mother cells is functional and cytokinesis accompanies meiosis. Usually it is the chalazal megaspore of the linear tetrad which develops into the Polygonum type embryo sac, but in *Schizomeria* and sometimes in *Weinmannia*, the subchalazal megaspore functions. The synergids are pyriform, the polar nuclei fuse before fertilization, and the secondary nucleus moves close to the 3 ephemeral antipodal cells. Starch grains are common in the embryo sacs of all species, but a hypostase has been reported only in *Ceratopetalum apetalum*.

Endosperm formation is Nuclear and the tissue becomes cellular only after many free nuclei have formed.

Embryogeny is unknown.

Dahlgren, 1939a • Mauritzon, 1939c.

CUSCUTACEAE

The anther is tetrasporangiate and its wall development follows the Dicotyledonous type. The endothecium develops fibrous thickenings, the middle layer is ephemeral, and the cells of the glandular tapetum become 2–4 nucleate, the 1-nucleate condition being restored by fusion in *Cuscuta epithymum*. Ubisch granules have been reported in several species. Simultaneous cytokinesis in the microspore mother cells follows meiosis and the microspore tetrads are tetrahedral, isobilateral or decussate. Pollen grains are usually 3-celled when shed, but those of *C. monogyna* and *C. reflexa* are 2-celled. Multinucleate pollen grains and polyspory have been reported in *C. epithymum* and *C. reflexa*.

The ovule is anatropous, unitegmic, and tenuinucellar. The archesporial cell functions directly as the megaspore mother cell where usually cytokinesis accompanies meiosis and the chalazal megaspore of a linear tetrad develops into a Polygonum type embryo sac. In *C. reflexa*, however, wall formation following the homotypic division is suppressed and an Allium type embryo sac forms from the chalazal dyad cell. The synergids are beaked and in *C. reflexa* one enlarges and persists into embryogeny with a suspected haustorial function. The polar nuclei fuse before fertilization and the 3 antipodal cells are ephemeral. Starch grains are present in the embryo sac and a placental obturator develops in *C. reflexa*.

Endosperm formation is Nuclear and according to Smith (1934) more than 1500 free nuclei are present in the embryo sac of *C. rostrata* before the endosperm becomes cellular. In *C. reflexa* the inner endosperm cells gelatinize and become mucilaginous.

Embryogeny in different species suggests either the Caryophyllad or the Solanad type but it does not conform satisfactorily to either. The fully developed embryo shows no development of cotyledons. The suspensor consists of a few uninucleate cells in *C. epithymum*, *C. hyalina*, and *C. planifolia* but in *C. monogyna* it forms an aggressive haustorium of large multinucleate cells whereas in *C. reflexa* both suspensor types occur as well as intermediate forms. Polyembryony is of occasional occurrence in *C. reflexa*, where the additional embryo is of supposedly synergid origin.

Asplund, 1920 • Coulter and Chamberlain, 1903 • Dahlgren, 1922, 1927a • Fedortschuk, 1931 • Finn, 1937a • Hofmeister, 1859 • B. M. Johri, 1951 • B. M. Johri and Nand, 1934 • B. M. Johri and Tiagi, 1952 • Kamensky, 1928 • Koch, 1877a • Macpherson, 1921 • K. Peters, 1908 • B. E. Smith, 1934 • Svensson, 1925 • Tiagi, 1951a.

CYCLANTHACEAE

The anther is tetrasporangiate with a persistent epidermis in *Carludovica*, *Cyclanthus*, and *Dicranopygium*. The endothecium develops fibrous thickenings, the middle layer is ephemeral, and the cells of the glandular tapetum become 2–4-nucleate. Ubisch granules are of general occurrence. Successive cytokinesis in the microspore mother cells accompanies meiosis and the microspore tetrads are isobilateral or decussate. Pollen grains are 2-celled when shed.

The ovule is anatropous, bitegmic and crassinucellar, with the slightly zigzag micropyle formed by both integuments. The archesporial cell cuts off a primary parietal cell which gives rise to 2 parietal layers and the apical cells of the nucellar epidermis divide periclinally to form a nucellar cap 2 or 3 cells in thickness. Cytokinesis in the megaspore mother cell accompanies meiosis and the chalazal mega-spore of a linear tetrad develops into a Polygonum type embryo sac. The synergids are pyriform, the polar nuclei fuse before fertilization, and the life of the 3 antipodal cells is variable.

Endosperm formation and embryogeny have not been investigated.

Drude, 1877 • Harling, 1946, 1958 • B. Palm, 1920 • Süssenguth, 1919.

CYNOCRAMBACEAE

Anther development and structure have not been described but in the microspore mother cells simultaneous cytokinesis follows meiosis and the microspore tetrads are tetrahedral. The pollen grains are 3-celled when shed.

The ovule is amphitropous, unitegmic, and crassinucellar. The archesporial cell cuts off a primary parietal cell which gives rise to several parietal layers and a nucellar cap is formed by periclinal divisions of the nucellar epidermis. Cytokinesis in the megaspore mother cell accompanies meiosis and the chalazal megaspore of a linear tetrad develops into a Polygonum type embryo sac. The polar nuclei fuse in the center of the embryo sac at or before fertilization and the 3 antipodal cells degenerate soon after.

Endosperm formation, in its initial stages, has not been described but in *Thelygonum cynocrambe* the tissue is cellular at the 3-celled stage of the proembryo.

Embryogeny follows the Chenopodiad type and a uniseriate sus-pensor of about 9 cells is present in the heart-shaped embryo.

Dahlgren, 1916 • Mauritzon, 1934b • H. Schneider, 1914 • Woodcock, 1929.

CYPERACEAE

The anther is tetrasporangiate with a persistent epidermis of en-larged or papillate cells and its wall development conforms to the Monocotyledonous type. The endothecium develops fibrous thicken-ings, the middle layer is ephemeral, and the cells of the glandular tapetum may become 2-nucleate, commonly exhibiting Ubisch gran-ules on their inner surfaces. During meiosis, the microspore mother cells assume a variety of forms which Shah (1962) attributes to irreg-ular density of the cytoplasm and which in other angiosperms would indicate abnormality. The initiation of an ephemeral cell plate across the heterotypic spindle is of common occurrence and after the homotypic division the microspore nuclei are arranged in a tetrahedral, decussate, or isobilateral manner. While one nucleus remains in the center of the microspore mother cell and increases in size, the remaining 3 nuclei pass to the periphery where they are delimited by a membraneous septum. The formation of membranes between the individual nuclei is not invariable but in some instances where they are ephemeral, the membranes may have been overlooked. These nonfunctional microspore nuclei occasionally undergo an abortive mitosis before their degeneration and at pollen grain maturity their remains are still recognizable as dark streaks against the exine. The functional microspore nucleus behaves normally and, as the male gametes are formed before dehiscence of the anther, the pollen grains are 3-celled when shed and often contain starch grains. Shah (1962) considers that the reports of 2-celled pollen grains are based on immature material. Because there is no formation of true tetrads and the wall of the microspore mother cell becomes the wall of the functional microspore, Selling (1947) describes the pollen grain as *pseudomonad*, although Erdtman (1952) prefers the term *cryptotetrad*.

The ovule is anatropous, bitegmic, and crassinucellar, with the micropyle formed by the inner integument. The archesporial cell cuts off a primary parietal cell which forms up to 4 parietal layers and the nucellar epidermis does not divide periclinally. Cytokinesis in the megaspore mother cell accompanies meiosis and the chalazal megaspore of a linear tetrad develops into a Polygonum type embryo sac. The synergids are hooked, the polar nuclei fuse just prior to fertilization, and the 3 antipodal cells are ephemeral. A well-developed hypostase has been reported in *Cyperus* and *Kyllinga* and a funicular obturator in *Cyperus rotundus* and *C. triceps*.

Endosperm formation is Nuclear and the tissue later becomes cellular.

Embryogeny conforms to the Onagrad type and polyembryony has been reported in *Carex maritima* and *C. maxima*.

Braun, 1860 • Carniel, 1962a,b • Dnyansagar, 1956a,b • Elfving, 1879 • Erdtman, 1952 • A. Fischer, 1880 • J.-L. Guignard, 1961a, 1962a • N. N. Gupta, 1958, 1959, 1962 • Guttenberg and Semlow, 1957 • Heilborn, 1918 • Hofmeister, 1858, 1861 • Jönsson, 1879–1880, 1881 • Juel, 1900b • Khanna, 1956, 1963 • Kostrioukoff, 1930 • Masters, 1869 • Mirbel, 1815 • Moquin-Tandon, 1841 • Padhye, 1959, 1960 • Padhye and Moharir, 1958 • Piech, 1924a,b, 1928a,b • Pointeau, 1809 • Schnarf, 1931a • H. Schneider, 1932 • Selling, 1947 • C. K. Shah, 1962, 1964, 1965 • Shiam, 1963 • Stout, 1912 • Strasburger, 1884 • Süssenguth, 1919, 1921a • Tanaka, 1939a,b, 1940, 1941, 1950 • Tieghem, 1897a • Turpin, 1837 • Vesque, 1879b • Wille, 1882a, 1886 • Wulff, 1939a.

CYRILLACEAE

The anther is tetrasporangiate but apart from the report that the endothecium is "ribbed" in *Cliftonia monophylla* and *Cyrilla racemiflora*, there is no information on its structure and development. According to Copeland (1953) the pollen grains are probably 2-celled when shed.

The ovule is anatropous, unitegmic, and, according to Mauritzon (1936d), tenuinucellar, or weakly crassinucellar. The formation of the embryo sac has not been described but the mature structure is elongated and narrow with an enlarged micropylar portion. The polar nuclei fuse before fertilization and the 3 antipodal cells stain deeply.

Endosperm formation is *ab initio* Cellular and Copeland (1953) considers that it probably passes through a 4-celled stage from which the 2 central cells develop into the endosperm proper and the terminal ones form the micropylar and chalazal haustoria.

Embryogeny has not been investigated.

Copeland, 1953 • Mauritzon, 1936d.

CYTINACEAE

The anther is tetrasporangiate but there is no information on the development and structure of its wall or that of the pollen grains except that simultaneous cytokinesis in the microspore mother cells follows meiosis.

The ovule is orthotropous (*Cytinus*), bitegmic, and tenuinucellar, with the micropyle formed by the inner integument. The outer integument is very much reduced and in *Mitrastemon yamamotoi* its development is suppressed and the ovule is unitegmic. The archesporial cell functions directly as the megaspore mother cell in which cytokinesis accompanies meiosis and the chalazal megaspore of a linear tetrad develops into a Polygonum type embryo sac. The synergids are pyriform, the polar nuclei fuse before or during fertilization, and in *Cytinus hypocistis* the 3 antipodal cells persist into early embryogeny.

Endosperm formation is Nuclear but the tissue becomes cellular after 8–16 free nuclei have formed.

Embryogeny probably conforms either to the Caryophyllad or the Solanad type because the early cleavages are transverse. When the seed is shed, only a proembryo is present which consists of 4 cells in *Mitrastemon* and 10 cells in 6 tiers in *Cytinus*.

Arcangeli, 1876 • Bernard, 1903 • Chodat and Bernard, 1902a • Dahlgren, 1927a • Endriss, 1902 • Ernst and Schmid, 1909, 1913 • Guzowska, 1964 • Heinricher, 1917, 1934 • Hofmeister, 1858, 1859 • Schürhoff, 1926b • Solms-Laubach, 1874, 1898 • Warming, 1913 • Watanabe, 1933, 1936 • H. Winkler, 1927.

DAPHNIPHYLLACEAE

Development and structure of the anther and pollen grains have not been described.

The ovule is anatropous and bitegmic but it is uncertain whether a parietal cell is formed. According to Schnarf (1931) embryo sac development is of the "normal" type. The synergids bear a prominent filiform apparatus and the antipodals are short-lived.

Endosperm formation is *ab initio* Cellular, but the embryogeny has not been investigated.

Schnarf, 1931 • Ventura, 1930b.

DATISCACEAE

Development and structure of the anther and pollen grains have not been investigated.

The ovule is anatropous, bitegmic, and crassinucellar, with the micropyle formed by both integuments. The archesporial cell cuts off a primary parietal cell which forms about 5 parietal layers and the apical cells of the nucellar epidermis undergo a single periclinal division. Cytokinesis in the megaspore mother cell follows only the heterotypic nuclear division and the chalazal dyad cell develops into an Allium type embryo sac. The synergids are pyriform, the polar nuclei fuse early, and the 3 antipodal cells may persist until after fertilization.

Endosperm formation is Nuclear, but after walls are formed around the embryo, the tissue becomes cellular throughout.

Embryogeny in *Datisca cannabina* follows the Onagrad type.

Crété, 1951d, 1952c • Himmelbaur, 1909 • Mauritzon, 1936b • Montemartini, 1905 • Sandt, 1921.

DIALYPETALANTHACEAE

Embryologically unknown.

DIAPENSIACEAE

The anther is bisporangiate in *Galax aphylla* but otherwise it is tetrasporangiate and its epidermis is persistent. The endothecium develops fibrous thickenings, in *Diapensia* 2 or 3 middle layers are formed, and the cells of the glandular tapetum become 2-nucleate. Development of the pollen grains has not been described but they are 3-celled at maturity and are liberated singly.

The ovule is hemianatropous to campylotropous, unitegmic, and tenuinucellar. The archesporial cell develops directly into the megaspore mother cell in which cytokinesis accompanies meiosis, and usually the chalazal megaspore of the linear tetrad develops into a Polygonum type embryo sac. The synergids may exhibit the filiform apparatus (*Diapensia*), the polar nuclei fuse before fertilization, and the 3 antipodal cells usually persist into early embryogeny. In *Shortia* the antipodals undergo secondary multiplication and up to 40 cells have been reported in *S. galacifolia*. Although the developing embryo sac comes into direct contact with the integument after breakdown of the nucellus, an endothelium is not always differentiated.

Endosperm formation is *ab initio* Cellular and the orientation of the first wall varies from transverse to longitudinal. All cells contribute to the endosperm proper.

Embryogeny probably conforms to the Solanad type.

Graef, 1958 • Hagerup, 1928 • Palser, 1963 • Petersen, 1912 • Safijowska, 1960 • Samuelsson, 1913.

DIDIEREACEAE

Embryologically unknown.

DILLENIACEAE

The anther is tetrasporangiate with a persistent epidermis whose cells, in *Wormia burbidgei*, develop fibrous thickenings. In general the endothecium is not well developed and, although fibrous bands are formed on some cells in *Acrotrema* and *Hibbertia*, they are absent in *Dillenia* and *Wormia*. The 2 or 3 midde layers are ephemeral and the cells of the glandular tapetum become binucleate. An amoeboid tapetum has been reported in *Wormia suffruticosa*. Simultaneous cytokinesis in the microspore mother cells follows meiosis and the microspore tetrads are tetrahedral, isobilateral, or linear. Pollen grains are 2-celled when shed.

The ovule is anatropous to amphitropous, bitegmic, and crassinucellar, with the zigzag micropyle formed by both integuments. The archesporial cell cuts off a primary parietal cell which gives rise to up to 5 parietal layers and a nucellar cap is formed by periclinal divisions of the apical nucellar epidermal cells. Cytokinesis in the megaspore mother cell accompanies meiosis and the chalazal megaspore of a linear or T-shaped tetrad develops into a Polygonum type embryo sac. The synergids are hooked in *Hibbertia*, the polar nuclei fuse before fertilization, and the 3 antipodal cells are ephemeral. An aril is frequently developed although it is rudimentary in *Hibbertia* and absent in *Dillenia indica*.

Endosperm formation is Nuclear but walls are formed later at the periphery of the embryo sac and the tissue becomes cellular throughout.

Embryogeny probably follows the Onagrad type. A zygotic mantle has been reported in *Acrotrema* and *Wormia* where it persists during early embryogeny with "coralloid protuberances" projecting among the adjacent endosperm cells.

Mauritzon, 1936b • Paetow, 1931 • A. N. Rao, 1955a, 1957b, 1961 • Sastri, 1958a • Schnarf, 1924 • Svedelius, 1911 • Swamy and Periasamy, 1955.

DIOSCOREACEAE

The anther epidermis is persistent but the number of component sporangia has not been reported. Anther wall development in *Dioscorea oppositifolia* conforms to the Monocotyledonous type. The endothecium develops fibrous thickenings, the middle layer is ephemeral, and the cells of the glandular tapetum become 2-nucleate. Simultaneous cytokinesis in the microspore mother cells follows meiosis and the microspore tetrads are tetrahedral or isobilateral. Pollen grains are 2-celled when shed.

The ovule is anatropous, bitegmic, and crassinucellar, with the micropyle formed by both integuments. The archesporial cell cuts off a primary parietal cell which forms several parietal layers within the nucellar epidermis. Cytokinesis in the megaspore mother cell accompanies meiosis and the chalazal megaspore of a linear tetrad develops into a Polygonum type embryo sac. The synergids are hooked, the polar nuclei fuse before fertilization, and the 3 antipodal cells degenerate soon afterwards. A hypostase is present.

Endosperm formation is Nuclear but the tissue later becomes cellular from the chalazal pole throughout the embryo sac.

Embryogeny follows the Asterad type and in *Tamus communis* the suspensor is broad and multicellular.

Friemann, 1910 • J.-L. Guignard, 1963a • A. N. Rao, 1951, 1953a, 1954, 1955c • P. M. Smith, 1916 • Solms-Laubach, 1878 • Süssenguth, 1921a,b • Täckholm and Söderberg, 1918 • Tischler, 1915.

DIPENTODONTACEAE

Embryologically unknown.

DIPSACACEAE

The anther is tetrasporangiate and its wall development conforms to the Dicotyledonous type. The endothecium develops fibrous thickenings, the middle layer is ephemeral, and the cells of the amoeboid tapetum become multinucleate. Simultaneous cytokinesis in the microspore mother cells follows meiosis and the microspore tetrads are tetrahedral. The pollen grains are 3-celled when shed.

The ovule is anatropous, unitegmic, and tenuinucellar. The archesporial cell functions directly as the megaspore mother cell in which cytokinesis accompanies meiosis and the chalazal megaspore of a linear tetrad develops into a Polygonum type embryo sac. The synergids are pyriform, the polar nuclei fuse before fertilization, and the 3 antipodal cells become 2-nucleate in *Cephalaria ambrosioides* while in *Morina longifolia* they undergo secondary multiplication. An endothelium is differentiated and a hypostase is present in *Dipsacus* and *Knautia*.

Endosperm formation is ab initio Cellular.

Embryogeny has been investigated only in *Scabiosa succisa* where the zygote divides by an almost vertical wall and consequently must be accommodated in the Piperad type. Polyembryony has been reported in *Cephalaria alpina* and *Scabiosa atropurpurea*.

Asplund, 1920 • Balicka-Iwanowska, 1899 • Braun, 1860 • Carniel, 1863 • T. Coulter, 1823 • Doll, 1927 • A. Fischer, 1880 • L. Guignard, 1882b • Hegelmaier, 1885 • Hofmeister, 1858b • Juel, 1915 • Lavaille, 1925a,b,c, 1926 • Molliard, 1895 • Poddubnaja-Arnoldi, 1933c • Razi and Subramanyam, 1953 • Risse, 1926, 1929 • Schnarf, 1931a • Souèges, 1937b, 1962, 1963a,b • Strasburger, 1882, 1889 • Wulff, 1934a.

DIPTEROCARPACEAE

The anther is tetrasporangiate and its wall development follows the Dicotyledonous type. The endothecium does not develop fibrous thickenings, the 3 middle layers are ephemeral, and the cells of the glandular tapetum become 2-nucleate. Simultaneous cytokinesis in the microspore mother cells follows meiosis and the microspore tetrads are tetrahedral, isobilateral, or decussate. Pollen grains are 2-celled when shed.

The ovule is anatropous, bitegmic, and crassinucellar, with the micropyle formed by the inner integument. The archesporial cell cuts

off a primary parietal cell which forms about 5 layers of parietal cells within the nucellar epidermis. Cytokinesis in the megaspore mother cell accompanies meiosis and the chalazal megaspore of a linear or T-shaped tetrad develops into a Polygonum type embryo sac. The synergids are hooked, the polar nuclei fuse toward the center of the embryo sac, and the 3 antipodal cells degenerate soon after fertilization. In *Vateria indica* a long antipodal haustorium develops after fertilization.

Endosperm formation is Nuclear but walls develop at the micropylar pole and the tissue becomes cellular throughout except in *Vateria* where it remains free-nuclear.

Embryogeny conforms to no definite type since cleavage planes are irregular after the initial transverse or oblique division, although in *Shorea rubusta* there are resemblances to the Asterad type.

A. N. Rao, 1953b, 1955b, 1956a,c, 1962.

DIRACHMACEAE

Embryologically unknown.

DONATIACEAE

Embryologically unknown.

DROSERACEAE

The anther is tetrasporangiate and its wall development follows the Monocotyledonous type. The endothecium develops fibrous thickenings, the middle layer is ephemeral, and the cells of the glandular tapetum become multinucleate but finally uninucleate by fusion. In *Drosera indica* and *D. peltata* tapetal cells may obtrude into each loculus and divide it into several chambers. An amoeboid tapetum has been described in *D. binata* and *D. capensis*. Simultaneous cytokinesis in the microspore mother cells follows meiosis and the microspore tetrads are tetrahedral or isobilateral, remaining as permanent tetrads in all except *Drosophyllum*. The mature pollen grains are 3-celled although the 2-celled condition is common in *Drosera burmanni*.

The ovule is anatropous, bitegmic, and either crassinucellar or tenuinucellar, with the micropyle formed by the inner integument. In most representatives the archesporial cell cuts off a primary parietal cell which forms up to 4 parietal layers but in *Drosera indica* and *D. peltata* it functions directly as the megaspore mother cell and in *D. rotundifolia* either condition may occur. Cytokinesis in the megaspore mother cell accompanies meiosis and the chalazal megaspore of a linear or T-shaped tetrad develops into a Polygonum type embryo sac. The synergids are hooked and exhibit the filiform apparatus, the polar nuclei fuse early, and the 3 antipodal cells degenerate soon after fertilization. The lateral nucellar cells become radially elongated and form a conspicuous jacket around the mature embryo sac while those at the base elongate in a longitudinal direction.

Endosperm formation is Nuclear but walls are formed later at the micropylar pole and the tissue finally becomes cellular throughout. The chalazal extremity of the embryo sac may show weak haustorial activity while it contains nuclear endosperm.

Embryogeny in *Drosera* shows features characteristic of both Solanad and Caryophyllad types, whereas in *Dionaea muscipula* ca divides vertically, indicating either the Asterad or Onagrad type.

Berghs, 1905b • Eichinger, 1908 • Hofmeister, 1858, 1859 • K. Jones, 1964 • Lang, 1901 • Levine, 1915 • Narasimhachar, 1949, 1951b • Pace, 1912 • Patankar, 1956 • C. A. Peters, 1897–1898 • Rosenberg, 1899, 1909a • Samuelsson, 1913 • Schnarf, 1930 • Schürhoff, 1924a • C. M. Smith, 1929 • Souèges, 1936c • Trankowsky, 1938 • Venkatasubban, 1950a,b • Warming, 1913.

EBENACEAE

The anther is tetrasporangiate and in *Diospyros kali* its wall is composed of nonfibrous endothecium, 2 middle layers, and an unspecified type of tapetum whose cells become multinucleate. Simultaneous cytokinesis in the microspore mother cells follows meiosis and the microspore tetrads are tetrahedral, isobilateral, or decussate. Pollen grains in *D. virginiana* are 2-celled but in *D. kali* they are 1-celled and of doubtful fertility.

The ovule is anatropous, bitegmic, and tenuinucellar, with the micropyle formed by the inner integument. Cytokinesis in the megaspore mother cell accompanies meiosis and the chalazal megaspore of a linear tetrad develops into a Polygonum type embryo sac which frequently degenerates. Fusion of polar nuclei does not always occur and the 3 antipodal cells are small and ephemeral. A well-developed endothelium is differentiated during development of the embryo sac.

Endosperm formation is Nuclear, but the tissue later becomes cellular and finally ruminate.

Embryogeny has not been investigated but polyembryony has been reported in *D. virginiana*.

Chatin, 1870 • Hague, 1911 • Longo, 1909b • Periasamy, 1962b • Tamari, 1901 • Warming, 1913 • Wettstein, 1908 • Woodburn, 1911 • Yasui, 1915.

EHRETIACEAE

The anther is tetrasporangiate and its wall development follows the Dicotyledonous type. The endothecium develops fibrous thickenings, the middle layer is ephemeral, and the cells of the glandular tapetum become multinucleate. In *Ehretia laevis* the tapetum may be irregularly 2-layered because of occasional periclinal divisions. Simultaneous cytokinesis in the microspore mother cells follows meiosis and the microspore tetrads are tetrahedral, isobilateral, or decussate, with frequent polyspory in *Ehretia*. Pollen grains are 2-celled when shed and in *Coldenia procumbens* they may germinate *in situ*. Branching pollen tubes have been reported in *E. laevis*.

The ovule is hemianatropous, unitegmic, crassinucellar or, in *Cordia*, tenuinucellar. The archesporial cell usually cuts off a primary parietal cell which forms 1 or 2 parietal layers, but in *Cordia* it functions directly as the megaspore mother cell. The overlying cells of the nucellar epidermis in *Ehretia* undergo considerable radial elongation but their periclinal division has only been reported in *E. macrophylla*. Cytokinesis in the megaspore mother cell accompanies meiosis and the chalazal megaspore of a linear tetrad develops into a Polygonum type embryo sac, except in *E. laevis* where wall formation after the homotypic division is usually suppressed and the embryo sac is of the Allium type. The synergids are hooked, the polar nuclei fuse early, and the 3 antipodal cells degenerate at about the time of fertilization. Starch grains have been reported in the embryo sac of *Coldenia procumbens* and an endothelium is differentiated in all members.

Endosperm formation is *ab initio* Cellular and in the course of its development a 4-celled micropylar haustorium and 2- or 4-celled chalazal haustorium is formed.

Embryogeny conforms to the Chenopodiad type in *Coldenia procumbens* and the Asterad type in *Ehretia laevis*.

B. M. Johri, and Vasil, 1956 • Junell, 1938 • Svensson, 1925 • Vasil, 1955 • Venkateswarlu and Atchutaramamurti, 1955a,b,c.

ELAEAGNACEAE

Neither the structure of the anther nor microsporogenesis has been described, but when the pollen grains of *Elaeagnus angustifolia* are shed their generative nuclei are in prophase or metaphase.

The ovule is anatropous, bitegmic, and crassinucellar. The archesporial cell cuts off a primary parietal cell which forms several parietal layers and cytokinesis in the megaspore mother cell accompanies meiosis. The chalazal megaspore of a linear tetrad develops into a Polygonum type embryo sac whose components have not been described.

Endosperm formation is Nuclear but embryogeny has not been investigated.

Fuchs, 1936 • Schnarf, 1929b, 1931a • Servettaz, 1909 • B. Singh, 1964.

ELATINACEAE

The anther is tetrasporangiate and its wall development follows the Basic type. The endothecium develops fibrous thickenings, the 2 middle layers are ephemeral, and the cells of the glandular tapetum become binucleate. Simultaneous cytokinesis in the microspore mother cells follows meiosis and the microspore tetrads are tetrahedral or isobilateral. Pollen grains are 2-celled when shed in *Bergia* spp. but in *Elatine* some are commonly 3-celled and in the cleistogamous flowers of *E. triandra* germination takes place *in situ.*

The ovule is anatropous, bitegmic, and crassinucellar, with the micropyle formed by both integuments. A multicellular archesporium differentiates but only one cell is functional and cuts off a primary parietal cell which gives rise to 3 or 4 parietal layers. The apical cells of the nucellar epidermis divide periclinally and form a nucellar cap only in *Bergia capensis.* Cytokinesis in the megaspore mother cell accompanies meiosis and the chalazal megaspore of a linear or T-shaped tetrad develops into a Polygonum type embryo sac. The synergids are hooked in *B. annamioides,* the polar nuclei fuse before fertilization, and the 3 antipodal cells are ephemeral.

Endosperm formation is Nuclear but, following the development of walls at the micropylar (*Bergia*) or the chalazal (*Elatine*) pole, the tissue becomes cellular throughout.

Embryogeny conforms to the Solanad type and a uniseriate suspensor of 3 or 4 cells is formed.

Frisendahl, 1927 • Jönsson, 1879–1880, 1881 • Kajale, 1939 • Lemesle, 1929a • K. Müller, 1847 • Raghaven and Srinivasan, 1940b.

EMPETRACEAE

The anther is tetrasporangiate with 2 undifferentiated wall layers and a tapetum of undescribed type. Development of the pollen grains has not been investigated but the microspores are retained in permanent tetrads and the pollen grains, individually, are 2-celled.

The ovule is anatropous, unitegmic, and tenuinucellar. The archesporial cell functions directly as the megaspore mother cell in which cytokinesis accompanies meiosis, and the chalazal megaspore of a linear tetrad develops into a Polygonum type embryo sac. The synergids are pyriform, the polar nuclei fuse before fertilization, and the 3 antipodal cells degenerate soon after. An endothelium encloses the embryo sac.

Endosperm formation is *ab initio* Cellular with the development of terminal haustoria.

Embryogeny of *Corema album* conforms to the Solanad type and cleavage polyembryony has been reported in *Empetrum nigrum*.

Crété, 1951d • Don, 1827 • Hagerup, 1922, 1946 • Samuelsson, 1913 • Veillet-Bartoszewska, 1959c.

EPACRIDACEAE

The anther is bisporangiate and its persistent epidermis forms an exothecium. The development of the wall is undescribed but a fibrous endothecium is not differentiated and the cells of the glandular tapetum remain 1-nucleate in *Styphelia longiflora*. Simultaneous cytokinesis in the microspore mother cells follows meiosis and the microspore tetrads are liberated as units. In the tribe Stphelieae usually only one microspore per tetrad is functional and the 3 nonfunctional microspores persist as relics in the permanent tetrad. The individual pollen grains are 3-celled at maturity and in *Leucopogon juniperinus* they contain plastids and starch grains.

The ovule is anatropous, unitegmic, and tenuinucellar. The archesporial cell functions directly as the megaspore mother cell and cytokinesis accompanies meiosis. The chalazal megaspore of a linear tetrad develops into a Polygonum type embryo sac and the reports of a functional micropylar megaspore in *Leucopogon juniperinus* and *Styphelia longiflora* are based on misinterpreting the 3 antipodal cells as nonfunctional megaspores. The synergids exhibit the filiform apparatus, the polar nuclei fuse prior to fertilization, and the 2 or 3 antipodal cells are usually short lived but in *L. ericoides* they undergo secondary multiplication. An endothelium differentiates around the lower two-thirds of the embryo sac.

Endosperm formation is *ab initio* Cellular. Terminal haustoria are developed in *Epacris*, *Brachyloma*, and *Sprengelia*, although the chalazal one is rudimentary in *Brachyloma*. In *Styphelia* only a micropylar haustorium is formed.

Embryogeny follows the Caryophyllad type but in *Dracophyllum secundum* there are certain resemblances to the Solanad type.

Artopoeus, 1903 • Brough, 1923, 1924 • Copeland, 1954 • Crété, 1951d • Hofmeister, 1859 • Paterson, 1961 • Payer, 1857 • Samuelsson, 1913 • Smith-White, 1955a,b, 1959 • Veillet-Bartoszewska, 1961.

EREMOSYNACEAE

Embryologically unknown.

ERICACEAE

The anther is tetrasporangiate and the cells of the persistent epidermis are often darkly pigmented. In *Loiseleuria* an exothecium is formed and in *Phyllodoce* some epidermal cells develop fibrous thickenings. Wall formation in *Gaultheria ovatifolia, G. procumbens,* and *G. shallon* conforms to the Reduced type and the single parietal layer breaks down late in anther development. In other genera 2 or 3 hypodermal layers are formed which remain undifferentiated except in *Bejaria, Enkianthus, Phyllodoce,* and *Rhodothamnus* where a fibrous endothecium is formed. The cells of the glandular tapetum usually become 2-nucleate. Simultaneous cytokinesis in the microspore mother cells follows meiosis and the microspore tetrads are liberated as units, except in *Enkianthus* spp. and *Erica stricta* where they disintegrate into separate microspores. The individual pollen grains are 2- or 3-celled when shed and in *E. perulatus* they often germinate *in situ*.

The ovule is anatropous to hemianatropous or almost campylotropous, unitegmic, and tenuinucellar. The archesporial cell functions directly as the megaspore mother cell and cytokinesis usually accompanies meiosis. The chalazal megaspore of a linear tetrad develops into a Polygonum type embryo sac, but in *Cassiope mertensiana,* where wall formation occurs only after the homotypic division, the embryo sac is of the Allium type. The synergids are often hooked and in *Epigaea repens* they extend deeply into the micropyle. The polar nuclei fuse before or at fertilization and the 3 antipodal cells are often small and ephemeral, but in *Gaultheria* spp. they occupy up to half the embryo sac and in *Leucothoe racemosa* and *L. recurva* they undergo secondary multiplication. Starch grains have been reported in the embryo sacs of many species and an endothelium is differentiated which may enclose only the chalazal portion of the embryo sac.

Endosperm formation is *ab initio* Cellular except in *Rhododendron japonicum* where the first two nuclear divisions are not accompanied by cytokinesis. Terminal endosperm haustoria are developed.

Embryogeny conforms to the Solanad type.

Artopoeus, 1903 • Beijerinck, 1940 • Bell and Burchill, 1955b • Bowers, 1931 • Brisseau-Mirbel, 1815 • Chatin, 1870 • Chou, 1952 • Copeland, 1933, 1943 • Coulter and Chamberlain, 1903 • Creeche, 1955 • Crété, 1951d • Doyel, 1942 • Elfving, 1879 • Fritzsche, 1832 • P. S. Ganapathy and Palser, 1964 • Hagerup, 1928, 1954 • Hofmeister, 1858, 1859 • Hubert, 1896 • Jönsson, 1879–1881 • Matthews and Knox, 1926 • Matthews and Taylor, 1926 • Palser, 1951a,b, 1952, 1954, 1958, 1959, 1961 • Peltrisot, 1904 • Purkinje, 1830 • Rübel, 1908 • K. Y. Rudenko, 1961a • Safijowska, 1955, 1960 • Samuelsson, 1913 • Schnarf, 1931b • Schürhoff, 1926a • Shilova, 1962 • N. E. Stevens, 1911, 1919 • Strasburger, 1884 • Veillet-Bartoszewska, 1957b, 1959a,b, 1960b,c, 1961a, 1963 • Vesque, 1878, 1879 • Warming, 1878.

ERIOCAULACEAE

The anther is tetrasporangiate. The endothecium develops fibrous thickenings but otherwise its wall structure is undescribed. Simultaneous cytokinesis in the microspore mother cells follows meiosis but the shape of the microspore tetrads has not been reported. The pollen grains are 3-celled when shed.

The ovule is orthotropous, bitegmic, and tenuinucellar, with the micropyle formed by the inner integument. The archesporial cell functions directly as the megaspore mother cell in which cytokinesis accompanies meiosos and the chalazal megaspore of a linear tetrad develops into a Polygonum type embryo sac. The synergids are pyriform, the polar nuclei fuse before fertilization close to the 3 ephemeral antipodal cells.

Endosperm formation is reported to be Nuclear and later the tissue becomes cellular throughout, but the basal position of the primary endosperm nucleus suggests the Helobial type.

Embryogeny conforms to the Asterad type and polyembryony has been reported in *Eriocaulon septangulare*. *

Carvel, 1869 • B. Palm, 1920 • R. W. Smith, 1910.

ERYTHROPALACEAE

The development and structure of the anther and pollen grains have not been described.

The ovule of *Erythropalum scandens* is anatropous, unitegmic, and tenuinucellar. The archesporial cell functions directly as the megaspore mother cell in which cytokinesis accompanies meiosis and the chalazal megaspore of a linear tetrad develops into a Polygonum type embryo sac. The synergids are pyriform, the polar nuclei become closely associated near the egg, and the 3 antipodal cells are small. Starch grains are present in the embryo sac.

Endosperm formation and embryogeny have not been investigated.

Fagerlind, 1946b.

ERYTHROXYLACEAE

The anther is tetrasporangiate with a persistent epidermis. The endothecium develops fibrous thickenings, the 1 or 2 middle layers are ephemeral, and the cells of the glandular tapetum become 2-nucleate. Simultaneous cytokinesis in the microspore mother cells follows meiosis and the microspore tetrads are tetrahedral. Pollen grains are 3-celled when shed.

The ovule of *Erythroxylum* is anatropous to hemianatropous, bitegmic, and crassinucellar, with the micropyle formed by the inner integument. The archesporial cell cuts off a primary parietal cell which forms 2–5 parietal layers within the nucellar epidermis. Cytokinesis in the megaspore mother cell accompanies meiosis and the chalazal megaspore of a linear tetrad develops into a Polygonum type embryo sac. The synergids exhibit the filiform apparatus, the polar nuclei fuse before fertilization, and the 3 antipodals degenerate soon after their formation. The mature embryo sac is small in proportion to the chalazal nucellus and appears stalked. An endothelium is differentiated and extends to the base of the nucellus.

Endosperm formation is Nuclear and the tissue later becomes cellular throughout.

Embryogeny conforms to the Solanad type.

Mauritzon, 1934d • L. L. Narayana, 1960b, 1964a • Schnarf, 1931a • Schürhoff, 1924b.

ESCALLONIACEAE

Development and structure of the anther and pollen grains have not been described.

The ovule is anatropous, bitegmic (*Brexia*) or unitegmic (*Escallonia*), tenuninucellar or crassinucellar. In *Escallonia* and *Polyosma* the archesporial cell functions directly as the megaspore mother cell but in *Brexia madagascariensis* it cuts off a primary parietal cell which divides only anticlinally and forms a single parietal layer. Cytokinesis in the megaspore mother cell accompanies meiosis and the chalazal megaspore of a linear tetrad develops into a Polygonum type embryo sac. The synergids are elongated, the polar nuclei fuse before fertilization, and the 3 antipodal cells disorganize at embryo sac maturity. An endothelium differentiates around the lower two-thirds of the embryo sac.

Endosperm formation is Nuclear but embryogeny has not been investigated.

Dahlgren, 1927a • Elst, 1909 • Jönsson, 1879–1880 • Mauritzon, 1933a • Warming, 1913.

EUCOMMIACEAE

The anther of *Eucommia ulmoides* is tetrasporangiate with a persistent epidermis. The endothecium is 2-layered and develops fibrous thickenings, the 1–2 middle layers are ephemeral, and the cells of the glandular tapetum become 2–6-nucleate. Simultaneous cytokinesis in the microspore mother cells follows meiosis and the microspore tetrads are tetrahedral. Pollen grains are 2-celled when shed and the pollen tubes may be branched.

The ovule is anatropous, unitegmic, and crassinucellar. A multicellular archesporium is common, each cell of which cuts off a primary parietal cell that gives rise to 2 or 3 parietal layers. A nucellar cap about 3 cells in thickness is formed by periclinal divisions of the apical nucellar epidermal cells. Cytokinesis accompanies meiosis, often in more than one megaspore mother cell, and the chalazal megaspore of each linear tetrad enlarges, but only one completes development into a Polygonum type embryo sac. The synergids are pyriform, the polar nuclei fuse before fertilization, and 3 antipodal cells are formed.

Endosperm formation is *ab initio* Cellular but embryogeny has not been investigated.

Eckardt, 1957, 1963 • Harms, 1933 • Tang, 1962.

EUCRYPHIACEAE

Embryologically unknown.

EUPHORBIACEAE

The anther is usually tetrasporic but the bisporic condition occurs in *Acalypha* spp., *Chrozophora* spp., *Euphorbia dracunculoides*, and

E. microphylla. Its wall development conforms to the Dicotyledonous type in *Euphorbia* but the Monocotyledonous type in *Acalypha* and *Phyllanthus.* The endothecium develops fibrous thickenings, the middle layer is ephemeral, and in *Hevea brasiliensis, Sebastiana chamaelea,* and *Tragia involucrata* 2 such layers are present. The tapetum is glandular and its cells usually become 2 or 3-nucleate, but in *Acalypha indica* an amoeboid tapetum has been reported (Johri and Kapil, 1953). Ubisch granules are of common occurrence. Simultaneous cytokinesis in the microspore mother cells follows meiosis and the microspore tetrads are tetrahedral, isobilateral, or decussate. Pollen grains are 2 or 3-celled when shed, but in *Euphorbia dulcis* they are sterile and seldom develop beyond the 1-celled condition.

The ovule is orthotropous (*Breynia patens*), hemianatropous or anatropous, bitegmic, and crassinucellar, with the micropyle usually formed by both integuments. A multicellular archesporium is common but although each cell cuts off a primary parietal cell, only one undergoes further development. A parietal tissue of several cell layers is formed and the apical cells of the nucellar epidermis divide periclinally and give rise to a nucellar cap. In *Acalypha* spp., *Euphorbia geniculata, E. tiruncalli, Pedilanthus tithymaloides,* and *Tragia involucrata* the nucellus forms a beak which extends beyond the inner integument and comes in contact with the placental obturator which occupies the exostome. An extreme development of the nucellus occurs when it becomes tonguelike and passes beyond both integuments, finally reaching the obturator outside the ovule. This condition has been described in *Agyneia, Ceramanthus, Chrozophora, Euphorbia hypericifolia, Glochidion, Jatropa, Phyllanthus, Scepasma,* and *Trigonostemon.* Cytokinesis in the megaspore mother cell accompanies meiosis and the chalazal megaspore develops into a Polygonum type embryo sac in species of *Agyneia, Chrozophora, Euphorbia, Jatropa, Mercurialis, Micrococca, Phyllanthus, Sebastiana,* and *Tragia.* In *Codiaeum variegatum* var. *pictum,* "strike" is exhibited by the 3 chalazal nuclei of the 4-nucleate stage with the result that the mature structure is 5-nucleate and lacks antipodals. Suppression of cytokinesis and the development of the chalazal dyad cell into an Allium type embryo sac occurs in *Chrozophora rottleri, Euphorbia amygdaloides, E. characias, E. lagascae,* and *E. mauretanica.* Tetrasporic embryo sac development is represented by the Drusa type in *Mallotus alba* and *M. japonicus,* the Fritillaria type in *E. dulcis,* and the Penaea type in *Acalypha australis, A. brachystachya, A. malabarica, Euphorbia palustris, E. procera,* and *Mallotus philippensis.* A type of embryo sac development intermediate between the Penaea and the Plumbago types occurs in *Acalypha ciliata, A. fallax, A. indica,* and *A. rhomboidea* where more than 4 nuclei form the secondary nucleus while in *A. lanceolata* only the egg and a single synergid are differentiated and the remaining 14 nuclei fuse in the center of the embryo sac (Peperomia hispidula type). The synergids may be hooked but a filiform apparatus has only been reported in *Mallotus philippensis.* The polar nuclei fuse before or at fertilization, and the 3 antipodal cells are usually short-lived, but in *Jatropa gossypifolia* a small degree of secondary multiplication occurs and 4 or 5 cells may be present. Starch grains are common in the embryo sac and a hypostase is usually differentiated.

Endosperm formation is Nuclear but the tissue later becomes cellular throughout, except in *Chrozophora rottleri* where the free-nucleate condition persists. In *Croton klotzschianus* and *C. sparsiflorus* a chalazal haustorium is formed which remains free-nucleate and may reach 1000 μ in length.

Embryogeny usually follows the Onagrad type but the Solanad type occurs in *Phyllanthus* and in *Euphorbia preslii* and *E. rothiana* the zygote divides vertically and consequently conforms to the Piperad type. In *E. dulcis* the egg degenerates and adventive embryony may result in the formation of up to 13 embryos. Polyembryony is of common occurrence and was first described by Petit-Thouars (1808) in *E. rosea.*

Amato, 1939, 1946b • Arnoldi, 1911, 1912 • Baillon, 1858a • Banerji, 1949, 1951 • Banerji and Dutt, 1944 • Bhalla, 1941a,b • Bohn, 1924 • Bouharmont, 1961, 1962 • Braun, 1857, 1860 • Candolle, 1827 • Carano, 1915b, 1925, 1926 • Cesca, 1961a • C. B. Clarke, 1887 • Dang-Van-Liem, 1959, 1962 • P. K. Deshpande, 1959 • Dessiatoff, 1911 • Dickey and Reuther, 1940 • Donati, 1912, 1913 • M. K. Dutt, 1943 • Elfving, 1879 • Galimberti, 1963 • Gopinath and Gopalkrishnan, 1949 • L. Guignard, 1882b • Hanstein, 1877 • Hegelmaier, 1885, 1901, 1903 • Heusser, 1919 • Hofmeister, 1858 • Hubert, 1896 • Jennings, 1963 • B. M. Johri, 1952 • B. M. Johri, and Kapil, 1953 • Jönsson, 1879–1880, 1881 • Jörgensen, 1923 • Kajale, 1954b • Kajale and Murthy, 1954 • Kajale and Rao, 1943 • Kapil, 1955, 1956a,b, 1960, 1961 • Kayser, 1892, 1893a • Kelkar, 1960 • Kenoyer, 1919 • Landes, 1946 • Lundberg, 1931 • F. M. Lyon, 1898 • Maas, 1919 • P. Maheshwari, 1942, 1945 • P. Maheshwari and Chowdhury, 1937 • P. Maheshwari and Johri, 1940, 1941 • Malte, 1910 • A. P. Mani, 1960 • Markowski, 1912 • Martinoli, 1940b • Masters, 1869 • Mathé, 1928 • L. P. McCann, 1942, 1945 • L. O. T. Mendes, 1947 • J. Modilewski, 1909a, 1910, 1911 • Mohan Ram and Satsangi, 1963 • Moore and Lindsay, 1953 • Moquin-Tandon, 1841 • Mukherjee, 1957, 1958, 1961a,c, 1962, 1964 • Mukherjee and Padhye, 1964 • Muzik, 1954 • Nair and Abraham, 1963 • Nair and Maitreyi, 1962 • Narasimha, 1962 • Petit-Thouars, 1908 • Py, 1929 • Raju and Rao, 1953 • A. N. Rao, 1956b, 1964a • P. N. Rao, 1962 • Roeper, 1824 • Sanchez, 1938 • Sateishi, 1927 • Schacht, 1850 • Schlotterbeck, 1898 • Schmidt, 1907 • Schürhoff, 1924b, 1926b

• Schweiger, 1905 • G. Sharma, 1956 • K. D. Sharma, 1955 • R. P. Singh, 1954, 1956, 1959, 1962 • Souèges, 1924f, 1925f • R. K. Srivastava, 1952 • R. K. Srivastava and Agarwal, 1953 • Strasburger, 1877, 1878, 1909c, 1910b • Swamy and Balakrishna, 1946 • Sykes, 1909 • Tateishi, 1927 • Thathachar, 1952, 1953a,b • Venkateswarlu and P. N. Rao, 1963 • Ventura, 1930b, 1933, 1934, 1940 • Weniger, 1917 • Wille, 1886.

EUPOMATIACEAE

Anther development and structure have not been described. Simultaneous cytokinesis in the microspore mother cells follows meiosis and the microspore tetrads are tetrahedral, isobilateral, decussate, or occasionally, linear. The constituents of the mature pollen grains are unknown.

Development and nature of the embryo sac, endosperm, and embryo have not been investigated.

Hotchkiss, 1958.

FAGACEAE

The number of sporangia comprising the anther has not been recorded but in *Quercus velutina* 2–4 parietal layers are formed, and the innermost forms the glandular (?) tapetum whose cells become at least 2-nucleate. The microspore tetrads are tetrahedral and the pollen grains are 2-celled when shed. In *Q. robur* the pollen tubes form short branches and in *Fagus sylvatica* they branch in the ovarian cavity.

The ovule is anatropous, bitegmic (unitegmic in *Nothofagus*), and crassinucellar. A multicellular archesporium is differentiated but only one cell is functional and cuts off a primary parietal cell which gives rise to a single parietal layer. In *Fagus sylvatica*, however, about 13 cell layers are present above the megaspore mother cell and these originate from periclinal divisions of the parietal and nucellar epidermal cells. Cytokinesis in the megaspore mother cell accompanies meiosis and the chalazal megaspore of a linear or T-shaped tetrad develops into a Polygonum type embryo sac. The synergids of *Quercus velutina* exhibit the filiform apparatus, the polar nuclei fuse prior to fertilization, and in *Castanea vulgaris* the 3 antipodal cells undergo some secondary multiplication. The development of a lateral caecum results in bifurcation of the base of the embryo sac and although the antipodals remain *in situ*, the secondary nucleus migrates into the caecum where it is fertilized.

Endosperm formation is Nuclear but the tissue later becomes cellular except in the chalazal portion of the embryo sac, which is occupied by a large vacuole.

Embryogeny in *Quercus robur* and *Q. velutina* follows the Onagrad type but cleavages in *ca* are very irregular. In the former species Hjelmqvist (1957) reports the degeneration of the suspensor cell and the formation of a secondary suspensor from the embryo proper. Polyembryony has been reported in *Q. alba* and *Q. robur*.

Bagda, 1948, 1952 • Benson, 1894 • Berridge, 1914 • Braun, 1860 • A. H. Conrad, 1900 • Finn, 1928a • Harvey 1917 • Hjelmqvist, 1948, 1953, 1957 • Hofmeister, 1858 • Klebelsberg, 1910 • Langdon, 1939 • Poole, 1952 • Stenzel, 1890.

FICOIDACEAE

The anther is tetrasporangiate and in *Sesuvium portulacastrum* its wall development follows the Basic type. The endothecium develops fibrous thickenings, the 2 middle layers are ephemeral, and the cells of the glandular tapetum become 2-nucleate. Ubisch granules occur in *Sesuvium*. Simultaneous cytokinesis in the microspore mother cells follows meiosis and the microspore tetrads are tetrahedral or isobilateral. The pollen grains are 3-celled when shed.

The ovule is anacampylotropous to campylotropous, bitegmic, and crassinucellar, with the micropyle formed by the inner integument. The archesporial cell cuts off a primary parietal cell which gives rise to 1 or 2 parietal layers and the lateral cells of the nucellar epidermis undergo several periclinal divisions. The apical epidermal cells elongate radially and form a single-layered nucellar cap. Cytokinesis in the megaspore mother cell accompanies meiosis and the chalazal megaspore of a linear tetrad develops into a Polygonum type embryo sac, although the Adoxa type has been reported in *Mesembryanthemum pseudotruncatellum*. Frequently, wall formation after the homotypic division is suppressed in the micropylar dyad cell and a "triad" results. Hooked synergids have only been described in *Sesuvium portulacastrum*, the polar nuclei fuse before fertilization, and the 3 antipodal cells are ephemeral. Starch grains are present in the mature embryo sac.

Endosperm formation is Nuclear but the tissue finally becomes cellular, although in *Trianthema portulacastrum* its chalazal portion is still free-nuclear 11 days after pollination.

Embryogeny follows the Solanad type and the suspensor is either slender or massive. Polyembryony has been reported in *T. portulacastrum*. An aril almost encloses the mature seed.

Bhargava, 1935b • Buxbaum, 1948 • Dahlgren, 1916, 1927c • Dnyansagar and Malkhede, 1963 • L. Guignard, 1882 • Huber, 1924 • Hubert, 1896 • Jönsson, 1879–1880 • Kajale, 1940b • H. S. Narayana, 1962c • Raghavan, 1940a • W. Schmid, 1925 • Woodcock, 1930.

FLACOURTIACEAE

The anther is tetrasporangiate with a persistent epidermis. The endothecium develops fibrous thickenings, the 1 or 2 middle layers are ephemeral, and the cells of the glandular tapetum become 2–4-nucleate. Simultaneous cytokinesis in the microspore mother cells follows meiosis and the microspore tetrads are tetrahedral or isobilateral. Pollen grains are 2-celled when shed.

The ovule is orthotropous (*Casearia*), anatropous (*Kiggelaria*), or hemianatropous (*Idesia*), bitegmic, and crassinucellar, with the slightly zigzag micropyle formed by both integuments. The archesporial cell cuts off a primary parietal cell that forms 3–7 parietal layers below the nucellar epidermis in which an occasional cell undergoes a single periclinal division in *Kiggelaria africana*. Cytokinesis in the megaspore mother cell accompanies meiosis and the chalazal megaspore of a linear tetrad develops into a Polygonum type embryo sac. The synergids are hooked and in *Casearia tomentosa* they show the filiform apparatus, the polar nuclei fuse before or at fertilization, and the 3 antipodal cells are ephemeral. Except in *Kiggelaria*, the embryo sac becomes much elongated during maturation and its apex penetrates the micropyle to the exostome. A hypostase is differentiated in *Casearia*.

Endosperm formation is Nuclear but the tissue later becomes cellular.

Embryogeny has not been investigated.

Corti, 1948 • Gopinath, 1946 • Mauritzon, 1936b • Narayanaswami and Sawhney, 1959 • Ventura, 1937.

FLAGELLARIACEAE

Anther development and structure have not been described. Successive cytokinesis follows meiosis in the rectangular and very small microspore mother cells of *Flagellaria indica* and the microspore tetrads are isobilateral or linear.

Development and the nature of the embryo sac, endosperm, and embryo are unknown.

B. Palm, 1920.

FOUQUIERIACEAE

Development and structure of the anther and pollen grains have not been described.

The ovule is anatropous, bitegmic, and tenuinucellar, with the micropyle formed by the inner integument whose distal portion is expanded and liplike. The archesporial cell functions directly as the megaspore mother cell in which cytokinesis accompanies meiosis, although it may be suppressed in the micropylar dyad cell after the homotypic division. The chalazal megaspore of a linear tetrad or "triad" develops into a Polygonum type embryo sac. The synergids are pyriform, the polar nuclei fuse before fertilization, and the 3 antipodal cells degenerate soon after. An endothelium encloses the embryo sac.

Endosperm formation is *ab initio* Cellular. In *Fouquieria splendens*, the first cell division forms a small micropylar chamber and a large chalazal one from which a lateral haustorium is given off. The endosperm proper develops from a cell formed at the apex of the chalazal chamber whose nucleus then passes into the haustorium.

Embryogeny of *F. peninsularis* conforms to the Asterad type.

Johansen, 1936 • R. Khan, 1943 • Mauritzon, 1936b.

FRANCOACEAE

Development and structure of the anther and pollen grains have not been described.

The ovule of *Francoa* is anatropous, bitegmic, and crassinucellar, with the micropyle formed by both integuments. The archesporial cell cuts off a primary parietal cell which forms up to 6 parietal layers, and an occasional cell of the nucellar epidermis undergoes a single periclinal division. Cytokinesis in the megaspore mother cell accompanies meiosis and the chalazal megaspore of a linear tetrad develops into a Polygonum type embryo sac. The synergids are hooked, the polar nuclei fuse before fertilization and the 3 antipodal cells are ephemeral.

Endosperm formation is Nuclear. Following the initiation of walls at the micropylar pole and around the embryo, the tissue becomes cellular, although in the distended base of the embryo sac the free-nucleate condition persists for a considerable time.

Embryogeny is unknown.

Dahlgren, 1930c • Elst, 1909 • Gäumann, 1918, 1919 • Mauritzon, 1933a • Tieghem, 1898.

FRANKENIACEAE

Anther development and structure have not been described but the cells of the glandular tapetum become 2-nucleate. Simultaneous cytokinesis in the microspore mother cells follows meiosis and the microspore tetrads are tetrahedral. Pollen grains are 2-celled when shed.

The ovule of *Frankenia hirsuta* is anatropous, bitegmic, and pseudocrassinucellar, with the micropyle formed by the inner integument. The archesporial cell functions directly as the megaspore mother cell which becomes very elongated and cytokinesis accompanies meiosis to form a linear tetrad of megaspores. Owing to the unusual length of the megaspore mother cell, the chalazal megaspore is deeply embedded and when the 3 nonfunctional megaspores degenerate they are replaced by lateral nucellar cells which form a thick tissue between the developing Polygonum type embryo sac and the nucellar epidermis. The synergids are hooked, the polar nuclei fuse before fertilization, and the 3 antipodal cells are large.

Endosperm formation and embryogeny have not been investigated.

Dahlgren, 1928b • Mauritzon, 1933c, 1936b.

FUMARIACEAE

In *Dicentra* and *Fumaria* each stamen is tripartite and bears a central tetrasporangiate anther and lateral bisporangiate ones. Anther wall development follows the Monocotyledonous type and the epidermis is persistent. The endothecium develops fibrous thickenings, the middle layer is ephemeral, and the cells of the glandular tapetum become 2- or more nucleate. Simultaneous cytokinesis in the microspore mother cells follows meiosis and the microspore tetrads are tetrahedral, isobilateral, or decussate. Pollen grains are 2-celled when shed and those of *D. scandens* may germinate *in situ*.

The ovule is anatropous to campylotropous, bitegmic, and crassinucellar, with the micropyle formed by both integuments. The archesporial cell cuts off a primary parietal cell which forms 2 or 3 parietal layers below the nucellar epidermis. Cytokinesis in the megaspore mother cell accompanies meiosis and the chalazal megaspore of a linear tetrad develops into a Polygonum type embryo sac. The synergids of *Fumaria parviflora* exhibit the filiform apparatus, the polar nuclei fuse before fertilization, and the 3 antipodal cells of *Fumaria* are very large and resemble the egg apparatus.

Endosperm formation is Nuclear but centripetal wall development is initiated after the formation of several hundred free nuclei and the tissue becomes cellular throughout.

Embryogeny follows the Caryophyllad type but the suspensor shows considerable variation in origin and morphology. In *Hypecoum* it is a swollen unicellular structure derived directly from *cb*, whereas in *Corydalis* it is composed of 3 vesicular multinucleate cells, only one of which is derived from *cb*, and in *Fumaria cb* alone gives rise to a very massive multicellular suspensor which at first exceeds in size the embryo proper. Polyembryony has been reported in *Dicentra scandens*.

Dahlgren, 1915a • L. Guignard, 1891, 1903b • Hegelmaier, 1878, 1880b, 1885 • Hofmeister, 1858 • Hubert, 1896 • Huss, 1906 • Il'ina, 1964 • Jönsson, 1879–1880 • Němec, 1910b • Petit, 1928 • Saksena, 1954 • D. Singh and Negi, 1962 • Souèges, 1941f,g, 1943a,b, 1946a,b,c,j • Strasburger, 1879b, 1880b • Tischler, 1900 • Vesque, 1879.

GARRYACEAE

The anther of *Garrya elliptica* is tetrasporangiate and the endothecium probably develops fibrous thickenings. The middle layer is ephemeral and the cells of the amoeboid tapetum become 2-nucleate before periplasmodium formation. Simultaneous cytokinesis in the microspore mother cells follows meiosis and the microspore tetrads are tetrahedral. Pollen grains are 2-celled when shed.

The ovule is anatropous, unitegmic, and crassinucellar. The archesporial cell cuts off a primary parietal cell which remains undivided, but the apical cells of the nucellar epidermis give rise to a nucellar cap 2 or 3 cells in thickness. Cytokinesis in the megaspore mother cell accompanies meiosis and the chalazal megaspore of a linear tetrad develops into a Polygonum type embryo sac. The egg is very elongated and extends almost to the middle of the embryo sac, the polar nuclei fuse before fertilization, and the 3 antipodal cells undergo secondary multiplication. An obturator is formed from the funicle or placenta.

Endosperm formation is Nuclear but after walls are formed at the micropylar pole, the tissue becomes cellular throughout.

Embryogeny conforms to the Solanad type and a long uniseriate suspensor is formed which, in *G. veatchii*, gives rise to additional embryos by budding although only the zygotic embryo reaches maturity.

Eyde, 1964 • Hallock, 1930 • Horne, 1914 • P. R. M. Rao, 1963.

GEISSOLOMATACEAE

Development and structure of the anther and pollen grains have not been investigated.

The ovule of *Geissoloma marginata* is anatropous and bitegmic, with the micropyle formed by both integuments. The youngest material examined contained a 2-nucleate embryo sac and consequently its origin was not determined although Stephens (1910) was of the opinion that it was monosporic. The polar nuclei fuse at the chalazal end of the embryo sac before fertilization, the 3 antipodal cells are ephemeral, and numerous starch grains are present, particularly around the polar nuclei.

The endosperm is cellular during later stages but there is no information on its early development or that of the embryo.

Stephens, 1910.

GENTIANACEAE

The anther is tetrasporangiate and the formation of its wall follows the Dicotyledonous type in *Swertia carolinensis*. The endothecium develops fibrous thickenings, except in *Cotylanthera* and *Exacum* where pore dehiscence occurs. The middle layer in *Exacum bicolor, E. petiolare,* and *Swertia carolinensis* divides periclinally to form 3 or 4 similar layers which are persistent, and the tapetum is glandular except in *Canscora* spp. and *Gentiana diffusa* where it is amoeboid. Ubisch granules have been reported in *Exacum,* while in *Gentiana* and *Swertia* each loculus may be subdivided by partitions of sterile cells. Simultaneous cytokinesis in the microspore mother cells follows meiosis and the microspore tetrads are tetrahedral or isobilateral. Pollen grains are 2- or 3-celled when shed and in *Canscora diffusa* both conditions occur in the same anther.

The ovule is anatropous, unitegmic, and tenuinucellar. The archesporial cell functions directly as the megaspore mother cell in which cytokinesis accompanies meiosis and the chalazal megaspore of a linear tetrad develops into a Polygonum type embryo sac. The synergids are pyriform, the polar nuclei fuse before fertilization, and the 3 antipodal cells degenerate at embryo sac maturity except in *Swertia carolinensis* where secondary multiplication occurs. Starch grains are present in the embryo sac of *Canscora* and an endothelium has been reported in *Exacum pumilum.*

Endosperm formation is usually Nuclear but it becomes cellular after centripetal wall formation, and *ab initio* Cellular endosperm has been reported in *Voyria coerulea* and *Voyriella parviflora*. Embryogeny conforms to the Solanad type.

Arekal, 1961a • Baum, 1948b • Billings, 1901 • Crété, 1949a,d,e, 1955e, 1959a • Figdor, 1897 • Goebel, 1923 • Guérin, 1903, 1904, 1924, 1925, 1926 • L. Guignard, 1901d • Holm, 1897 • Jacobsson-Paley, 1920d • Johow, 1885, 1889 • Maheswari Devi, 1962 • McCoy, 1949 • Oehler, 1927 • K. Y. Rudenko, 1961a • Schnarf, 1923 • Srinivasan, 1941 • Steffen and Landmann, 1958 • Stolt, 1921, 1927 • Süssenguth, 1927 • Svedelius, 1902 • Wóycicki, 1932.

GERANIACEAE

The anther is tetrasporangiate and the endothecium develops fibrous thickenings, while the middle layer is ephemeral. The tapetum is glandular in *Monsonia senegalensis* and its cells become 2-nucleate, but in *Pelargonium zonale* it is amoeboid. Simultaneous cytokinesis in the microspore mother cells follows meiosis and the pollen grains are 3-celled when shed in *Erodium circutarium* and *P. zonale* but 2-celled in *M. senegalensis*.

The ovule is anatropous to campylotropous, bitegmic, and crassinucellar. The archesporial cell cuts off a primary parietal cell whose behavior has not been described and cytokinesis in the megaspore mother cell accompanies meiosis. The chalazal megaspore of a linear tetrad develops into a Polygonum type embryo sac in which the polar nuclei fuse before fertilization and the 3 antipodal cells are very ephemeral. The pollen tube is persistent throughout embryogeny in *M. senegalensis*.

Endosperm formation is Nuclear but the tissue later becomes cellular throughout.

Embryogeny conforms to the Asterad type in *Erodium circutarium* but the Onagrad type in *Geranium molle*, while a combination of both types occurs in *M. senegalensis* and *P. zonale*. A suspensor haustorium has been reported in *P. zonale* but requires confirmation in view of the occurrence of a persistent pollen tube in *M. senegalensis*.

Billings, 1901 • Elfving, 1879 • Hegelmaier, 1878 • Hofmeister, 1858, 1859 • Juel, 1915 • Nagl, 1962 • H. S. Narayana and Arora, 1963a,b • Samuelsson, 1913 • Schürhoff, 1924b • Souèges, 1923b,c • Strasburger, 1882a, 1884b.

GESNERIACEAE

The number of sporangia comprising the anther has not been recorded but its wall development conforms to the Dicotyledonous type.

The epidermis is persistent, the endothecium develops fibrous thickenings, and the middle layer is ephemeral. The cells of the glandular tapetum become multinucleate and finally uninucleate by fusion. Simultaneous cytokinesis in the microspore mother cells follows meiosis and the microspore tetrads are tetrahedral or decussate. Pollen grains are 2-celled when shed.

The ovule is anatropous, unitegmic, and tenuinucellar. The archesporial cell functions directly as the megaspore mother cell in which cytokinesis accompanies meiosis and the chalazal megaspore of a linear tetrad develops into a Polygonum type embryo sac. The synergids are slender and in *Didymocarpus tomentosa*, *Klugia zeylanica*, and *Rhynchoglossum obliquum* their long tapering tips enter the micropyle and extend throughout its length. The polar nuclei fuse just before or at fertilization, the 3 antipodal cells are very ephemeral, and starch grains are present in the embryo sac of *Rhytidophyllum*. An endothelium is differentiated around only the slender proximal portion of the embryo sac.

Endosperm formation is *ab initio* Cellular with terminal haustoria. The aggressive chalazal haustorium is 1 or 2-nucleate and reaches the epidermis of the ovule while the 2-celled micropylar haustorium is increasingly active during later stages of embryogeny and becomes extramicropylar in *Didymocarpus*.

Embryogeny conforms to the Onagrad type.

Arekal, 1961b • Balicka-Iwanowska, 1899 • Berg, 1898 • M. T. Cook, 1907a • Crété, 1942, 1949c, 1951d, 1955a,f • Dahlgren, 1927a • Elfving, 1879 • Glišic, 1924, 1927, 1934 • Hielscher, 1879 • Hofmeister, 1849 • V. Laurent, 1923 • Oehlkers, 1923 • Padmanabhan, 1961a • Schnarf, 1917b, 1921b, 1923 • Strasburger, 1877, 1878, 1884b • Swamy and Padmanabhan, 1961b • Thathachar, 1942b, 1943 • Vesque, 1878 • Warming, 1878.

GLOBULARIACEAE

The development and structure of the anther and pollen grains have not been investigated.

The ovule is anatropous, unitegmic, and tenuinucellar. The archesporial cell functions directly as the megaspore mother cell in which cytokinesis accompanies meiosis, and the chalazal megaspore of a linear tetrad develops into a Polygonum type embryo sac. The synergids are pyriform, the polar nuclei fuse before fertilization, and the 3 large antipodal cells become disorganized soon after. *Globularia vulgaris* is highly apomictic and several chalazal cells may develop into unreduced embryo sacs by somatic apospory.

Endosperm formation is *ab initio* Cellular with aggressive terminal haustoria, both of which become extra-ovular and invade the ovary wall. The micropylar haustorium is initially 4-celled but on degeneration of the intervening walls it becomes unicellular and coenocytic, with at least 7 nuclei occurring in that of *G. cordifolia*. The chalazal haustorium forms directly from the primary chalazal endosperm chamber whose nucleus undergoes a single division.

Embryogeny conforms to the Onagrad type.

Billings, 1901 • Crété, 1943, 1951d • Hauss, 1927 • Hofmeister, 1858, 1859 • Jönsson, 1879-1880, 1881 • Magnus, 1913 • Rosén, 1940b.

GOMORTEGACEAE

Embryologically unknown.

GONYSTYLACEAE

Embryologically unknown.

GOODENIACEAE

The anther is tetrasporangiate with a persistent epidermis. The endothecium develops fibrous thickenings, the middle layer is ephemeral, and the cells of the glandular tapetum become multinucleate, but in *Scaevola lobelia* the uninucleate condition is restored by fusion. Simultaneous cytokinesis in the microspore mother cells follows meiosis and the microspore tetrads are tetrahedral or isobilateral. Pollen grains are 2-celled when shed, and in *Leschenaultia* they are retained in permanent tetrads.

The ovule is anatropous, unitegmic, and tenuinucellar. The archesporial cell functions directly as the megaspore mother cell in which cytokinesis accompanies meiosis and the chalazal megaspore of a linear tetrad develops into a Polygonum type embryo sac. The synergids are elongate and those of *Dampiera stricta* exhibit the filiform apparatus, the polar nuclei fuse before fertilization, and the 3 antipodal cells are still present during early postfertilization stages. An endothelium is differentiated but does not enclose the extremities of the embryo sac.

Endosperm formation is *ab initio* Cellular.

Embryogeny conforms to the Solanad type.

Billings, 1901 • Brough, 1927 • Hamilton, 1885, 1894 • Haviland, 1885, 1914 • Kausik, 1939c • Rosén, 1937, 1946.

GOUPIACEAE

Embryologically unknown.

GRAMINEAE

The anther is tetrasporangiate and its wall development follows the Monocotyledonous type. The endothecium develops fibrous thickenings, the middle layer is ephemeral, and the cells of the glandular tapetum usually become 2-nucleate, although the uninucleate condition is retained in *Pennisetum typhoideum*. Successive cytokinesis in the microspore mother cells accompanies meiosis and the microspore tetrads are isobilateral or, occasionally, T-shaped or linear. Pollen grains are 3-celled when shed but pollen abortion is commonly associated with apomixis.

The ovule is anatropous, hemianatropous, or campylotropous, bitegmic, and usually pseudocrassinucellar, with the micropyle commonly formed by the inner integument, although in *Panicum miliaceum* both integuments are involved. In *Pennisetum clandestinum,* however, the outer integument is weakly developed and, as the inner one fails to enclose the nucellus, no micropyle is formed. Further reduction in size of the outer integument to little more than a relic occurs in *Phyllostachys* and the absence of both integuments has been reported in *Melocanna*. The archesporial cell functions directly as the megaspore mother cell and usually periclinal divisions of the apical nucellar epidermal cells form a nucellar cap up to 6 cells in thickness. In the Pooideae, however, the nucellar epidermis typically remains as a single layer and the ovule is tenuinucellar. Cytokinesis in the megaspore mother cell accompanies meiosis and the chalazal megaspore of a linear tetrad develops into a Polygonum type embryo sac. The synergids may be hooked and their apices frequently present a hyaline appearance, while the polar nuclei fuse before or at fertilization. The 3 antipodal cells undergo considerable size increase in *Bromus inermis, Eleusine coracana,* and *E. indica,* but secondary multiplication is a characteristic of the family and in *Sasa paniculata* about 300 antipodal cells are present in a chalazal diverticulum. In the Pooideae the antipodals become laterally situated in the embryo sac. Apomixis is of common occurrence and is often, but not invariably, associated with polyploidy. In the Panicoideae apomictic embryo sacs are usually 4-nucleate and lack antipodals as well as either a polar nucleus or one of the synergids. In *Poa* somatic and gonial apospory, as well as sexual reproduction, have all been reported while, according to Nygren (1949), young plants of *Calamagrostis purpurea* reproduce sexually but, on aging, become apomictic and their pollen is then abortive. In somatic apospory in *Pennisetum clandestinum* although the enlargement of one or more nucellar cells usually crushes the megaspore tetrad, both sexual and apomictic embryo sacs may reach maturity within the same ovule. Multiple embryo sac formation is common and may result from the functioning of more than one megaspore, from the development of several nucellar cells by somatic apospory, or from a combination of these processes.

Endosperm formation is Nuclear and the tissue becomes cellular only after a large number of free nuclei have formed. The peripheral cell layer behaves as a secondary cambium and forms the aleurone layer of the seed, although in *Echinochloa frumentosa* Narayanaswami (1955) found no evidence of meristematic activity in the endosperm. In apomictic embryo sacs fertilization may still be required for endosperm formation although the unreduced egg develops autonomously, but if the meiotic failure which precedes gonial apospory also results in pollen abortion, endosperm formation must necessarily be independent of fertilization. During seed maturation the endosperm normally becomes hard and dry but in *Helictotrichon, Koeleria, Sphenopholis,* and *Trisetum* it remains liquid for years.

Embryogeny conforms to the Asterad type. Polyembryony is common and is frequently associated with multiple embryo sac formation.

Afanas'eva, 1962, 1964 • Åkerberg, 1936, 1939, 1943 • Aleksandrov and Aleksandrova, 1938 • Alicja and Marja, 1934 • A. M. Anderson, 1927 • Anikiev, 1963 • Armstrong, 1937 • Artschwager, Brandes, and Starrett, 1929 • Artschwager and McGuire, 1949 • Avery, 1932 • G. N. R. Ayyangar and Krishnaswami, 1930 • G. N. R. Ayyangar and V. P. Rao, 1935 • Bannikova, 1963 • Bashaw, 1962 • Bashaw and Hoit, 1958 • Batikyan and Cholakhyan, 1962 • Batygina, 1962a,b • Batygina, Terekhin, Alimova, and Yakovlev, 1963 • Beaudry, 1951 • Beck and Horton, 1932 • Belitser, 1963 • Bennett, 1944 • Bohutinsky, 1914 • Boyes and Thompson, 1937 • Braun, 1860 • Bremer, 1946, 1959 • Bremner, 1946, 1959 • Bremner, Eckersall, and Scott, 1963 • Brenchley, 1909, 1912 • Brink and Cooper, 1944 • C. M. Brown, 1964 • W. L. Brown, 1941 • W. L. Brown and Emery, 1957a,b, 1958 • W. V. Brown, 1949, 1955, 1959, 1960 • W. V. Brown and Coe, 1951 • Bruns, 1892 • Cannon, 1900 • Carniel, 1961, 1962a • Cassini, 1828 • Celakovsky, 1897 • Celarier and Harlan, 1957 • Chandra, 1962, 1963a,b • Cho, 1938 • Cholakhyan and Sogomonyan, 1961 • Christoff, 1942 • G. L. Church, 1929a,b • Collins, 1909 • D. C. Cooper, 1937, 1951 • Coulon, 1922, 1923 • Cruz, 1957 • Cummins, 1929 • R. M. Datta and Paul, 1951 • Demoor, 1853 • Diakonu, 1962 • Dmitrieva and Zhukova, 1961 • Dore, 1956 • N. L. Dutt and Krishnaswami, 1932 • N. L. Dutt and Rao, 1933 • Duvick, 1955 • Dzyubenko, 1960 • Eichinger, 1910 • Elfving, 1879 • Emery, 1957 • Emery and Brown, 1957, 1958 • Engelbert, 1940, 1941 • Eyster,

1931 • Farquharson, 1955 • A. Fischer, 1880 • W. D. Fischer, Bashaw, and Holt, 1954 • Gaines and Aase, 1926 • Gering and Zorina, 1961 • Gioelli, 1935 • Goebel, 1933 • Golinski, 1893 • Gordon, 1922 • Graham, 1927 • Guérin, 1899 • J.-L. Guignard, 1961c, 1962a, 1963b • L. Guignard, 1882b, 1901a • Guttenberg, Heydel, and Pankow, 1954 • Hair, 1956 • Håkansson, 1943, 1944, 1948, 1953 • Håkansson and Ellerström, 1950 • Halsted, 1890 • W. Hansen, 1920 • Hanstein, 1870 • H. V. Harlan, 1920 • H. V. Harlan and Pope, 1925 • J. R. Harlan, 1949 • J. R. Harlan, Brooks, Borgaonkar, and de Wet, 1964 • Harrington and Crocker, 1923 • Hayman, 1956 • Hegelmaier, 1874a • Hérail, 1889 • Hofmeister, 1849, 1858, 1861 • Hoshikawa, 1961a,b • Hubert, 1896 • Hutchison and Bashaw, 1964 • G. H. Jensen, 1918 • Johnston, 1953 • J. W. Jones, 1928 • Jost, 1907 • Juliano and Aldana, 1937 • Kalinina, 1959 • Kamra, 1960 • Kandelaki, 1961 • Kennedy, 1900 • Khosla, 1946 • Kiellander, 1935, 1937, 1941 • Kiesselbach, 1926a,b, 1949 • Komura, 1922 • Konstantinov, 1963 • Kordyum, 1963 • Körnicke, 1896 • Korobov, 1961, 1962 • Kostoff, 1939, 1940 • Koul, 1959 • Koul and Gahi, 1962 • Krauss, 1933 • Krishnaswamy and Ayyangar, 1930, 1937 • Kumar, 1942 • Kuwada, 1910a,b, 1911 • Lampe, 1931 • La Rue and Avery, 1938 • Levan, 1941 • Lima-de-Faria, 1947 • Lötscher, 1905 • Lowe and Nelson, 1946 • MacLeod and McCorquodale, 1958 • Merry, 1941 • Merwe, 1957 • Miller, 1920 • K. C. Misra, 1948 • Modilevski and Beilis, 1937, 1938 • Morrison, 1955 • Mowery, 1929–1930 • Müntzing, 1933, 1940 • Narayan, 1955, 1962 • Narayanaswami, 1940, 1952, 1953, 1954, 1955a,b,c, 1956 • Němec, 1910b • Neuffer, 1964 • Nielsen, 1945, 1946, 1947a,b • Nishimura, 1922a,b • Noguchi, 1929 • Nörner, 1881 • Nygren, 1946, 1949, 1950a,b • Palamarchuk, 1962 • Palamarchuk and Gogoleva, 1962 • Palm, 1920 • Paul and Datta, 1950, 1953 • Percival, 1921 • Persidsky, 1940 • Petit-Thouars, 1810 • Petrova and Drozdov, 1963 • Poddubnaja-Arnoldi and Pashchenko, 1962 • Poindexter, 1903 • Pointeau, 1809 • Pope, 1937, 1943a,b, 1946 • A. J. Pritchard, 1962 • Ramiah, Parthasarathy and Ramanusam, 1935 • Randolph, 1936 • Randolph and Fischer, 1939 • Rangasamy, 1935 • Raspail, 1824 • Reeder, 1953, 1956, 1957, 1959, 1962 • Reeves, 1928 • Reusch, 1961 • Richard, 1811 • Rodrigo, 1926 • Roth, 1955, 1957, 1959 • Rowlee and Doherty, 1898 • Rowley, 1963 • Rychlewski, 1958, 1961 • Sandeen, 1868 • Santos, 1933 • Sargant and Arber, 1915 • Sass, 1946 • Sass and Sprague, 1950 • K. Sax, 1921, 1922 • Schacht, 1850, 1858 • Schilbersky, 1890 • Schleiden, 1839b • Schnarf, 1926 • Schrenk, 1894 • Shadowsky, 1926 • Sharman, 1942 • Sheth, Yu, and 1961 • Skalińska, 1952, 1959 • B. W. Smith, 1948 • Snyder, 1957 • Snyder, Hernan-Edwardson, 1956 • Shkurenko, 1961 • Simonyan, 1963 • S. P. Singh and Hadley, 1961 • Skalińska, 1952, 1959 • B. W. Smith, 1948 • Snyder, 1957 • Snyder, Hernan-dez, and Warmke, 1955 • Solntseva and Yakovlev, 1964 • Souèges, 1924b • G. F. Sprague, 1932 • Stapf, 1904 • Stenar, 1932a • Stover, 1937 • Strasburger, 1884b • Stratton, 1923 • Süssenguth, 1919 • Swamy, 1944a • Täckholm and Söderberg, 1918 • Tannert, 1905 • Terada, 1928 • Tieghem, 1897a • Tinney, 1940 • True, 1893 • Turpin, 1837 • Ustinova, 1960a,b,c • Venkateswarlu and Devi, 1964 • Vijayaraghavan and Rao, 1936 • Vukolov, 1929 • Wakakuwa, 1934 • Warmke, 1954 • Weatherwax, 1916, 1917, 1919, 1926, 1930, 1934, 1955 • Weir and Dale, 1960 • Westermaier, 1890 • Wet and Borgaonkar, 1963 • Wordsell, 1916 • Yakovlev, 1950 • Yamaura, 1933 • Yasui, 1936 • Zimmermann, 1911.

GREYIACEAE

Development and structure of the anther and pollen grains have not been described.

The ovule is anatropous, bitegmic, and crassinucellar, with the micropyle formed by both integuments. The archesporial cell of *Greyia sutherlandii* cuts off a primary parietal cell which gives rise to 4 parietal layers, and the apical cells of the nucellar epidermis divide periclinally to form a nucellar cap 4 cells in thickness. Cytokinesis in the megaspore mother cell accompanies meiosis and the chalazal megaspore of a linear or T-shaped tetrad develops into a Polygonum type embryo sac, whose structure has not been described.

Endosperm formation and embryogeny are unknown.

Mauritzon, 1936d.

GROSSULARIACEAE

The anther is tetrasporangiate. The endothecium develops fibrous thickenings, 2 middle layers are formed, and the cells of the glandular (?) tapetum become multinucleate. Simultaneous cytokinesis in the microspore mother cells follows meiosis and the microspore tetrads are tetrahedral or isobilateral. Pollen grains are 2-celled when shed.

The ovule is anatropous, bitegmic, and crassinucellar. The archesporial cell cuts off a primary parietal cell which gives rise to several parietal layers, and cytokinesis in the megaspore mother cell accompanies meiosis. The chalazal megaspore of a linear tetrad develops into a Polygonum type embryo sac in which the synergids are hooked and bear apical "caps." The polar nuclei fuse before fertilization and the 2 or 3 antipodal cells degenerate soon afterwards. A funicular aril has been described in *Ribes aureum* where its disintegration forms a pulpy mass which encloses the seeds.

Endosperm formation is *ab initio* Cellular in *R. orientale, R. rubrum,* and *R. silvestre* but the Helobial type occurs in *R. bureiense, R. divaricatum, R. grossularia, R. missouriense,* and *R. oxyacanthoides,* where the small chalazal endosperm chamber becomes multicellular.

Embryogeny is very irregular after the formation of a row of 4 cells and on present information it cannot be assigned to a definite type.

Dahlgren, 1930c • Elst, 1909 • A. Fischer, 1880 • L. Guignard, 1882b • Himmelbaur, 1911 • Hofmeister, 1858b • Janczewski, 1903, 1907, 1908 • Jönsson, 1881 • Mauritzon, 1933a • Pohl, 1922 • Tischler, 1906 • Vesque, 1878, 1879b • Warming, 1878 • Yen, 1936.

GRUBBIACEAE

The development and structure of the anther and pollen grains have not been described.

The ovule is anatropous, unitegmic, and tenuinucellar, with a long micropyle. The archesporial cell of *Grubbia tomentosa* functions directly as the megaspore mother cell in which cytokinesis accompanies meiosis. The chalazal megaspore of a linear tetrad develops into a Polygonum type embryo sac whose tip invades the micropyle, but there is no account of its structure. An endothelium is differentiated from the innermost layer of the integument.

Endosperm formation has not been described but later stages are cellular and its epidermal layer is covered by thick cuticle. Micropylar and chalazal haustoria are present.

Embryogeny is unknown.

Fagerlind, 1947e • B. M. Johri and Bhatnagar, 1960 • Tieghem, 1896b.

GYROSTEMONACEAE

Embryologically unknown.

HAEMODORACEAE

Anther structure has not been described but the tapetum is usually amoeboid and its cells become 2-nucleate, although in *Lanaria plumosa* a glandular tapetum has been reported. Successive cytokinesis in the microspore mother cells accompanies meiosis in all members except *Lanaria*, where cytokinesis is simultaneous. The microspore tetrads are tetrahedral or isobilateral and pollen grains are 2-celled when shed.

The ovule is hemianatropous to anatropous, bitegmic, and crassinucellar, with the micropyle formed by either both integuments (*Anigozanthos, Lanaria*) or only the inner one (*Dilatis, Wachendorfia*). The archesporial cell cuts off a primary parietal cell which gives rise to 2–4 parietal layers and the apical cells of the nucellar epidermis divide periclinally to form a nucellar cap 2–4 cells in thickness. Cytokinesis in the megaspore mother cell accompanies meiosis, and the chalazal megaspore of a linear tetrad develops into a Polygonum type embryo sac. The synergids are pyriform, the polar nuclei fuse just before fertilization close to the 3 antipodal cells, which soon degenerate.

Endosperm formation is Helobial and the chalazal chamber becomes multinucleate in *Lanaria*, but otherwise gives rise to 4 large cells, and may show some weak haustorial activity. The micropylar chamber, after a period of free-nuclear division, becomes cellular and forms the endosperm proper.

Embryogeny conforms to the Asterad type.

Dellert, 1933 • Stenar, 1927b, 1938b • Süssenguth, 1919, 1921 • Vos, 1956, 1961, 1963.

HALORRHAGACEAE

The anther is tetrasporangiate and its wall development follows the Monocotyledonous type. The endothecium develops fibrous thickenings, the middle layer is ephemeral and the cells of the glandular tapetum become 2-nucleate. Simultaneous cytokinesis in the microspore mother cells follows meiosis and the microspore tetrads are tetrahedral or decussate. The pollen grains are 2-celled when shed in *Gunnera* and *Laurembergia* but they are 3-celled in *Hippuris*.

The ovule is hemianatropous to anatropous, unitegmic (*Hippuris*) or bitegmic, and crassinucellar, with the micropyle formed by both integuments. The archesporial cell cuts off a primary parietal cell which gives rise to 2 parietal layers and the apical cells of the nucellar epidermis may undergo periclinal divisions and form a nucellar cap. According to Juel (1910, 1911) the archesporial cell of *Hippuris vulgaris* functions directly as the megaspore mother cell and the ovule is tenuinucellar. In *Hippuris*, *Laurembergia*, and *Myriophyllum* cytokinesis in the megaspore mother cell accompanies meiosis and the chalazal megaspore of a linear tetrad develops into a Polygonum type embryo sac. The synergids exhibit the filiform apparatus, the polar nuclei fuse early, and the 3 antipodal cells persist until after fertilization. In *Gunnera chilensis*, *G. insignis* and *G. macrophylla*, however, the embryo sac is tetrasporic and of the 16-nucleate Peperomia type in which the large secondary nucleus is formed by the fusion of 7 nuclei, and the 6 antipodal cells degenerate after fertilization.

Endosperm formation is usually *ab initio* Cellular but in *Laurembergia* it is Nuclear, and later the tissue becomes cellular throughout.

Embryogeny in *Hippuris* follows the Onagrad type and a large haustorial suspensor is formed, but in *Laurembergia* and *Myriophyllum* it conforms to the Caryophyllad type and *cb* divides longitudinally to form a pair of juxtaposed haustorial cells which resemble persistent synergids.

Bley, 1925 • Ernst, 1908a,b • Fagerlind, 1944c • Hegelmaier, 1870, 1878 • Jönsson, 1879–1880, 1881 • Jørgensen, 1923 • Juel, 1910, 1911 • Kellermann, 1881 • J. Modilewski, 1908a • Samuels, 1912 • Schnegg, 1902 • Souèges, 1922c, 1940d • Stolt, 1928 • Tieghem, 1898 • Unger, 1849 • Virkki, 1962 • Warming, 1913.

HAMAMELIDACEAE

The anther is tetrasporangiate (*Corylopsis, Fothergilla, Liquidambar*) or bisporangiate (*Hamamelis*). The endothecium develops fibrous thickenings, the middle layer is ephemeral, and the cells of the glandular tapetum become 2–4 nucleate. Simultaneous cytokinesis in the microspore mother cells follows meiosis and the microspore tetrads are tetrahedral. Pollen grains are 2-celled when shed.

The ovule is anatropous, bitegmic, and crassinucellar and, although in *Hamamelis* the zigzag micropyle is formed by both integuments, in *Corylopsis* only the inner one is involved. The archesporial cell cuts off a primary parietal cell which gives rise to 5–10 parietal layers below the nucellar epidermis. Cytokinesis in the megaspore mother cell accompanies meiosis and the chalazal megaspore of a linear tetrad develops into a Polygonum type embryo sac. In *Liquidambar* the homotypic division is suppressed in the micropylar dyad cell and a "triad" of megaspores is formed. The synergids are pyriform, the polar nuclei fuse before fertilization, and the secondary nucleus moves close to the 3 antipodal cells, which commence degeneration soon after their formation. According to Shoemaker (1905) about one week intervenes between fertilization and pollination in *Fothergilla gardeni* and *Liquidambar styracifolia*, but in *Hamamelis arborea* the interval is 2 months and in *H. virginiana* it is 5–7 months.

Endosperm formation is Nuclear but later the tissue becomes cellular throughout.

Embryogeny has not been investigated.

Flint, 1957a,b, 1959a • Horne, 1914 • Shoemaker, 1902, 1905 • Tong, 1930.

HELLEBORACEAE

The anther is tetrasporangiate with a persistent epidermis. The endothecium develops fibrous thickenings, the 2 or 3 middle layers are ephemeral, and the cells of the glandular tapetum become at least 2-nucleate before fusions restore the 1-nucleate condition. *Actaea spicata* is exceptional in possessing an amoeboid tapetum which becomes irregularly 2-layered during development. Simultaneous cytokinesis in the microspore mother cells follows meiosis and the microspore tetrads are tetrahedral, decussate, or isobilateral. Pollen grains are 2-celled when shed.

The ovule is anatropous, bitegmic, and crassinucellar, with the micropyle formed by the inner integument. Although a multicellular archesporium is common, only one cell is functional and cuts off a primary parietal cell which, with derivatives of the nucellar epidermis, forms up to 6 cell layers. Cytokinesis in the megaspore mother cell accompanies meiosis, and the chalazal megaspore of a linear tetrad develops into a Polygonum type embryo sac. The synergids are pyriform, the polar nuclei fuse before fertilization, and the 3 antipodal cells increase in size. In *Aconitum napellus* the upper antipodal extends almost to the egg apparatus. Nuclear multiplication in the antipodal cells is common and is often followed by fusions, but secondary multiplication of cells has been reported only in *Actaea cimifuga*, where 4 cells may occur. The antipodals persist, in an apparently healthy condition, into early embryogeny. In *Consolida arvensis* fertilization takes place 3–19 hours after pollination.

Endosperm formation is Nuclear, but following centripetal wall development, the tissue becomes cellular throughout.

Embryogeny conforms to the Onagrad type except in *Isopyrum fumarioides*, where it follows the Solanad type. Polyembryony has been attributed to synergid fertilization in *Aconitum napellus* and *Delphinium elatum* and according to Derschau (1918) it follows fertilization of antipodal cells in *Nigella arvensis*.

Arzt, 1933 • Berghs, 1905 • Dahlgren, 1915a, 1924, 1927a • Derschau, 1918 • Dunn, 1900 • Earle, 1938 • A. Fischer, 1880 • Grafl, 1941 • L. Guignard, 1882a, 1889, 1900 1901c • Habermann, 1906 • Hegelmaier, 1878, 1885 • Hofmeister, 1858 • Huss, 1906 • Jalan, 1960, 1963 • John, 1907 • Jönsson, 1879–1880, 1881 • Kapil and Jalan, 1962 • Kordyum, 1961a • Lötscher, 1905 • Lundegårdh, 1909 • Ly Thi Ba, 1961b,c • Mottier, 1895, 1897, 1898, 1905 • Nawaschin, 1900a,b • Osterwalder, 1898 • Overton, 1905 • Persidsky, 1914 • Poddubnaja-Arnoldi, 1936 • Py, 1929 • Raciborski, 1893 • Schürhoff, 1924a • Strasburger, 1877, 1878, 1879a, 1880b, 1882a • Süssenguth, 1919, 1921 • E. M. Thomas, 1900a,b • Tschermak-Woess, 1956 • Tulasne, 1855 • Vesque, 1878, 1879 • Warming, 1913 • Westermaier, 1890, 1898.

HERNANDIACEAE

Embryologically unknown.

HETEROPYXIDACEAE

Embryologically unknown.

HETEROSTYLACEAE

The anther of the terminal male flower of *Lilaea subulata* is tetrasporangiate and those of the lateral flowers are bisporangiate. The endothecium develops fibrous thickenings and, of the 2 middle layers, the inner is ephemeral and the outer persists until the pollen grains are almost mature. The cells of the amoeboid tapetum are uninucleate and an extensive periplasmodium is formed. Successive cytokinesis in the microspore mother cells accompanies meiosis and the microspore tetrads are usually tetrahedral. Pollen grains are 2-celled when shed.

The ovule is anatropous, bitegmic, and crassinucellar, with the micropyle formed by the inner integument. Although a multicellular archesporium is common, only one cell cuts off a primary parietal cell and this forms 5 or 6 layers of parietal tissue. Cytokinesis in the megaspore mother cell accompanies meiosis, and the chalazal megaspore of a linear tetrad develops into a Polygonum type embryo sac. The synergids are beaked, the polar nuclei fuse before fertilization, and although the 3 antipodals degenerate during early embryogeny, vestiges still remain as the seed approaches maturity.

Endosperm formation is Nuclear and the tissue does not become cellular before it is digested by the embryo.

Embryogeny conforms to the Caryophyllad type and *cb* enlarges into a short unicellular suspensor.

Agrawal, 1952 • Campbell, 1898 • Wulff, 1939b.

HIMANTANDRACEAE

Embryologically unknown.

HIPPOCASTANACEAE

The anther is tetrasporangiate with a glandular tapetum. Simultaneous cytokinesis in the microspore mother cells follows meiosis and the pollen grains are 2-celled when shed.

The ovule is anatropous, bitegmic, and crassinucellar. The archesporium is multicellular and several cells each cuts off a primary parietal cell. Cytokinesis accompanies meiosis in each functional megaspore mother cell and several linear tetrads are formed. Although embryo sac development is presumably of the Polygonum type, it has not been described.

Endosperm formation is Nuclear but embryogeny has not been described in detail. According to List and Steward (1965) the zygote of *Aesculus woerlitzensis* is divided by a transverse, oblique, or vertical wall and subsequent divisions are very variable.

Guérin, 1901 • Jönsson, 1879–1880 • Juel, 1915 • Kayser, 1893b • List and Steward, 1965 • Schürhoff, 1926b.

HIPPOCRATEACEAE

The anther is tetrasporangiate with a persistent epidermis whose cells become papillate in *Hippocratea grahamii*. The endothecium develops fibrous thickenings, the 2 middle layers are ephemeral, and the cells of the glandular tapetum become multinucleate. Simultaneous cytokinesis in the microspore mother cells follows meiosis and the microspore tetrads are tetrahedral or decussate. Pollen grains are 2-celled when shed.

The ovule is anatropous, bitegmic, and usually crassinucellate, with the micropyle formed by the inner integument. The archesporial cell usually cuts off a primary parietal cell which divides only anticlinally, except in *Salacia oblonga* where it forms 4 parietal layers. In *H. grahamii*, however, the archesporial cell functions directly as the megaspore mother cell and the ovule is tenuinucellar. Cytokinesis in the megaspore mother cell accompanies meiosis and the chalazal megaspore of a linear tetrad develops into a Polygonum type embryo sac. The synergids of *H. grahamii* are hooked and exhibit the filiform apparatus, the polar nuclei fuse before fertilization, and the 3 antipodal cells are commonly ephemeral. An endothelium is differentiated in *Hippocratea*.

Endosperm formation is Nuclear but embryogeny has not been described.

Adatia and Gavole, 1962 • David, 1938 • Mauritzon, 1936c,d.

HOPLESTIGMATACEAE

Embryologically unknown.

HUACEAE

Embryologically unknown.

HUMIRIACEAE

The development and structure of the anther and pollen grains have not been described.

The ovule is anatropous, bitegmic, and crassinucellar, with the micropyle formed by both integuments. The archesporial cell cuts off a primary parietal cell which gives rise to about 6 parietal layers. The mature embryo sac is 8-nucleate in *Humiria* but its development has not been recorded.

Endosperm formation in *Vantanea* is "probably Nuclear" (Mauritzon, 1934c), but embryogeny is unknown.

Mauritzon, 1934c.

HYDNORACEAE

Development and structure of the anther and pollen grains have not been described.

The ovule is orthotropous, unitegmic, and tenuinucellar. The archesporial cell functions directly as the megaspore mother cell in which cytokinesis follows only the heterotypic division in *Prosopanche bertoniensis* and the chalazal dyad cell develops into an Allium type embryo sac. In *Hydnora africana*, however, cytokinesis in the megaspore mother cell is suppressed and the embryo sac is of the tetrasporic Adoxa type. The synergids are pyriform, the polar nuclei fuse before fertilization, and the 3 antipodal nuclei degenerate soon after their formation.

Endosperm formation has not been investigated.

Embryogeny in *H. africana* is unusual in that the early cleavages are all transverse and a uniseriate filament of up to 15 cells is formed before longitudinal divisions take place. The embryo proper is reported to develop from cells at the center of the proembryo and, although the suspensor degenerates, the distal remains of the proembryo persist. Johansen considers that such development conforms best to the Solanad type but a reinvestigation is desirable.

Bary, 1868 • Chodat, 1916 • Dastur, 1922 • Johansen, 1950 • Solms-Laubach, 1874 • Tieghem, 1897b.

HYDRANGEACEAE

Development and structure of the anther and pollen grains are undescribed.

The ovule is anatropous, unitegmic, and tenuinucellar. The archesporial cell functions directly as the megaspore mother cell but the origin of the embryo sac has not been traced, although Mauritzon's figures suggest that in *Kirengeshoma palmata* it may be of the Allium type. The synergids are hooked, the polar nuclei fuse before fertilization, and in *Kirengeshoma* the 3 antipodal cells become 2-nucleate and haustorial. An endothelium encloses the lower half of the embryo sac.

Endosperm formation is *ab initio* Cellular but embryogeny has not been investigated.

Elst, 1909 • Mauritzon, 1933a • Tieghem, 1898.

HYDROCHARITACEAE

The anther is tetrasporangiate or rarely bisporangiate (*Elodea canadensis, Philotria*) with a persistent epidermis which in *Vallisneria spiralis* forms an exothecium, and its wall development conforms to the Monocotyledonous type. The endothecium develops fibrous thickenings in the chasmogamous flowers of *Ottelia* but otherwise it is undifferentiated, 1 or 2 middle layers are formed, and the cells of the amoeboid tapetum remain 1-nucleate. According to Padhye and Rao (1960) no tapetal periplasmodium is formed in *Lagarosiphon roxburghii*. Successive cytokinesis in the microspore mother cells accompanies meiosis and the microspore tetrads are isobilateral, decussate, or linear. Pollen grains are usually 3-celled when shed but in *Blyxa* and *Ottelia* they are 2-celled. In *Ottelia ovalifolia* the pollen grains germinate *in situ* in both cleistogamous and chasmogamous flowers.

The ovule is orthotropous in *Nechamandra* and *Vallisneria* but is otherwise anatropous, bitegmic, and crassinucellar, with the micropyle formed by the inner integument except in *Blyxa oryzetorum* where both integuments are involved. The archesporial cell cuts off a primary parietal cell which gives rise to 2–4 parietal layers and the apical cells of the nucellar epidermis divide periclinally to form a nucellar cap 2 or 3 cells in thickness. Cytokinesis in the megaspore mother cell accompanies meiosis and the chalazal megaspore of a linear, T-shaped, or tetrahedral tetrad develops into a Polygonum type embryo sac. In *Blyxa* the micropylar dyad cell degenerates soon after its formation and the homotypic division takes place only in the chalazal dyad cell. The synergids are large and in *Enalus acoroides* and *Ottelia lancifolia* they exhibit the filiform apparatus whereas the synergids of *Nechamandra alternifolia* are hooked. The polar nuclei fuse just before fertilization and the secondary nucleus moves close to the 3 small antipodal cells, which persist into early embryogeny in a short pouch.

Endosperm formation is Helobial and free-nuclear divisions take place in the micropylar chamber, which after wall formation gives rise to the endosperm proper. The small chalazal endosperm chamber remains 1-nucleate and may exhibit some haustorial activity and in

Halophila ovata the walls of the adjacent nucellar cells degenerate and liberate the protoplasts, so that the chalazal chamber becomes secondarily coenocytic. The formation of a lateral caecum from the micropylar chamber has been reported in *Blyxa octandra*.

Embryogeny conforms to the Caryophyllad type and the short suspensor terminates in a large basal cell. Polyembryony has been reported in *Nechamandra alternifolia*.

Baude, 1956 • Burr, 1903 • Claussen, 1927 • Elfving, 1879 • Ernst-Schwarzenbach, 1945a,b, 1956 • A. Fischer, 1880 • Govindappa and Naidu, 1956 • Haccius, 1952 • Islam, 1950 • Kausik, 1939b, 1940b, 1941a • Kausik and Rao, 1942 • Kerner, 1891 • Kny, 1878 • Lakshmanan, 1961, 1963a,b • P. Maheshwari, 1933b, 1934a, 1943a • P. Maheshwari and B. M. Johri, 1950b • S. K. N. Murthy, 1935a • Padhye, 1962a • Padhye and Rao, 1960, 1963 • B. Palm, 1915 • Rangasamy, 1934, 1941b • Riddle, 1905a • Rosenberg, 1901a,b • Schürhoff, 1926b • Souèges, 1954a • Svedelius, 1904, 1932 • Swamy and Lakshmanan, 1962 • Sykes, 1909 • Tassi, 1900 • Troll, 1931 • Tuschnjakowa, 1929b • Wager, 1928 • Witmer, 1937 • Wylie, 1904, 1923.

HYDROPHYLLACEAE

Anther development has not been described but the tapetum is glandular and its cells remain 1-nucleate. Simultaneous cytokinesis in the microspore mother cells follows meiosis but the form of the microspore tetrads and details of the pollen grains have not been reported.

The ovule is anatropous, unitegmic, and tenuinucellar. The archesporial cell functions directly as the megaspore mother cell in which cytokinesis accompanies meiosis and the chalazal megaspore of a linear tetrad develops into a Polygonum type embryo sac. In *Hydrolea zeylanica* the synergids possess large basal and apical vacuoles and the filiform apparatus is exhibited in *Phacelia tanacetifolia*. The polar nuclei fuse before fertilization and the 3 antipodal cells are ephemeral, but in *Hydrolea* they degenerate as free nuclei. An endothelium encloses the embryo sac.

Endosperm formation is *ab initio* Cellular in *Nemophila aurita*, *Phacelia congesta*, *P. viscidula*, and *Romanzoffia sitchensis*, but in *P. malvifolia* and *P. tanacetifolia* it is Nuclear. In *P. parryi*, however, the endosperm is of an intermediate type because after the formation of a row of 4 cells, each undergoes free-nuclear division followed by wall formation and the tissue ultimately becomes cellular. The development of a chalazal endosperm haustorium is common and, although it is little more than a short pouch in *Phacelia congesta*, *P. parryi*, and *P. tanacetifolia*, a 1–2-nucleate diverticulum is present in *P. malvifolia* and *P. viscidula*. A similar structure occurs in *Nemo-*

phila insignis, where it arises from the base or side of the lowest endosperm cell, whereas in *N. aurita* there is a micropylar and two chalazal haustoria. No such haustoria have been reported in *Hydrolea* or *Romanzoffia.*

Embryogeny conforms to the Solanad type.

Billings, 1901 • Crété, 1946e • Hofmeister, 1858, 1859 • Jönsson, 1879–1880 • Kainradl, 1927 • Mitra, 1945, 1947a • Strasburger, 1884b • Svensson, 1925 • Wulff and Raghavan, 1937 • Yamazaki, 1957.

HYDROSTACHYACEAE

The anther is tetrasporangiate but its wall development and that of the pollen grains have not been investigated. The pollen grains are shed as permanent tetrads.

The ovule is anatropous, unitegmic, and tenuinucellar. The archesporial cell functions directly as the megaspore mother cell in which cytokinesis accompanies meiosis and the chalazal megaspore of a linear tetrad develops into a Polygonum type embryo sac. The synergids are pyriform, the polar nuclei fuse before fertilization, but the behavior of the 3 antipodal nuclei is not clear. Starch grains are present in the mature embryo sac.

Endosperm formation is *ab initio* Cellular with no haustorial development.

Embryogeny has not been described, but in *Hydrostachys imbricatus* the basal suspensor cell becomes vesicular and coenocytic and finally irregularly cellular.

Dahlgren, 1927c • Erdtman, 1952 • Mauritzon, 1933b, 1939c • B. Palm, 1915 • Subramanyam, 1962 • Warming, 1882.

HYPERICACEAE

The anther is bisporangiate in *Hypericum* and its epidermal cells contain darkly staining granules. The endothecium develops fibrous thickenings, the 1 or 2 middle layers are ephemeral, and the cells of the glandular tapetum become 2-nucleate. Simultaneous cytokinesis in the microspore mother cells follows meiosis and the microspore tetrads are tetrahedral, isobilateral, or decussate. Pollen grains are 2-celled when shed.

The ovule is anatropous, bitegmic and tenuinucellar, with the micropyle formed by both integuments. The archesporial cell functions directly as the megaspore mother cell in which cytokinesis accompanies meiosis and the chalazal megaspore of a linear tetrad develops into a Polygonum type embryo sac. The synergids are pyriform, the polar nuclei fuse before fertilization and the 3 antipodal cells usually commence degeneration soon after. In *Hypericum gentianoides* and *H. punctatum,* however, secondary multiplication may result in the formation of about 7 antipodals which persist into early embryogeny. Starch grains are present in the mature embryo sac.

Endosperm formation is Nuclear. In *Hypericum,* following division of the primary endosperm nucleus, the two daughter nuclei move to opposite poles of the embryo sac and the micropylar nucleus undergoes free-nuclear division. The chalazal nucleus, however, becomes enclosed in dense cytoplasm, forming a coenocytic cystlike body which merges finally with the general endosperm. Wall formation is initiated at the micropylar pole when embryogeny is well advanced, and the tissue becomes cellular throughout.

Embryogeny conforms to the Solanad type and synergid polyembryony has been reported in *H. maculatum*

Braun, 1860 • Crété, 1936 • Dahlgren, 1923, 1927c • Govindappa, 1956b • L. Guignard, 1893 • Hoar and Haertl, 1932 • Myers, 1964 • Noack, 1939 • B. Palm, 1922a • A. N. Rao, 1957 • Schnarf, 1914 • Souèges, 1925a, 1936b,g • Stenar, 1938a • Swamy, 1946d • Vesque, 1878.

HYPOXIDACEAE

The anther is tetrasporangiate with a persistent epidermis. The endothecium develops fibrous thickenings, the number of middle layers has not been reported, and the amoeboid tapetum forms an extensive periplasmodium. Successive cytokinesis in the microspore mother cells accompanies meiosis and the pollen grains are 2-celled when shed.

The ovule is hemianatropous (*Forbesia, Pauridia*) or anatropous (*Curculigo, Hypoxis, Ianthe*), bitegmic, and pseudocrassinucellar, with the slightly zigzag micropyle formed by both integuments. The apical cells of the nucellar epidermis divide periclinally to form a nucellar cap 2 cells in thickness. The archesporial cell functions directly as the megaspore mother cell in which cytokinesis accompanies meiosis, and the chalazal megaspore of a linear or T-shaped tetrad develops into a Polygonum type embryo sac. In *Forbesia plicata,* however, wall formation after the homotypic division is suppressed and the chalazal dyad cell develops into an Allium type embryo sac. The synergids of *I. aquatica* exhibit the filiform apparatus, the polar nuclei fuse prior to fertilization, and the 3 antipodal cells are usually ephemeral, but occasionally in *Ianthe* a small degree of secondary multiplication occurs.

Endosperm formation is Nuclear in *Pauridia* but Helobial in *Curculigo* and *Hypoxis*, where the small chalazal chamber is haustorial, and both endosperm types occur in *Ianthe* and *Spiloxene*.

Embryogeny in *Ianthe* conforms to the Asterad type.

Dellert, 1933 • B. Palm, 1920 • Stenar, 1924a, 1925b • Vos, 1948, 1949, 1956, 1961.

ICACINACEAE

The number of sporangia comprising the anther has not been reported. The endothecium develops fibrous thickenings, the 1 or 2 middle layers are ephemeral, and the cells of the glandular tapetum become 5- or 6-nucleate. Simultaneous cytokinesis in the microspore mother cells follows meiosis and the microspore tetrads are tetrahedral. Pollen grains are 2-celled when shed.

The ovule is anatropous, unitegmic, and usually crassinucellar. The archesporium is multicellular and, although each archesporial cell cuts off a primary parietal cell, only one undergoes further development. Up to 5 layers of parietal cells are formed below the nucellar epidermis. In *Phytocrene dasycarpa*, however, the functional megaspore mother cell forms directly from an archesporial cell and the ovule is tenuinucellar. Cytokinesis in the megaspore mother cell accompanies meiosis and the chalazal megaspore of a linear tetrad develops into a Polygonum type embryo sac. The synergids exhibit the filiform apparatus and are hooked in *Gomphandra polymorpha* and *Phytocrene dasycarpa*. The polar nuclei fuse before fertilization and the 3 antipodal cells are small and ephemeral in *Gomphandra*, but are large and pyriform in *Phytocrene*. Starch grains are present in the embryo sac.

Endosperm formation is Nuclear in *Gomphandra*, where it later becomes cellular but does not develop the haustorial structure described in *Nothapodytes foetida*. In this species the basal endosperm cell acts as a haustoria initial and gives off a short intercellular caecum which establishes protoplasmic continuity with the chalazal nucellar cells.

Embrogeny is unknown.

Fagerlind, 1945c • Mauritzon, 1936c,d • Padmanabhan, 1961c • Swamy and Ganapathy, 1957a.

ILLECEBRACEAE

The anther is tetrasporangiate and its wall development in *Polycarpon loeflingiae* conforms to the Dicotyledonous type. The endothecium develops fibrous thickenings, the middle layer is ephemeral, and the cells of the glandular tapetum become 2-nucleate. The microspore tetrads are tetrahedral or isobilateral and the pollen grains are 3-celled when shed.

The ovule is hemianatropous, bitegmic, and crassinucellar, with the micropyle formed by the inner integument. Although a multicellular archesporium is common, only one cell develops further and cuts off a primary parietal cell which divides only anticlinally. Cytokinesis in the megaspore mother cell accompanies meiosis, although the homotypic division may be suppressed in the micropylar dyad cell, and the chalazal megaspore of a linear tetrad or "triad" develops into a Polygonum type embryo sac. The synergids are pyriform, the polar nuclei fuse before fertilization, and the 3 antipodal cells are ephemeral, but in *P. tetraphyllum* the antipodal nuclei degenerate soon after they are formed.

Endosperm formation is Nuclear but the tissue becomes cellular throughout following the initiation of walls at the micropylar pole.

Embryogeny conforms to the Solanad type in *Herniaria* and *Polycarpon* but to the Caryophyllad type in *Scleranthus*. Polyembryony has been reported in *P. loeflingiae*.

Dahlgren, 1916, 1940a • Dambroise, 1947 • N. Pal, 1952 • Rocén, 1926, 1927 • Souèges, 1938c,g, 1945d.

ILLICIACEAE

The anther is tetrasporangiate. The endothecium develops fibrous thickenings, the middle layers are ephemeral, and the glandular tapetum may become irregularly 2-layered. Simultaneous cytokinesis in the microspore mother cells follows meiosis and the microspore tetrads are tetrahedral. Pollen grains are 2-celled when shed, and in *Illicium floridanum* germination takes place by the exine splitting into three portions.

The ovule is anatropous, bitegmic, and crassinucellar. The archesporial cell cuts off a primary parietal cell which gives rise to the parietal tissue and cytokinesis in the megaspore mother cell accompanies meiosis. The chalazal megaspore of a linear tetrad develops into a Polygonum type embryo sac with 3 ephemeral antipodals.

Endosperm formation is *ab initio* Cellular and embryogeny conforms to the Asterad type.

Hayashi, 1960, 1963a • Wodehouse, 1935 • Vesque, 1878.

IRIDACEAE

The anther is tetrasporangiate but the development and structure of its wall have not been described, except for the report of a glandular tapetum. Simultaneous cytokinesis in the microspore mother cells follows meiosis and the microspore tetrads are isobilateral or tetrahedral. The pollen grains are usually 2-celled when shed, but occasionally they are 3-celled and in *Iris japonica* Yasui and Sawada (1940) found that only 63% of the pollen grains were viable.

The ovule is anatropous, bitegmic, and crassinucellar, with the micropyle formed by the inner integument. The archesporial cell cuts off a primary parietal cell which forms one or more parietal layers, and cytokinesis in the megaspore mother cell accompanies meiosis. The chalazal megaspore of a linear or T-shaped tetrad develops into a Polygonum type embryo sac in which the synergids of *I. tenax* exhibit the filiform apparatus and those of *I. japonica* are hooked. The polar nuclei fuse before fertilization and the 3 antipodal cells of *I. tenax* persist into early endosperm formation. According to Yasui and Sawada (1940) at least 86% of the ovules are sterile in *I. japonica*.

Endosperm formation is Nuclear and in *I. tenax* the division of the primary endosperm nucleus takes place about 70 hours after fertilization.

Embryogeny in *I. pseudacorus* conforms to the Asterad type and the suspensor is short and multiseriate, but in *Crocus vernus* it follows the Caryophyllad type and *cb* remains undivided.

Berg, 1898 • Dodel, 1891 • Elfving, 1879 • C. H. Farr, 1922 • Ferraris, 1902 • Fleischer, 1874 • J.-L. Guignard, 1926b • L. Guignard, 1882b, 1886, 1889, 1915a,b • Habermann, 1906 • Haeckel, 1930 • Hérail, 1889 • Himmelbaur, 1926 • Hofmeister, 1849, 1858, 1861, 1867 • Hubert, 1896 • Inariyama, 1929 • Jönsson, 1879–1880 • Juel, 1915 • Jungers, 1931 • Karag'ozova, 1963 • Koerniche, 1901a,b • Riley, 1942 • Sawyer, 1917 • Schacht, 1858 • Simonet, 1932, 1934 • Smith and Clarkson, 1956 • Soltwedel, 1882 • Strasburger, 1879, 1884b, 1887, 1895 • Vesque, 1878, 1879 • Westermaier, 1890, 1897a • Yasui and Sawada, 1940.

IRVINGIACEAE

Embryologically unknown.

IXONANTHACEAE

Embryologically unknown.

JUGLANDACEAE

The anther is tetrasporangiate with a persistent epidermis whose cells in *Hicoria pecan* become radially elongated. Whether a fibrous endothecium is differentiated is not clear, but the 2–4 middle layers are ephemeral and the cells of the glandular tapetum become multi-nucleate. Sometimes periclinal wall formation follows the first nuclear division and the tapetum becomes irregularly 2-layered. Simultaneous cytokinesis in the microspore mother cells follows meiosis and the microspore tetrads are tetrahedral or isobilateral. Pollen grains are 2-celled when shed.

The ovule is orthotropous, unitegmic, and crassinucellar. The arche-sporial cell cuts off a primary parietal cell which gives rise to 3–7 parietal layers, while in *Juglans* the apical cells of the nucellar epidermis may undergo a single periclinal division and in *Hicoria* a nucellar cap 3 cells in thickness is formed. Cytokinesis in the mega-spore mother cell accompanies meiosis, and the chalazal megaspore of a linear tetrad develops into a Polygonum type embryo sac. Karsten (1902) found that in *J. cordiformis* each of the 2 basal megaspores had an equal chance of development and that occasionally the embryo sac was tetrasporic. In *Carya glabra* and *H. pecan* the polar nuclei fuse soon after their formation, but in *J. regia* Nast (1941) found they were still distinct nuclei when the pollen tube entered the micro-pyle and in *J. niger* Karsten (1902) concluded that their fusion oc-curred very late, if at all. The 3 antipodal cells degenerate soon after fertilization. Chalazogamy is of normal occurrence in *Carya* and *Jug-lans* and porogamy in *Hicoria*, where the interval between pollination and fertilization has been reported to be 5–7 weeks by Woodroof and Woodroof (1927) and 2 weeks by Shuhart (1932).

Endosperm formation is Nuclear and in *J. regia*, according to Nast (1935), about 1000 free nuclei are present before the zygote divides. Later, wall formation takes place and the tissue becomes cellular.

Embryogeny in *Carya glabra* and *Juglans mandshurica* conforms to the Asterad type and polyembryony has been reported in *J. nigra*.

Adriance, 1931 • Benson, 1894 • Benson and Welsford, 1909 • Billings, 1903 • Candolle, 1862 • Chodat and Bernard, 1902b • Isbell, 1928 • Kabets'ka, 1964 • Karsten, 1902 • Langdon, 1934, 1939 • Lubbock, 1891 • McKay, 1947 • Nast,

1935, 1941 • Nawaschin, 1895a, 1897, 1909 • Nawaschin and Finn, 1912, 1913 • O. Neumann, 1939 • Nicoloff, 1904–1905 • Robyns, 1938, 1941 • Rowlee and Hastings, 1898 • Schacht, 1850 • Schanderl, 1964 • Shuhart, 1927, 1932 • Tieghem, 1861 • Warming, 1878 • J. G. Woodroof, 1926, 1930 • J. G. Woodroof and N. C. Woodroof, 1926, 1927 • N. C. Woodroof, 1928 • Woodworth, 1930b.

JULIANACEAE

Embryologically unknown.

JUNCACEAE

The anther is tetrasporangiate. The endothecium develops fibrous thickenings and in *Juncus effusus* and *J. prismatocarpus* it may become irregularly 2-layered. The middle layer is ephemeral except in *Oxychloe andina*, where it is persistent and some of its cells develop fibrous thickenings. The cells of the glandular tapetum usually remain 1-nucleate but in *Oxychloe* a single nuclear division occurs and when this is followed by periclinal wall formation, the tapetum is irregularly 2-layered. Simultaneous cytokinesis in the microspore mother cells follows meiosis and the microspore tetrads are tetrahedral or isobilateral. Pollen grains are shed as permanent tetrads, and are individually 3-celled.

The ovule is anatropous, bitegmic, and crassinucellar, with the micropyle formed by the inner integument. The archesporial cell cuts off a primary parietal cell which forms 1 or 2 parietal layers, and in *Juncus* the overlying cells of the nucellar epidermis elongate radially. Cytokinesis in the megaspore mother cell accompanies meiosis and the chalazal megaspore of a linear tetrad develops into a Polygonum type embryo sac. The synergids are large, the polar nuclei fuse before fertilization, and the 3 small antipodal cells may persist into early embryogeny.

Endosperm formation is Helobial. Free-nuclear divisions in the large micropylar chamber are followed by cell formation and it gives rise to the endosperm proper, but the small chalazal chamber remains 1-nucleate in *J. bufonius*, and in *J. effusus* and *J. prismatocarpus* 8 free nuclei are formed before it degenerates.

Embryogeny conforms to the Onagrad type and a 2-celled suspensor is formed.

Almeida and Sampayo, 1950 • Brenner, 1922 • Elfving, 1879 • Fischer, 1880 • M. Laurent, 1903a,b, 1904 • C. K. Shah, 1963 • Souèges, 1923d, 1933 • Strasburger, 1884b • Täckholm and Söderberg, 1918 • Werth and Drygalski, 1911 • Wille, 1882a • Wulff, 1939a • Zaman, 1950.

JUNCAGINACEAE

The anther is tetrasporangiate with a persistent epidermis, and although the endothecium forms a distinct layer, fibrous thickenings have not been described. The 1 or 2 middle layers are ephemeral and the cells of the amoeboid tapetum remain 1-nucleate. Successive cytokinesis in the microspore mother cells accompanies meiosis and the microspore tetrads are isobilateral. Pollen grains are 2- or 3-celled when shed.

The ovule is anatropous, bitegmic, and crassinucellar. The archesporial cell cuts off a primary parietal cell which forms 2 parietal layers below the nucellar epidermis. Cytokinesis in the megaspore mother cell accompanies meiosis and the chalazal megaspore of a linear or T-shaped tetrad develops into a Polygonum type embryo sac. In *Triglochin maritimum* the polar nuclei do not fuse until after fertilization and the 3 antipodal cells undergo secondary multiplication and persist into early embryogeny.

Endosperm formation is Nuclear and small in amount, with the free nuclei being confined to the peripheral cytoplasm.

Embryogeny conforms to the Caryophyllad type and polyembryony has been reported in *T. palustre*.

Buchenau, 1882 · Buchet and Gatin, 1908 · Claussen, 1927 · A. Fischer, 1880 · Guttenberg, 1960 · Hill, 1900 · Hofmeister, 1858, 1861 · Schnarf, 1925 · Souèges, 1943c · Täckholm and Söderberg, 1918 · Vesque, 1879 · Wulff, 1939b.

KOEBERLINIACEAE

Embryologically unknown.

KRAMERIACEAE

Embryologically unknown.

LABIATAE

The anther is tetrasporangiate with a persistent epidermis and its wall development follows the Dicotyledonous type. The endothecium develops fibrous thickenings, the middle layer is ephemeral, and the cells of the glandular tapetum become multinucleate. In *Salvia mellifera* the tapetal cells adjacent to the connective become considerably elongated radially, which results in each sporangium being reniform in cross section. Simultaneous cytokinesis in the microspore mother cells follows meiosis and the microspore tetrads are tetrahedral or decussate. The pollen grains are 2- or 3-celled when shed and in the cleistogamous flowers of *Lamium amplexicaule* they germinate *in situ* and no fibrous endothecium is differentiated.

The ovule is hemianatropous to anatropous, unitegmic, and tenuinucellar. The archesporial cell functions directly as the megaspore mother cell and the nucellar epidermis remains as a single layer, except in *Anisomeles indica* and *Leonurus sibiricus* where its 2 upper cells undergo a single periclinal division. Cytokinesis in the megaspore mother cell accompanies meiosis and the chalazal megaspore of a linear tetrad develops into a Polygonum type embryo sac. Multiple embryo sac formation is common in *Leonurus sibiricus* and results from the development of several megaspore mother cells. The synergids are hooked in *Anisomeles, Leonurus, Mentha, Orthosiphon,* and *Stachys,* and the polar nuclei fuse before or at the time of fertilization. The 3 antipodal cells undergo secondary multiplication only in *Physostegia virginiana,* and although they usually commence degeneration before fertilization, sometimes they may persist into early embryogeny. Except in *Lallemantia iberica, Salvia greggii, S. leucantha,* and *S. splendens* an endothelium differentiates, but the extent to which it encloses the embryo sac varies from the lower fifth in *Ballota nigra* to the more usual half to three-quarters. A funicular obturator is commonly present.

Endosperm formation is *ab initio* Cellular in which the primary endosperm cell divides transversely and, according to the planes of division in the two chambers, Schnarf (1917b) recognized 4 endosperm types. In the commonest condition, the chalazal chamber develops directly into a 2-nucleate haustorium which functions only during the formation of the endosperm proper, and the aggressive micropylar haustorium becomes coenocytic and invades the integument.

Embryogeny conforms to the Onagrad type.

Admiral'skaya, 1960 • Billings, 1909 • Bushnell, 1936 • E. M. Carlson and Stuart, 1936 • Chatin, 1874 • Crété, 1942, 1951d, 1963b • Elfving, 1879 • Finn, 1939 • Ganguli, 1948 • Gorczyński, 1929 • Guérin, 1917, 1919 • L. Guignard, 1882b, 1893 • Habermann, 1906 • Hofmeister, 1858, 1859 • Hubert, 1896 • Jönsson, 1879–1880, 1881 • Junell, 1934, 1937 • Laws, 1930 • Leitner, 1942 • Lietz, 1929 • S. N. Murthy, 1940, 1941a, 1942, 1946, 1947 • Rupert, 1902 • Ruttle, 1931, 1932 • Schacht, 1850 • Schnarf, 1917b • Schürhoff, 1927 • Sharp, 1911 • Soltwedel, 1882 • Souèges, 1921c,d • Strasburger, 1879a, 1889 • Tulasne, 1855 • Vesque, 1878, 1879 • Warming, 1873, 1878 • Wolf, 1929.

LACISTEMACEAE

Development and structure of the anther and pollen grains have not been described.

The ovule is anatropous, bitegmic, and crassinucellar. The megaspore mother cell is deeply buried in the nucellus but neither the origin of the overlying tissue nor that of the embryo sac has been investigated.

Endosperm formation in *Lacistema* is Nuclear but its embryogeny is unknown.

Chirtoiu, 1918 • D. S. Johnson, 1905, 1907.

LACTORIDACEAE

Embryologically unknown.

LARDIZABALACEAE

The anther is tetrasporangiate with a persistent epidermis. The endothecium develops fibrous thickenings, the 2 or 3 middle layers are ephemeral, and the cells of the glandular tapetum become 2–5-nucleate. Simultaneous cytokinesis in the microspore mother cells follows meiosis and the microspore tetrads are tetrahedral or decussate. Pollen grains are 2-celled when shed and in the female flowers of *Holboellia latifolia* 1-nucleate pollen grains are formed before the anthers degenerate.

The ovule is orthotropous to anatropous, bitegmic, and crassinucellar, with the micropyle formed by the inner integument. The archesporial cell cuts off a primary parietal cell which gives rise to 3 or 4 parietal layers and in *Holboellia* periclinal division of the apical nucellar epidermal cells forms a nucellar cap 2 cells in thickness. Cytokinesis in the megaspore mother cell accompanies meiosis and the chalazal megaspore of a linear or T-shaped tetrad develops into a Polygonum type embryo sac. The synergids are pyriform, the polar nuclei fuse before fertilization, and the 3 antipodal cells are ephemeral in *Holboellia* but otherwise they persist into early embryogeny.

Endosperm formation is *ab initio* Cellular but embryogeny has not been investigated.

Bhatnagar, 1965a • Swamy, 1953a • Velser, 1913 • Vesque, 1879b.

LAURACEAE

The anther is bisporangiate in *Cassytha, Cinnamomum, Litsea,* and *Persea* but tetrasporangiate in *Sassafras* whereas in *P. gratissima* both types of anther, alternate in the flower. The epidermis persists and the endothecium either develops fibrous thickenings or, as in *Sassafras verifolium,* its cell walls become much thickened. The 2 or 3 middle layers are compressed but not destroyed and the tapetal cells become 2–4-nucleate. In most genera the tapetum is amoeboid and forms a periplasmodium, but in *Cassytha* it is glandular. Successive cytokinesis in the microspore mother cells accompanies meiosis and the microspore tetrads are tetrahedral, isobilateral, and, occasionally, T-shaped or linear. Pollen grains are 2-celled when shed.

The ovule is anatropous, bitegmic, and crassinucellar, with the micropyle formed by both integuments except in *Sassafras* where only the inner integument is involved, and in *Cassytha* the wide micropyle is occupied by nucellar tissue. A multicellular archesporium is common but usually only one cell cuts off a primary parietal cell and undergoes further development. In *Cassytha,* however, the hypodermal archesporial cells each give rise to a primary parietal cell and those in a subhypodermal position function directly as megaspore mother cells. Up to 6 parietal layers are formed and in *Litsea sebifera* the apical cells of the nucellar epidermis divide periclinally to form a nucellar cap 3 cells in thickness. Cytokinesis in the megaspore mother cell accompanies meiosis and the chalazal megaspore of a linear tetrad develops into a Polygonum type embryo sac. In *Cassytha,* where 25–40 megaspore mother cells are present, a large number of megaspore tetrads form and up to 6 embryo sacs reach maturity. Synergids exhibiting the filiform apparatus have been reported in *Laurus nobilis, Litsea sebifera,* and *Umbellaria californica.* The polar nuclei fuse before fertilization and the 3 antipodal nuclei of *Cassytha* and *Persea* are very ephemeral while in *Cinnamomum* and *Sassafras* they are enclosed in cells before degenerating. In *Litsea* the antipodals persist into early embryogeny, but their secondary multiplication has been reported only in *Laurus nobilis.*

Endosperm formation is usually Nuclear followed by wall formation early in embryogeny and the tissue becomes cellular throughout. In *Cassytha* and *Umbellaria,* however, it is *ab initio* Cellular.

Embryogeny in *Cinnamomum* and *Litsea* conforms to the Onagrad type and in *Persea* to the Asterad type, but in *Cassytha,* although the first cleavage is transverse, later ones appear to follow no definite pattern.

154   DESCRIPTIONS OF THE FAMILIES

Bambacioni-Mezzetti, 1935, 1937, 1938, 1941 • Battaglia, 1947a • J. K. Choudhury and Mitra, 1953 • Coy, 1928 • Giuliani, 1928 • Kasapligil, 1951 • Mirande,
1905 • Pellegrini, 1955 • Reece, 1939 • Sastri, 1952, 1956b, 1957a, 1958b, 1962,
1963 • Schaffner, 1904 • Schroeder, 1952, 1955 • Täckholm and Söderberg, 1917,
1918 • Tongiorgi, 1935.

LECYTHIDACEAE

The anther is tetrasporangiate with a persistent epidermis and in
Barringtonia acutangula its wall development conforms to the Basic
type. The endothecium develops fibrous thickenings, the 2 middle
layers are ephemeral, and the cells of the amoeboid tapetum become
2-nucleate. Simultaneous cytokinesis in the microspore mother cells
follows meiosis and the microspore tetrads are tetrahedral or isobilateral. Pollen grains are 3-celled when shed.

The ovule is anatropous, bitegmic, and tenuinucellar, with the micropyle formed by the inner integument. The archesporial cell functions directly as the megaspore mother cell in which cytokinesis accompanies meiosis, but this may be suppressed in the micropylar dyad
cell. The chalazal megaspore of a linear or T-shaped tetrad or "triad"
develops into a Polygonum type embryo sac. The synergids are pyriform, the polar nuclei fuse just before or at fertilization, and the
3 small antipodal cells are ephemeral. An endothelium encloses the
embryo sac.

Endosperm formation is Nuclear but embryogeny has not been
described.

Mauritzon, 1939c • Treub, 1884 • Venkateswarlu, 1952b.

LEDOCARPACEAE

Embryologically unknown.

LEITNERIACEAE

The anther is tetrasporangiate with a persistent epidermis. The
endothecium develops fibrous thickenings, the middle layer is ephemeral, and the tapetum is glandular. Development of the pollen grains
has not been investigated.

The ovule is amphitropous, bitegmic, and crassinucellar, with the
micropyle formed by both integuments. The archesporial cell cuts
off a primary parietal cell which gives rise to about 9 parietal layers
and the apical cells of the nucellar epidermis undergo a single periclinal division to form a shallow nucellar cap. Cytokinesis in the

megaspore mother cell accompanies meiosis and the chalazal megaspore of a linear tetrad develops into a Polygonum type embryo sac. The synergids are broadly triangular and nonvacuolate, fusion of the polar nuclei has not been observed, and the 3 antipodal cells are ephemeral.

Endosperm formation is Nuclear but walls are formed later and the tissue becomes cellular.

Embryogeny of *Leitneria floridana* is reported to be initiated by a transverse or vertical division of the zygote followed by cell divisions in all planes, and consequently cannot be allocated to a definite type.

W. M. Pfeiffer, 1912.

LEMNACEAE

The anther is bisporangiate (*Wolffia*) or tetrasporangiate (*Lemna*) and its wall development conforms to the Reduced type. The endothecium develops fibrous thickenings, no middle layer is formed, and the cells of the amoeboid tapetum remain 1-nucleate. Successive cytokinesis in the microspore mother cells accompanies meiosis and the microspore tetrads are tetrahedral or isobilateral. The pollen grains are 3-celled when shed and those of *W. arrhiza* contain starch grains.

The ovule is anatropous in *Spirodela polyrrhiza* but in *Lemna paucicostata* it is initially orthotropous and later it becomes almost hemianatropous after fertilization, bitegmic, and crassinucellar. The micropyle is formed by the inner integument except in *Spirodela* where both integuments are involved. The archesporial cell cuts off a primary parietal cell which, in *Spirodela* and *Wolffia*, divides only anticlinally, but in *Lemna* it forms 2–3 parietal layers which persist after breakdown of the lateral nucellus. Cytokinesis in the megaspore mother cell accompanies meiosis in *Spirodela* although the micropylar dyad cell degenerates soon after its formation and the chalazal dyad gives rise to 2 unequal megaspores, of which the larger chalazal one develops into a Polygonum type embryo sac. In *Lemna* and *Wolffia*, however, cytokinesis follows only the heterotypic division and embryo sac formation is of the Allium type. The synergids are pyriform, the polar nuclei fuse before fertilization, and the 3 antipodal cells are ephemeral except in *Spirodela* where they persist during early endosperm formation. A postfertilization operculum is usually formed by elongation of the cells at the lip of the inner integument.

Endosperm formation is *ab initio* Cellular. In *Wolffia microscopica* and probably *Spirodela polyrrhiza* the primary chalazal chamber develops directly into a haustorium, but in *Lemna paucicostata* it undergoes a transverse division before elongating as a narrow caecum. The endosperm proper is derived from the primary micropylar chamber.

Embryogeny in *Lemna* conforms to the Onagrad type but in *Wolffia* the early cleavages are irregular. A short suspensor is formed but no radicle is differentiated.

Blodgett, 1923 • Caldwell, 1899 • B. L. Gupta, 1935 • Hegelmaier, 1868, 1871 • Hofmeister, 1858 • Jönsson, 1879–1880, 1881 • Lawalrée, 1952 • S. C. Maheshwari, 1954, 1956a,b, 1958, 1959 • S. C. Maheshwari and Kapil, 1963a,b, 1964 • S. C. Maheshwari and N. Maheshwari, 1963 • H. L. Mason, 1938 • C. McCann, 1942 • Rostowzew, 1905.

LENNOACEAE

The anther is tetrasporangiate with a persistent epidermis. A well-developed endothecium is formed, but Copeland's figure of *Pholisma arenarium* shows no fibrous thickenings. The middle layer is ephemeral and the cells of the glandular tapetum are 1- or 2-nucleate. The pollen grains are 2-celled and shed singly, but their development has not been described.

The ovule is anatropous, unitegmic, and tenuinucellar. The archesporial cell functions directly as the megaspore mother cell in which cytokinesis accompanies meiosis and the chalazal megaspore of a linear tetrad develops into a Polygonum type embryo sac. The synergids are pyriform, the polar nuclei fuse before fertilization, and the 3 antipodal cells persist into early embryogeny.

Endosperm formation is *ab initio* Cellular and embryogeny in *Lennoa madreporoides* follows the Caryophyllad type, but the suspensor is much reduced.

Copeland, 1935b • Solms-Laubach, 1870 • Süssenguth, 1927.

LENTIBULARIACEAE

The anther is tetrasporangiate with a persistent epidermis. The endothecium develops fibrous thickenings, the middle layer is ephemeral, and the cells of the glandular tapetum become 2- or 3-nucleate. Simultaneous cytokinesis in the microspore mother cells follows meiosis and the microspore tetrads are tetrahedral, decussate, or isobilateral. The pollen grains are 3-celled when shed and may be dimorphic in *Utricularia flexuosa*. Pollen germination *in situ* is common *U. flexuosa* and *U. stellaris*.

The ovule is anatropous, unitegmic, and tenuinucellar. The archesporial cell functions directly as the megaspore mother cell in which cytokinesis accompanies meiosis and the chalazal megaspore of a linear tetrad develops into a Polygonum type embryo sac. The synergids are hooked in *U. reticulata* and the polar nuclei usually fuse before fertilization, but in *Pinguicula vulgaris* triple fusion is usual. The 3 antipodal cells are small except in *P. vulgaris* and occasionally in *U. flexuosa* where they enlarge and the upper cell may occupy almost half the embryo sac after the lower 2 degenerate. Abundant starch grains have been reported in the embryo sacs of *U. exoleta* and *U. flexuosa.* An endothelium is differentiated and usually encloses only the lower portion of the embryo sac while in *Polypompholyx* and *Utricularia* the apical portion of the embryo sac becomes extraovular and makes direct contact with the placenta where it exhibits some haustorial activity.

Endosperm formation is *ab initio* Cellular with the formation of aggressive terminal haustoria in *Utricularia* in which the micropylar haustorium penetrates deeply into the placenta.

Embryogeny in *Pinguicula leptoceras, P. vulgaris,* and *U. flexuosa* follows the Onagrad type, in *P. alpina* the Asterad type, and in *U. stellaris* the Chenopodiad type. Polyembryony has been reported in *U. flexuosa.*

Buchenau, 1865 • Caspary, 1867 • Crété, 1956a,b • Farooq, 1958a, 1965 • Farooq and Siddiqui, 1964a,b • Haccius and Hartl-Baude, 1956 • Jacobsson-Stiasny, 1914b • Kamiénsky, 1877 • Kausik, 1935a, 1938c • Kausik and Raju, 1955, 1956 • R. Khan, 1953, 1954 • Kopczynska, 1964 • Lang, 1901 • Merl, 1915 • Merz, 1897 • Samuelsson, 1913 • Shivaramiah, 1964a,b • Stolt, 1936 • Treviranus, 1839 • Wylie and Jocom, 1923.

LEPIDOBOTRYACEAE

Embryologically unknown.

LILIACEAE

The anther is tetrasporangiate and its wall development follows the Monocotyledonous type. The endothecium develops fibrous thickenings, the 2 or 3 middle layers are usually ephemeral but only the innermost layer behaves in this way in *Amianthium* and *Iphigenia*. The cells of the glandular tapetum become multinucleate but nuclear fusions may occur and Ubisch granules are common. Successive cytokinesis in the microspore mother cells accompanies meiosis in most cases, but the simultaneous method has been reported in *Asphodelus, Asphodeline, Bulbine, Eremurus, Kniphofia,* and *Tofieldia*. The microspore tetrads are isobilateral, decussate, or tetrahedral and the pollen grains are usually 2-celled when shed but 3-celled grains may occur in *Chlorophytum attenuatum, Polygonatum multiflorum*, and *Tulipa gesneriana*. Stow (1930) reported the occurrence of giant embryo-sac-like pollen grains in the anthers of *Hyacinthus orientalis* when the plants had been subjected to high temperatures during meiosis.

The ovule is hemianatropous, anatropous, or orthotropous, bitegmic, and either tenuinucellar or crassinucellar, with the micropyle formed by the inner integument. The archesporial cell functions directly as the megaspore mother cell in *Erythronium, Gagea, Gloriosa, Iphigenia, Lilium, Theropogon, Tricyrtis*, and *Uvularia*, but it cuts off a primary parietal cell in *Albuca, Aletris, Asphodelus, Blandfordia, Camassia, Chionographis, Chlorophytum, Convallaria, Dipcadi, Drimiopsis, Eremurus, Eucomis, Fritillaria, Gagea, Gasteria, Heloniopsis, Lilium, Metanarthecium, Scilla, Tofieldia, Urginea, Veratrum*, and *Zygadenus*. Both types of behavior of the archesporial cell have been reported in *Amianthium muscaetoxicum, Hemerocallis fulva, Ophiopogon wallichianus, Polygonatum communatum*, and *Smilacina* spp. The primary parietal cell usually divides only anticlinally, but a more extensive parietal tissue of up to 4 cell layers occurs in *Eucomis, Gloriosa*, and *Polygonatum* while the formation of a nucellar cap from periclinal divisions of the apical nucellar epidermal cells has been described in *Albuca, Amianthium, Blandfordia, Chionographis, Gloriosa, Iphigenia, Leucocrinum, Ophiopogon*, and *Smilacina*. In most records cytokinesis in the megaspore mother cell accompanies meiosis and the chalazal megaspore of a linear or T-shaped tetrad develops into a Polygonum type embryo sac. However, suppression of wall formation after the homotypic division results in the formation of an embryo sac of the Allium type (*Polygonatum, Smilacina*) or Scilla type (*Agraphis, Scilla, Smilacina*). Absence of cytokinesis in conjunction with meiosis results in tetrasporic embryo sac formation of the Adoxa type (*Agraphis, Amana, Camassia, Erythronium*), the Drusa type (*Maianthemum*), or the Fritillaria type (*Cardiocrinum, Erythronium, Fritillaria, Gagea, Lilium*). In *Clintonia borealis* and *C. uniflora* the 3 chalazal megaspore nuclei degenerate and fuse into an irregular mass, while the nuclei of the embryo sac (pseudomonosporic) develop only from the micropylar megaspore nucleus. Variation in embryo sac formation frequently occurs within a genus and in *Tulipa* spp. Romanov (1959) has reported 5 different types of development. The synergids are hooked and exhibit the filiform apparatus (*Asphodelus, Blandfordia, Camassia, Chlorophytum, Drimiopsis*), they are only hooked (*Dipcadi*), or they lack hooks but show the filiform apparatus (*Amianthium, Eremurus, Hesperocallis,*

Lachenalia, Scilla, Urginea). The polar nuclei fuse before fertilization and the secondary nucleus moves close to the antipodals except in *Eucomis* where it passes into an embryo sac haustorium. The antipodals remain as 3 naked nuclei in *Scilla nonscripta*, although in *S. pratensis* they are enclosed in cells which become much enlarged, but commonly the cells are ephemeral (*Asphodelus, Calochortus, Camassia, Cardiocrinum, Chlorophytum, Lilium, Ophiopogon, Tulipa*). In *Tricyrtis* the antipodals increase in size until they occupy one-third of the embryo sac and persist into endosperm formation. Multinucleate antipodal cells have been reported in *Amianthium, Gloriosa, Heloniopsis, Iphigenia,* and *Veratrum* while secondary multiplication with the formation of up to 11 cells occurs in *Iphigenia, Smilacina* and *Veratrum*. A hypostase is common and an integumentary obturator develops in *Aletris aurea* which grows over the micropyle towards the funicle, while in *Asphodelus* an aril is formed.

Endosperm formation is Helobial and the small chalazal chamber is usually ephemeral and 2–4-nucleate, but in *Asphodelus* it may persist during embryogeny and in *Blandfordia* and *Eremurus* up to 32 nuclei may form. Many free-nuclear divisions take place in the large micropylar chamber before walls develop and the tissue becomes cellular. Nuclear endosperm formation has been reported in *Asphodelus, Colchicum, Iphigenia, Liriope, Scilla* and *Tricyrtis*, but it is possible that a small chalazal chamber was overlooked.

Embryogeny conforms to the Onagrad type (*Erythronium, Lilium*), Asterad type (*Heloniopsis, Muscaria*), Caryophyllad type (*Dipcadi*), and perhaps Chenopodiad type (*Asphodelus, Calochortus*). Adventive polyembryony has been described in *Funkia* and *Smilacina* but in *Erythronium* and *Tulipa* the embryo apex undergoes cleavage and in *Iphigenia* and *Lilium* an extra embryo has been attributed to fertilization of a synergid.

Afzelius, 1918 • Agrawal, 1950 • Alden, 1912 • Amato, 1949a • L. E. Anderson, 1939 • Atkinson, 1899 • Bally, 1916 • Bambacioni, 1927, 1928a,b,c • Bambacioni and Giombini, 1930 • Bambacioni-Mezzetti, 1931a,b, 1932, 1947 • Baranov, 1926 • Battaglia, 1958b,c,d, 1959 • Battaglia and Feeley, 1959 • Beal, 1939 • Bellows and Bamford, 1941 • Berghs, 1904a,b, 1905 • Bernard, 1937 • Bianchi, 1946 • Blackman and Welsford, 1913 • Botschanzeva, 1937 • Braun, 1860 • Brock, 1955 • Browne, 1961 • Buchner, 1948 • Buxbaum, 1937a,b • Campbell, 1898 • Capoor, 1937a • Cave, 1941, 1942b, 1948, 1953 • Chamberlain, 1897b, 1898, 1914a • Chandler, Porterfield, and Stout, 1937 • Chennaveeraiah and Mahabale, 1962 • Conant and Haquist, 1944 • D. C. Cooper, 1934, 1935a, 1936, 1939, 1943 • Coulter and Chamberlain, 1903 • Coulter, Chamberlain, and Schaffner, 1897 • Crété, 1952a,b, 1954 • Dahlgren, 1927a • Desole, 1947 • Dixon, 1895, 1946 • Eigsti, 1941 • Elfving, 1879 • Erickson, 1948 • Ernst, 1901, 1902, 1910 • Eunus, 1949, 1950a,b, 1951a,b,

1952 • Fagerlind, 1941c, 1946c • Ferguson, 1907 • F. F. Flint and Johansen, 1958 • L. H. Flint and Moreland, 1943 • Fullmer, 1899 • Fulvio and Cave, 1964 • Furlani, 1904 • Geitler, 1941 • Gerassimova, 1956 • Gerassimova-Navashina, 1962 • Gerassimova-Navashina and Batygina, 1958 • Gerassimova-Navashina and Korobova, 1959 • Golaszewska, 1934a,b • Gorham, 1953 • Govindappa, 1956 • Govindappa and Sheriff, 1951 • Guérin, 1927, 1930, 1931, 1937 • L. Guignard, 1882b, 1884, 1885, 1889, 1891, 1899b,c, 1900a,b • Guttenberg and Heydel, 1957 • Guttenberg and Jakuszeit, 1957 • Haberlandt, 1922b • Habermann, 1906 • Hannig, 1909 • Haque, 1951 • Heimann-Winawer, 1919 • Heimans, 1928 • Hérail, 1889 • Herrig, 1919, 1922 • Hoare, 1934 • Hofmeister, 1849, 1858, 1861 • Hrubý, 1934, 1938 • Hu, 1963 • Hubert, 1896 • Ikeda, 1902 • Jeffrey, 1895 • Johnston, 1941, 1959 • M. M. Johri, 1962 • Jönsson, 1879–1880, 1881 • A. C. Joshi, 1937c, 1939b, 1940 • Juel, 1897 • Kostriukova, 1939b • Krupko, 1928 • Langlet, 1927 • Lechmere, 1910 • Leffingwell, 1930 • Lenoir, 1927 • Lewitzky, 1925 • Lidfors, 1897 • Linskens, 1958 • Lötscher, 1905 • MacKenney, 1898 • Mahabale and Chennaveeraiah, 1961 • P. Maheshwari, 1932, 1933a, 1934c, 1946b • P. Maheshwari and Singh, 1930 • Martins, 1909 • McAllister, 1909, 1913, 1914 • McCarthy, 1928 • McKenney, 1898, 1904 • Mellink, 1880 • Mezzetti-Bambacioni, 1940, 1943 • Moffatt, 1932 • Mottier, 1897, 1898b • Naithani, 1937 • Nawaschin, 1898b, 1899a, 1910 • Nemec, 1898, 1912, 1931 • Newton, 1926 • T. Noguchi, 1940 • Nothnagel, 1918 • Ogura, 1964 • Oikawa, 1937, 1940, 1950, 1956, 1959, 1961a,b • O'Mara, 1933 • Ono, 1926, 1928, 1929 • E. Overton, 1891 • B. Palm, 1920 • Prosina, 1930a • Raju, 1957 • Randall and Rich, 1945 • Robbins and Borthwick, 1925 • Rodkiewicz, 1961 • Roever, 1935 • Romanov, 1936, 1938, 1939, 1957, 1959 • Rosenberg, 1946 • Santos, 1937 • Sargant, 1896a,b, 1897 • Sauer, 1909 • K. Sax, 1916 • J. H. Schaffner, 1897c, 1901 • Schnarf, 1923, 1928a,b, 1929a, 1931, 1944, 1948 • Schnarf and Wunderlich, 1939 • J. M. Schneider, 1908 • Schniewind-Thies, 1901 • Seelieb, 1924 • Shoji and Nakamura, 1928 • Showalter, 1921 • Silva, 1945 • Sienicka, 1929 • Simoni, 1937 • F. H. Smith, 1933, 1942, 1943, 1955 • R. W. Smith, 1911 • Soltwedel, 1882 • Souèges, 1918b, 1926c, 1931a, 1932a • Stenar, 1925b, 1927, 1928a,b, 1931, 1934, 1937b, 1941, 1949, 1950, 1951a, 1952, 1953 • Stiffler, 1925 • Stow, 1930, 1934 • Strasburger, 1877, 1878, 1879b, 1880b, 1882b, 1884b, 1895, 1908 • Subramanyam and Govindu, 1949 • Subramanyam and Rao, 1952 • Sulbha, 1954a,b • Sundar Rao, 1940b • Süssenguth, 1919, 1921 • Swamy, 1949c • Täckholm and Söderberg, 1917, 1918 • Timm, 1928 • Tischler, 1915 • Trankowski, 1930 • Treub and Mellink, 1880 • Tulasne, 1855 • Upcott, 1936 • Varitchat, 1940 • Vesque, 1878, 1879b • Walker, 1944 • Warming, 1878 • Welsford, 1914 • Weniger, 1918 • Went and Blaauw, 1906 • Westergård, 1936 • Wiegand, 1899, 1900 • Wimmel, 1950 • Wunderlich, 1936, 1937 • Yamaha, 1926 • Yasui, 1935.

LIMNANTHACEAE

The anther is tetrasporangiate with a persistent epidermis. The endothecium develops fibrous thickenings, the 2 middle layers are ephemeral, and the cells of the glandular tapetum become 2-nucleate. Simultaneous cytokinesis in the microspore mother cells follows meiosis and the microspore tetrads are tetrahedral, decussate, or, occasionally, isobilateral. The pollen grains are 2-celled when shed.

The ovule is anatropous, unitegmic, and tenuinucellar. The archesporium is multicellular but only one cell is functional and this undergoes direct development into the megaspore mother cell. Cytokinesis in the megaspore mother cell is suppressed and embryo sac formation is of the Drusa type with varying degrees of "strike." In *Limnanthes* the chalazal nucleus of each meiotic division usually degenerates and, because its 4 nuclei are then all derived from the micropylar megaspore nucleus, the embryo sac may be regarded as pseudomonosporic. In *Floerkea*, however, "strike" does not become effective until both meiotic divisions are completed, and the embryo sac is 6-nucleate. The synergids are large and hooked, with a filiform apparatus in *Limnanthes*. Only one polar nucleus is present in a 4-nucleate embryo sac but otherwise 2 are formed and these become closely associated near the egg while the number of antipodals is determined by the number of nuclei remaining after the formation of the egg apparatus and the polar nuclei.

Endosperm formation is Nuclear but the tissue does not become cellular and in *Floerkea* a lateral haustorial pocket develops.

Embryogeny in *Limnanthes* conforms to the Onagrad type and a long uniseriate suspensor is formed.

Eysel, 1937 • Fagerlind, 1939a • L. Guignard, 1893 • Hofmeister, 1858b • B. M. Johri and P. Maheshwari, 1951 • P. Maheshwari and Johri, 1956 • C. T. Mason, 1949 • N. Mathur, 1956 • Russell, 1919 • Stenar, 1925a.

LINACEAE

The anther is tetrasporangiate and its wall development conforms to the Monocotyledonous type. The endothecium develops fibrous thickenings, the 1 or 2 middle layers are ephemeral, and the cells of the glandular tapetum become 2-nucleate. Simultaneous cytokinesis in the microspore mother cells follows meiosis and the microspore tetrads are tetrahedral. The pollen grains are 3-celled when shed and contain starch grains.

The ovule is anatropous and bitegmic, and both tenuinucellar and crassinucellar conditions have been reported. The micropyle is formed by the inner integument. The archesporial cell functions directly as the megaspore mother cell in several species of *Linum* and *Radiola linoides*, but in *Hugonia mystax*, *L. grandiflorum*, *L. mysorense*, and *Reinwardtia trigyna* it cuts off a primary parietal cell which forms 1–4 parietal layers. Cytokinesis in the megaspore mother cell accompanies meiosis and the chalazal megaspore of a linear tetrad develops into a Polygonum type embryo sac. The synergids are hooked and exhibit the filiform apparatus in *L. mysorense*, the polar nuclei fuse before fertilization, and although the 3 antipodal nuclei are naked in *Linum*, they are enclosed in cells in *Radiola*. In *Hugonia* and *Reinwardtia* the embryo sac contains starch grains. An endothelium is differentiated and in *L. mysorense* a funicular obturator is present.

Endosperm formation is Helobial with a chalazal haustorium in *Linum flavum, L. perenne,* and *L. usitatissimum* but in *L. mysorense* and *Radiola linoides* it is Nuclear and in *L. mysorense* the chalazal end of the embryo sac undergoes postfertilization haustorial development.

Embryogeny conforms to the Solanad type and a 4–9-celled suspensor is formed although in *L. usitatissimum* there is a single large suspensor cell.

Billings, 1901 • Dorasami and Gopinath, 1945 • Gopinath, 1942 • L. Guignard, 1893 • Hegelmaier, 1891 • Hofmeister, 1849 • Jönsson, 1879–1880 • Juel, 1915 • Kantor, 1957 • Kappert, 1933 • Mauritzon, 1934d • L. L. Narayana, 1964b • D. Rao and Narayana, 1965 • Schnarf, 1931a • Schürhoff, 1924b • Sizova, 1958, 1961, 1963 • Souèges, 1924c,h, 1937h, 1953b.

LISSOCARPACEAE

Embryologically unknown.

LOASACEAE

Development of the anther and pollen grains has not been investigated.

The ovule is hemianatropous to anatropous, unitegmic, and tenuinucellar. The archesporial cell functions directly as the megaspore mother cell in which cytokinesis accompanies meiosis. In *Loasa bergii* the chalazal megaspore of a linear tetrad develops into a Polygonum type embryo sac but according to Kratzer (1918) the micropylar megaspore is functional. The synergids are pyriform and, although a subchalazal haustorium is formed, the 3 antipodal cells remain *in situ* and persist in a shallow pouch during early postfertilization stages. It is doubtful that the polar nuclei fuse before fertilization. An endothelium is differentiated but in *Blumenbachia hieronymi* it encloses only the middle portion of the embryo sac.

Endosperm formation is *ab initio* Cellular with the development of terminal haustoria. The micropylar haustorium in *Loasa* is coenocytic and gives off aggressive caeca which invade the integument, funicle, and sometimes the placenta, but in the other genera it is smaller and less active. The chalazal haustorium of *Loasa* is 1-nucleate and vesicular but in *Blumenbachia* a similar structure gives off branching caeca which invade the integument. In *Cajophora* and *Mentzelia* a multicellular chalazal haustorium is formed which in the former is much branched basally.

Embryogeny conforms to the Solanad type.

Crété, 1946a,b • Garcia, 1962a,b • Hofmeister, 1849, 1858b, 1859 • Kratzer, 1918 • Samuelsson, 1913 • Soltwedel, 1882.

LOBELIACEAE

The anther is tetrasporangiate with a persistent epidermis and its wall development conforms to the Dicotyledonous type. The endothecium develops fibrous thickenings, the middle layer is ephemeral, and the cells of the glandular tapetum become 2-nucleate. Simultaneous cytokinesis in the microspore mother cells follows meiosis and the microspore tetrads are tetrahedral or isobilateral. The pollen grains are 3-celled when shed and in *Isotoma fluviatilis* contain starch grains whereas those of *Lobelia pyramidalis* and *L. trialata* may sometimes germinate *in situ*.

The ovule is anatropous, unitegmic, and tenuinucellar. The archesporial cell functions directly as the megaspore mother cell in which cytokinesis accompanies meiosis and the chalazal megaspore of a linear tetrad develops into a Polygonum type embryo sac. The synergids are long tapering cells in which the filiform apparatus has been reported in *L. cardinalis*, *L. pyramidalis*, and *I. fluviatilis*. The polar nuclei fuse at about the time of fertilization when the 3 antipodal cells usually degenerate, although in *L. cardinalis* they persist into early endosperm formation. Starch grains occur in the embryo sac of *I. fluviatilis*. An endothelium is differentiated around the lower two-thirds of the embryo sac.

Endosperm formation is *ab initio* Cellular with the development of terminal haustoria. The micropylar haustorium is 2-celled but, although the chalazal haustorium consists of 2 basally expanded cells in *L. pyramidalis*, it is unicellular in *I. longiflora, Laurentia michelii,* and *Lobelia cardinalis*, whereas in *L. pyramidalis* either type may form.

Embryogeny follows the Solanad type and polyembryony has been reported in *I. longiflora* and *L. syphilitica*.

Armand, 1912, 1913, 1921 • Billings, 1901 • G. O. Cooper, 1942b • Crété, 1938a,b, 1951d, 1956e • L. Guignard, 1882b • Hewitt, 1939 • Jönsson, 1879–1880,

1881 • Kausik, 1935b, 1938d • Kausik and Subramanyam, 1945a,b, 1946a,b, 1947b • P. Maheshwari, 1944a,b • Ohlendorf, 1907 • Rosén, 1932, 1949 • Schlotterbeck, 1896 • Schürhoff, 1926b • Subramanyam, 1949, 1951b,e,f, 1953 • Vesque, 1878 • Ward, 1880b • Warming, 1878.

LOGANIACEAE

Development of the anther and pollen grains has not been investigated.

The ovule is hemianatropous to anatropous, unitegmic, and tenuinucellar. The archesporial cell functions directly as the megaspore mother cell in which cytokinesis accompanies meiosis and the chalazal megaspore of a linear tetrad develops into a Polygonum type embryo sac. In *Polypremum procumbens* the apex of the embryo sac penetrates the micropyle and reaches the surface of the ovule. The polar nuclei fuse before fertilization and the 3-antipodal cells degenerate soon after. An endothelium is differentiated in *Polypremum* but not in *Gelsemium* or *Geniostoma*.

Endosperm formation is *ab initio* Cellular with terminal haustoria which in *Polypremum* are narrow, cylindrical, and multicellular.

Embryogeny conforms to the Onagrad type.

Dahlgren, 1922 • Dop, 1923 • Mohrbutter, 1936 • Moore, 1948.

LORANTHACEAE

[Barlow (1964) erected the family VISCACEAE to accommodate the subfamily Viscoideae].

The anther is tetrasporangiate (*Atkinsonia, Dendrophthoe, Helicanthes, Macrosolen, Peraxilla, Tolypanthus, Tupeia*) or bisporangiate (*Loranthus, Phoradendron*) but in *Arceuthobium* there is a single annular microsporangium around a central columella. Its wall development follows the Monocotyledonous type and the epidermis may degenerate very early. Except in *Lepeostegeres*, the endothecium develops fibrous thickenings, and the 1 or 2 middle layers are usually ephemeral, but in *Korthalsella* the outermost layer persists and in *Amyema* some of its cells enlarge and become fibrous. The cells of the glandular tapetum become 1–4-nucleate and nuclear fusions occur in *Nuytsia* and *Peraxilla*. Ubisch granules are common. Reports of a periplasmodium in *Arceuthobium, Hyphear*, and *Phoradendron* may be based on the occurrence of degenerating microspore mother cells. Simultaneous cytokinesis in the microspore mother cells follows meiosis and the microspore tetrads are tetrahedral or decussate. Pollen grains are 2-celled when shed and in *Barathranthus* some have been reported to germinate *in situ*. Partition walls in the anther loculi have been reported in *Amyema* and *Elytraria*.

Ovules, as such, are not present. In *Elytraria, Lysiana, Macrosolen, Nuytsia,* and *Peraxilla* a lobed mamelon arises from the base of the loculus and, since its lobes contain the archesporial cells, they are interpreted as much reduced ovules borne on a modified placenta. Below the mamelon is a tube- or saucer-shaped collenchymatous band. A derived condition is exhibited by *Arceuthobium, Helicanthes, Korthalsella,* and *Phoradendron* in which the mamelon is reduced to a smooth papilla, and in *Barathranthus, Dendrophthoe falcata, Helixanthera, Moquiniella, Scurrula, Tapinanthus, Taxillus, Tupeia* and *Viscum* a mamelon is not formed and the archesporial cells are differentiated from subepidermal cells of the ovary floor. A reverse tendency is seen in *Amyema, Dendrophthoe neelgherrensis,* and *Tolypanthus* in which a pseudomamelon forms as the result of elongation of the megaspore mother cells which causes localized elevation of the floor of the loculus. The archesporium is usually multicellular and each cell functions directly as a megaspore mother cell. In the Loranthoideae, cytokinesis accompanies meiosis and the basal megaspores of each linear tetrad develop into a Polygonum type embryo sac. Multiple embryo sac formation is usual and frequently more than one megaspore of each tetrad may undergo development. At the 4-nucleate stage of development each embryo sac elongates, carrying 2 of the nuclei in its tip, and several reach the base of the style, but the distance they penetrate the style is generically characteristic. In *Macrosolen* the embryo sacs do not extend beyond the base of the style, whereas in *Barathranthus, Helixanthera, Tapinostemma,* and *Tupeia* they reach the apex of the stigma, and those of other genera attain intermediate positions. An extreme condition has been reported in *Moquiniella* (B. M. Johri and Raj, 1965) where, after the tip of the embryo sac reaches almost to the surface of stigma, it bends and grows downwards through the style for about 4 mm. The final embryo sac mitosis takes place first in the 2 lower nuclei and a short 6-nucleate stage is passed through before the 2 upper nuclei divide and the 8-nucleate condition is attained. The synergids are hooked and exhibit the filiform apparatus, the polar nuclei fuse just before fertilization close to the egg in the apex of the embryo sac, and the 3 antipodal cells remain at its base. During its maturation, the lower extremity of the embryo sac elongates as a caecum, leaving the antipodals *in situ*, until it reaches the collenchymatous tissue which prevents further growth. In *Nuytsia* the development of a short caecum at the proximal end of the embryo sac has been reported. In the Viscoideae, however, cytokinesis in the megaspore mother cell only accompanies the heterotypic division and embryo sac development is of the Allium type. In *Dendrophthora, Korthalsella,* and *Phoradendron,* when the embryo sac becomes 4-nucleate, its basal end curves upwards and it is in this arm that the egg apparatus differentiates when it penetrates the carpellary tissue and the final embryo sac mitosis is completed. In the shorter (originally "upper") arm, the 3 antipodal cells are organized. In the other members of the Viscoideae the embryo sac is straight or only slightly curved and there is no reversal of polarity.

Endosperm formation is *ab initio* Cellular and the division of the primary endosperm nucleus occurs after its migration to the base of the embryo sac. In the Loranthoideae the developing endosperm in adjacent embryo sacs fuses into a common mass but in the Viscoideae that of each embryo sac retains its own identity.

Embryogeny in the Loranthoideae follows the Piperad type. In the long biseriate proembryo, only the 2 lowest tiers form the embryo proper and the remainder become the long coiled suspensor which is reported to push the functional apex through the developing endosperm to the base of the embryo sac where further stages in embryogeny take place. In the Viscoideae, however, cleavage of the zygote is transverse except in *Arceuthobium* and *Korthalsella,* and a suspensor is not differentiated. Polyembryony commonly follows formation of proembryos in several embryo sacs but usually only one completes development.

Agrawal, 1954 • Barlow, 1964 • Billings, 1932, 1933 • Braun, 1860 Cohen, 1962 • Dixit, 1954a,b, 1955a,b, 1956, 1958a,b, 1961 • Dowding, 1931 • Ernst, 1908b, 1942 • Fagerlind, 1945b • Garg, 1958 • Gill, 1935 • Goebel, 1933a • Griffith, 1838, 1843 • Hawksworth, 1961 • Heinricher, 1915a,b • Hofmeister, 1858, 1859 • T. Johnson, 1888 • B. M. Johri and Agrawal, 1954 • B. M. Johri, Agrawal, and Garg, 1957 • B. M. Johri and Bhatnagar, 1960 • B. M. Johri and Prakash, 1965 • B. M. Johri and Raj, 1965 • B. L. Jones and Gordon, 1965 • Jost, 1888 • Kuijt, 1954 • P. Maheshwari and Johri, 1950a • P. Maheshwari, Johri, and Dixit, 1957 • P. Maheshwari and Singh, 1952 • R. Narayana, 1954a,b, 1955, 1956, 1958a,b • Pienaar, 1952 • Pisek, 1922, 1923, 1924 • Prakash, 1960, 1961, 1963 • L. Radlkofer, 1856 • Rauch, 1936 • Rutishauser, 1935a, 1937 • Schacht, 1855 • Schaeppi and Steindl, 1942, 1945 • Schnarf, 1929b • Schürhoff, 1922b • Scrobischewsky, 1884 • B. Singh, 1950, 1952a, 1962 • Smart, 1952 • Staedtler, 1923 • Steindl, 1935 • Stevenson, 1934 • Thoday and E. T. Johnson, 1930 • Tieghem, 1895a,b • Treub, 1881, 1882, 1883a,d, 1885 • Wefelscheid, 1911 • York, 1913.

LOWIACEAE

Embryologically unknown.

LYTHRACEAE

The anther is tetrasporangiate and in *Ammania baccifera* its wall development follows the Dicotyledonous type. The endothecium develops fibrous thickenings, the 2 middle layers are ephemeral, and the cells of the glandular tapetum become multinucleate. Simultaneous cytokinesis in the microspore mother cells follows meiosis and the microspore tetrads are tetrahedral. Pollen grains are 2-celled when shed. Degeneration of sporogenous tissue is common in *Lawsonia* and *Nesaea* and occurs occasionally in *Ammania*.

The ovule is anatropous, bitegmic, and crassinucellar, with the micropyle formed by both integuments. In *Nesaea myrtifolia* the ovules towards the base and apex of the loculus are amphitropous. The archesporium is multicellular but usually only one cell undergoes further development and cuts off a primary parietal cell which forms 2–7 parietal layers. In *Pemphis acidula* the apical cells of the nucellar epidermis divide periclinally to form a nucellar cap 2 cells in thickness. Cytokinesis in the megaspore mother cell accompanies meiosis and the chalazal megaspore of a linear tetrad develops into a Polygonum type embryo sac. The synergids are hooked, the polar nuclei fuse just before fertilization, and the 3 antipodal cells are ephemeral. The occurrence of multiple embryo sacs is common in *Lawsonia inermis* and embryo sac degeneration has been reported in *Lagerstroemia*, *Lawsonia*, and *Woodfordia*. A hypostase is usually present.

Endosperm formation is Nuclear. The first 2 nuclei move to opposite poles of the embryo sac, where cytoplasmic accumulations occur, and the nuclei divide rapidly. After wall formation the tissue becomes cellular and in *Ammania* and *Peplis* the chalazal end of the embryo sac extends back to the hypostase in the pouchlike manner.

Embryogeny conforms to the Onagrad type, with the formation of a uniseriate suspensor in *Ammania* spp., *Nesaea*, and *Peplis* but a multiseriate one in *Ammania* spp. and *Cuphea*.

L. Guignard, 1882b • Hofmeister, 1858 • Hubert, 1896 • Jönsson, 1879–1880, 1881 • A. C. Joshi, 1939a • A. C. Joshi, and Venkateswarlu, 1935a,b,c,d, 1936a,b • Mauritzon, 1934a • Souèges, 1925b • Tassi, 1898 • Tischler, 1917, 1918 • Venkateswarlu, 1937a • Warming, 1878.

MAGNOLIACEAE

The anther is tetrasporangiate with a persistent epidermis. The endothecium develops fibrous thickenings, and in *Magnolia liliflora* about 4 middle layers are formed. The cells of the glandular tapetum become multinucleate and frequently the tapetum becomes irregularly 2- or 3-layered. Simultaneous cytokinesis in the megaspore mother cells follows meiosis and the microspore tetrads are isobilateral or decussate. Pollen grains are 2-celled when shed.

The ovule is anatropous, bitegmic, and crassinucellar, with the micropyle formed by both integuments. The archesporial cell cuts off a primary parietal cell which forms about 8 parietal layers. Cytokinesis in the megaspore mother cell accompanies meiosis and the chalazal megaspore of a linear tetrad develops into a Polygonum type embryo sac. The synergids are pyriform, the polar nuclei fuse just before fertilization, and the 3 antipodal cells are ephemeral. A funicular obturator is formed in *Liriodendron*.

Endosperm formation is *ab initio* Cellular. Two weeks after fertilization in *L. tulipifera* the endosperm forms a narrow tissue 2 cells in thickness but after another week it has filled the embryo sac.

Embryogeny conforms to the Onagrad type. In *Michelia champaca* cleavage of the zygote occurs only after the formation of a considerable amount of endosperm.

Andrews, 1902 • Canright, 1953 • Earle, 1938 • Farr, 1918 • Gray, 1857 • Guard, 1943 • L. Guignard, 1897, 1898 • Hayashi, 1960, 1964, 1965 • Kaeiser and Boyce, 1962 • Maneval, 1914 • Padmanabhan, 1960b • Schürhoff, 1926b • Stoudt, 1960 • Swamy, 1949b • Vesque, 1878 • Wefelscheid, 1911 • Yamaha, 1926 • Yasui, 1937.

MALESHERBIACEAE

Embryologically unknown.

MALPIGHIACEAE

The anther is tetrasporangiate with a persistent epidermis. The endothecium develops fibrous thickenings, the 2 middle layers are ephemeral, and the cells of the glandular tapetum become multinucleate. Simultaneous cytokinesis in the microspore mother cells follows meiosis and the microspore tetrads are tetrahedral, isobilateral, or decussate. The pollen grains are 2-celled when shed.

The ovule is hemianatropous, bitegmic, and crassinucellar, with the micropyle formed either by the inner integument (*Hiptage, Malpighia, Tristellateia*), the outer integument (*Banisteria, Malpighia coccifera, Stigmatophyllum*), or by both (*Thryallis*). The archesporium is multicellular and each cell cuts off a primary parietal cell which undergoes periclinal divisions. The parietal tissue cannot be clearly distinguished from cells derived from periclinal divisions of the apical nucellar epidermal cells and the massive nucellar beak frequently occupies the micropyle. Only one megaspore mother cell undergoes further development and usually meiosis is not accompanied by cytokinesis so that embryo sac formation is tetrasporic. The megaspore nuclei take up a cruciform arrangement and undergo two divisions to form a Penaea type embryo sac, after which one nucleus from each quartet moves to the center and fusion results in a $4n$ secondary nucleus. Degeneration of the embryo sac frequently occurs before further organization takes place. In *Galphinia gracilis, Malpighia glauca,* and *Thryallis glauca* the heterotypic meiotic division is followed by cytokinesis and an Allium type embryo sac is formed in which the 2 polar nuclei fuse early and the 3 antipodal cells are ephemeral.

Endosperm formation is Nuclear with the development of a chalazal haustorium which remains free-nuclear after the endosperm proper has become cellular. *M. glabra* is the only species in which fertilization has been reported and in the other members the secondary nucleus forms the endosperm autonomously.

Embryogeny in *M. glabra* conforms to the Solanad type but in the other species adventive embryos are formed by budding from the apical nucellar tissue and polyembryony is common. In *Hiptage madablota* Subba Rao (1937) described the enlargement of several nucellar cells before fusion of the polar nuclei.

Braun, 1860 • Cortini, 1958 • Fotidar, 1939 • Narasimhachar, 1938 • Ritzerow, 1908 • Schürhoff, 1924b • B. Singh, 1959, 1961a,b • Stenar, 1937a • Subba Rao, 1937, 1939, 1940b, 1941.

MALVACEAE

The anther is bisporangiate with a persistent epidermis and wall development follows the Dicotyledonous type. The endothecium develops fibrous thickenings, the middle layer is ephemeral, and the cells of the amoeboid tapetum become multinucleate. Simultaneous cytokinesis in the microspore mother cells follows meiosis and the microspore tetrads are tetrahedral and decussate. The pollen grains are 2-celled when shed and are frequently polysiphonous, up to 10 pollen tubes being given off from each pollen grain of *Althaea rosea,* 14 from those of *Malva neglecta,* and 20–30 from those of *Anoda hastata* and *Lavatera.* The pollen tube of *Hibiscus trianon* branches extensively when it reaches the nucellus.

The ovule is anatropous to campylotropous, bitegmic, and crassinucellar, with the zigzag micropyle formed by both integuments. The archesporial cell cuts off a primary parietal cell which forms up to 12 parietal layers and the apical cells of the nucellar epidermis may undergo one or more periclinal divisions, sometimes forming a nucellar cap. Cytokinesis in the megaspore mother cell accompanies meiosis and the chalazal megaspore of a linear or T-shaped tetrad develops into a Polygonum type embryo sac. The synergids of *Gossypium* and *Sida* exhibit the filiform apparatus, and those of *Sida* and *Thespesia* are hooked. The polar nuclei fuse just before fertilization. The 3 antipodal cells are often ephemeral, but in *Abutilon indicum, A. theophrasti, Althaea rosea, Gossypium herbaceum* and *Hibiscus micranthus*, they undergo secondary multiplication to form at least 20 cells which may persist into early endosperm development.

Endosperm formation is Nuclear and several hundred free nuclei are present before wall formation is initiated and the tissue becomes cellular.

Embryogeny conforms to the Asterad type and polyembryony is common in *Gossypium*.

P. Abraham, 1934 • G. S. Ayyangar, 1948 • Balesubramanian, 1932 • Balls, 1905, 1906 • Byxbee, 1900 • Cannon, 1903 • Constantin, 1964 • Coulter and Chamberlain, 1903 • Denham, 1924 • Elfving, 1879 • Gore, 1932 • L. Guignard, 1882b, 1893, 1900b, 1904 • Harland, 1936 • Hegelmaier, 1885 • Hofmeister, 1849, 1858, 1867 • Hubert, 1896 • N. K. Iyengar, 1938 • Jönsson, 1879–1880, 1881 • Juel, 1915 • Lantis, 1912 • Lebegue, 1954 • Luxemburg, 1927 • Quintanilha, Cabral, and Quintanilha, 1947 • R. G. Reeves and Valle, 1934 • Saakyar, 1962 • Silow and Stephens, 1944 • Souèges, 1922e • Stenar, 1925b • Strasburger, 1884b • Vasil, 1962 • Venkata Rao, 1952a, 1954b, 1955a • J. B. Weaver, 1957, 1958 • Webber, 1938 • Wefelscheid, 1911 • Winter, 1960 • Wóycicki, 1911b, 1917, 1922, 1923 • Yamaha, 1926 • Youngman, 1927.

MARANTACEAE

Development and structure of the anther and pollen grains have not been described.

The ovule is anatropous to anacampylotropous, bitegmic, and crassinucellar, with the micropyle formed usually by the inner integument, but in *Phrynium* both integuments are involved. The archesporial cell cuts off a primary parietal cell which divides only anticlinally and the apical cells of the nucellar epidermis become elongated while the lateral ones undergo several periclinal divisions. Cytokinesis in the megaspore mother cell accompanies meiosis and the chalazal megaspore of a linear tetrad develops into a Polygonum type embryo sac. The synergids are pyriform, the polar nuclei fuse before fertilization, and the 3 antipodal cells are ephemeral in *Thalia*, but they persist at least until fertilization in *Maranta, Phrynium,* and *Stromanthe,* while in *Calathea* they become 2-nucleate and secondary multiplication may occur.

Endosperm formation in Nuclear and embryogeny follows the Chenopodiad type.

Hofmeister 1861 • J. E. Humphrey, 1896 • Jönsson, 1881 • Mauritzon, 1936e • Schachner, 1924 • Süssenguth, 1919 • Venkataswarlu, 1937.

MARCGRAVIACEAE

The anther is tetrasporangiate with a persistent epidermis. The endothecium develops fibrous thickenings, the 3 or 4 middle layers are ephemeral, and the cells of the glandular tapetum remain 1-nucleate. Simultaneous cytokinesis in the microspore mother cells follows meiosis but the tetrad types and pollen grains have not been described. Those of *Marcgravia* frequently germinate *in situ.*

The ovule is anatropous, bitegmic, and tenuinucellar, with the micropyle formed by the inner integument. The archesporial cell functions directly as the megaspore mother cell in which cytokinesis accompanies meiosis and the chalazal megaspore of a linear tetrad develops into a Polygonum type embryo sac. The polar nuclei fuse before fertilization and, although Mauritzon (1939a) reported the presence in *Marcgravia umbellata* of 3 antipodal cells, in *M. cuyuniensis* and *M. purpurea* Swamy (1948) found naked nuclei which degenerated soon after their formation and before the chalazal elongation of the embryo sac. A weak endothelium is differentiated.

Endosperm formation is *ab initio* Cellular with the development of 7 or 8 cells in a linear series before any longitudinal walls are formed. In *Marcgravia* the lowest of these cells enters the micropyle and becomes haustorial.

Embryogeny has not been investigated.

Juel, 1887 • Mauritzon, 1939a • Swamy, 1948.

MARTYNIACEAE

The development and structure of the anther have not been described, but simultaneous cytokinesis in the microspore mother cells follows meiosis and the microspore tetrads are tetrahedral or isobilateral. Pollen grains are usually 2-celled when shed but those of *Proboscidea louisiana* are 3-celled.

The ovule is anatropous, unitegmic, and tenuinucellar. The arche-sporial cell of *Martynia louisiana* and *Proboscidea lutea* functions directly as the megaspore mother cell in which cytokinesis accompanies meiosis and the chalazal megaspore of a linear tetrad develops into a Polygonum type embryo sac. The synergids are large and pyriform, the polar nuclei fuse just before fertilization, and the 3 antipodal cells persist into embryogeny. An endothelium is differentiated.

Endosperm formation is *ab initio* Cellular and, according to Anderson (1922), the chalazal haustorium of *Martynia* is a postfertilization development of the antipodal cells.

Embryogeny in *Martynia* conforms to the Onagrad type and a long slender suspensor is formed.

F. Anderson, 1922 • Balicka-Iwanowska, 1899 • Eseltine, 1929 • Gaiser, Sutherland, and Moore, 1943 • Hofmeister, 1849 • Martini, 1939 • Samuelsson, 1913 • Schacht, 1850.

MAYACACEAE

Embryologically unknown.

MEDUSAGYNACEAE

Embryologically unknown.

MEDUSANDRACEAE

Embryologically unknown.

MELASTOMACEAE

The anther is tetrasporangiate with a persistent epidermis whose tangential walls become cutinized in *Melastoma* and *Oxyspora*, in both of which the endothecium is poorly developed and becomes crushed. In *Mouriria* the walls of the endothecial cells become heavily thickened and fibrous bands are formed in *Memecylon*. An ephemeral middle layer is usually present but in *Melastoma malabathricum* about 7 middle layers are formed, of which the outer 2—3 layers are persistent and the remainder degenerate. The cells of the glandular tapetum remain 1-nucleate, and in *Memecylon heyneanum* an irregularly 2-layered tapetum is formed. Simultaneous cytokinesis in the microspore mother cells follows meiosis and the microspore tetrads are tetrahedral. Pollen grains are 3-celled when shed.

The ovule is anatropous, bitegmic, and crassinucellar, with the micropyle formed by both integuments. The archesporial cell cuts off a primary parietal cell which gives rise to 2–6 parietal layers below the nucellar epidermis. Cytokinesis in the megaspore mother cell accompanies meiosis and the chalazal megaspore of a linear tetrad develops into a Polygonum type embryo sac. The synergids are hooked, the polar nuclei fuse before fertilization, and the 3 antipodal cells are ephemeral. According to Subramanyam (1951) nearly 50% of the ovules of *Oxyspora paniculata* show double embryo sac formation either by the functioning of 2 archesporial cells or of 2 megaspores of a tetrad. A hypostase is differentiated.

Endosperm formation is Nuclear and the tissue is digested by the embryo in the free-nucleate condition.

Embryogeny conforms to the Onagrad type in *Bertolonia maculata, Calvoa orientalis, Clidemia hirta,* and *Oxyspora paniculata* where the multicellular suspensor is short and massive. In *Melastoma malabathricum,* however, it follows the Solanad type and a uniseriate suspensor of 4 cells is formed. A modification of this last type has been reported in *Sonerila wallichii* where *cb* divides vertically to form a tier of 6 somewhat swollen cells. Polyembryony has been described in *Melastoma.*

Chatin, 1870 • Crété, 1956f, 1957a, 1960a,d • George, 1938 • Hofmeister, 1858 • Iconomides, 1958 • Mellink, 1880 • Morley, 1953 • Ruys, 1924 • Subramanyam, 1942, 1944, 1946, 1948a, 1949, 1951a,c • Tassi, 1898a • Venkatesh, 1955 • Warming, 1878 • Ziegler, 1925.

MELIACEAE

The anther is tetrasporangiate with a persistent epidermis which, in *Azadirachta, Cipadessa,* and *Melia,* becomes conspicuously tuberculate at maturity. The endothecium develops fibrous thickenings and usually 2 or 3 ephemeral middle layers are formed, although only a single one is present in *Cipadessa.* The cells of the glandular tapetum become multinucleate and nuclear fusions are common. An intrusive tapetum which subdivides the loculus has been reported in *Chisocheton divergens.* Simultaneous cytokinesis in the microspore mother cells follows meiosis and the microspore tetrads are tetrahedral, decussate, or isobilateral. The pollen grains are 2- or 3-celled when shed, and often contain abundant starch grains. Degeneration of microspore mother cells or young pollen grains is common in *Azadirachta, Cipadessa,* and *Melia.*

The ovule is anatropous, bitegmic, and crassinucellar, with the micropyle formed by the inner integument, except in *Dysoxylum ramiflorum* where Paetow (1931) reported it was the outer integument concerned. A multiple archesporium is of common occurrence but only one cell usually cuts off a primary parietal cell which gives rise to a parietal tissue of 4–7 cell layers. In addition, the apical cells of the nucellar epidermis divide periclinally and form a nucellar cap 2–9 cells in thickness. Cytokinesis in the megaspore mother cells accompanies meiosis and the chalazal megaspore of a linear or T-shaped tetrad develops into a Polygonum type embryo sac. The synergids are hooked and in *Azadirachta* they exhibit the filiform apparatus whereas in *Cipadessa baccifera* their colorless apex is bordered basally by a narrow striated band. The polar nuclei fuse before fertilization, the 3 antipodal cells are ephemeral, and starch grains occur in the embryo sacs of *Azadirachta, Melia,* and *Sandoricum.* An obturator of multicellular glandular hairs from the placenta is formed in *Cipadessa.* Nair (1959) found that in *Melia azedarach* over 50% of the ovules contained degenerated gamotophytes. Multiple embryo sac formation has been reported in several genera.

Endosperm formation is Nuclear with a chalazal aggregation of nuclei. Walls are initiated at the micropylar pole and the tissue becomes cellular when embryogeny is well advanced.

Embryogeny conforms to the Onagrad type and polyembryony has been described in *Aphanamixis, Azadirachta,* and *Melia.*

Garudamma, 1956, 1957 • Gavde, 1963 • R. B. Ghosh, 1962a • Juliano, 1934a,b • Karsten, 1891 • Mauritzon, 1935e • Nair, 1956, 1958, 1959a,b • Nair and Kanta, 1961 • Narasimhachar, 1936 • L. L. Narayana, 1958 • Paetow, 1931 • Wiger, 1935, 1936.

MELIANTHACEAE

The anther is tetrasporangiate with a persistent epidermis. The endothecium in *Melianthus major* does not develop fibrous thickenings, the 3 middle layers are ephemeral, and the cells of the glandular tapetum become multinucleate. Simultaneous cytokinesis in the microspore mother cells follows meiosis and the microspore tetrads are tetrahedral or isobilateral. Pollen grains are 2-celled when shed but in *Melianthus* there is a high degree of sterility.

The ovule is anatropous, bitegmic, and crassinucellar, with the micropyle formed by the inner integument in *Melianthus* but in *Bersama* both integuments are involved. The archesporial cell cuts off a primary parietal cell which gives rise to 6–13 parietal layers and the apical cells of the nucellar epidermis divide periclinally to form a nucellar cap 3 or 4 cells in thickness. Cytokinesis in the megaspore mother cell accompanies meiosis and the chalazal or subchalazal megaspore develops into a Polygonum type embryo sac. The synergids are hooked, the polar nuclei fuse before fertilization, and the 3 antipodal cells are ephemeral.

Endosperm formation is Nuclear but embryogeny is unknown.

Guérin, 1901 • Khushalani, 1963a • Mauritzon, 1936d.

MENISPERMACEAE

The anther is tetrasporangiate with a persistent epidermis and in *Tiliacora racemosa* its wall development follows the Dicotyledonous type. The endothecium develops fibrous thickenings, the 2 middle layers are ephemeral, and the cells of the glandular tapetum become 2-nucleate. The tapetum may become irregularly 2-layered when the formation of a periclinal wall follows nuclear division. Simultaneous cytokinesis in the microspore mother cells follows meiosis and the microspore tetrads are tetrahedral or isobilateral. Pollen grains are 2-celled when shed and in *Tiliacora* they are filled with starch grains. Dimorphic pollen has been reported in *Tripodandra grandiflora*.

The ovule is hemianatropous to amphitropous, bitegmic (*Tiliacora*) or unitegmic (*Cissampelos, Cocculus, Stephania, Tinospora*), and crassinucellar. The micropyle is formed by the inner integument in *Tiliacora* and in *Tinospora cordifolia* it is zigzag because one lip of the single integument becomes tucked under the other. The archesporial cell cuts off a primary parietal cell which gives rise to 3–11 parietal layers and the apical cells of the nucellar epidermis divide periclinally to form a nucellar cap 2–4 cells in thickness. Cytokinesis in the megaspore mother cell accompanies meiosis and the chalazal megaspore of a linear tetrad develops into a Polygonum type embryo sac. The synergids of *Cocculus villosus* bear small hooks and filiform apparatus, the polar nuclei fuse before fertilization, and the 3 antipodal cells are ephemeral in *Tiliacora* but in *Cocculus* and *Tinospora* they may persist into early embryogeny and in *Tinospora cordifolia* secondary multiplication has been reported.

Endosperm formation is Nuclear but the tissue later becomes cellular throughout and ruminations commonly develop by infoldings of the integument.

Embryogeny conforms to the Onagrad type.

Abraham, 1935 • Ernst, 1886 • A. C. Joshi, 1937b, 1939c • A. C. Joshi and B. V. R. Rao, 1934, 1935 • R. E. Lee, 1961 • Sahni, 1934 • Sastri, 1954a,b, 1964 • Seshagiriah, 1934 • B. Singh, 1934 • Tiwary, 1934.

MENYANTHACEAE

The anther is tetrasporangiate with a persistent epidermis. The endothecium develops fibrous thickenings, the 1 or 2 middle layers are ephemeral, and the cells of the glandular tapetum become multinucleate but nuclear fusions are frequent. Simultaneous cytokinesis in the microspore mother cells follows meiosis and the pollen grains are 3-celled when shed.

The ovule is anatropous, unitegmic, and tenuinucellar. The archesporial cell functions directly as the megaspore mother cell in which cytokinesis accompanies meiosis and the chalazal megaspore of a linear tetrad develops into a Polygonum type embryo sac. The synergids are pyriform, the polar nuclei fuse before fertilization, and in *Limnanthemum cristatum* and *Nymphoides peltatum* the 3 antipodal nuclei degenerate immediately but in *L. indicum* and *Menyanthes trifoliata* they are enclosed in cells which may persist into early postfertilization stages. An endothelium is always differentiated and a hypostase is present in *L. cristatum*.

Endosperm formation is *ab initio* Cellular and in *Villarsia reniformis* a row of 8 cells is formed before longitudinal divisions occur.

Embryogeny conforms to the Asterad type and polyembryony has been reported in *L. indicum*.

Billings, 1901 • Crété, 1956c • Guérin, 1925, 1926 • Maheswari Devi, 1962 • Souèges, 1943e • A. R. Srinivasan, 1941 • Stolt, 1921, 1927 • Stover, 1932 • Warming, 1878.

MIMOSACEAE

The anther is tetrasporangiate with a persistent epidermis. The endothecium develops fibrous thickenings, the 1 or 2 middle layers are ephemeral, and the cells of the glandular tapetum remain 1-nucleate. Simultaneous cytokinesis in the microspore mother cells follows meiosis and the microspore tetrads are tetrahedral or isobilateral. In *Desmanthus, Neptunia,* and *Prosopis* the microspores are liberated from the tetrads but in *Mimosa* they remain attached and form permanent tetrads while in *Acacia, Pithecolobium,* and some others they form polyads. Individual pollen grains are 2-celled when shed and those of *Mimosa pudica* often germinate *in situ.* Starch occurs in the pollen grains of *Desmanthus* and *Prosopis.*

The ovule is hemianatropous to anatropous, bitegmic, and crassinucellar, with the micropyle formed by the outer integument except in *M. pudica* where it is zigzag and formed by both integuments. The archesporial cell cuts off a primary parietal cell which gives rise to 2–7 parietal layers and periclinal divisions of the apical nucellar epidermal cells form a nucellar cap 2 or 3 cells in thickness. Cytokinesis in the megaspore mother cell accompanies meiosis and the chalazal megaspore of a linear tetrad develops into a Polygonum type embryo sac. The synergids are hooked and exhibit the filiform apparatus, the polar nuclei fuse shortly before or at fertilization, and the 3 antipodal cells are ephemeral although their remains may persist until early postfertilization stages. Starch grains are present, sometimes in great numbers, in the embryo sac.

Endosperm formation is Nuclear, but after walls are formed at the micropylar pole, the tissue becomes cellular although the tubular chalazal extremity remains free-nuclear until the initiation of cotyledons by the embryo.

Embryogeny conforms to the Onagrad type but no suspensor is formed.

Dnyansagar, 1949a, 1951a,b • 1952, 1954a,b,c,d,e, 1955, 1956, 1957, 1958 • Elfving, 1879 • L. Guignard, 1881c,d, 1882a,b • B. M. Johri and Garg, 1959 • Jönsson, 1879–1880 • P. Maheshwari, 1931 • Narasimhachar, 1948, 1951a • Neumann, 1939 • Neuman, 1933, 1934a,b,c • Rosanoff, 1865 • B. Singh and Shivapuri, 1935 • Täckholm and Söderberg, 1918 • Venkatesh, 1951 • Warming, 1873.

MOLLUGINACEAE

The anther is tetrasporangiate with a persistent epidermis, and its wall development follows the Monocotyledonous type. The endothecium develops fibrous thickenings, the middle layer is ephemeral, and the cells of the glandular tapetum become multinucleate. Ubisch granules have been reported in *Orygia decumbens*. Simultaneous cytokinesis in the microspore mother cells follows meiosis and the microspore tetrads are tetrahedral, decussate, or isobilateral. Pollen grains are 3-celled when shed and in *Mollugo nudicaulis* they may occasionally germinate *in situ*.

The ovule is anatropous to anacampylotropous, bitegmic, and crassinucellar, with the micropyle formed by the inner integument. The archesporial cell cuts off a primary parietal cell which gives rise to 1 or 2 parietal layers and the apical cells of the nucellar epidermis usually divide periclinally to form a nucellar cap 2 or 3 cells in thickness. In *Mollugo oppositifolia* the cells of the nucellar epidermis adjacent to the micropyle undergo considerable radial elongation but do not divide periclinally. Cytokinesis in the megaspore mother cell accompanies meiosis and the chalazal megaspore of a linear or T-shaped tetrad develops into a Polygonum type embryo sac. The synergids in *Gisekia pharnaceoides* are hooked and exhibit the filiform apparatus, the polar nuclei fuse before fertilization, and the 3 antipodal cells degenerate before or at fertilization except in *Limeum indicum* where they persist into endosperm formation. A placental obturator is present in *Mollugo* and *Orygia* and a funicular one in *Glinus* and *Limeum*.

Endosperm formation is Nuclear but after walls are initiated at the micropylar pole the tissue becomes cellular throughout. During postfertilization stages the embryo sac elongates into the chalaza and becomes curved.

Embryogeny conforms to the Caryophyllad type in *Gisekia* and *Limeum* but to the Solanad type in *Orygia*.

H. R. Bhargava, 1934 • A. C. Joshi and V. R. Rao, 1936 • Kshirsagar, 1960 • H. S. Narayana and Jain, 1962 • H. S. Narayana and Lodha, 1961, 1963 • Payne, 1935 • Raghavan, 1940a.

MONIMIACEAE

The anther is tetrasporangiate with a 5- or 6-layered wall and the tapetum is glandular. Simultaneous cytokinesis in the microspore mother cells accompanies meiosis, the microspore tetrads are tetrahedral, and in *Hedycarya angustifolia* they do not disintegrate into individual microspores. The pollen grains are 2-celled when shed.

The ovule is anatropus, bitegmic (*Peumus*) with the micropyle formed by the inner integument or unitegmic (*Siparuna*), and crassinucellar. The archesporial cell cuts off a primary parietal cell which gives rise to 2 or 3 parietal layers and the apical cells of the nucellar epidermis divide periclinally to form a nucellar cap 2–4 cells in thickness. In *Siparuna eggersii* the archesporium is multicellular and each cell cuts off a primary parietal cell which divides periclinally to form the 2–4 parietal layers. Cytokinesis accompanies meiosis in all megaspore mother cells and the chalazal megaspore of the central linear tetrad elongates into a narrow tube which penetrates the chalaza as far as the hypostase where it becomes coiled and vesicular. Degeneration of this abortive embryo sac follows the rupture of the chalazal vesicle and the plant is sterile. According to Peter (1920) embryo sac formation in *Mollinedia* is "normal," but in *Peumus boldus* its origin is not clear although there is an indication that the Allium type of development may be followed on some occasions, at least. In *P. boldus* the synergids are pyriform, the polar nuclei fuse just before fertilization at the chalazal end of the embryo sac, and the antipodal cells undergo secondary multiplication to form 5–20 cells.

Endosperm formation in *Peumus boldus* is *ab initio* Cellular and its embryogeny conforms to the Asterad type.

Heilborn, 1931 • Mauritzon, 1935c • Money, Bailey, and Swamy, 1950 • Perkins, 1898 • Peter, 1920.

MONOTROPACEAE

The anther is tetrasporangiate with a persistent epidermis which forms an exothecium, and the 2 hypodermal cell layers are undifferentiated. The cells of the glandular tapetum remain 1-nucleate. Simultaneous cytokinesis in the microspore mother cells follows meiosis and the microspore tetrads are isobilateral or decussate. Pollen grains are shed singly and are 2-celled.

The ovule is anatropous, unitegmic, and tenuinucellar. The archesporial cell functions directly as the megaspore mother cell in which cytokinesis accompanies meiosis and the chalazal megaspore of a linear or T-shaped tetrad develops into a Polygonum type embryo sac. In *Pterospora andromedea* Bakshi (1959) reported the occasional suppression of wall formation after the homotypic division and the development of an Allium type embryo sac. The polar nuclei fuse before or at fertilization and the 3 antipodal cells may persist into early embryogeny.

Endosperm formation is *ab initio* Cellular with the development of terminal haustoria in *Sarcodes*.

Embryogeny conforms to the Caryophyllad type.

Bakshi, 1959 • Batygina, Teriokhin, Alimova, and Yakovlev, 1963 • Copeland, 1933, 1934, 1935a, 1937, 1938b, 1939, 1941, 1943 • Doyel and Goss, 1941 • Elfving, 1879 • Hagerup, 1954 • Hofmeister, 1849, 1858b • Koch, 1880, 1882 • K. Müller, 1847 • Oliver, 1890 • Peltrisot, 1904b • Samuelsson, 1913 • Schacht, 1850 • Shibata, 1902a,b • Strasburger, 1877, 1878, 1879, 1884b, 1900a • Teriokhin, 1962b, 1963.

MORACEAE

The anther is tetrasporangiate with a heavily cutinized epidermis and its wall development follows the Monocotyledonous type. The endothecium develops fibrous thickenings and 2 ephemeral middle layers are usually formed but 4 or 5 are present in *Ficus religiosa*. The cells of the glandular tapetum become 2–4-nucleate and when a periclinal division follows a nuclear division, the tapetum becomes irregularly 2-layered. Simultaneously cytokinesis in the microspore mother cells follows meiosis and the microspore tetrads are tetrahedral, decussate, or isobilateral. Pollen grains are 2-celled when shed and in *F. religiosa* they contain starch grains. In *Morus* spp. Singh (1954) reported complete degeneration of sporogenous tissue in some loculi and in *M. alba* he found a few instances of abortive sporangia in the ovary wall.

The ovule is hemianatropous to anatropous, bitegmic, and crassinucellar, with the micropyle formed by the inner integument and visible only in the young ovule. The archesporium is multicellular and each cell cuts off a primary parietal cell which gives rise to 5–8 parietal layers and the apical cells of the nucellar epidermis divide periclinally to form a nucellar cap 3–5 cells in thickness. Only one megaspore mother cell is functional and cytokinesis accompanies meiosis to form a linear or T-shaped tetrad of which the chalazal megaspore develops into a Polygonum type embryo sac. Gonial apospory has been reported in several species of *Dorstenia*. The synergids are pyriform and in *Artocarpus* they are very large, the polar nuclei fuse before fertilization, and the 3 antipodal cells are ephemeral except in *Dorstenia* spp. where secondary multiplication forms about 8 cells. Nucellar budding in some ovules of *Ficus carica* results in local proliferation of cells and occasionally in secondary primordia containing archesporial cells. No perceptible difference occurs in the embryo sacs of long-styled ("seed") flowers and short-styled ("gall") flowers of *Ficus* and those "gall" flowers which escape oviposition by *Blastophaga* produce perfect seeds but larvae may also develop in the ovaries of "seed" flowers. In *Morus* embryo sac collapse after pollination failure is followed by parthenocarpic fruit development. A hypostase is present in *Streblus asper*.

Endosperm formation is Nuclear but the number of free nuclei present when the tissue becomes cellular is smaller in the "seed" flowers than in the "gall" flowers, where wall formation may enclose several nuclei in each cell. In *Artocarpus* the endosperm remains free-nuclear until late in embryogeny.

Embryogeny conforms to the Asterad type but in the "gall" flowers of *Ficus* the embryo does not develop beyond the octant stage. Tricotyly has been reported in *Ficus religiosa* and *Morus multicaulis*.

Banerji and Hakim, 1954 • Bessey, 1908 • Condit, 1926, 1928, 1932, 1938 • Cunningham, 1889 • Das, 1961 • R. M. Datta, 1941 • Hofmeister, 1858 • Hubert, 1896 • B. M. Johri and Konar, 1955, 1956 • Leclerc du Sablon, 1908, 1910 • Longo, 1905b, 1909a, 1911a,b • Modilewski, 1908b • Padmanabhan, 1961b • M. A. Rau, 1942 • Ravasini, 1912a,b • S. P. Singh, 1954 • Subba Rao, 1940a • Tahara, 1910 • Tischler, 1912 • Treub, 1902 • Zamotailov, 1955.

MORINGACEAE

The anther of *Moringa oleifera* is usually bisporangiate but occasionally tetrasporangiate, and Puri (1941) considers that the former condition is secondarily derived. Anther wall development has not been described, but 4–6 parietal layers are formed and the glandular tapetum is dimorphic with its radially elongated cells adjacent to the connective becoming multinucleate and finally 1-nucleate by fusion. Ubisch granules are present on the inner and radial tapetal walls. Simultaneous cytokinesis in the microspore mother cells follows meiosis and the microspore tetrads are tetrahedral, isobilateral, or decussate. Pollen grains are 3-celled when shed.

The ovule is anatropous, bitegmic, and crassinucellar, with the zigzag micropyle formed by both integuments. The archesporial cell cuts off a primary parietal cell which forms 2–4 parietal layers below the nucellar epidermis. Cytokinesis in the megaspore mother cell accompanies meiosis and the chalazal megaspore of a linear or T-shaped tetrad develops into a Polygonum type embryo sac. The synergids are hooked and bear a faint filiform apparatus, the polar nuclei fuse in association with a male gamete, and the 3 antipodal cells are very ephemeral.

Endosperm formation is Nuclear with an aggregation of nuclei at the micropylar pole where wall formation is initiated and the tissue finally becomes cellular throughout.

Embryogeny conforms to the Asterad type but no suspensor is formed.

Hedayetullah, 1935b • Narayana, 1962a • Puri, 1934, 1941 • Rutgers, 1922, 1923b.

MUSACEAE

Anther development and structure have not been investigated, but successive cytokinesis in the microspore mother cells accompanies meiosis. The nature of the microspore tetrads and the pollen grains has not been reported.

The ovule is anatropous, bitegmic, and crassinucellar. with the micropyle formed by both integuments. The archesporial cell cuts off a primary parietal cell which forms 1 or 2 parietal layers and the apical cells of the nucellar epidermis become much elongated radially, forming a plug which projects into the base of the micropyle. Cytokinesis in the megaspore mother cell accompanies meiosis and the chalazal megaspore of a linear, T-shaped or ⊥-shaped tetrad develops into a Polygonum type embryo sac. The synergids are pyriform and the polar nuclei undergo triple fusion close to the 3 ephemeral nuclei or cells. The mature embryo sac is very broad with a short antipodal appendix.

Endosperm formation is Nuclear and often there are local accumulations of dense cytoplasm containing free nuclei ("endosperm nodules"). In *Musa acuminata* ssp. *burmannica* the endosperm becomes cellular 55 days after fertilization.

Embryogeny has not been described but the zygote divides transversely 2–4 weeks after fertilization. The edible polyploid bananas are highly sterile through meiotic irregularities, failure of fertilization, or postfertilization development.

Angremont, 1912, 1915 • Bouharmont, 1963 • Dodds, 1943, 1945 • Gatin, 1905, 1908 • J. E. Humphrey, 1896 • Juliano and Alcala, 1933 • McGahan, 1961 • Shepherd, 1954, 1960 • Simmonds, 1961 • Tischler, 1910b, 1912 • P. R. White, 1928.

MYOPORACEAE

The development and structure of the anther and pollen grains have not been investigated but the tapetum is glandular and its cells become 2-nucleate.

The ovule is anatropous, unitegmic, and tenuinucellar. The archesporial cell functions directly as the megaspore mother cell in which cytokinesis accompanies meiosis and the chalazal megaspore of a linear tetrad develops into a Polygonum type embryo sac. The synergids are pyriform, the polar nuclei fuse before fertilization, and the 3 small antipodal cells persist into early endosperm formation. An endothelium encloses the lower two-thirds of the embryo sac.

Endosperm formation is *ab initio* Cellular with the development of terminal haustoria. The chalazal haustorium is small and 4-celled while the micropylar one is multicellular in *Eremophila duttoni, E. longifolia,* and *Myoporum acuminatum,* but composed of 4 large cells in *Oftia africana.*

Embryogeny conforms to the Onagrad type and a slender uniseriate suspensor at least 7 cells in length is formed in *Eremophila* and *Myoporum.*

Billings, 1901 • David, 1938 • Junell, 1934 • P. Maheshwari, 1946a • Vos, 1947.

MYRICACEAE

The development and structure of the anther have not been described. In *Myrica gale,* simultaneous cytokinesis in the microspore mother cells follows meiosis but the nature of the mature pollen grains has not been reported.

The ovule is orthotropous, unitegmic, and crassinucellar. The archesporial cell cuts off a parietal cell which gives rise to 4–6 parietal layers and the apical cells of the nucellar epidermis undergo a single periclinal division. Cytokinesis in the megaspore mother cell accompanies meiosis and the chalazal megaspore of a linear tetrad develops into a Polygonum type embryo sac which occupies only the upper portion of a very long nucellus. The synergids are pyriform, the polar nuclei fuse before fertilization, and the 3 antipodal cells are ephemeral. According to Håkansson (1955) 4–5 weeks intervene between pollination and fertilization in *Myrica gale* and in *M. rubra* Yen (1950) reported the interval to be 6–7 weeks.

Endosperm formation is Nuclear but following the initiation of walls at the micropylar pole, the tissue becomes cellular throughout.

Embryogeny is unknown.

B. Clarke, 1858 • Hagerup, 1934 • Håkansson, 1955 • Kershaw, 1900a,b • Treub, 1891 • Yen, 1950.

MYRISTICACEAE

The anther is tetrasporangiate. The endothecium develops fibrous thickenings, the 2 middle layers are ephemeral, and the cells of the glandular tapetum remain 1-nucleate. Successive cytokinesis in the microspore mother cells accompanies meiosis and the microspore tetrads are isobilateral. Pollen grains are 2-celled when shed.

The ovule is anatropous, bitegmic, and crassinucellar, with the micropyle formed by the inner integument. The archesporial cell cuts off a primary parietal cell which forms several parietal layers. Cytokinesis in the megaspore mother cell accompanies meiosis and the chalazal megaspore of a linear tetrad develops into a Polygonum type embryo sac whose structure has not been described. An aril develops from the outer integument and in *Myristica* it forms a network over the surface of the mature seed. The pollen tube persists in the micropyle until early embryogeny.

Endosperm formation is Nuclear but the tissue later becomes cellular and finally ruminate through infoldings of the inner integument.

Embryogeny has not been investigated.

Camp and Hubbard, 1963 • A. C. Joshi, 1943, 1946 • Mauritzon, 1939c • Nair and Bahl, 1956 • Periasamy, 1961 • Sastri, 1955b, 1959 • Voigt, 1888.

MYROTHAMNACEAE

Embryologically unknown.

MYRSINACEAE

The development of the anther and microspores has not been investigated but Chatin (1870) reported a nonfibrous endothecium in *Badula*. Pollen grains are 2-celled when shed.

The ovule is anatropous, bitegmic, and tenuinucellar, with the micropyle formed by the inner integument. The archesporial cell functions directly as the megaspore mother cell in which cytokinesis accompanies meiosis and the chalazal megaspore of a linear tetrad develops into a Polygonum type embryo sac. The structure of the mature embryo sac has not been described but it is enclosed by an endothelium.

Endosperm formation is Nuclear, but the tissue later becomes cellular.

Embryogeny probably conforms to the Onagrad type and a long suspensor is formed. Polyembryony is common.

Braun, 1860 • Chatin, 1870 • Dahlgren, 1916 • Hofmeister, 1858 • Jaensch, 1905 • Schürhoff, 1926 • Warming, 1878, 1913.

MYRTACEAE

The anther is tetrasporangiate and its epidermis degenerates. The endothecium develops fibrous thickenings, the 1 or 2 middle layers are ephemeral, and the cells of the glandular tapetum become 2-nucleate. Pollen grains are 2-celled when shed.

The ovule is anatropous, usually bitegmic, and crassinucellar, with the micropyle formed by both integuments except in *Thryptomene* and *Wehlia* where only the inner integument is involved. Only a single integument is present in *Eugenia fruticosa, E. jambos, E. paniculata, Syzygium caryophyllifolium,* and *S. cumini.* The archesporial cell is always described as subhypodermal and as functioning directly as the megaspore mother cell, but presumably a primary parietal cell is cut off so early that its formation has escaped detection. A parietal tissue of 2–12 layers is formed but the nucellar epidermis remains as a single layer except in *Psidium* where its apical cells divide periclinally to form a nucellar cap 2 or 3 cells in thickness. Cytokinesis in the megaspore mother cell accompanies meiosis and the chalazal megaspore of a linear tetrad develops into a Polygonum type embryo sac. The synergids are commonly hooked and those of *Eugenia jambos* and *Tristania suaveolens* exhibit the filiform apparatus. The polar nuclei usually fuse before fertilization but in *Myrtus communis,*

Syzygium cumini, and *S. caryophyllifolium* fusion occurs after one has been fertilized and a secondary nucleus is not formed. The 3 antipodals degenerate soon after their formation and definite cells are not always formed.

Endosperm formation is Nuclear and in *Syzygium* there is an accumulation of cytoplasm and free nuclei at the chalazal pole. Wall formation is initiated at the micropylar end of the embryo sac and the tissue becomes cellular throughout.

Embryogeny in *Myrtus communis* conforms to the Onagrad type but in most representatives the zygote degenerates. Adventive embryogeny by budding from nucellar cells is the usual method of embryo formation and in *Eugenia jambos* Pijl (1934) reported the formation of nucellar embryos before pollination. Polyembryony is of common occurrence and although it is usual for only one embryo to survive, in *S. caryophyllifolium* 45–50% of the seeds were found to be polyembryonic (Roy and Sahai, 1962), and in *E. hookeri* Johnson (1936) found 2–21 embryos in all seeds.

Baranov, Baranova, and Polunina, 1955 • Briggs, 1964 • Cook, 1907d • Fohn, 1935 • Friesendahl, 1912 • Greco, 1930 • Gurbel, 1952 • Irmisch, 1876 • A. M. Johnson, 1936 • Mauritzon, 1939c • Narayanaswami and Roy, 1960a,b • Pijl, 1931, 1934 • Polunina, 1957, 1958 • S. K. Roy, 1953, 1955, 1960, 1961 • S. K. Roy and Sahai, 1962 • Somego and Kawandbe, 1961 • Souèges, 1940b • Tiwary, 1925, 1926a,b • Tiwary and V. S. Rao, 1934.

MYZODENDRACEAE

The anther of *Myzodendron recurvum* is bisporangiate with a persistent epidermis, but the development of its wall and of the pollen grains has not been investigated.

The ovule is little more than a curved papilla of nucellus, and is ategmic and tenuinucellar. The archesporial cell functions directly as the megaspore mother cell in which cytokinesis accompanies meiosis and the chalazal megaspore of a linear or T-shaped tetrad develops into a Polygonum type embryo sac. The synergids are pyriform, the polar nuclei fuse before fertilization, and the 3 antipodals are ephemeral.

Endosperm formation is *ab initio* Cellular with the development of a long branching chalazal haustorium which penetrates the funicle and finally reaches the placenta and the pedicel of the flower.

Embryogeny has not been investigated.

T. Johnson, 1889 • B. M. Johri and Bhatnagar, 1960 • Skottsberg, 1913.

NAJADACEAE

The anther is tetrasporangiate with a persistent epidermis and its wall development follows the Reduced type in which only 2 parietal layers are formed. The subepidermal layer does not develop fibrous thickenings and is soon crushed while the second layer differentiates as the amoeboid tapetum whose cells remain 1-nucleate. Successive cytokinesis in the microspore mother cells accompanies meiosis and the microspore tetrads are tetrahedral, isobilateral, or, rarely, linear or T-shaped. The microspores are already 2-celled when liberated from the tetrad and the pollen grains are 3-celled when shed and contain starch grains.

The ovule is anatropous, bitegmic, and crassinucellar, with the micropyle formed by the inner integument. The archesporial cell cuts off a primary parietal cell which forms 1 or 2 parietal layers below the nucellar epidermis. Cytokinesis in the megaspore mother cell accompanies meiosis and the chalazal megaspore of a linear tetrad develops into a Polygonum type embryo sac. The synergids are pyriform, the polar nuclei fuse at fertilization, and the 3 antipodal cells persist into early embryogeny.

Endosperm formation is Nuclear but walls are initiated later at the micropylar pole and the tissue becomes cellular throughout.

Embryogeny of *Najas graminea* and *N. lacerata* conforms to the Caryophyllad type and *cb* becomes much enlarged as the terminal cell of the short suspensor.

Campbell, 1897 • L. Guignard, 1899a,e, 1901b • Hofmeister, 1858b, 1861 • Jönsson, 1881 • Magnus, 1869, 1870 • Strasburger, 1882a • Swamy and Lakshmanan, 1962a • Venkatesh, 1956b • Wunderlich, 1954, 1959.

NANDINACEAE

Embryologically unknown.

NEPENTHACEAE

The anther of *Nepenthes ampullaria* and *N. melamphora* is tetrasporangiate but its structure has not been described. The development of the pollen grains has not been investigated but they are liberated as permanent tetrahedral tetrads.

The ovule is anatropous bitegmic, and crassinucellar, with the micropyle formed by both integuments. The archesporial cell cuts off a primary parietal cell which forms a single parietal layer below the nucellar epidermis. Cytokinesis in the megaspore mother cell accompanies meiosis and the chalazal megaspore of a linear tetrad develops into a Polygonum type embryo sac. The synergids are pyriform, the polar nuclei fuse before fertilization, and 3 antipodal cells are formed.

Endosperm formation and embryogeny have not been described.

Kühl, 1933 • Stern, 1917.

NOLANACEAE

The development and structure of the anther have not been described, but the cells of the glandular tapetum become 2-nucleate. Simultaneous cytokinesis in the microspore mother cells follows meiosis and the microspore tetrads are tetrahedral or decussate. Pollen grains are 2-celled when shed.

The ovule is hemianatropous, unitegmic, and tenuinucellar. The archesporial cell functions directly as the megaspore mother cell in which cytokinesis accompanies meiosis and the chalazal megaspore of a linear tetrad develops into a Polygonum type embryo sac. The synergids are pyriform, the polar nuclei fuse before fertilization, and the 3 antipodal cells degenerate soon after. An endothelium is differentiated.

Endosperm formation is *ab initio* Cellular without the development of haustoria.

Embryogeny in *Nolana prostrata* conforms to the Solanad type and the slender uniseriate suspensor is up to 9 cells in length.

Campin, 1925 • Crété, 1957c • S. Datta, 1933 • Gioelli, 1933 • Rosén, 1947 • Samuelsson, 1913.

NYCTAGINACEAE

The anther is tetrasporangiate with a persistent epidermis and its wall development follows the Basic type. The endothecium develops fibrous thickenings, the 2 middle layers are still recognizable at dehiscence in *Bougainvillea*, and the cells of the glandular tapetum become 2-nucleate. Simultaneous cytokinesis in the microspore mother cells follows meiosis and the microspore tetrads are tetrahedral or isobilateral. Pollen grains are usually 3-celled when shed but they are 2-celled in *B. repandra* whereas in *B. glabra* all pollen is abortive.

The ovule is hemianatropous to anacampylotropous, bitegmic (*Bougainvillea, Oxybaphus, Pisonia*) or unitegmic (*Ambronia, Boerhaavia, Mirabilis*), and crassinucellar, with the micropyle formed by the inner integument. The archesporial cell cuts off a primary parietal cell which gives rise to up to 14 parietal layers and the apical cells of the nucellar epidermis divide periclinally to form a nucellar cap. Cytokinesis in the megaspore mother cell accompanies meiosis and the chalazal megaspore of a linear tetrad develops into a Polygonum type embryo sac, except in *Bougainvillea glabra* where sporogenesis is abortive. The synergids are hooked, the polar nuclei fuse before fertilization, and the 3 antipodal cells persist into early postfertilization stages, undergoing a small degree of secondary multiplication in *Boerhaavia diffusa, B. repandra, M. jalapa,* and *O. viscosus.* During postfertilization stages the embryo sac elongates into the chalaza and becomes curved.

Endosperm formation is Nuclear and the tissue later becomes cellular, except for its chalazal extremity which remains free-nuclear.

Embryogeny conforms to the Asterad type and polyembryony has been reported in *B. repandra.*

H. R. Bhargava, 1932 • D. C. Cooper, 1931a ,, 1932, 1933b, 1949 • Dahlgren, 1916 • Dambroise, 1947 • D'Yakova, 1962 • Fiedler, 1910 • A. Fischer, 1880 • L. Guignard, 1882b • Hedemann, 1931 • Hegelmaier, 1885 • Heimerl, 1887 • Hofmeister, 1858b • Kajale, 1936, 1937a, 1938 • P. Maheshwari, 1929, 1930 • P. Maheshwari and B. M. Johri, 1950b • Nair and Nair, 1963 • Rocén, 1924b, 1927 • Showalter, 1935 • Souèges, 1938d • Tischler, 1908 • Venkateswarlu, 1947b • Woodcock, 1929a • Yamaha, 1926.

NYMPHACEAE

The anther is tetrasporangiate with a persistent epidermis. The endothecium develops fibrous thickenings and in *Euryale ferox* 4 or 5 middle layers are present in the anthers of the outer stamens but only 2 or 3 layers in those of the inner stamens. The cells of the glandular tapetum become multinucleate. Simultaneous cytokinesis in the microspore mother cells follows meiosis and the microspore tetrads are tetrahedral or isobilateral. The pollen grains are 3-celled when shed and in *Nelumbium speciosum* germination is preceded by rupture of the exine.

The ovule is anatropous, bitegmic, and crassinucellar, with the micropyle formed by the inner integument. The archesporial cell cuts off a primary parietal cell which gives rise to 1–5 parietal layers, and although the nucellar epidermis remains as a single layer in *Euryale,* in the other genera its apical cells divide periclinally to form a nucellar cap 2–4 cells in thickness. Cytokinesis in the megaspore mother cell accompanies meiosis and the chalazal megaspore of a linear tetrad develops into a Polygonum type embryo sac. The synergids are pyriform, the polar nuclei fuse just before or at fertilization, and the 3 antipodal cells are very ephemeral. Starch grains occur in the embryo sac of *Castalia odorata* and in *E. ferox* an aril develops from 4 funicular outgrowths.

Endosperm formation in *Castalia, Nelumbo,* and *Nymphaea* is *ab initio* Cellular and the primary chalazal chamber forms a 1-nucleate haustorium. In *Euryale,* however, the endosperm is Nuclear but it becomes cellular at the micropylar pole before division of the zygote and the antipodal end of the embryo sac forms a tubular haustorium which penetrates deeply into the chalaza.

Embryogeny is of the Asterad type and polyembryony has been reported in *Euryale ferox* and *Nymphaea advena.*

H. S. Conrad, 1902, 1905 • M. T. Cook, 1902, 1906, 1909a • Elfving, 1879 • C. H. Farr, 1922a • L. Guignard, 1897 • Hegelmaier, 1886 • Hofmeister, 1858 • Khanna, 1964 • Lubimenko and Maige, 1907 • H. L. Lyon, 1901 • Meier, 1960 • Melikyan, 1964 • Nitzchke, 1914 • Ohga, 1937 • Pointeau, 1809 • Raciborsky, 1894 • J. H. Schaffner, 1904 • Seaton, 1908 • Strasburger, 1900b • Süssenguth, 1919 • Tischler, 1915 • Trécul, 1845 • Venkateswarlu and Seshavataram, 1964 • Wefelscheid, 1911 • York, 1904.

NYSSACEAE

Anther and pollen grain development and structure have not been investigated.

The ovule is anatropous, unitegmic, and crassinucellar? The apical cells of the nucellar epidermis divide periclinally and give rise to a nucellar cap 2 or 3 cells thick but the behavior of the archesporial cell and embryo sac development have not been described. In *Davidia involucrata* the initiation of multiple embryo sacs is common but only one completes development. An endothelium is differentiated.

Endosperm formation is *ab initio* Cellular but embryogeny is unknown.

Horne, 1909, 1914 • Warming, 1913.

OCHNACEAE

The anther is tetrasporangiate. The endothelium develops fibrous thickenings, the middle layer is ephemeral, and the tapetum is glandular. Simultaneous cytokinesis in the microspore mother cells follows meiosis and the microspore tetrads are tetrahedral. Pollen grains are 2-celled when shed.

The ovule is anatropous, bitegmic, and tenuinucellar, with the micropyle formed by both integuments. The archesporial cell functions directly as the megaspore mother cell in which cytokinesis accompanies meiosis and the chalazal megaspore of a linear or T-shaped tetrad develops into a Polygonum type embryo sac. The synergids exhibit the filiform apparatus, the polar nuclei fuse before fertilization, and the 3 antipodal cells are large. Gonial and somatic apospory as well as embryo sac abnormalities are common in *Ochna multiflora* and *O. serrulata*.

Endosperm formation is Nuclear, but after the initiation of walls at the micropylar pole, the tissue becomes cellular throughout.

Embryogeny has not been described.

Chiarugi and Francini, 1929, 1930 • Chikkanniah, 1954 • Francini, 1928 • R. B. Ghosh, 1964 • Tieghem, 1902.

OCTOKNEMACEAE

Development and structure of the anther and pollen grains have not been investigated.

The ovule is anatropous and undifferentiated but little is known of embryo sac development, which, according to Fagerlind (1948a) resembles that of the Olacaceae. In the embryo sac of *Octoknema* the synergids are beaked, the polar nuclei become closely associated in a central position, and 3 antipodal cells are present.

Endosperm formation and embryogeny have not been described.

Fagerlind, 1948a • B. M. Johri and Bhatnagar, 1960 • C. F. Reed, 1955 • Stauffer, 1957.

OLACACEAE

The anther is tetrasporangiate with a persistent epidermis. The endothecium develops fibrous thickenings and in *Strombosia* it may be irregularly 2-layered. The outermost of the 2 or 3 middle layers may also develop fibrous thickenings in *Olax* and the cells of the glandular tapetum become 2–4-nucleate. Simultaneous cytokinesis in the microspore mother cells follows meiosis and the microspore tetrads are tetrahedral, decussate, or isobilateral. The pollen grains of *Olax* are 3-celled when shed but those of *Strombosia* are 2-celled and sometimes germinate *in situ*.

The ovule is anatropous, unitegmic (*Anacolosa, Olax scandens, O. stricta, O. wightiana, Strombosia, Tetrastylidium*), bitegmic (*Coula, Heisteria, Macrotheca, Minquairta, Ximenia*), or ategmic (*Liriosma*,

Olax imbricata, Ptychopetalum), and tenuinucellar but it is occasionally pseudocrassinucellar in *Olax*. The archesporial cell functions directly as the megaspore mother cell and the chalazal megaspore of a linear or T-shaped tetrad develops into a Polygonum type embryo sac. In *O. wightiana*, however, the micropylar dyad cell degenerates early and the chalazal dyad cell develops into an Allium type embryo sac. The synergids are hooked and exhibit the filiform apparatus, the polar nuclei fuse before fertilization, and the 3 antipodal cells are ephemeral. In *Olax* the antipodal nuclei may be distributed between 2 cells and occasionally the antipodals are represented by a single 3-nucleate cell. Starch grains are present in the embryo sac of *Strombosia*. In *Olax* a lateral caecum develops near the base of the embryo sac and after penetrating the chalaza it branches on entering the funicle whereas in *O. stricta* it reaches the placenta. Extraovular development of the embryo sac takes place in *Chaunochiton, O. scandens*, and *O. wightiana*, where, at the 4-nucleate stage, its tip passes through the micropyle and grows towards the stylar canal.

Endosperm formation is *ab initio* Cellular in *Strombosia* where the chalazal endosperm chamber elongates as a 1-nucleate haustorium which reaches the funicle. In *Olax*, however, endosperm development follows the Helobial type and the 4-nucleate chalazal haustorium penetrates the funicle and finally branches extensively in the pedicel of the flower.

Embryogeny is little known but in *Strombosia* it is variable because *ca* may divide either transversely or longitudinally before giving rise to the embryo proper, but the suspensor is derived entirely from *cb*.

Agarwal, 1961b, 1963a,b • Fagerlind, 1946b, 1947h, 1948a • B. M. Johri, 1962b • B. M. Johri and Bhatnagar, 1960 • Shamanna, 1954, 1961.

OLEACEAE

The number of sporangia comprising the anther has not been recorded. The endothecium develops fibrous thickenings, the 1 or 2 middle layers are ephemeral, and the cells of the glandular tapetum become multinucleate but nuclear fusions may occur. In *Fraxinus* and *Nyctanthus* the tapetum may become irregularly 2-layered. Simultaneous cytokinesis in the microspore mother cells follows meiosis and the microspore tetrads are tetrahedral, isobilateral, or occasionally T-shaped or linear. Pollen grains are 2-celled when shed.

The ovule is anatropous, unitegmic, and tenuinucellar. The archesporial cell functions directly as the megaspore mother cell in which cytokinesis accompanies meiosis and the chalazal megaspore of a linear or T-shaped tetrad develops into a Polygonum type embryo sac. In *Olea*, however, the micropylar dyad cell degenerates and the chalazal cell develops into an Allium type embryo sac. The synergids in *Nyctanthus arbortristis* are hooked, the polar nuclei fuse before fertilization, and the 3 antipodal cells are ephemeral. An endothelium differentiates during embryo sac development.

Endosperm formation is *ab initio* Cellular.

Embryogeny has not been described in detail but as the early cleavages are transverse it probably follows either the Solanad or Caryophyllad type. Polyembryony has been reported to occur with a frequency of 0.71% in *Fraxinus nigra* and 7% in *F. velutina*.

Andersson, 1931 • Battaglia and Breviglieri, 1955 • Billings, 1901 • Borgenstam, 1922 • Copeland, 1960 • Dahlgren, 1923 • L. Guignard, 1882b • Haberlandt, 1922b • Hofmeister, 1858b • G. W. Johnson, 1941 • Jönsson, 1881 • Juel, 1900b, 1915 • King, 1938 • Messeri, 1950 • Moore and Behney, 1908 • Nicolayeva, 1962 • N. K. Patel, 1960 • Sommer, 1929 • Souèges, 1942b • Steinbauer, 1943 • Stolt, 1921 • Tischler, 1908 • Warming, 1878 • Westermaier, 1896, 1897 • Wille, 1886.

OLINIACEAE

The number of sporangia comprising the anther has not been recorded. The endothecium develops fibrous thickenings, the middle layer is ephemeral, and the cells of the glandular (?) tapetum become 2-nucleate. Development of the pollen grains has not been investigated.

The ovule of *Olinia capensis* is hemianatropous, bitegmic, and crassinucellar, with the micropyle formed by both integuments. The archesporial cell cuts off a primary parietal cell which gives rise to 2 parietal layers and occasionally the nucellus protrudes and prevents the formation of a micropyle. Cytokinesis in the megaspore mother cell accompanies meiosis and the chalazal megaspore of a linear tetrad develops into a Polygonum type embryo sac. The synergids are pyriform and the 3 small antipodal cells are ephemeral.

Endosperm formation is Nuclear and several hundred free nuclei are present when the proembryo is 2-celled.

Embryogeny is unknown.

Mauritzon, 1939c.

ONAGRACEAE

The anther is tetrasporangiate but the formation and structure of its wall have not been investigated. Simultaneous cytokinesis in the microspore mother cells follows meiosis and the microspore tetrads are tetrahedral. Pollen grains are 2-celled when shed and those of *Oenothera* contain starch grains.

The ovule is anatropous, bitegmic, and crassinucellar, with the micropyle formed by both integuments. The archesporial cell cuts off a primary parietal cell which gives rise to two parietal layers in *Jussieua repens* but usually forms a massive tissue. The apical cells of the nucellar epidermis undergo an occasional periclinal division in *Jussieua* but in *Fuchsia* a nucellar cap 5 cells in thickness is formed. Cytokinesis in the megaspore mother cell accompanies meiosis and usually the micropylar megaspore of a linear tetrad develops into the 4-nucleate Oenothera type embryo sac. The synergids exhibit the filiform apparatus and bear lateral indentations in *Oenothera* and *Taraxia*. The single polar nucleus lies close to the egg and antipodals are absent. Starch grains occur in the embryo sac of *Taraxia*. A hypostase is present in many species.

Endosperm formation is Nuclear and in *Jussieua repens* at least 900 free nuclei are present before the tissue becomes cellular, although rarely more than 20 nuclei are formed in *Gayophytum ramosissimum*.

Embryogeny conforms to the Onagrad type and polyembryony has been reported in *Taraxia ovata*.

Bartels, 1956 • Beer, 1906, 1907 • Beth, 1938 • Cleland, 1924 • B. M. Davis, 1909, 1910 • Gates, 1909, 1911, 1914, 1928 • Gates and Sheffield, 1929 • Geerts. 1908, 1909 • Gerhard, 1929 • L. Guignard, 1882b • Haberlandt, 1921a, 1927, 1938a • Håkansson, 1924, 1925 • Hanstein, 1870 • Hiorth, 1926 • Hoeppener and Renner, 1929 • Hofmeister, 1847, 1849, 1858 • Hulbary and Rao, 1959 • Ishikawa, 1918 • Johansen, 1928a,b, 1929, 1930a,b, 1931a,b,c, 1933, 1934 • R. Khan, 1942 • Kistner, 1955 • Langendorf, 1930 • Lebègue, 1948a,c • Lehmann, 1924 • Luerssen, 1869 • P. Maheshwari and Gupta, 1934 • Michaelis, 1925 • Modilewski, 1909b • O'Neal, 1923 • Pagni, 1958 • Renner, 1914, 1921 • Rudloff and Schmidt, 1933 • Rutgers, 1923a • Souèges, 1920e, 1935a, 1946h • Stomps, 1930, 1931 • Strasburger, 1877, 1882a, 1884b, 1889 • Subramanyam and Govindu, 1948 • Täckholm, 1914, 1915 • Tschistiakoff, 1876 • Vesque, 1879b • Ward, 1880b • Warming, 1873 • Warth, 1923, 1925 • Weidner-Rauh, 1939 • Werner, 1915 • Yamaha, 1926.

OPILIACEAE

The anther is tetrasporangiate and in *Cansjera rheedii* its wall development follows the Dicotyledonous type. The endothecium develops fibrous thickenings, the middle layer is ephemeral and the cells of the glandular tapetum becomes 2–4-nucleate. Simultaneous cytokinesis in the microspore mother cells follows meiosis and the microspore tetrads are tetrahedral. The pollen grains are 2-celled when shed.

The ovule is anatropous, unitegmic, and tenuinucellar, with a much reduced nucellus and very slender micropyle. The archesporial cell functions directly as the megaspore mother cell in which cytokinesis accompanies meiosis and the chalazal megaspore of a linear tetrad develops into a Polygonum type embryo sac. The synergids of *Opilia* are hooked and exhibit the filiform apparatus, the polar nuclei fuse before fertilization, the 3 antipodal cells are ephemeral, and in *Cansjera* many compound starch grains are present. At maturity, a chalazal caecum develops and passes into the funicle so that the embryo sac becomes U-shaped.

Endosperm formation is *ab initio* Cellular and the chalazal chamber becomes a uninucleate haustorium which grows from the funicle toward the base of the ovary. In *Opilia amentacea* the haustorium is unbranched and reaches the pedicel of the flower, but in *Cansjera rheedii* it branches prolifically and secondary haustoria develop from adjacent endosperm cells.

Embryogeny has not been investigated.

Fagerlind, 1948a • B. M. Johri and Bhatnagar, 1960 • Shamanna, 1955 • Swamy, 1960 • Swamy and Rao, 1963.

ORCHIDACEAE

The anther is tetrasporangiate with a persistent epidermis and its wall development conforms to the Monocotyledonous type. The endothecium develops fibrous thickenings, the 1 or 2 middle layers are ephemeral, and the cells of the glandular tapetum remain 1-nucleate except in *Paphiopedilum druryi* where they become 2-nucleate. Simultaneous cytokinesis in the microspore mother cells follows meiosis and the microspore tetrads are tetrahedral or isobilateral, but subsequent behavior is variable. In most diandrous orchids and a few monandrous genera (*Cephalanthera, Vanilla*, etc.) single pollen grains are formed, but in several members of the Neotiinae the tetrads are retained as compound pollen grains. An extension of this condition occurs in the Ophrydinae where the tetrads are grouped into massulae, and in the more advanced monandrous tribes the contents of each anther loculus adhere as pollinia. The individual pollen grains are 2-celled at dehiscence.

The ovule is anatropous, usually bitegmic (unitegmic in *Epipogium, Gastrodia, Paphiopedilum*), and tenuinucellar, with the micropyle formed by the inner integument. The archesporial cell functions directly as the megaspore mother cell and in most species cytokinesis accompanies meiosis and the chalazal megaspore of a linear tetrad (or "triad") develops into a Polygonum type embryo sac. The diandrous orchids, however, are characterized by the formation of an Allium type embryo sac. Both Allium and Adoxa types of development are of occasional occurrence in species which normally form the Polygonum type embryo sac. The phenomenon of "strike" is common and results in embryo sacs with 6, 5, or 4 nuclei, depending on the stage at which mitosis is inhibited in the chalazal nuclei, but a 6-nucleate embryo sac may also form following fusion of the chalazal spindles during the last embryo sac mitosis. The synergids are pyriform and in *Aa* they exhibit the filiform apparatus, whereas in *Spiranthes* they occupy about one-third of the embryo sac. The polar nuclei fuse prior to or at fertilization but in *Spiranthes* they degenerate without the formation of a secondary nucleus. The 3 antipodal cells are ephemeral but sometimes the nuclei degenerate before cytokinesis (*Cymbidium, Dendrobium, Satyrium*). In *Epidendron* they are either free-nuclear or cellular and in *Spiranthes* the single antipodal cell is 3-nucleate. When pollination occurs, the embryo sac is undifferentiated and in *Dendrobium phalaenopsis* the embryo sac is not fully mature until 55–65 days later. Somatic apospory has been described in *Zygopetalum mackayi*.

Endosperm formation, when it occurs, is Nuclear but only 2–4 endosperm nuclei are formed except in *Vanilla planifolia* where 10 free nuclei have been reported. Usually either the secondary nucleus or the primary endosperm nucleus degenerates soon after its formation.

Embryogeny is very variable and has been discussed fully by Johansen (1950), but the embryo is always immature in the ripe seed. Outgrowths of the suspensor may become conspicuous structures and in *Goodyera discola cb* forms an immensely elongated but unbranched cell. Adventive embryony is common in *Cephalanthera, Epipactis, Listera, Nigritella, Orchis*, and *Zeuxine* and cleavage polyembryony has been reported in *Cymbidium, Eulophea, Gastrodia, Gymnadenia*, and *Spiranthes*.

Afzelius, 1916, 1922, 1928, 1932, 1954, 1959 • Amici, 1847 • Baranov, 1915, 1916, 1918, 1925a,b • H. N. Barber, 1942 • Braun, 1860 • Brongniart, 1831 • W. H. Brown, 1909 • W. H. Brown and Sharp, 1911 • M. C. Carlson, 1940, 1945 • Chamberlain, 1914 • Chodat, 1913 • Cocucci, 1964 • Dahlgren, 1915a • Dumée, 1910 • Duthrie, 1915 • Elfving, 1879 • Fleischer, 1874 • Francini, 1930, 1931, 1945 • Friemann, 1910 • Fuchs and Ziegenspeck, 1924, 1927 • Geitler, 1956 • Gilliland, 1960 • Goebel, 1880 • L. Guignard, 1882c, 1884, 1886c,d, 1891, 1897,

1915 • Hagerup, 1944, 1945, 1947 • Hall, 1902 • Heusser, 1914, 1915 • Hildebrand, 1863 • K. Hoffman, 1929, 1930 • Hofmeister, 1849, 1861, 1876 • Hubert, 1896 • Hurst, 1900 • Irmisch, 1853 • Johansen, 1950 • Johow, 1885, 1889 • Krupko, Israelstam, and Martinovic, 1954 • Kusano 1915 • Leavitt, 1900, 1901 • P. Maheshwari and Narayanaswami, 1951 • Modilewski, 1918 • Montéverdé, 1880 • Müller, 1847 • Nawaschin, 1900a,c • Niimoto and Sagawa, 1961, 1962 • Pace, 1907, 1909, 1914 • B. Palm, 1915, 1920 • Pastrana and Santos, 1931 • Pfitzer, 1880 • Poddubnaja-Arnoldi, 1964b • Prosina, 1930b • A. N. Rao, 1964b • Razmologov, 1958 • Reichenbach, 1852 • Rohrbach, 1866 • Sagawa and Niimoto, 1961 • Schacht, 1850 • Semianinova, 1925 • Seshagiriah, 1932a,b, 1941 • Sharp, 1912 • Soltwedel, 1882 • Stenar, 1937c, 1940 • Strasburger, 1877, 1878, 1879b, 1884b, 1900a • Süssenguth, 1919, 1923 • Swamy, 1941b, 1942b,c, 1943a,b, 1944d, 1945a, 1946a,c,f, 1947, 1948a,b, 1949a,b • Treub, 1879, 1883b,f • Tuschnajakowa, 1929 • Vermoesen, 1911 • Vesque, 1878 • Ward, 1880a • Wille, 1886 • Wirth and Withner, 1959 • Yamaha, 1926.

OROBANCHACEAE

The anther is tetrasporangiate with a persistent epidermis and its wall development conforms to the Dicotyledonous type. The endothecium usually develops fibrous thickenings which in *Aeginetia* are also formed on some cells of the epidermis and outer middle layer, but in *Cistanche* the endothecial cells merely become thick-walled. In *Aeginetia* and *Cistanche* there are 2 middle layers and the outer persists, but in *Orobanche* only occasional cells of the single middle layer divide periclinally. The cells of the glandular tapetum become at least 2-nucleate and in *Orobanche* the 4–6 nuclei undergo fusions which restores the 1- or 2-nucleate condition. Simultaneous cytokinesis in the microspore mother cells follows meiosis and the microspore tetrads are tetrahedral, isobilateral, or decussate. Pollen grains are 2-celled when shed.

The ovule is anatropous, unitegmic, and tenuinucellar. The archesporial cell functions directly as the megaspore mother cell in which cytokinesis accompanies meiosis and the chalazal megaspore of a linear tetrad develops into a Polygonum type embryo sac. The synergids are hooked and exhibit the filiform apparatus in *Cistanche tubulosa*, the polar nuclei fuse just before or at fertilization, and the remains of the 3 antipodal cells persist throughout embryogeny. Starch grains occur in the embryo sac and an endothelium is differentiated.

Endosperm formation is *ab initio* Cellular with the formation of terminal haustoria. The aggressive micropylar haustorium is 2-celled and its branches penetrate the integument whereas the chalazal haustorium is binucleate and less active.

Embryogeny conforms to the Onagrad type but the embryo is undifferentiated in the mature seed.

Bernard, 1903 • Brooks, 1960 • Carter, 1928 • Caspary, 1854 • Cassera, 1935 • Cooke and Shively, 1904 • Crété, 1942 • 1951d, 1955f • Dahlgren, 1938 • Finn and Rudenko, 1930 • Gates, 1925 • Gates and Latter, 1927 • Glišić, 1929, 1931–1932 • Gourgenov, 1928 • Heinricher, 1896, 1931 • Hofmeister, 1851, 1858b, 1859 • Jönsson, 1879–1880 • Juliano, 1935c • Kadry, 1952, 1953, 1955 • Koch, 1877b,c, 1878, 1887 • Kusano, 1908 • Persidsky, 1926 • T. Rudenko, 1930 • Schacht, 1850 • E. Schmid, 1906 • A. C. Smith, 1904 • G. L. Srivastava, 1939 • Tiagi, 1950, 1951b, 1952a,b, 1963 • Wordsell, 1897.

OXALIDACEAE

The anther is tetrasporangiate. The endothecium develops fibrous thickenings, the 1 or 2 middle layers are ephemeral, and the cells of the glandular tapetum become 2–4-nucleate. Ubisch granules have been reported in *Oxalis rosea*. Simultaneous cytokinesis in the megaspore mother cells follows meiosis and the microspore tetrads are tetrahedral or decussate. Pollen grains are 3-celled when shed in *Oxalis* but 2-celled in *Biophytum*.

The ovule is anatropous, bitegmic, and tenuinucellar, with the micropyle formed by both integuments, and in *Biophytum* the outer integument is prolonged into a long, tubular structure. The archesporial cell functions directly as the megaspore mother cell in which cytokinesis accompanies meiosis and the chalazal megaspore of a linear or T-shaped tetrad develops into a Polygonum type embryo sac. The synergids are pyriform and hooked in *Biophytum*, the polar nuclei fuse at fertilization, and the 3 antipodal cells degenerate soon after.

Endosperm formation is Nuclear but later the tissue becomes cellular following peripheral wall formation.

Embryogeny conforms to the Asterad type and in *O. corniculata* the formation of a multicellular suspensor has been reported.

Billings, 1901 • Dahlgren, 1915a • Elfving, 1879 • Fleischer, 1874 • Gorczynski, 1929 • Govindappa and Boriah, 1956 • H. S. Hammond, 1908 • Hofmeister, 1858b, 1859 • Jönsson, 1879–1880, 1881 • Krupko, 1944 • Mauritzon, 1934d • L. L. Narayana, 1962 • Noll, 1935 • Samuelsson, 1913 • Schürhoff, 1924b • Soltwedel, 1882 • Souèges, 1939f • Thathachar, 1942a • Ubisch, 1927 • Vignoli, 1937a.

PAEONIACEAE

The anther is tetrasporangiate with a glandular tapetum but the development and structure of its wall have not been described. Simultaneous cytokinesis in the microspore mother cells follows meiosis and the pollen grains are 2-celled when shed.

The ovule is anatropous, bitegmic, and crassinucellar, with the micropyle formed by both integuments. The hypodermal cells of the multicellular archesporium each cut off a primary parietal cell and about 9 parietal layers are formed, in addition to a nucellar cap 3 cells in thickness derived from periclinal divisions of the apical nucellar epidermal cells. Meiosis accompanied by cytokinesis takes place in all or most of the megaspore mother cells and the chalazal megaspore of each linear or T-shaped tetrad begins development into a Polygonum type embryo sac. Up to 4 mature embryo sacs are formed and Yakovlev and Yoffe (1959) reported fusion between them. The synergids exhibit the filiform apparatus, the polar nuclei fuse early, and the 3 antipodal cells may persist during early postfertilization stages. A hypostase is differentiated and an aril develops from the funicle.

Endosperm formation is Nuclear but after walls are formed at the micropylar pole, the tissue becomes cellular except in the chalazal extremity which elongates as a haustorium.

Embryogeny in *Paeonia* spp. has been the subject of considerable controversy. According to Yakovlev and Yoffe (1957), Cave et al. (1961), Matthiessen (1962), and Walters (1962) division of the zygotic nucleus is not followed by wall formation and the proembryo becomes coenocytic. After the formation of a considerable number of nuclei, walls develop and certain peripheral cells give rise to embryonal primordia. Murgai (1959, 1962), however, reported wall formation after division of the zygote nucleus and considered that the large coenocytic cell, *cb*, had been mistaken for the whole proembryo and the small cell, *ca*, had been overlooked because of its degeneration soon after its formation. Agreement between workers has now been reached that the embryo is formed by budding from *cb*. Although more than one embryo sac may be fertilized and several embryonal initials originate from each proembryo, usually only one embryo in each ovule completes development.

Camp and Hubbard, 1963 • Cave, Arnott, and Cook, 1961 • Dahlgren, 1915a • Dark, 1936 • Hofmeister, 1858 • Huss, 1906 • Jönsson, 1879–1880, 1881 • Kumazawa, 1935 • Matthiessen, 1962 • Moskov, 1964 • Murgai, 1959, 1962 • B. Palm, 1915 • Stebbins, 1938 • Strasburger, 1884b • Walters, 1962 • Wefelscheid, 1911 • Wille, 1886 • Yakovlev and Yoffe, 1957, 1959.

PALMACEAE

The anther is tetrasporangiate with a persistent epidermis. The endothecium develops fibrous thickenings, the 2–6 middle layers are ephemeral, and the glandular tapetum may become irregularly 2-layered. Simultaneous cytokinesis in the microspore mother cells follows meiosis, except in *Nipa fruticans* and *Pinanga disticha* where the successive type has been reported. The microspore tetrads are isobilateral, tetrahedral, or, occasionally, T-shaped or linear and the pollen grains are 2-celled when shed.

The ovule is anatropous to hemianatropous, bitegmic, and crassinucellar, with the micropyle formed by both integuments. The archesporial cell cuts off a primary parietal cell which in *Hyphaene indica* and *Nipa fruticans* forms a single parietal layer, but at least 2 layers are commonly present and up to 6 have been reported in *Areca catechu* and *Cocos nucifera*. In addition, the apical cells of the nucellar epidermis may divide periclinally and form a nucellar cap. In most species cytokinesis in the megaspore mother cell accompanies meiosis and the chalazal megaspore of a linear tetrad develops into a Polygonum type embryo sac. In *Chaemodorea latifolia*, *Hyphaene indica*, and *Nipa fruticans*, however, wall formation does not follow the homotypic nuclear division and an Allium type embryo sac results. The synergids are pyriform, the polar nuclei fuse before fertilization, and the 3 antipodals may remain as naked nuclei (*Hyphaene indica*) or form cells which in *Calyptocalyx* and *Pinanga* become 2- or 3-nucleate before they degenerate. Although the antipodals are usually ephemeral, they persist into early embryogeny in *Nephrosperma* and *Verschaffeltia* whereas in *Areca catechu* they become aggressive and are possibly haustorial.

Endosperm formation is Nuclear but later it becomes cellular although in *Cocos nucifera* wall formation does not extend to the center of the embryo sac and the peripheral endosperm cells divide actively and function as a meristematic layer.

Embryogeny conforms to the Onagrad type in *Actinophloeus* and *Areca* but the Asterad type in *Chamaerops*.

A. Abraham and Mathew, 1963 • Bauch, 1911 • Bosch, 1947 • Cutter and Freeman, 1954 • Cutter, Katherine, and Freeman, 1955 • Drude, 1877 • M. Dutt, 1953, 1955 • Gassner, 1941 • Gatin, 1905c, 1906 • Guevara, 1961 • J.-L. Guignard, 1961b, 1962a • Harling, 1958 • Henry, 1956 • Jönsson, 1879–1880 • Juliano and Quisumbing, 1931 • Kajale and Ranade, 1952, 1953 • Karsten, 1891 • Knapp, 1959 • Lloyd, 1910 • Long, 1943 • Lötscher, 1905 • Mahabale and Chennaveeraiah, 1957 • Nambiar and Swaminathan, 1960 • Osenbrüg, 1894 • B. Palm, 1920 • Poerck, 1950 • Quisumbing and Juliano, 1927 • Radermacher, 1924 • Santos, 1928 • Schnarf, 1931a • Schürhoff, 1926b • Söderberg, 1919 • Süssenguth, 1919, 1921b • Swamy, 1942a • Tischler, 1900 • Venkata Rao, 1955b,c, 1956, 1958 • Voigt, 1888.

PANDACEAE

Embryologically unknown.

PANDANACEAE

The development of the anther and pollen grains has not been investigated but the tapetum is glandular and the pollen grains are 2-celled when shed.

The ovule is anatropous, bitegmic, and crassinucellar, with the micropyle formed by the inner integument except in *Freycinetia javanica* where both integuments are involved. The archesporial cell cuts off a primary parietal cell which in *Pandanus* forms 3 or 4 cell layers and the apical cells of the nucellar epidermis divide periclinally to form a nucellar cap 3 or 4 cells in thickness. In *Freycinetia*, however, the cells elongate radially and only a few undergo a periclinal division. Cytokinesis in the megaspore mother cell accompanies meiosis in *Freycinetia* where the chalazal megaspore of a linear or T-shaped tetrad develops into a Polygonum type embryo sac. In *Pandanus*, however, wall formation after the homotypic division is suppressed and an Allium type embryo sac is formed whose constitution is complicated by the addition of migrating nuclei from adjacent nucellar cells. In *Freycinetia* the polar nuclei fuse normally and 3 small antipodal cells are formed, but in *Pandanus*, according to Campbell (1911), the upper polar nucleus fuses with a varying number of nuclei from the chalazal region and 64 or more antipodal cells may form, but according to Stromberg (1956), up to 200 antipodals are secondarily added by migrating nuclei. A hypostase is differentiated.

Endosperm formation is Nuclear and a large number of nuclei are present before the tissue becomes cellular in a centripetal manner.

Embryogeny has not been investigated but in *Pandanus* the embryo is small and undifferentiated in the mature seed.

Campbell, 1908, 1909, 1910, 1911 • Fagerlind, 1940a • Harling, 1958 • Solms-Laubach, 1878a • Strasburger, 1884b • Stromberg, 1956.

PAPAVERACEAE

The anther is tetrasporangiate with a persistent epidermis. The endothecium develops fibrous thickenings, the 1—3 middle layers are usually ephemeral, but in *Argemone* the outermost layer persists and some of its cells may develop fibrous thickenings similar to those of the endothecium. The cells of the glandular tapetum become multinucleate followed by nuclear fusions. In *Argemone* the tapetum may become irregularly 2- or 3-layered following periclinal wall formation after nuclear division. Simultaneous cytokinesis in the microspore mother cells follows meiosis and the microspore tetrads are tetrahedral, isobilateral, or decussate. Pollen grains are 2-celled when shed in *Argemone, Eschscholtzia,* and *Sanguinaria* but 3-celled in *Papaver,* and those of *Eschscholtzia* contain numerous starch grains.

The ovule is anatropous, bitegmic, and crassinucellar, with the micropyle formed by both integuments. A multicellular archesporium is common but only one cell is functional and cuts off a primary parietal cell which forms 2–5 parietal layers. In addition, the apical cells of the nucellar epidermis divide periclinally to form a nucellar cap about 3 cells in thickness. Cytokinesis in the megaspore mother cell accompanies meiosis and the chalazal megaspore of a linear or T-shaped tetrad develops into a Polygonum type embryo sac. The synergids are hooked and exhibit the filiform apparatus, the polar nuclei fuse before fertilization, and the 3 antipodal cells continue to enlarge after fertilization and may persist until the endosperm has become cellular. In *Papaver somniferum* fertilization takes place 48 hours after pollination.

Endosperm formation is Nuclear and in *Eschscholtzia californica* nuclear fusions in the chalazal region form large irregular masses which remain in the free-nucleate condition for a considerable time after the remainder of the endosperm has become cellular.

Embryogeny conforms to the Solanad type but in *Argemone* the early cleavages are very irregular. Polyembryony has been reported in *Argemone.*

A. V. Beatty, 1940, 1943 • Bose, 1937 • Bose and Banerji, 1933 • Carano, 1911 • Crété, 1956g, 1957b • Elfving, 1879 • Hegelmaier, 1878, 1885 • Hubert, 1896 • Huss, 1906 • Il'ina, 1961, 1962a • A. C. Joshi, 1933 • Ljungdahl, 1922 • Mottier, 1905 • A. N. Rao, and Shamanna, 1963 • Sachar, 1953, 1955, 1956a • Sachar and Mohan Ram, 1958 • B. Schmid, 1902 • Shaw, 1904 • Souèges, 1926d,e,g, 1928, 1936e, 1937j, 1948a, 1949b,c • Strasburger, 1884b • Sulmont and Lebegue, 1964 • Surface, 1905 • Vesque, 1878, 1879b • Vilcins and Abele, 1927 • Warming, 1873, 1878.

PAPILIONACEAE

The anther is tetrasporangiate with a persistent epidermis and its wall development follows the Dicotyledonous type. The endothecium develops fibrous thickenings, the 1 or 2 middle layers are ephemeral, and the cells of the glandular tapetum remain 1-nucleate. In *Milletia ovalifolia* the tapetum may become irregularly 2-layered when a periclinal division accompanies a nuclear division. Simultaneous cytokinesis in the microspore mother cells follows meiosis and the microspore tetrads are tetrahedral, isobilateral, or decussate. Pollen grains are

2- or 3-celled when shed, both conditions occurring in *Clitoria*, and *in situ* germination takes place in the cleistogamous flowers of *Phaseolus vulgaris*. Polysiphonous pollen grains have been reported in *Lupinus*.

The ovule is anatropous, hemianatropous, amphitropous, or campylotropous, bitegmic, and crassinucellar, with the micropyle formed by both integuments and often markedly zigzag. A multicellular archesporium is common but only 1 cell is functional and cuts off a primary parietal cell which forms at least 2 parietal layers. The apical cells of the nucellar epidermis may divide periclinally and form a nucellar cap. Cytokinesis in the megaspore mother cell accompanies meiosis and the chalazal megaspore of a linear or T-shaped tetrad develops into a Polygonum type embryo sac. The synergids are hooked in *Gliricidia* and those of *Milletia* exhibit the filiform apparatus. The polar nuclei fuse before fertilization, the 3 antipodal cells are ephemeral, and the embryo sac of *Arachis hypogaea* contains many starch grains. In *Trifolium pratense* Hindmarsh (1964) has reported embryo sac development by somatic apospory.

Endosperm formation is Nuclear but the extent to which it becomes cellular is very variable and the development of a chalazal haustorium is usual. In *Lathyrus annuus* and *Stylosanthes mucronata* wall formation is suppressed and the endosperm remains free-nuclear, but in most species cell formation is initiated at the micropylar pole and proceeds toward the base. In *Cyamopsis psoralioides, Desmodium laburnaefolium,* and *D. pulchellum* even the chalazal haustorium becomes cellular but usually this remains free-nuclear, although in *D. gangeticum* it is partly cellular. In *Arachis hypogaea* the haustorium is rudimentary, degenerating while the endosperm in the embryo sac is still free-nuclear, and a lateral haustorium has been reported in *Rothia trifoliata*. An endothelium is usually differentiated although it is absent in *Crotalaria* and *Lupinus*, and in *Vigna catjang* Rau (1951a) has described similar layers being formed successively by the nucellus and inner integument. A "barrier tissue" in the chalaza has been reported in *Clitoria, Dalbergia, Glycine, Indigofera, Pongamia,* and *Tephrosia,* where it obstructs the growth of the chalazal haustorium.

Embryogeny conforms either to the Onagrad, Asterad, or Caryophyllad type and the suspensor shows great variation between and, sometimes, within species. In *Milletia ovalifolia* Pal (1960) reported that the suspensor may be either a small globular structure or narrow and very elongated, but sometimes it is rudimentary and composed only of a few hypertrophied cells. In *Medicago, Orobus, Pisum,* and

Vigna, however, the suspensor cells are large and coenocytic. Polyembryony in *Trifolium pratense* is often associated with multiple embryo sac formation but cleavage polyembryony has been described in *Crotalaria sagittalis.*

Atabekova, 1957 • Atabekova and Ling, 1962, 1963 • Banerjee and Datta, 1960 • Banerji, 1938 • Banerji and Samal, 1963 • Baranetzky, 1880 • Baum, 1948a • Bocsa and Mandy, 1964 • Braun, 1860 • Brink and Cooper, 1936 • M. M. Brown, 1917 • Bruyne, 1906 • Buscalioni, 1898 • Castetter, 1925 • Chandravadana, 1963, 1965 • Chubirko, 1952, 1962, 1964 • H. S. Coe and Martin, 1920 • M. T. Cook, 1924b • D. C. Cooper, 1933a, 1935b, 1938 • D. C. Cooper and Brink, 1940 • D. C. Cooper, Brink, and Albrecht, 1937 • Corti, 1930a, 1946, 1950 • Crété, 1951a,b, 1953b, 1958b • Danilina, 1959 • Das, 1953 • Dnyansagar, 1956 • Elfving, 1879 • Farley and Hutchinson, 1941 • Fedortschuk, 1935, 1944 • Fridriksson and Bolton, 1963 • Gerassimova-Navashina, 1959b • Goursat, 1961a,b,c • Greenshields, 1951, 1954 • R. P. Gregory, 1905 • L. Guignard, 1880b, 1881c,d, 1882a • H. W. Hansen, 1953 • Hanson, 1943, 1953 • Hanson and Cope, 1955 • Haque, 1946 • Hegelmaier, 1880a, 1885, 1886 • Hindmarsh, 1964 • Ho, 1963 • Hofmeister, 1849, 1858a • Jagannathrao and Subramanyam, 1934 • Jaranowski, 1961, 1962a,b • B. M. Johri and Garg, 1956, 1959 • Jönsson, 1879–1880, 1881, 1883 • A. C. Joshi, 1938 • Julen, 1950 • Kapuskar, 1959, 1964 • Kastikova, 1955, 1959 • Kempanna and Sastry, 1958 • J. C. Kirkwood, 1926 • Kozlov, 1954 • Latter, 1925, 1926 • Ledingham, 1940 • Maleeva, 1960 • J. N. Martin, 1913, 1914 • Mlyniec, 1961 • Moggi, 1950 • Nagl, 1962 • Němec, 1910a • O. Neumann, 1939 • Nikolov, 1963 • B. P. Pal, 1963 • B. P. Pal and Rao, 1941 • N. Pal, 1960 • Palamarchuk, 1959 • Pandey, 1955 • Pantulu, 1941, 1942 • J. S. Patel and Narayana, 1935 • Paul and Datta, 1950a • Poljakova, 1958 • Povilaitis and Boyes, 1956a,b, 1959, 1960 • S. Prakash, 1960a • M. A. Rau, 1950c,d, 1951a,b,c,d,e,f, 1953, 1954a,b, 1955 • E. L. Reed, 1924 • Reeve, 1948 • Reeves, 1930a,b • Roscoe, 1927a • B. Roy, 1933 • Samal, 1936 • Sato, 1956a,b, 1957, 1958 • Schindler, 1913 • Schleiden and Vogel, 1838 • Sciple and Johnston, 1963 • Scrobischewski, 1884 • N. K. Sen and Krishnan, 1961 • T. C. Shukla, 1954 • Silow, 1931 • Singh, 1958, 1959 • B. W. Smith, 1946, 1950, 1954, 1956a,b • Soltwedel, 1882 • Souèges, 1927a,b,c,d, 1929a,b,c, 1946d,e,f,g,i, 1947a,d,f,g,h, 1948b, 1949a,d, 1950c,d, 1951a, 1953c,d, 1955c, 1956a,b • Sterling, 1955a,b • Strasburger, 1875, 1879b, 1880a, 1882b, 1884b • Tischler, 1903a • Tulasne, 1855 • Valle, 1959 • Valle, Salminen, and Huokuna, 1960 • Vasil, 1962 • Veillet-Bartoszewska, 1956a,b • Voroshilova, 1964 • Ward, 1880b • Warming, 1873 • Weinstein, 1926 • Wille, 1886 • Young, 1905 • Zamotailov, 1960.

PARNASSIACEAE

The anther is tetrasporangiate but the development and structure of its wall have not been described. Simultaneous cytokinesis in the microspore mother cells follows cytokinesis and the microspore tetrads are tetrahedral. Pollen grains are 2-celled when shed.

The ovule is anatropous, bitegmic, and tenuinucellar, with the micropyle formed by both integuments. The archesporial cell functions directly as the megaspore mother cell in which the chalazal megaspore of a linear tetrad develops into a Polygonum type embryo sac. The synergids in *Parnassia palustris* are hooked and exhibit the filiform apparatus, the polar nuclei fuse before fertilization, and in *P. nubicola* the 3 antipodal cells are large and may undergo secondary multiplication to form about 5 cells.

Endosperm formation is Nuclear but the tissue later becomes cellular.

Embryogeny conforms to the Asterad type.

Chodat, 1903, 1904, 1907 • Eichinger, 1908 • Lebègue, 1953a • Mauritzon, 1933a • Pace, 1912 • Saxena, 1964b.

PASSIFLORACEAE

The anther is tetrasporangiate with a persistent epidermis. The endothecium develops fibrous thickenings, the 2 or 3 middle layers are ephemeral, and the cells of the glandular tapetum become multinucleate followed by nuclear fusions. In *Passiflora foetida* the tapetum becomes irregularly 2-layered when a periclinal division follows a nuclear division. Simultaneous cytokinesis in the microspore mother cells follows meiosis and the microspore tetrads are tetrahedral or isobilateral. Pollen grains are 2-celled when shed.

The ovule is anatropous, bitegmic, and crassinucellar, with the micropyle formed by both integuments. The archesporial cell cuts off a primary parietal cell which forms up to 20 parietal layers below the epidermis. Cytokinesis in the megaspore mother cell accompanies meiosis and the chalazal megaspore of a linear tetrad develops into a Polygonum type embryo sac. The synergids are hooked and may exhibit the filiform apparatus, the polar nuclei fuse before fertilization, and the 3 antipodal cells are ephemeral. The pollen tube is persistent and Cook (1909b) reported an instance in *P. adenophylla* where its convolutions filled the embryo sac.

Endosperm formation is Nuclear with aggregations of nuclei in dense cytoplasm at both ends of the embryo sac. Wall formation is centripetal and the endosperm finally becomes cellular throughout. In *P. foetida* the tissue is ruminate.

Embryogeny usually conforms to the Onagrad type but Padhye (1963) reported that in about 70% of the ovules of *P. foetida* the proembryonic development was of the Piperad type. The mature seed is enclosed in a succulent aril which originates from the funicle.

M. T. Cook, 1909b • Hofmeister, 1848, 1856, 1858, 1867 • Juel, 1915 • Kratzer, 1918 • Padhye, 1963 • Padhye and Deshpande, 1960 • Raju, 1952b, 1956a • D. Singh, 1961a, 1962b • Strasburger, 1889 • Warming, 1878.

PEDALIACEAE

The anther is tetrasporangiate with a persistent epidermis and its wall development conforms to the Dicotyledonous type. The endothecium develops fibrous thickenings, 2 or 3 ephemeral middle layers are formed, and the cells of the glandular tapetum become multinucleate. In *Pedalium murex* nuclear fusions occur and each tapetal cell finally contains a single polyploid nucleus. Ubisch granules have been reported in *Sesamum indicum*. Simultaneous cytokinesis in the microspore mother cells follows meiosis and the microspore tetrads are tetrahedral, isobilateral, decussate, or occasionally T-shaped. Pollen grains are 3-celled when shed.

The ovule is anatropous, unitegmic, and tenuinucellar. The archesporial cell functions directly as the megaspore mother cell in which cytokinesis accompanies meiosis and the chalazal megaspore of a linear tetrad develops into a Polygonum type embryo sac. The syngergids are elongated and pyriform, the polar nuclei fuse before fertilization, and the 3 antipodal cells are ephemeral. An endothelium encloses the lower two-thirds of the embryo sac and a hypostase is formed.

Endosperm formation is *ab initio* Cellular with terminal haustoria. The micropylar haustorium is short and 2- or 4-celled and the aggressive chalazal haustorium either is composed of 4 elongated cells (*Sesamum*) or is 4-nucleate (*Pedalium*).

Embryogeny follows the Onagrad type and a slender uniseriate suspensor is formed.

Balicka-Iwanowska, 1899 • Glück, 1940 • Hanawa, 1953 • Mauritzon, 1936a • Nohara, 1934 • Oliver, 1888 • Raghavan and Krishnamurty, 1947 • S. P. Singh, 1960a,b, 1963 • A. R. Srinivasan, 1942 • R. N. Srivastava, 1954.

PELLICIERACEAE

Embrylogically unknown.

PENAEACEAE

The development of the anther and pollen grains has not been described.

The ovule is anatropous, bitegmic, and crassinucellar, with the micropyle formed by both integuments. The archesporial cell cuts off a primary parietal cell which forms about 5 parietal layers below the nucellar epidermis. In *Brachysiphon, Penaea,* and *Sarcolla* cytokinesis in the megaspore mother cell does not accompany meiosis and the embryo sac is of the tetrasporic 16-nucleate Penaea type. Four quartets of nuclei are arranged in a cruciform manner and at cytokinesis one nucleus from each quartet moves to the center of the embryo sac and fusion results in a large $4n$ secondary nucleus, while the remaining nuclei of each quartet become organized into 3 cells which resemble an egg apparatus.

Endosperm formation is Nuclear but walls are formed when the embryo reaches the globular stage and the tissue becomes cellular.

Embryogeny conforms to the Asterad type but a suspensor is lacking. Stephens (1909) reported the occasional formation of embryos at the sides of the embryo sac, which suggests that each lateral group of cells may sometimes function as an egg apparatus.

Stephens, 1908, 1909a,b.

PENTADIPLANDRACEAE

Embryologically unknown.

PENTAPHYLACACEAE

The development and structure of the anther and pollen grains have not been investigated.

The ovule of *Pentaphylax euryoides* is anatropous, bitegmic, and crassinucellar, with the long micropyle formed by the inner integument. The archesporial cell is assumed to cut off a primary parietal cell but the parietal tissue is small in amount. There is no information on the development of the embryo sac, which is 8-nucleate and becomes curved.

Endosperm formation and embryogeny are unknown.

Mauritzon, 1936d.

PERIDISCACEAE

Embryologically unknown.

PERIPLOCACEAE

The anther is tetrasporangiate and its wall development conforms to the Dicotyledonous type. The endothecium develops fibrous thickenings, the 1 or 2 middle layers are ephemeral, and the cells of the glandular tapetum remain 1-nucleate (*Hemidesmus*) or become 2-nucleate (*Cryptostegia*). Simultaneous cytokinesis in the microspore mother cells follows meiosis and the microspore tetrads are tetrahedral, isobilateral, T-shaped, or linear. Pollen grains are 2-celled when shed in *Cryptostegia grandiflora* but 3-celled in *Hemidesmus indicus*, and are retained in permanent tetrads.

The ovule is anatropous, unitegmic, and tenuinucellar. The archesporial cell functions directly as the megaspore mother cell in which cytokinesis accompanies meiosis and the chalazal megaspore of a linear tetrad develops into a Polygonum type embryo sac. The synergids are hooked, the polar nuclei fuse before fertilization, the 3 antipodal cells are ephemeral, and starch grains are present in the embryo sac.

Endosperm formation is Nuclear, but following wall formation, the tissue later becomes cellular throughout.

Embryogeny conforms to the Solanad type and a long slender suspensor is developed.

Dop, 1902, 1903 • L. Guignard, 1903a • Maheswari Devi, 1964 • Nirula and Richharia, 1945 • Pardi, 1933a • Venkata Rao and S. R. Rao, 1954.

PETERMANNIACEAE

Embryologically unknown.

PETIVERIACEAE

The anther is tetrasporangiate with a persistent epidermis and its wall development conforms to the Monocotyledonous type. The endothecium develops fibrous thickenings, the middle layer is ephemeral, and the cells of the glandular tapetum become 2-nucleate. Simultaneous cytokinesis in the microspore mother cells follows meiosis and the microspore tetrads are tetrahedral or isobilateral. Pollen grains are 3-celled when shed.

The ovule is campylotropous, bitegmic, and crassinucellar, with the micropyle formed by the inner integument. The archesporial cell cuts off a primary parietal cell which forms 2 or 3 parietal layers and the apical cells of the nucellar epidermis divide periclinally to form a nucellar cap which may reach 17 cells in thickness at early embryogeny. Cytokinesis in the megaspore mother cell accompanies meiosis, but is often suppressed following the homotypic division in the micropylar dyad cell, and the chalazal megaspore of a linear tetrad or "triad" develops into a Polygonum type embryo sac. The synergids in *Petiveria alliacea* are hooked, the polar nuclei fuse before fertilization, and the 3 antipodal cells are usually ephemeral but those of *Rivina humilis* may undergo secondary multiplication resulting in the formation of up to 6 cells.

Endosperm formation is Nuclear but following wall formation the tissue becomes cellular.

Embryogeny conforms to the Chenopodiad type.

Dambroise, 1947 • A. C. Joshi, 1936a • Kajale, 1954a • Mauritzon, 1934b • Rocén, 1927.

PETROSAVIACEAE

Embryologically unknown.

PHILADELPHACEAE

The development and structure of the anther and pollen grains have not been described.

The ovule is anatropous, unitegmic, and tenuinucellar. The archesporial cell functions directly as the megaspore mother cell in which cytokinesis accompanies meiosis and the chalazal megaspore of a linear tetrad develops into a Polygonum type embryo sac. During its development in *Philadelphus* spp. the upper portion of the embryo sac passes through the micropyle and becomes extra-ovular. The synergids are pyriform, the polar nuclei fuse before fertilization, and the 3 antipodal cells may persist into early postfertilization stages. An endothelium is differentiated around the lower half of the embryo sac.

Endosperm formation is usually *ab initio* Cellular and in *Deutzia* and *Philadelphus* a micropylar haustorium of 2 or 4 much-elongated cells is formed. In *Fendlera*, however, the endosperm is at first Nuclear and the tissue does not become cellular until a few hundred free nuclei have formed.

Embryogeny has not been described.

Elst, 1909 • Gäumann, 1919 • Mauritzon, 1933a, 1939c.

PHILESIACEAE

The anther is tetrasporangiate with a persistent epidermis. The endothecium develops fibrous thickenings, the number of middle layers has not been reported, and the tapetum is probably glandular. Successive cytokinesis in the microspore mother cells accompanies meiosis and pollen grains are 2-celled when shed.

The ovule of *Luzuriaga latifolia* is campylotropous, bitegmic, and crassinucellar, with the micropyle formed by the inner integument. The archesporial cell cuts off a primary parietal cell which forms 2 parietal layers below the nucellar epidermis. Cytokinesis in the megaspore mother cell accompanies meiosis and the chalazal megaspore develops into a Polygonum type embryo sac. The synergids are pyriform, the polar nuclei fuse before fertilization, and the 3 antipodal cells are large.

Endosperm formation and embryogeny have not been investigated.

Stenar, 1952.

PHILYDRACEAE

The anther is bisporangiate. The endothecium develops fibrous thickenings, the 2 or 3 middle layers are ephemeral, and the cells of the glandular tapetum become 2-nucleate. Successive cytokinesis in the microspore mother cells accompanies meiosis and the microspore tetrads are isobilateral. Pollen grains are 2-celled when shed.

The ovule of *Philydrum lanuginosum* is anatropous, bitegmic, and crassinucellar. The archesporial cell cuts off a primary parietal cell which forms a single parietal layer. Cytokinesis in the megaspore mother cell accompanies meiosis and the chalazal megaspore of a linear tetrad develops into a Polygonum type embryo sac. The synergids are hooked, the polar nuclei fuse before fertilization, and the 3 antipodal cells degenerate soon after.

Endosperm formation is Helobial and both chambers later become cellular.

Embryogeny has been described only for the early stages, in which *ca* divides vertically and *cb* transversely, so there is insufficient information to distinguish between Onagrad and Asterad types.

Hamann, 1962, 1963.

PHRYMACEAE

Development and structure of the anther and pollen grains have not been investigated.

The ovule of *Phryma leptostachya* is orthotropous, unitegmic, and tenuinucellar. The archesporial cell functions directly as the megaspore mother cell in which cytokinesis accompanies meiosis and the chalazal megaspore of a linear tetrad develops into a Polygonum type embryo sac. The synergids exhibit the filiform apparatus, the polar nuclei fuse before fertilization, the 3 antipodal cells persist into early postfertilization stages, and starch grains are present in the embryo sac.

Endosperm formation is *ab initio* Cellular with the development of a 4-celled chalazal haustorium, which penetrates the chalaza until it reaches the hypostase.

Embryogeny conforms to the Solanad type and a long slender suspensor is developed.

D. C. Cooper, 1941.

PHYTOLACCACEAE

The anther is tetrasporangiate but the development of its wall has not been described. The cells of the glandular tapetum become multinucleate and simultaneous cytokinesis in the microspore mother cells follows meiosis. Pollen grains are 2- or 3-celled when shed.

The ovule is anacampylotropous, bitegmic, and crassinucellar. The archesporial cell cuts off a primary parietal cell which gives rise to two parietal layers and the apical cells of the nucellar epidermis divide periclinally to form a nucellar cap about 3 cells in thickness. Cytokinesis in the megaspore mother cell accompanies meiosis, although sometimes it does not occur after the homotypic division in the micropylar dyad cell, and the chalazal megaspore of a linear tetrad or "triad" develops into a Polygonum type embryo sac. The synergids are pyriform, the polar nuclei fuse before fertilization, and the 3 antipodal cells may persist into early postfertilization stages.

Endosperm formation is Nuclear but the tissue later becomes cellular.

Embryogeny conforms to the Caryophyllad type in *Phytolacca dioica* but the Onagrad type in *P. decandra*.

Buxbaum, 1949 • Dahlgren, 1916 • Hegelmaier, 1885 • Kajale, 1944c, 1954a • I. F. Lewis, 1905 • Mauritzon, 1934b • Woodcock, 1925.

PICRODENDRACEAE

Embryologically unknown.

PIPERACEAE

The anther is bisporangiate (*Peperomia*) or tetrasporangiate (*Piper, Pothomorphe*) with a persistent epidermis and its wall development conforms to the Monocotyledonous type. The endothecium develops fibrous thickenings, the 1 or 2 middle layers are ephemeral, and the cells of the glandular tapetum become 2-nucleate. In *Piper nigrum* the tapetum may become irregularly 2-layered. Simultaneous cytokinesis in the microspore mother cells follows meiosis and the microspore tetrads are tetrahedral, decussate, or isobilateral. Pollen grains are 2-celled when shed.

The ovule is orthotropous, unitegmic (*Peperomia*) or bitegmic (*Heckleria, Piper*), and crassinucellar, with the micropyle formed by both integuments in *Heckleria* but only the inner in *Piper*. The archesporial cell cuts off a primary parietal cell which forms 2–4 parietal layers below the epidermis. Cytokinesis in the megaspore mother cell does not accompany meiosis and the embryo sac is tetrasporic. In *Heckleria* and *Piper* embryo sac formation is of the Fritillaria type and the synergids are poorly differentiated, the polar nuclei fuse before fertilization, and the antipodal cells undergo secondary multiplication in *Piper*, up to 100 cells being reported in *P. nigrum*. In *Peperomica*, however, embryo sac formation is of the 16-nucleate Peporomia type. The egg and a single synergid are differentiated, and of the remaining nuclei either 8 fuse to form the secondary nucleus and 6 remain at the periphery of the embryo sac or, as in *P. hispidula*, all 14 fuse to form the very large secondary nucleus. Kanta (1961, 1962) has reported a high degree of sterility in *Piper nigrum*, where about half the ovules are not fertilized and in others an accumulation of calcium oxalate crystals appears to prevent division of the zygote, while some otherwise normal ovules were found to contain no sporogenous tissue.

Endosperm formation in *Heckleria* and *Peperomia* is *ab initio* Cellular, but in *Piper* it is Nuclear and later becomes cellular after wall formation is initiated at the periphery of the embryo sac.

Embryogeny conforms to the Piperad type, although in *P. nigrum* the zygote divides occasionally by a transverse wall. The embryo is undifferentiated in the mature seed.

Abele, 1923, 1924 • Balfour, 1957 • W. H. Brown, 1908 • Campbell, 1899a,b, 1901, 1902 • Fagerlind, 1939c,d • G. C. Fisher, 1914 • Gentry, 1955 • Häuser, 1916 • D. S. Johnson, 1900b, 1902a,b,c, 1905, 1907, 1910, 1914 • Jönsson, 1879–1880, 1881 • A. C. Joshi, 1944 • Kanta, 1961, 1962 • P. Maheshwari and Gangulee, 1942 • Martinoli, 1948 • Maugini, 1953 • Murty, 1959a,b • B. Palm, 1915 • Periasamy, 1965 • Süssenguth, 1919 • Swamy, 1944b, 1945b • Täckholm and Söderberg, 1918 • Warming, 1878 • Yoshida, 1960.

PITTOSPORACEAE

Development and structure of the anther have not been described except for the report of a glandular tapetum. Simultaneous cytokinesis in the microspore mother cells follows meiosis and the microspore tetrads are tetrahedral or isobilateral. Pollen grains are 3-celled when shed.

The ovule is anatropous, unitegmic, and tenuinucellar. The archesporial cell functions directly as the megaspore mother cell in which cytokinesis accompanies meiosis except in *Marianthus rigens* and *Sollya heterophylla* where the micropylar dyad cell remains undivided. The chalazal megaspore of a linear tetrad or "triad" develops into a Polygonum type embryo sac in which the polar nuclei fuse before fertilization and the 3 antipodal cells are ephemeral.

Endosperm formation is Nuclear but its later development and that of the embryo have not been investigated.

Bremer, 1915 • Mauritzon, 1939c • Schürhoff, 1929 • Tieghem, 1884.

PLANTAGINACEAE]

Development and structure of the anther have not been described except for the report of a glandular tapetum. Simultaneous cytokinesis in the microspore mother cells follows meiosis and in *Plantago media* the pollen grains are 2-celled when shed.

The ovule is hemianatropous to anatropous, unitegmic, and tenuinucellar. The archesporial cell functions directly as the megaspore mother cell in which cytokinesis accompanies meiosis and the chalazal megaspore of a linear tetrad develops into a Polygonum type embryo sac. The synergids are pyriform and those of *Plantago media* are hooked, the polar nuclei fuse before fertilization, and the 3 antipodal cells usually persist into early postfertilization stages. An endothelium encloses the embryo sac.

Endosperm formation is *ab initio* Cellular with the development of aggressive terminal haustoria. The micropylar haustorium is 4-celled and its branches penetrate the integument whereas the 1-cellular chalazal haustorium is 2-nucleate and in *P. media* it develops a lateral diverticulum.

Embryogeny conforms to the Onagrad type and polyembryony has been reported in *P. lanceolata*.

Balicka-Iwanowska, 1899 • Barnéoud, 1844 • Buscalioni, 1894 • G. O. Copper, 1942a • Crété, 1942 • Ekstrand, 1918 • Elfving, 1879 • Hofmeister, 1858, 1859 • Jönsson, 1879–1880, 1881 • R. C. Misra, 1964 • Nawaschin, 1895a • Rosén, 1940a • Rössler, 1917 • Schnarf, 1917a • Schürhoff, 1924c • Shadowsky, 1924 • Souèges, 1923e, 1926h • Vesque, 1879 • Warming, 1873.

PLATANACEAE

Development and structure of the anther have not been investigated but the tapetum is probably glandular and its cells become 2- or 4-nucleate. Simultaneous cytokinesis in the microspore mother cells follows meiosis, but details of the pollen grains have not been described.

The ovule of *Platanus* is orthotropous, bitegmic, and crassinucellar. The archesporial cell cuts off a primary parietal cell which gives rise to parietal tissue, but the development of the embryo sac has not been described.

Endosperm formation and embryogeny is unknown.

Bretzler, 1924 • Brouwer, 1923, 1924 • Nicoloff, 1911.

PLOCOSPERMACEAE

Embryologically unknown.

PLUMBAGINACEAE

The anther is tetrasporangiate. The endothecium develops fibrous thickenings, the middle layer is ephemeral, and the cells of the glandular (?) tapetum become 2-multinucleate. Simultaneous cytokinesis in the microspore mother cells follows meiosis and the microspore tetrads are tetrahedral or isobilateral. Pollen grains are 2- or 3-celled when shed.

The ovule is anatropous or circinnotropous (*Armeria, Vogelia*), bitegmic, and crassinucellar, with the micropyle formed by the inner integument. The archesporial cell cuts off a primary parietal cell which forms 2 or 3 parietal layers below the nucellar epidermis. Cytokinesis in the megaspore mother cell does not accompany meiosis and the embryo sac is tetrasporic. In *Ceratostigma*, *Plumbago*, and *Vogelia* embryo sac development follows the Plumbago type in which the megaspore nuclei first assume a cruciform arrangement and, after undergoing a postmeiotic mitosis, one nucleus from each group moves to the center of the embryo sac and fusion results in a $4n$ secondary nucleus. The 3 lateral and basal nuclei degenerate soon after becoming enclosed in cells and the mature embryo sac consists of the egg and large secondary nucleus. Fagerlind (1938a) reported the 16-nucleate Penaea type of embryo sac development in *Limonium eu-limonium* but all other species of *Limonium* and *Armeria vulgaris* var. *maritima* conform to the Fritillaria type, with the occasional occurrence of the Adoxa type. *Plumbagella micrantha,* however, has given its name to the Plumbagella type, in which the final postmeiotic mitosis of the Fritillaria type is omitted. After the second 4-nucleate stage of the developing embryo sac cytokinesis occurs and one nucleus becomes the egg, one an antipodal cell, and the remaining 2 nuclei fuse to form the $4n$ secondary nucleus. *Limonium oleaefolium* var. *confusum* and *L. transwallianum* are predominantly apomictic by gonial apospory.

Endosperm formation is Nuclear but the tissue later becomes cellular.

Embryogeny conforms to the Solanad type with the development of a massive multicellular suspensor.

Amato, 1940b,c, 1943, 1949b • Barnéoud, 1844 • Billings, 1901 • Boyes, 1939a,b, 1959 • Boyes and Battaglia, 1951a,b • H. C. Choudhury, 1942 • Claussen, 1919 • Dahlgren, 1915a,c, 1916, 1937 • Fagerlind, 1938a,c, 1939a • Haupt, 1934 • Hjelmqvist and Grazi, 1964 • Jönsson, 1879–1880, 1881 • K. L. Mathur, 1940 • K. L. Mathur and Khan, 1941 • Soltwedel, 1882 • Souèges, 1937d • Tieghem, 1900b • Veillet-Bartoszewska, 1958c • Warming, 1913 • Ya-E., 1941.

PODOACEAE

Embryologically unknown.

PODOPHYLLACEAE

The anther is tetrasporangiate with a persistent epidermis. The endothecium develops fibrous thickenings, the 1–2 middle layers are ephemeral, and the tapetum is probably glandular. Simultaneous cytokinesis in the microspore mother cells follows meiosis and the microspore tetrads are tetrahedral. Pollen grains are 2-celled when shed.

The ovule is anatropous, bitegmic, and pseudocrassinucellar, with the micropyle formed by both integuments. The archesporial cell functions directly as the megaspore mother cell, although the formation of a primary parietal cell has been reported in *Caulophyllum,* and the apical cells of the nucellar epidermis divide periclinally to form a nucellar cap 6 or 7 cells in thickness. Cytokinesis in the megaspore mother cell accompanies meiosis and the chalazal megaspore of a linear tetrad develops into a Polygonum type embryo sac. The synergids exhibit the filiform apparatus, the polar nuclei fuse before fertilization, the 3 antipodal cells in *Jeffersonia diphylla* occupy about half the embryo sac, and starch grains are present.

Endosperm formation is Nuclear with no haustoria.

Embryogeny conforms to the Onagrad type but the early cleavages are irregular in *Podophyllum emodi* and *P. peltatum*.

Andrews, 1895 • Arzt, 1933 • Butters, 1909 • Clark, 1923 • Darlington, 1936 • Holm, 1898 • Huss, 1906 • Koernicke, 1901 • C. E. Lewis, 1904 • Lublinerówna, 1925a,b,c • Mauritzon, 1936f • Mottier, 1897 • Overton, 1905 • Schnarf, 1931a • Täckholm and Söderberg, 1918 • Tören, 1950, 1954.

PODOSTEMACEAE

The anther is tetrasporangiate with a 4-layered wall, including the glandular tapetum. Successive cytokinesis in the microspore mother cells accompanies meiosis and the microspore tetrads are isobilateral or decussate. In *Lawia zeylanica* the tetrads break up into individual microspores but in other members permanent dyads are common. Individual pollen grains are 2-celled when shed.

The ovule is anatropous, bitegmic, and tenuinucellar, with the micropyle formed by the outer integument. The archesporial cell functions directly as the megaspore mother cell in which cytokinesis occurs only after the heterotypic meiotic division and the micropylar dyad cell degenerates. Following the homotypic division the chalazal dyad cell enlarges as the 2-nucleate embryo sac. In *Griffithella, Lawia, Podostemon,* and *Zeylanidium,* the lower nucleus degenerates and the upper one gives rise to 4 nuclei which differentiate as egg, 2 synergids, and a single polar cell or nucleus. Such an embryo sac is commonly referred to as a reduced Allium type but it is also pseudomonosporic, because its 4 nuclei are derived from a single megaspore nucleus. Another variation on the Allium type occurs in *Dicraea,* where both nuclei of the 2-nucleate embryo sac divide and cytokinesis results in the micropylar pair of nuclei being enclosed in 2 superposed cells while the chalazal pair forms juxtaposed cells. The arrangement of cells in this unique type of embryo sac is therefore ⊥-shaped, with the synergid occupying the micropylar pole, the 2 very ephemeral antipodal cells the chalazal pole, and the egg being intermediate in position. Mukkada (1964) considers that this embryo sac is sufficiently distinct to justify the erection of a special type, the Dicraea type.

Endosperm formation does not occur, but below the enlarging megaspore mother cell a large cavity containing dense cytoplasm and free nuclei develops in the nucellus and Mukkada (1962) suggests that this "pseudo-embryo sac" may function as endosperm.

Embryogeny in *Dicraea stylosa* conforms to the Solanad type and *cb* enlarges, becomes 2-nucleate, and gives rise to haustorial caeca which penetrate between the integuments. Similar caeca were reported in *D. elongata* by Magnus (1913).

Carano, 1914b • Cario, 1881 • Chiarugi, 1933 • Dahlgren, 1927c • Erdtman, 1945 • B. L. Hammond, 1937 • W. Magnus, 1913 • S. C. Maheshwari, 1955 • A. C. Martin, 1946 • Mauritzon, 1933b, 1939c • Mukkada, 1962, 1963, 1964 • Razi, 1949, 1955 • Steude, 1935 • Subramanyam, 1962 • Warming, 1882 • Went, 1909, 1910, 1912, 1926, 1929 • Wettstein, 1924.

POLEMONIACEAE

The anther of *Polemonium caeruleum* is tetrasporangiate and its wall development conforms to the Dicotyledonous type. The endothecium develops fibrous thickenings, the middle layer is ephemeral, and the cells of the amoeboid tapetum become 2-nucleate but finally 1-nucleate by fusion. Simultaneous cytokinesis in the microspore mother cells follows meiosis and the microspore tetrads are tetrahedral. Pollen grains are 2-celled when shed.

The ovule is anatropous, unitegmic, and tenuinucellar. The archesporial cell functions directly as the megaspore mother cell in which cytokinesis accompanies meiosis and the chalazal megaspore of a linear tetrad develops into a Polygonum type embryo sac. The synergids are pyriform, the polar nuclei fuse before fertilization, and the 3 antipodal cells are ephemeral. The embryo sac is enclosed in an endothelium.

Endosperm formation is Nuclear, but the tissue later becomes cellular.

Embryogeny follows the Chenopodiad type.

Billings, 1901 • D. C. Cooper, 1933b • Dahlgren, 1922 • Elfving, 1879 • Jönsson, 1879–1880 • Juel, 1915 • H. A. Miller and Wetmore, 1945 • Schnarf, 1921a, 1937b • Schürhoff, 1926b • Souèges, 1939c,g, 1942c, 1945c • Sundar Rao, 1940a.

POLYGALACEAE

The anther is tetrasporangiate, or bisporangiate by reduction, with a persistent epidermis and its wall development in *Epirrhizanthes* follows the Dicotyledonous type. The endothecium develops fibrous thickenings, the 1 or 2 middle layers are ephemeral, and the cells of the glandular tapetum become 2-nucleate. Simultaneous cytokinesis in the microspore mother cells follows meiosis and the microspore tetrads are tetrahedral or isobilateral. The pollen grains are 3-celled when shed in *Polygala vulgaris* and *Salomonia cantoniensis* but otherwise are 2-celled.

The ovule is anatropous to hemianatropous, bitegmic, and crassinucellar, with the micropyle formed usually by both integuments but only the outer is involved in *S. cantoniensis*. The archesporial cell cuts off a primary parietal cell which forms 2–10 parietal layers and usually the apical cells of the nucellar epidermis divide periclinally to form a nucellar cap 3 or 4 cells in thickness. Cytokinesis in the megaspore mother cell accompanies meiosis and the chalazal megaspore of a linear tetrad develops into a Polygonum type embryo sac except in *P. polygama* where Reeves (1957) reported tetrasporic (pseudomonosporic) development. The synergids are frequently hooked and those of *P. sibirica* and *P. vulgaris* exhibit the filiform apparatus. The polar nuclei fuse either before or at fertilization, and although the 3 antipodal cells are usually ephemeral, those of *P. chinensis, P. erioptera,* and *P. sibirica* may persist during early embryogeny. Secondary multiplication resulting in 4 binucleate cells may occur in *P. chinensis,* and in *P. sibirica* 7–12 antipodals are formed. A hypostase is differentiated.

Endosperm formation is Nuclear but the tissue later becomes cellular, although wall development may be delayed considerably in the narrow chalazal extremity.

Embryogeny conforms to the Asterad type.

Chodat, 1891 • Dahlgren, 1916 • Dube, 1962 • Guignard, 1882b • Hofmeister, 1858 • Jauch, 1918 • Karsmark, 1933 • Mauritzon, 1936d • Mukherjee, 1961b • A. N. Rao, 1964 • Reiser, 1911 • J. H. Reeves, 1957 • Schürhoff, 1924b • Shadowsky, 1912 • Souèges, 1941e • Srinivasachar, 1942 • Venkatesh, 1956a • Wirz, 1910.

POLYGONACEAE

The anther is tetrasporangiate with a persistent epidermis and its wall development conforms to the Monocotyledonous type. The endothecium develops fibrous thickenings, the middle layer is ephemeral, and the cells of the glandular tapetum become 2–4 nucleate. Simultaneous cytokinesis in the microspore mother cells follows meiosis and the microspore tetrads are tetrahedral. Pollen grains are 2-celled when shed in *Antigonon leptopus,* but otherwise are 3-celled and contain starch. Those of *Rumex crispus* may germinate *in situ.*

The ovule is orthotropous, bitegmic, and crassinucellar, with the micropyle formed by the inner integument. A multicellular archesporium is common but only one cell cuts off a primary parietal cell which gives rise to 1–3 parietal layers and in *Rumex* some apical cells of the nucellar epidermis may undergo a single periclinal division. Cytokinesis in the megaspore mother cell accompanies meiosis and the chalazal megaspore of a linear (*Antigonon, Polygonum*) or T-shaped (*Rheum, Rumex*) tetrad develops into a Polygonum type embryo sac. Hooked synergids occur in *Rumex dentatus* and those of *Antigonon leptopus* and *Polygonum divaricatum* exhibit the filiform apparatus. The polar nuclei fuse just before fertilization and the 3 antipodal cells are often ephemeral but in *Rumex* they become multinucleate. In *Muhlenbeckia platycladus* the ovules degenerate and the fruit develops parthenocarpically. A hypostase is present in *R. dentatus*.

Endosperm formation is Nuclear but later the tissue becomes cellular from the micropylar pole and in *Fagopyrum esculentum* the chalazal portion remains free-nuclear. The endosperm becomes ruminate in *Coccoloba uvifera*.

Embryogeny conforms to the Asterad type.

Bauer, 1922 • Bhargava and Sawhney, 1958 • Dahlgren, 1916 • Doida, 1960 • Dudgeon, 1918 • Edman, 1929, 1931 • Elfving, 1879 • Fink, 1899 • Hagerup, 1926 • Hegelmaier, 1885 • Hofmeister, 1849 • Jaretsky, 1927, 1928 • Kihara and Ono, 1923 • Lonay, 1922a,b, 1923 • Mahony, 1935, 1936 • Mar'yakhina, Mikulovich, and Baleva, 1961 • Ono, 1928c, 1935 • Periasamy, 1962b, 1964a • V. S. Rao, 1936b • Roth, 1906 • Schacht, 1850 • Schnarf, 1931a • Soltwedel, 1882 • Souèges, 1919a,b,c, 1920a,b, 1924a • Stevens, 1912a,b • Strasburger, 1877, 1879a • Tischler, 1912 • Warming, 1878 • Wefelscheid, 1911 • Wille, 1886 • Woodcock, 1914 • Zhebrak, 1961.

PONTEDERIACEAE

The anther is tetrasporangiate and its innermost wall layer forms the amoeboid tapetum, whose cells become 2-nucleate. Successive cytokinesis in the microspore mother cells accompanies meiosis and the microspore tetrads are isobilateral or decussate. Pollen grains are 2-celled when shed.

The ovule is anatropous, bitegmic, and crassinucellar, with the micropyle formed by both integuments. The archesporial cell cuts off a primary parietal cell which forms a single parietal layer below the epidermis. Cytokinesis in the megaspore mother cell accompanies meiosis and the chalazal megaspore of a linear tetrad develops into a Polygonum type embryo sac. The synergids of *Monochoria hastaefolia* exhibit the filiform apparatus, the polar nuclei fuse before fertilization, and the 3 antipodal nuclei (*M. hastaefolia*) or cells are ephemeral, although their remains commonly persist in an antipodal pocket during postfertilization stages.

Endosperm formation is Helobial. Free-nuclear divisions take place in both chambers and are usually followed by cell formation. In *Monochoria* spp. the large micropylar chamber gives off a pair of broad lateral haustorial arms which extend basally and enclose a column of nucellar tissue. The small chalazal chamber remains free-nuclear in *Monochoria* but in *Eichhornia, Heteranthera,* and *Pontederia* it becomes cellular before degenerating.

Embryogeny conforms to the Asterad type.

Arcangeli, 1897 • Banerji and Gangulee, 1937 • Banerji and Haldar, 1942 • Coker, 1907 • Hofmeister, 1858, 1861 • Juliano, 1931b • Ono, 1926, 1928 • B. Palm, 1920 • Schürhoff, 1922a • R. W. Smith, 1898, 1908 • Wylie, 1917.

PORTULACACEAE

The anther is tetrasporangiate with a persistent epidermis and its wall development conforms to the Monocotyledonous type. The endothecium develops fibrous thickenings, the middle layer is ephemeral, and the cells of the glandular tapetum become 2-nucleate and bear Ubisch granules. Simultaneous cytokinesis in the microspore mother cells follows meiosis and the microspore tetrads are isobilateral or tetrahedral. The pollen grains may contain starch grains and are 2-celled when shed in *Portulaca tuberosa,* but otherwise are 3-celled.

The ovule is anatropous to amphitropous, bitegmic, and crassinucellar, with the micropyle formed by the inner integument. The archesporial cell cuts off a primary parietal cell which forms 3 or 4 parietal layers and the apical cells of the nucellar epidermis may elongate radially while the lateral ones divide periclinally. Cytokinesis in the megaspore mother cell accompanies meiosis and the chalazal megaspore of a linear tetrad develops into a Polygonum type embryo sac. The synergids of *P. quadrifida* are hooked and those of *P. oleracea* exhibit the filiform apparatus. The polar nuclei fuse before or at fertilization, the 3 antipodal cells degenerate early, and starch grains are present in the embryo sac of *P. tuberosa.*

Endosperm formation is Nuclear but later the tissue becomes cellular from the micropylar pole, although in *P. oleracea* a narrow band of free-nuclear endosperm is retained around the embryo. The central part of nucellus, which becomes enclosed by the curvature of the embryo, forms the perisperm of the mature seed.

Embryogeny conforms to the Solanad type in *Portulaca* but in *Claytonia virginica* the Caryophyllad type is more appropriate and the basal cell of the uniseriate suspensor becomes much enlarged. Polyembryony has been reported in *P. oleracea.*

M. T. Cook, 1903a • D. C. Cooper, 1935c, 1940 • Dahlgren, 1916 • Haccius, 1954 • Hofmeister, 1858b • Hubert, 1896 • Kajale, 1942 • Raghavan and Srinivasan, 1941d • Rocén, 1924a, 1927 • Souèges, 1938b, 1945e • Woodcock, 1926a.

POSIDONIACEAE

Embryologically unknown.

POTALIACEAE

Development of the anther and pollen grains has not been investigated. Mohrbutter (1936) has reported that in *Fagraea fragrans* certain tapetal cells extend between the microspore mother cells and become multinucleate with frothy cytoplasm, which may indicate an amoeboid nature. Pollen grains are 2- or 3-celled when shed.

The ovule is anatropous, unitegmic, and tenuinucellar. The archesporial cell functions directly as the megaspore mother cell in which cytokinesis accompanies meiosis and the chalazal megaspore of a linear tetrad develops into a Polygonum type embryo sac. The synergids are pyriform, the polar nuclei fuse at fertilization, and the 3 antipodal cells are ephemeral.

Endosperm formation is Nuclear but embryogeny is unknown.

Mohrbutter, 1936.

POTAMOGETONACEAE

The number of sporangia comprising the anther has not been reported. The epidermis persists, the endothecium develops fibrous thickenings, and the middle layer is ephemeral. The cells of the amoeboid tapetum usually remain 1-nucleate and when an occasional nuclear division is followed by periclinal wall formation the tapetum becomes irregularly 2-layered. Successive cytokinesis in the microspore mother cells accompanies meiosis and the microspore tetrads are isobilateral. Pollen grains are 3-celled when shed.

The ovule is orthotropous, bitegmic, and crassinucellar, with the micropyle formed by the inner integument. The archesporial cell cuts off a primary parietal cell which forms up to 7 parietal layers and some of the apical nucellar epidermal cells may undergo a single periclinal division. Cytokinesis in the megaspore mother cell accompanies meiosis, although it may be suppressed in the micropylar dyad cell, and the chalazal megaspore of a linear or T-shaped tetrad or "triad" develops into a Polygonum type embryo sac. The synergids are broad at their bases, and the secondary nucleus lies close to the 3 antipodal cells. A hypostase occurs in *Potamogeton lucens*.

Endosperm formation is Helobial. The micropylar chamber becomes coenocytic following free-nuclear divisions but later becomes cellular, while the nucleus of the chalazal chamber increases in size and finally degenerates as the chamber becomes crushed.

Embryogeny conforms to the Caryophyllad type and the terminal suspensor cell becomes vesicular.

P. Claussen, 1927 • M. T. Cook, 1908 • Dahlgren, 1927a • B. L. Gupta, 1934 • Hofmeister, 1861 • Holferty, 1901 • Schacht, 1850 • Schürhoff, 1926b • Souèges, 1940e, 1954a • Tischler, 1915 • Wiegand, 1898, 1899, 1900 • Wiśniewska, 1931.

PRIMULACEAE

The anther is tetrasporangiate. The endothecium develops fibrous thickenings, the middle layer is ephemeral, and the cells of the glandular tapetum remain 1-nucleate. Simultaneous cytokinesis in the microspore mother cells follows meiosis, and the microspore tetrads are tetrahedral. Pollen grains are 2-celled when shed and those of *Anagallis pumila* sometimes germinate *in situ*.

The ovule is anatropous to hemianatropous, bitegmic, and tenuinucellar, with the micropyle formed by both integuments. The archesporial cell functions directly as the megaspore mother cell in which cytokinesis accompanies meiosis and the chalazal megaspore of a linear or T-shaped tetrad develops into a Polygonum type embryo sac. The synergids are elongated and pointed, the polar nuclei fuse at fertilization, and whereas the 3 antipodal cells of *Lysimachia vulgaris* are very similar to the synergids, those in *Anagallis* are small and ephemeral. The embryo sac is enclosed by an endothelium.

Endosperm formation is Nuclear but wall formation is initiated soon after division of the zygote and the tissue becomes cellular. In *Anagallis* usually 8 or 16 free nuclei are formed but in *Primula officinalis* Dahlgren (1916) has reported about 1000 nuclei before wall formation.

Embryogeny conforms to the Caryophyllad type and polyembryony by suspensor budding occurs in *P. auriculata*.

Billings, 1901 • Brokschmidt, 1904 • Dahlgren, 1914, 1915a, 1916 • Decrock, 1901 • Digby, 1912 • Duncan, 1873 • Elfving, 1879 • C. H. Farr, 1916 • R. P. Gregory, 1912, 1914 • Hofmeister, 1858 • Hubert, 1896 • Jönsson, 1879–1880, 1881 • Pax, 1882 • Pfeffer, 1872 • Raju, 1953 • Rudenko, 1961a • J. Scott, 1864 • Soltwedel, 1882 • Souèges, 1937a • Veillet-Bartoszewska, 1957a,c, 1963 • Vesque, 1878, 1879 • Warming, 1878, 1913.

PROTEACEAE

The anther is tetrasporangiate. The endothecium develops fibrous thickenings, the 2 or 3 middle layers are ephemeral, and the cells of the glandular tapetum become 2-nucleate. In *Lomatia tinctoria* the tapetum becomes 2-layered on the side of the connective. Simultaneous cytokinesis in the microspore mother cells follows meiosis and the microspore tetrads are tetrahedral or decussate. Pollen grains are 2-celled when shed and those of *Grevillea* and *Orites* contain starch grains. A high degree of pollen dimorphism occurs in *G. vestita*.

The ovules are orthotropous in *Bellendena, Brabejum, Conospermum, Macadamia,* and *Placospermum* but otherwise are hemianatropous to anatropous, bitegmic, and crassinucellar, with the micropyle formed by the inner integument. In *Macadamia ternifolia,* however, the integuments develop very slowly and do not enclose the nucellus until after fertilization. A multicellular archesporium is common and all cells may cut off a primary parietal cell although only one megaspore mother cell is functional except in *Synaphea*. Up to 10 parietal layers are formed and the apical cells of the nucellar epidermis usually divide periclinally to form a nucellar cap 3–8 cells in thickness which may form a conical protuberance. In *Placospermum* and *Synaphea,* however, only occasional cells of the nucellar epidermis divide and a nucellar cap is not formed. Cytokinesis in the megaspore mother cell accompanies meiosis and the chalazal megaspore of a linear or T-shaped tetrad develops into a Polygonum type embryo sac. The synergids are usually hooked and show the filiform apparatus, the polar nuclei fuse at fertilization, and the 3 antipodal cells are ephemeral or persist into early postfertilization stages. In *Protea lepidocarpon* the upper part of the embryo sac projects through the micropyle. Starch grains occur in the embryo sacs of *Conospermum, Grevillea,* and *Placospermum*.

Endosperm formation is Nuclear and wall formation commences at the micropylar pole. The chalazal endosperm remains coenocytic and in *Brabejum, Hakea* and *Macadamia* it gives off haustorial processes which invade the chalaza but in *Grevillea, Lomatia,* and *Orites* it forms a long, convoluted haustorial tube.

Embryogeny conforms to the Asterad type and no suspensor is formed.

Ballantine, 1909 • Brough, 1933 • Garside, 1946 • Haber, 1959 • Hamilton, 1931 • Hofmeister, 1858 • Jordaan, 1946 • Kausik, 1938a,b,e, 1939a, 1940a, 1941b, 1942 • Messeri, 1928 • Schacht, 1850 • Tassi, 1898 • Venkata Rao, 1957, 1960, 1961, 1962, 1963, 1964.

PTEROSTEMONACEAE

Embryologically unknown.

PUNICACEAE

Development and structure of the anther and pollen grains have not been described.

The ovule of *Punica granatum* is anatropous, bitegmic, and crassinucellar, with the micropyle formed by both integuments. The archesporial cell cuts off a primary parietal cell which forms 3 parietal layers, and King (1947) suggests that the apical cells of the nucellar epidermis may also divide periclinally during embryo sac formation. Cytokinesis in the megaspore mother cell accompanies meiosis and the chalazal megaspore of a linear tetrad develops into a Polygonum type embryo sac. The synergids are elongated and usually non-vacuolate, the polar nuclei fuse before fertilization, and the 3 antipodal cells are uninucleate.

Endosperm formation is Nuclear but the embryogeny is unknown.

King, 1947 • Mauritzon, 1939c.

PYROLACEAE

The anther is tetrasporangiate. The nature of the endothecium has not been described but a single middle layer is formed and the cells of the glandular tapetum become at least 2-nucleate. Microsporogenesis has not been described. In *Pyrola secunda* the 2-celled pollen grains are shed singly, but otherwise they adhere in permanent tetrads although those of *Chimaphila* are easily disrupted into single grains.

The ovule is anatropous, unitegmic, and tenuinucellar. The archesporial cell functions directly as the megaspore mother cell in which cytokinesis accompanies meiosis and the chalazal megaspore of a linear tetrad develops into a Polygonum type embryo sac. The synergids are slender with broad bases, the polar nuclei fuse before fertilization, and the 3 antipodal cells are uninucleate. The embryo sac is enclosed by an endothelium.

Endosperm formation is *ab initio* Cellular with the formation of short terminal 1-celled haustoria.

Embryogeny conforms to the Caryophyllad type.

Batygina, Teriokhin, Alimova, and Yakovlev, 1963 • Copeland, 1933, 1947 • Hagerup, 1954 • Hofmeister, 1858b, 1959 • Peltrisot, 1904 • Samuelsson, 1913 • Souèges, 1939e • Strasburger, 1877 • Teriokhin, 1962a,b, 1963 • Warming, 1912.

QUIINACEAE

Embryologically unknown.

RANUNCULACEAE

The anther is tetrasporangiate and its wall development follows the Dicotyledonous type. The endothecium develops fibrous thickenings, the 1 or 2 middle layers are ephemeral, and the cells of the glandular tapetum become 2–4-nucleate. Simultaneous cytokinesis in the microspore mother cells follows meiosis and the microspore tetrads are tetrahedral, isobilateral, or decussate. Pollen grains are 3-celled when shed in *Batrachium longirostris* and *Ranunculus delphinifolius* but otherwise are 2-celled and those of *Batrachium* contain starch grains.

The ovule is hemianatropous in *Ranunculus* but anatropous in other genera, and is unitegmic and pseudocrassinucellar (*Clematis, Myosurus, Ranunculus*) or bitegmic and crassinucellar (*Adonis, Thalictrum*). The archesporial cell either functions directly as the megaspore mother cell or cuts off a primary parietal cell which divides only anticlinally and forms a single parietal layer. The apical cells of the nucellar epidermis divide periclinally and give rise to a nucellar cap 2 or 3 cells in thickness. Cytokinesis in the megaspore mother cell accompanies meiosis and the chalazal megaspore of a linear or T-shaped tetrad usually develops into a Polygonum type embryo sac. In *Adonis aestivalis* and *A. annua*, however, cytokinesis is suppressed following the homotypic division and the chalazal dyad cell forms an Allium type embryo sac. The synergids are large and in *Adonis* and *Clematis* they bear hooks, while those of *A. aestivalis, Hepatica* and *Myosurus* exhibit the filiform apparatus. The polar nuclei fuse before fertilization and the 3 antipodal cells frequently become 2-nucleate, but up to 12 nuclei were reported in each cell of *Hepatica acutiloba* (Mottier, 1895). Secondary multiplication of antipodals has been described only in *Hepatica* and *Trautvettaria*, with 2–5 and 11 cells respectively.

Endosperm formation is Nuclear but the tissue later becomes cellular.

Embryogeny conforms to the Onagrad type but in *R. ficaria* the embryo consists of a club-shaped mass of undifferentiated parenchyma with one cotyledon suppressed.

Arcangeli, 1897 • Bessey, 1898 • Bhandari, 1962, 1963b • Braun, 1860 • Brouland, 1935 • Chamberlain, 1898 • Claussen, 1927 • Coulter, 1898 • Coulter and Chamberlain, 1903 • Dahlgren, 1915a, 1927a • Day, 1896 • Earle, 1938 • Elfving, 1879 • A. S. Foster, 1961 • L. Guignard, 1881b, 1882b, 1884, 1900b, 1901c • Habermann, 1906 • Häfliger, 1943 • Hegelmaier, 1878 • Hérail, 1889 • Hofmeister, 1858 • Huss, 1906 • Jalan and Bhandari, 1963 • Jönsson, 1879–1880 • Kapil and Jalan, 1962 • Kindler, 1914 • E. L. Kordyum, 1959 • Y. L. Kordyum, 1961 • Kuhn, 1928 • Lonay, 1901 • Loschnigg, 1926 • Lötscher, 1905 • G. Mann, 1893 • Marsden-Jones, 1935 • Mellink, 1881 • Metcalfe, 1936 • Mottier, 1895, 1905 • Němec, 1910b • Overton, 1902, 1904, 1905, 1909 • Rassner, 1932 • Riddle, 1905c • Rousi, 1956 • Rutishauser, 1953–1954, 1954 • Salisbury, 1931 • Schmid, 1902 • Schöffel, 1932 • Schürhoff, 1915, 1926b • B. Singh, 1936 • Souèges, 1910a,b,c,d, 1911a,b,c, 1912a,b,c, 1913a,b,c, 1914a • Strasburger, 1879a,b • Swingle, 1908 • E. M. Thomas, 1900b • Tschernoyarow, 1915, 1926 • Vijayaraghavan, 1962 • Vesque, 1878, 1879 • Ward, 1880b • Warming, 1873, 1913 • Westermaier, 1890 • Whyte, 1929 • Wolter, 1933 • Yamaha, 1926.

RAPATEACEAE

Embryologically unknown.

RESEDACEAE

The anther is tetrasporangiate but its wall structure has not been investigated. Simultaneous cytokinesis in the microspore mother cells follows meiosis and the microspore tetrads are isobilateral or tetrahedral. Pollen grains are 2-celled when shed.

The ovule is anatropous to campylotropous, bitegmic, tenuinucellar (*Astrocarpus, Oligomeris, Reseda alba, R. glauca, R. luteola*) or crassinucellar (*R. lutea, R. odorata*). A multicellular archesporium is common and in the crassinucellar species each archesporial cell cuts off a primary parietal cell. Cytokinesis in the functional megaspore mother cell accompanies meiosis and the chalazal megaspore of a linear tetrad develops into a Polygonum type embryo sac. The synergids are hooked, the polar nuclei fuse before fertilization, and the 3 antipodal cells are ephemeral. Multiple embryo sac formation may follow the development of more than one megaspore mother cell and fusion between 2 mature embryo sacs has been reported.

Endosperm formation is Nuclear but the tissue becomes cellular later.

Embryogeny conforms to the Onagrad type and a uniseriate suspensor is formed.

Chhonkar, 1961 • Crété, 1955c • Eigsti, 1937a • Gori, 1957 • L. Guignard, 1893, 1900b • Hennig, 1929 • Hofmeister, 1858 • Morstatt, 1902 • Oksijuk, 1929, 1935, 1937, 1938 • Orr, 1921d • Souèges, 1935e • Strasburger, 1880b.

RESTIONACEAE

The anther is bisporangiate with a persistent epidermis. The endothecium develops fibrous thickenings, the middle layer is ephemeral, and the cells of the glandular (?) tapetum remain 1-nucleate. The pollen grains are 2-celled when shed in *Chondropetalum* but 3-celled in *Hypodiscus*.

The ovule is orthotropous, bitegmic, and tenuinucellar, with the micropyle formed by both integuments. The apical cells of the nucellar epidermis elongate radially but remain as a single layer. The archesporial cell functions directly as the megaspore mother cell, although in *Hypodiscus aristatus* Krupko (1962) reported the presence of a subepidermal layer which was derived, presumably, from a primary parietal cell. Cytokinesis in the megaspore mother cell accompanies meiosis and the chalazal megaspore develops into a Polygonum type embryo sac. The synergids are large and may be hooked and exhibit the filiform apparatus in *Chondropetalum* and *Hypodiscus*. The polar nuclei fuse before or at fertilization and the 3 antipodal cells are usually ephemeral. In *Elegia dodii*, *Restio racemosa*, and *Thamnochortus fruticosus*, however, secondary multiplication occurs and up to 15 antipodal cells are formed and degenerate soon after fertilization. An unusual type of cytokinesis takes place in the embryo sac of *Chondropetalum hookerianum*, where, according to Krupko (1963), cross walls cut off 3-nucleate micropylar and chalazal chambers, in which the egg apparatus and antipodals are then organized. A hypostase is present in *Chondropetalum* and starch grains are present in its embryo sac.

Endosperm formation is Nuclear but the embryogeny is unknown.

Borwein, Coetsee, and Krupko, 1949 • Krupko, 1956–1957, 1962, 1963 • Mlodzianowski, 1964.

RHAMNACEAE

The number of sporangia comprising the anther has not been recorded, but its wall development follows the Basic type. The endothecium develops fibrous thickenings, the 2 middle layers are ephemeral, and the cells of the glandular tapetum become 2–4-nucleate. Ubisch granules have been reported in *Zizyphus jujuba*. Simultaneous cytokinesis in the microspore mother cells follows meiosis and the microspore tetrads are tetrahedral or isobilateral. Pollen grains are 2-celled when shed and those of *Z. rotundifolia* sometimes germinate *in situ*.

The ovule is anatropous, bitegmic, and crassinucellar, with the micropyle usually formed by the outer integument. A multicellular archesporium is common and each cell cuts off a primary parietal cell which gives rise to up to 13 parietal layers. In addition, the apical cells of the nucellar epidermis divide periclinally and form a nucellar cap 5–7 cells in thickness. In *Z. rotundifolia*, the nucellus becomes cone-shaped and its prominent beak protrudes through the micropyle. Cytokinesis in the megaspore mother cell accompanies meiosis in *Colletia, Hovenia, Paliurus,* and *Rhamnus,* where the chalazal megaspore of a linear or T-shaped tetrad develops into a Polygonum type embryo sac. In *Zizyphus,* however, cytokinesis is suppressed after the homotypic division and the chalazal dyad cell forms an Allium type embryo sac. The synergids are hooked and usually exhibit the filiform apparatus, the polar nuclei fuse at about the time of fertilization, and the 3 antipodal cells become enlarged and sometimes coenocytic. A hypostase is present in *Z. rotundifolia,* which also possesses a persistent pollen tube.

Endosperm formation is Nuclear but the tissue later becomes cellular from the micropylar pole, although in *Scutia* and *Zizyphus* the chalazal end of the embryo sac remains free-nuclear.

Embryogeny conforms to the Asterad type in *Ceanothus* and *Rhamnus,* but the Solanad type is followed in *Zizyphus* where polyembryony is of occasional occurrence.

Arora, 1953 · Chiarugi, 1927a, 1930 · Dolcher, 1947 · Juel, 1929 · Kajale, 1944a,b · Lindau, 1891, 1928 · Souèges, 1939d, 1941d · Srinivasachar, 1940b.

RHIZOPHORACEAE

The development of the anther and pollen grains has not been described.

The ovule is anatropous to hemianatropous, bitegmic, and crassinucellar, with the zigzag micropyle formed by both integuments in *Bruguiera, Ceriops,* and *Rhizophora,* although in *Gynotroches* only the inner integument is involved. The archesporial cell cuts off a primary parietal cell which forms 2 parietal layers below the nucellar epidermis. Cytokinesis in the megaspore mother cell accompanies meiosis and the chalazal megaspore of a linear tetrad develops into a Polygonum type embryo sac. The synergids are pyriform, the polar nuclei fuse before fertilization, and the 3 antipodal cells are uninucleate.

Endosperm formation is Nuclear and in *Gynotroches axillaris* it becomes cellular only at the chalazal pole. According to Carey (1934), in *Ceriops candolleana* and *Rhizophora mucronata* the endosperm protrudes through the micropyle, finally reaching the ovary wall, and in *Ceriops* chalazal haustorial processes are formed.

Embryogeny has not been described but in *Ceriops* and *Rhizophora* the suspensor is massive.

Carey, 1934 • M. T. Cook, 1907b • Haberlandt, 1895 • Karsten, 1891 • Kumar, 1942b • Mauritzon, 1939c • Warming, 1883.

RHOIPTELEACEAE

Embryologically unknown.

ROSACEAE

The anther is tetrasporangiate with a persistent epidermis. The endothecium develops fibrous thickenings, the 2 or 3 middle layers are ephemeral, and the cells of the glandular tapetum become 2–8-nucleate. Simultaneous cytokinesis in the microspore mother cells follows meiosis and the microspore tetrads are tetrahedral. Pollen grains are 2-celled when shed.

The ovule is anatropous to hemianatropous, unitegmic (*Adenostoma, Alchemilla, Aphanes, Arunculus, Geum, Holodiscus, Neviusia, Potentilla, Rhodotypus, Rubus, Sibiraea, Spiraea, Ulmaria*) or bitegmic, and crassinucellar. In the bitegmic members the micropyle is formed of both integuments in *Cotoneaster, Cydonia, Neillia, Physocarpus, Pyrus*, and *Sorbaria* but only the inner integument is involved in *Cercocarpus, Chamaebatia, Cowania, Dryas, Exochorda, Gillenia, Nuttallia*, and *Purshia*. Although a multicellular archesporium is common and all cells cut off a primary parietal cell, usually only one megaspore mother cell undergoes further development. Up to 9 parietal layers are formed and the apical cells of the nucellar epidermis divide periclinally to form a nucellar cap 2–7 cells in thickness. Cytokinesis in the megaspore mother cell accompanies meiosis and the chalazal megaspore of a linear tetrad develops into a Polygonum type embryo sac, although in *Rosa* it is usually the micropylar megaspore which is concerned and in *Rubus* any megaspore may function. An unusual condition has been described in *Alchemilla, Aphanes, Cotoneaster, Rubus,* and *Sorbus* where the megaspore mother cell degenerates and is replaced by one or more secondary megaspore mother cells which undergo meiosis and give rise to embryo sacs in the usual way. The synergids are pyriform and the polar nuclei fuse just before fertilization or undergo triple fusion. The 3 antipodal cells are either ephemeral or degenerate during early postfertilization stages, but in *Alchemilla* spp. they may persist into early embryogeny and in *A. orbiculata* they undergo a small amount of secondary multiplication. Starch grains occur in the embryo sac of *Spiraea* and a funicular obturator is developed in *Cotoneaster* and *Malus*. In the family generally, but particularly in the polyploid members, there is a strong tendency to apomixis. One or more nucellar, parietal or nucellar epidermal cells may develop by somatic apospory into unreduced embryo sacs in competition with the sexual one which is often crushed in the process. Gonial apospory also occurs.

Endosperm formation is Nuclear but later the tissue becomes cellular throughout, commencing at the micropylar pole. In *Prunus* and *Rubus*, however, the chalazal part of the embryo sac remains free-nuclear and forms a long, narrow haustorial tube which penetrates the chalaza.

Embryogeny conforms to the Asterad type and polyembryony is of occasional occurrence. A case of vivipary was reported by Mani (1947) in *Pyrus malus* where 8 seedlings about one inch in length were found in a fruit.

Albanese, 1904 • Bessey, 1898 • Böös, 1917, 1920, 1924 • Bradbury, 1929 • Braun, 1860 • Bryant, 1935 • Cherenky, 1962 • Christen, 1950 • Christoff and Papasova, 1943 • Chuvashina and Gorshkova, 1962 • R. D. Cole, 1917 • Czapik, 1961, 1962 • Dermen, 1936 • Dorsey, 1919 • Einset, 1951 • Elfving, 1879 • Elssmann and Veh, 1931 • Esaulova, 1958 • Fagerlind, 1948b • Filimonova, 1962 • Fischer, 1880 • Forenbacher, 1913, 1914 • Gentscheff, 1938 • Gentscheff and Gustafsson, 1940 • Gorczynski, 1934 • Grevtsova, 1962 • L. Guignard, 1882b • Gustafsson, 1930, 1931 • Håkansson, 1946 • Hanstein, 1870 • Harrold, 1935 • Hjelmqvist, 1956a, 1957, 1959a,b, 1962 • Hoar, 1916 • Hofmeister, 1849, 1858 • Howlett, 1931, 1938 • Hunziker, 1954 • Hurst, 1931 • Ivanovskaya, 1960, 1962, 1963 • Jacobsson-Stiasny, 1914a • Johnston, 1961 • Jönsson, 1879–1880, 1881 • Juel, 1918, 1927 • Juliano, 1931a • Kerr, 1954 • Konstantinov, 1958, 1960, 1961 • Krzyzan et al., 1963 • Lebègue, 1952a • Liljefors, 1934, 1953 • Longley, 1924a,b • Longo, 1898, 1914 • V. K. S. Mani, 1947 • Mauritzon, 1939c • C. F. Meyer, 1958, 1959 • Mildenberger, 1963 • A. Müntzing and G. Müntzing, 1941, 1945 • Murbeck, 1897, 1901a,b, 1902a, 1916 • Olden, 1953 • Orlova, 1963 • Osterwalder, 1910 • Péchoutre, 1901, 1902 • Penland, 1923 • Popoff, 1935 • Pratt and Einset, 1955 • Radionenko, 1963 • Rudloff, 1930 • Ruehle, 1924 • Rutishauser, 1939, 1943a,b, 1945a,b, 1946, 1948, 1949 • Sarfatti, 1958, 1960, 1961, 1962 • H. J. Sax, 1954 • Schacht, 1850 • Schanderl, 1949 • Schneider, 1953 • J. S. Shoemaker, 1926, 1928 • Shmarhon, 1964 • U. P. Singh, 1959 • Solntseva, 1961 • Sommer, 1929 • Souèges, 1922a,b, 1923h, 1935b,g,h, • Steinegger, 1933 • Strasburger, 1877, 1879, 1884b, 1904, 1905b, 1909a • Surkova and Skipina, 1963 • Täckholm, 1923 • P. T. Thomas, 1940 • P. A. Thompson, 1963 • Tischler, 1908 • Tukey, 1933, 1934, 1936 • Tukey and Lee, 1937 • Tupitsyn, 1957 • Vesque, 1879 • Wanscher, 1939 • Warming, 1878 • Webb, 1902 • Went, 1887a • Wille, 1886.

ROXBURGHIACEAE

The anther is tetrasporangiate but neither its structure nor the development of the pollen grains have been investigated, apart from Palm's (1920) report that the microspore mother cells of *Stemona* are very small and undergo successive cytokinesis.

The ovule is anatropous, bitegmic, and crassinucellar, with the micropyle formed by the inner integument. The archesporial cell cuts off a primary parietal cell which forms 2 parietal layers below the nucellar epidermis. Cytokinesis in the megaspore mother cell accompanies meiosis and the chalazal megaspore of a linear tetrad develops into a Polygonum type embryo sac. The synergids are hooked and exhibit the filiform apparatus, the polar nuclei fuse at fertilization, and the 3 antipodals are very ephemeral.

Endosperm formation is Nuclear but after wall formation is initiated at the micropylar pole, the tissue becomes cellular throughout. Embryogeny has not been investigated.

Lachner-Sandoval, 1892 • B. Palm, 1920 • Swamy, 1964a.

RUBIACEAE

The anther is tetrasporangiate with a persistent epidermis and its wall development conforms to the Dicotyledonous type. The endothecium develops fibrous thickenings, the middle layer is ephemeral, and the cells of the glandular tapetum remain 1-nucleate. Simultaneous cytokinesis in the microspore mother cells follows meiosis and the microspore tetrads are tetrahedral, isobilateral, and decussate. In *Coffea, Hydrophylax, Knoxia,* and *Rondeletia* the pollen grains are 2-celled when shed, but otherwise they are 3-celled and Farooq (1958b) reported one instance in *Oldenlandia corymbosa* where they had germinated *in situ.*

The ovule is anatropous to hemianatropous, unitegmic, and tenuinucellar. The family is characterized by poor development of the nucellus, which reaches its greatest development in *Cephalanthus, Chiococca, Hoffmannia, Phyllis,* and *Psychotria* which comprise the Phyllis type (Fagerlind, 1937). In the Vaillantia and Bouvardia types the nucellus is represented by a 4–5-celled cap, but in the Oldenlandia type only a single epidermal cell is present above the archesporium, and finally in the Houstonia type the nucellus is eliminated and the integument alone encloses the archesporial cell. A side development of this evolutionary tendency is seen in the Rubia olivierri type where the 3 cells of the nucellar epidermis become considerably elongated and extend through the micropyle to the surface of the ovule. Owing to the reduced nature of the nucellus, the archesporium is situated almost in the chalaza and the micropyle is very long and slender. A multicellular archesporium is common but usually only one cell functions as a megaspore mother cell. Cytokinesis accompanies meiosis and the chalazal megaspore of a linear tetrad develops into a Polygonum type embryo sac. In *Galium lucidum* and *Putoria calabrica* haustorial processes are given off by the megaspores and invade the integument, sometimes reaching the funicle. An Allium type embryo sac has been reported in *Scyphiphora hydrophyllacea* (Karsten, 1891) and the Peperomia type in *Crucianella* spp. and *Rubia oliverii* (Fagerlind, 1937). The synergids are often beaked and the polar nuclei fuse just before or at fertilization. The 3 antipodal cells are very ephemeral in *Dentella, Knoxia,* and *Oldenlandia* but in *Galium, Hydrophylax, Phyllis,* and *Putoria* the chalazal cell becomes considerably elongated and sometimes coenocytic. Secondary multiplication of antipodals is of occasional occurrence in *Asperula montana* and *Coffea arabica.* Starch grains are present in the embryo sac of *Rondeletia amoena* and a funicular obturator is common.

Endosperm formation is Nuclear except in *Ophiorrhiza mungos* where it is *ab initio* Cellular. In *Coffea arabica* Mendes (1941) has reported that division of the primary endosperm nucleus takes place 21–27 days after fertilization and that wall formation follows the second nuclear division. Ruminate endosperm occurs in *Psychotria, Randia,* and *Tarenna.*

Embryogeny conforms to the Solanad type and suspensor haustoria occur in *Asperula, Crucianella, Galium,* and *Rubia.* Polyembryony has been reported in *Coffea arabica.*

Crété, 1956d • Dahlgren, 1927a,c • Faber, 1912 • Fagerlind, 1936a,b, 1937, 1939b • Farooq, 1952b, 1953, 1958b, 1959, 1960 • P. M. Ganapathy, 1956a,b • Graner, 1936, 1938 • Hanausek, 1895 • Hegelmaier, 1886 • Hille Ris Lambers, 1930 • Hofmeister, 1858b • Houk, 1936, 1938 • Jönsson, 1881 • A. C. Joshi, 1938a • Juel, 1915 • Karsten, 1891 • Krug, 1934, 1937 • Krug and Carvalho, 1939 • Leliveld, 1938 • Lloyd, 1899, 1902, 1904, 1905 • Ly Thi Ba, 1960, 1961a • Mathewson, 1906 • Mayne, 1937 • A. J. T. Mendes, 1941 • Periasamy, 1962b, 1964 • Periasamy and Parameswaran, 1962 • Pierpaoli, 1917 • Raghavan and Rangaswamy, 1941 • Raghavan and Srinivasan, 1941a • Raman, 1954 • Schleiden, 1837 • Schürhoff, 1926b • Shivaramiah and Dutt, 1964 • Shivaramiah and Ganapathy, 1961 • Souèges, 1924d, 1925e, 1951c • N. E. Stevens, 1912b • Sybenga, 1960 • Venkateswarlu and Rao, 1954, 1958 • Vesque, 1878, 1879 • Warming, 1873, 1878 • Wormer, 1963.

RUPPIACEAE

The structure of the anther has not been described apart from the report of an amoeboid tapetum. The microspore tetrads are isobilateral and the pollen grains are 3-celled when shed.

The ovule of *Ruppia* is campylotropous, bitegmic, and crassinucellar, with the micropyle formed by both integuments. The archesporial cell cuts off a primary parietal cell, which forms a single parietal layer below the nucellar epidermis. Cytokinesis in the megaspore mother cell accompanies meiosis and the chalazal megaspore of a linear or T-shaped tetrad develops into a Polygonum type embryo sac. The polar nuclei fuse before fertilization and the 3 ephemeral antipodal cells occupy a small pouch at the base of the embryo sac.

Endosperm formation is Helobial.

Embryogeny in *R. maritima* and *R. rostellata* conforms to the Caryophyllad type and *cb* forms the 1-celled vesicular suspensor.

Graves, 1908 • Hofmeister, 1852, 1861 • Murbeck, 1902b • Wille, 1882b.

RUSCACEAE

The structure of the anther has not been described except for the endothecium, which develops fibrous thickenings. Successive cytokinesis in the microspore mother cells accompanies meiosis and the microspore tetrads are isobilateral. Pollen grains are 2- or 3-celled when shed.

The ovule is orthotropous to hemianatropous, bitegmic, and tenuinucellar. The archesporial cell in *Ruscus aculeatus* functions directly as the megaspore mother cell which, in the carpellate flowers, undergoes cytokinesis only after the heterotypic division and the chalazal dyad cell develops into an Allium type embryo sac. The synergids are hooked and exhibit the filiform apparatus, the polar nuclei fuse before fertilization, and the secondary nucleus is located at the base of the embryo sac. The 3 antipodal cells undergo secondary multiplication to form 5 cells which occupy a chalazal diverticulum, and these degenerate soon after fertilization.

Endosperm formation and embryogeny have not been investigated.

Elfving, 1879 • Geitler, 1935 • Phillipis, 1936.

RUTACEAE

The anther is tetrasporangiate with a persistent epidermis. The endothecium develops fibrous thickenings, the 2 or 3 middle layers are ephemeral, and the cells of the glandular tapetum become 2-multi-nucleate, with frequent nuclear fusions. Occasionally a nuclear division is followed by periclinal wall formation and the tapetum becomes irregularly 2- or 3-layered. Simultaneous cytokinesis in the microspore mother cells follows meiosis and the microspore tetrads are tetrahedral, decussate, or isobilateral. Pollen grains are 3-celled when shed in *Citrus grandis* but otherwise are 2-celled.

The ovule is anatropous to hemianatropous, bitegmic, and crassinucellar, with the micropyle formed of both integuments except in *Calodendrum capense* where only the outer integument is involved. A multicellular archesporium is common but only 1 cell cuts off a primary parietal cell which gives rise to 2–10 parietal layers. Except in *Feronia elephantum*, the apical cells of the nucellar epidermis divide periclinally and form a nucellar cap 2–5 cells in thickness. Cytokinesis in the megaspore mother cell accompanies meiosis and the chalazal megaspore of a linear or T-shaped tetrad develops into a Polygonum type embryo sac. The synergids are hooked in *Aegle, Citrus, Dictamnus,* and *Feronia* and those of *A. marmelos* exhibit the filiform apparatus. The polar nuclei fuse before fertilization, the 3 antipodal cells are ephemeral, and starch grains are present in the embryo sac of *Glycosmis pentaphylla*. In *Xanthoxylum* the embryo sac is 4-nucleate and after degeneration of the egg apparatus the single polar nucleus forms endosperm autonomously, while in *Skimmia* no archesporium is formed and the 6–8-nucleate embryo sac arises by somatic apospory. A hypostase is usually present and in *Coleonema album* an aril forms from the base of the ovule which it envelops.

Endosperm formation is Nuclear but after the initiation of cell walls at the micropylar pole the tissue becomes cellular throughout. In *Aegle marmelos* the chalazal extremity of the embryo sac elongates as an aggressive haustorium.

Embryogeny in *Citrus trifoliata* conforms to the Solanad type but the Onagrad type is followed by the other members. Adventive embryony accompanied by polyembryony is obligate in *Xanthoxylum*, but throughout the family the formation of such embryos is common and the zygotic embryo seldom reaches maturity. In *Citrus* cleavage polyembryony also occurs.

Bacchi, 1943 • Bajpai and Maurya, 1963 • Banerji, 1954 • Biermann, 1896 • Braun, 1860 • Cappaletti, 1929 • Chakravarty, 1935, 1936 • Desai, 1961, 1962a,b • Elfving, 1879 • Fagerlind, 1939c • Farooq, 1952a • Fohn, 1935 • Franchino, 1951 • Frost, 1926, 1938 • Furusato, 1951, 1953 • Furusato, Ohta, and Ishibashi, 1957 • L. Guignard, 1882b • Gurbel, 1952 • Hofmeister, 1858 • Honsell, 1954 • B. M. Johri and Ahuja, 1956, 1957 • Jönsson, 1879–1880, 1881 • Leroy, 1947

• Longley, 1925 • Longo, 1908 • Mauritzon, 1935b, 1936d • L. L. Narayana, 1963a • Osawa, 1912 • Schlotterbeck, 1896 • Schürhoff, 1924b • Sokolškaja, 1938 • Soltwedel, 1882 • Souèges, 1925c, 1926f, 1953e • Strasburger, 1878 • Torres, 1936 • Vasil, 1962 • Vesque, 1879 • H. J. Webber, 1931 • H. J. Webber and Batchelor, 1946 • J. M. Webber, 1940 • Westermaier, 1897a.

SABIACEAE

The number of sporangia comprising the anther has not been recorded. In *Meliosma* the endothecium develops fibrous thickenings, the 2 middle layers are ephemeral, and the cells of the glandular tapetum become 2-nucleate. Development of the pollen grains has not been described but they are 2-celled when shed.

The ovule is hemianatropous, unitegmic, and crassinucellar, but as the integument fails to grow over the dome-shaped nucellus, no micropyle is formed. The archesporial cell cuts off a primary parietal cell which gives rise to at least 4 parietal layers and the apical cells of the nucellar epidermis undergo a single periclinal division. Cytokinesis in the megaspore mother cell accompanies meiosis and the chalazal megaspore of a linear tetrad develops into a Polygonum type embryo sac. The synergids of *M. arnottiana* are hooked, the polar nuclei fuse before fertilization, and the secondary nucleus migrates into a short chalazal diverticulum while the 3 ephemeral antipodal cells remain *in situ*.

Endosperm formation is Helobial. The endosperm proper develops from the micropylar chamber and the small chalazal chamber becomes 2-nucleate before giving off one or more haustorial processes.

Embryogeny has not been investigated.

Mauritzon, 1936d • Raju, 1952a.

SALICACEAE

The anther is tetrasporangiate with a persistent epidermis and its wall development conforms to the Monocotyledonous type. The endothecium develops fibrous thickenings, the 1 or 2 middle layers are ephemeral, and the cells of the glandular tapetum become 2-nucleate. Simultaneous cytokinesis in the microspore mother cells follows meiosis and the microspore tetrads are tetrahedral, decussate, or isobilateral. Pollen grains are 2-celled when shed.

The ovule is anatropous, usually unitegmic, and crassinucellar. In *Populus canadensis* and *P. canescens* the bitegmic condition occurs, but the inner integument is very weakly developed. A multicellular archesporium is common but usually only one cell is functional and cuts off a primary parietal cell which forms 2–6 parietal layers. Cytokinesis in the megaspore mother cell accompanies meiosis and the chalazal megaspore of a linear tetrad develops into a Polygonum type embryo sac. The synergids exhibit the filiform apparatus in *Populus deltoides*, the polar nuclei fuse before fertilization, and the 3 antipodal cells are ephemeral.

Endosperm formation is Nuclear but the tissue later becomes cellular in a centripetal manner.

Embryogeny conforms usually to the Asterad type but the Onagrad type is followed in *P. deltoides* where polyembryony has been reported.

Campo, 1963 • Camus, 1904, 1905 • Chamberlain, 1897a, 1898 • Dahlgren, 1915a • Erlanson and Hermann, 1927 • Fagerlind, 1938c • M. J. Fischer, 1928 • Graf, 1921 • Gramuglio, 1962 • Håkansson, 1929, 1954 • Heizmann and Shull, 1944 • Hjelmqvist, 1948 • Hofmeister, 1858 • Ikeno, 1916, 1922 • Jönsson, 1879–1880, 1881 • Kimura, 1952, 1955a,b, 1963 • P. Maheshwari and Roy, 1951 • Moore and Behney, 1908 • Nagaraj, 1952 • Souèges, 1923f • Suda, 1963 • Tieghem, 1900a.

SALVADORACEAE

The development and structure of the anther and pollen grains have not been described.

The ovule is anatropous, bitegmic, and crassinucellar, with the micropyle formed by the inner integument. The archesporial cell cuts off a primary parietal cell which forms up to 10 parietal layers below the nucellar epidermis. Cytokinesis in the megaspore mother cell accompanies meiosis but it is frequently suppressed in the micropylar dyad cell and the chalazal megaspore of a linear tetrad or "triad" develops into a Polygonum type embryo sac. The synergids are pyriform, the polar nuclei fuse before fertilization, and the 3 antipodal cells are large.

Endosperm formation in *Salvadora persica* is Nuclear but embryogeny has not been investigated.

David, 1938 • Mauritzon, 1936d.

SANTALACEAE

The anther is tetrasporangiate and its wall development conforms to the Dicotyledonous type. In *Osyris* and *Santalum* the epidermis is strongly cutinized and persistent, but in other members it is destroyed during anther maturation. The endothecium develops fibrous thickenings, the 1 or 2 middle layers are ephemeral, and the cells of the glandular tapetum are 1-multinucleate. The tapetum may become irregularly 2-layered when a nuclear division is followed by periclinal cell division. Simultaneous cytokinesis in the microspore mother cells follows meiosis and the microspore tetrads are tetrahedral, decussate, and isobilateral. Pollen grains are 2-celled when shed in *Comandra*, *Exocarpos*, *Osyris*, and *Thesium* but 3-celled in *Mida* and *Santalum*. In *S. album*, *S. yasi*, and *T. wightiana* germination *in situ* is common.

The ovule is orthotropous in *Exocarpos* and *Leptomeria* but otherwise is anatropous to hemianatropous, unitegmic and tenuinucellar. The nucellus is much reduced and in *Buckleya*, *Exocarpos*, *Leptomeria* and *Santalum* it is not distinguishable from the integument whose growth may be arrested. Although a multicellular archesporium is common, usually only 1 cell undergoes further development and functions directly as the megaspore mother cell. Usually cytokinesis accompanies meiosis and the chalazal megaspore of a linear tetrad develops into a Polygonum type embryo sac, which in *Thesium* remains within the ovule. In *Osyris*, however, its tip protrudes into the loculus and in *Exocarpos*, *Leptomeria*, *Mida*,' *Quinchamalium* and *Santalum* it reaches the base of the style. In *Buckleya lanceolata* cytokinesis is suppressed after the homotypic division and embryo sac formation is of the Allium type. The synergids usually are hooked and exhibit the filiform apparatus, but in *Thesium* they are small cells and in *O. chilense* their tips elongate as tubular outgrowths which extend up the style for a third of its length. The polar nuclei fuse before fertilization and 3 ephemeral antipodal cells are formed except in *Quinchamalium* where the nuclei are enclosed in a single cell. Starch grains are present in the embryo sac of *Buckleya*. The embryo sac exhibits a variety of aggressive haustorial structures. Its base may elongate as a chalazal haustorium which penetrates the funicle and reaches the placenta (*Buckleya*, *Leptomeria*, *Mida*, *Quinchamalium*) or a lateral caecum may develop and follow the same path (*Comandra*, *Osyris*, *Santalum*, *Thesium*). In *Comandra* secondary haustoria originate at the base of the caecum and in *Exocarpos* numerous finger-like processes arise from the middle of the embryo sac and enclose its lower half.

Endosperm formation is *ab initio* Cellular (*Comandra*, *Exocarpos*, *Osyris*, *Quinchamalium*, *Thesium*) or Helobial in which the chalazal chamber is haustorial (*Leptomeria*, *Mida*, *Santalum*). In *Exocarpos* the 2 basal endosperm cells and in *Quinchamalium* the 4 basal cells become separated longitudinally and form independent haustoria which reach the base of the ovary.

Embryogeny is variable and often irregular so that it is not possible to recognize definite types. Polyembryony by proliferation of suspensor cells has been reported in *Exocarpos sparteus*.

Agarwal, 1961a, 1962 • Bhatnagar, 1959a,b, 1960, 1961, 1964, 1965b • Fagerlind, 1948a, 1959 • Ghosh, 1955 • Griffith, 1836, 1843 • L. Guignard, 1885 • Habermann, 1906 • Henfrey, 1856 • Hofmeister, 1858, 1859 • G. S. Iyengar, 1937 • B. M. Johri, 1962b • B. M. Johri and Bhatnagar, 1960 • Jönsson, 1879–1880, 1881 • P. C. Joshi, 1960 • P. Maheshwari and Ghosh, 1955 • Modilewski, 1928b • Paliwal, 1956 • Raj, 1964 • Ram, 1957, 1959a,b,c • L. N. Rao, 1942 • Rutishauser, 1937 • Schacht, 1850, 1865, 1866 • Schaeppi, 1942 • Schaeppi and Steindl, 1937 • Schulle, 1933 • Srimathi and Sreenivasaya, 1962 • Strasburger, 1877, 1878, 1885 • Tieghem, 1896b • Warming, 1878.

SAPINDACEAE

The anther is tetrasporangiate. The endothecium develops fibrous thickenings, the 1 or 2 middle layers are ephemeral, and the cells of the glandular tapetum are 1- or 2-nucleate. Simultaneous cytokinesis in the microspore mother cells follows meiosis and the microspore tetrads are tetrahedral or isobilateral. Pollen grains are 2-celled when shed and those of *Cardiospermum halicacabum* contain starch grains.

The ovule is anatropous to hemianatropous, bitegmic, and crassinucellar, with the micropyle formed by both integuments (*Diplopeltis, Dodonaea, Koelreuteria, Litchi, Sapindus*) or only the inner one (*Cardiospermum*). The archesporial cell cuts off a primary parietal cell which gives rise to 6–15 parietal layers and in *Cardiospermum hirsutum* the apical cells of the nucellar epidermis sometimes undergo a single periclinal division. Cytokinesis in the microspore mother cell accompanies meiosis and the chalazal megaspore of a linear tetrad develops into a Polygonum type embryo sac. The synergids are hooked, the polar nuclei fuse before fertilization, and although the 3 antipodal cells are usually ephemeral, Nair and Joseph (1960) report secondary multiplication in *C. halicacabum* with the formation of up to 14 cells, many of which are multinucleate.

Endosperm formation is Nuclear and the tissue is digested before it becomes cellular.

Embryogeny in *C. halicacabum* conforms to the Asterad type.

Banerji and Chaudhuri, 1944 • Chaudhuri, 1940 • David, 1938 • Guérin, 1901 • Kadry, 1946, 1950, 1960 • A. R. Khan, 1939 • Mauritzon, 1936d • Nair and Joseph, 1960 • Perrot and Guérin, 1903 • Pijl, 1957, 1960 • P. K. Sen, 1938.

SAPOTACEAE

The anther is tetrasporangiate but its development and that of the pollen grains have not been investigated.

The ovule is anatropous, unitegmic, and tenuinucellar. The archesporial cell functions directly as the megaspore mother cell in which cytokinesis accompanies meiosis and the chalazal megaspore of a linear or T-shaped tetrad develops into a Polygonum type embryo sac. The synergids are hooked, the polar nuclei fuse before fertilization, and the 3 antipodal nuclei degenerate before becoming enclosed in cells.

Endosperm formation is Nuclear but the tissue later becomes cellular in a centripetal manner.

Embryogeny has not been described but in *Achras sapota* the cells of the massive multicellular suspensor are of varying sizes.

S. N. Murthy, 1941b • Warming, 1913.

SARCOLAENACEAE

Embryologically unknown.

SARCOSPERMACEAE

Embryologically unknown.

SARGENTODOXACEAE

Embryologically unknown.

SARRACENIACEAE

The anther of *Sarracenia purpurea* is tetrasporangiate with a persistent epidermis. The endothecial cells become thickened on their inner and lateral walls, 1–3 middle layers are formed, and the cells of the 2- or 3-layered glandular tapetum become 2-nucleate. Simultaneous cytokinesis in the microspore mother cells follows meiosis and the microspore tetrads are tetrahedral. Pollen grains are 2-celled when shed.

The ovule is anatropous, unitegmic, and tenuinucellar. The archesporial cell functions directly as the megaspore mother cell in which cytokinesis accompanies meiosis and the chalazal megaspore of a linear tetrad develops into a Polygonum type embryo sac. The synergids are pyriform, the polar nuclei fuse at fertilization, and the 3 antipodal cells persist in a degenerated form during early postfertilization stages. An endothelium encloses the embryo sac.

Endosperm formation is *ab initio* Cellular and a row of 8 cells is produced before longitudinal divisions occur.

Embryogeny has not been described in detail but possibly follows the Caryophyllad type. A slender 7-celled uniseriate suspensor is formed.

Nichols, 1908 • Schweiger, 1909 • Shreve, 1905, 1906.

SAURAUIACEAE

The development and structure of the anther and pollen grains have not been investigated.

The ovule of *Saurauia nepalensis* is anatropous, unitegmic, and tenuinucellar. The archesporial cell functions directly as the megaspore mother cell in which cytokinesis accompanies meiosis and the chalazal megaspore of a linear tetrad develops into a Polygonum type embryo sac. The synergids are hooked, the polar nuclei fuse before fertilization, and the 3 antipodal cells are ephemeral. An endothelium encloses the lower half of the embryo sac.

Endosperm formation is *ab initio* Cellular but the embryogeny has not been described.

A. N. Rao, 1953c • Schnarf, 1924 • Tieghem, 1899.

SAURURACEAE

The anther is tetrasporangiate with a persistent epidermis. The endothecium develops fibrous thickenings, the middle layer is ephemeral, and the cells of the glandular tapetum become 2-nucleate. Simultaneous cytokinesis in the microspore mother cells follows meiosis and the microspore tetrads are tetrahedral, decussate, or isobilateral. The pollen grains are 2-celled when shed.

The ovule is orthotropous, bitegmic, and tenuinucellar or crassinucellar, with the micropyle formed by both integuments. In *Houttuynia cordata* the archesporial cell functions directly as the megaspore mother cell but in *Anemopsis californica* and *Saururus cernuus* it cuts off a primary parietal cell which forms 2 parietal layers. Cytokinesis in the megaspore mother cell accompanies meiosis but may be suppressed in the micropylar dyad cell, and the chalazal megaspora of a linear or T-shaped tetrad or "triad" develops into a Polygonum type embryo sac. The synergids in *Houttuynia* are hooked, the polar nuclei fuse before fertilization, and the 3 antipodal cells are ephemeral.

Endosperm formation is *ab initio* Cellular in which the primary chalazal chamber develops into a 1-nucleate haustorium and the primary micropylar chamber forms the endosperm proper.

Embryogeny in *Houttuynia* conforms to the Asterad type and the short suspensor is uniseriate.

Crété, 1957d,e • Häuser, 1916 • Johnson, 1900a, 1905 • Murty, 1960 • Okabe, 1930 • Quibell, 1941 • Raju, 1961 • Shibata and Miyake, 1908 • Täckholm and Söderberg, 1918.

SAXIFRAGACEAE

The anther is tetrasporangiate with a persistent epidermis. The endothecium develops fibrous thickenings, the 1 or 2 middle layers are ephemeral, and the cells of the glandular tapetum remain 1-nucleate. Simultaneous cytokinesis in the microspore mother cells follows meiosis and the microspore tetrads are tetrahedral. Pollen grains are 2- or 3-celled when shed.

The ovule is anatropous, unitegmic in *Peltiphyllum* but otherwise bitegmic, and crassinucellar, with the micropyle formed by both integuments. The archesporial cell cuts off a primary parietal cell which forms 2–6 parietal layers and in *Heuchera brixoides* the apical cells of the nucellar epidermis may undergo a single periclinal division. Cytokinesis in the megaspore mother cell accompanies meiosis and the chalazal megaspore of a linear or T-shaped tetrad develops into a Polygonum type embryo sac. The synergids are hooked and usually exhibit the filiform apparatus, the polar nuclei fuse before fertilization, and the 3 antipodal cells persist into early postfertilization stages except in most *Saxifraga* spp. and *Tiarella cordifolia* where they are ephemeral. Secondary multiplication of antipodals has only been reported in *S. diversifolia* where 5 cells may be formed.

Endosperm formation is *ab initio* Cellular (*Astilbe* spp., *Boykinia occidentalis*, *Heuchera* spp., *Mitella pentandra*, *Peltiphyllum peltatum*, *Tellima grandiflora*) or Helobial (*Boykinia tellimoides*, *Chrysoplenium* spp., *Mitella diphylla*, *Saxifraga* spp.). In each case a transverse wall separates a small primary chalazal chamber from a large micropylar one but in the Helobial type both chambers are at first free-nuclear. In *Mitella pentandra* a nonaggressive haustorium of 4 juxtaposed cells is formed from the chalazal chamber.

Embryogeny conforms to the Solanad type.

Chapman, 1933 • Dahlgren, 1923, 1927a, 1930a,b • Eichinger, 1907 • Elst, 1909 • Gäumann, 1918, 1919 • L. Guignard, 1882b • Hegelmaier, 1886 • Hermsen, 1939 • Herr, 1954 • Jönsson, 1879–1880, 1881 • Juel, 1907 • Lebègue, 1949, 1950, 1952c • Mauritzon, 1933a, 1939c • Pace, 1912 • M. A. Rau, 1962 • Rocén, 1928 • Rudenko, 1961 • Samuelsson, 1913 • Saxena, 1963, 1964a • Schürhoff, 1925a • Souèges, 1936a,g • Subramanyam, 1962 • Vesque, 1878, 1879b • Warming, 1877 • Webb, 1902 • Wiggins, 1959.

SCHEUCHZERIACEAE

The anther is tetrasporangiate. Apart from the report of an amoeboid tapetum in *Scheuchzeria palustris*, its wall structure has not been traced and there is no information on microsporogenesis. Pollen grains are 3-celled when shed.

The ovule is anatropous, bitegmic, and crassinucellar, with the micropyle formed by the inner integument. The archesporial cell cuts off a primary parietal cell which forms 4 parietal layers below the nucellar epidermis. Cytokinesis in the megaspore mother cell accompanies meiosis and the chalazal megaspore of a linear tetrad develops into a Polygonum type embryo sac. The synergids are pyriform, the polar nuclei fuse before fertilization, and the secondary nucleus moves close to the 3 ephemeral antipodal nuclei.

Endosperm formation is Helobial. The micropylar chamber becomes coenocytic but later it becomes cellular and forms the endosperm proper, while the small chalazal chamber remains 1-nucleate and exhibits no haustorial activity.

Embryogeny probably conforms to the Caryophyllad type since the suspensor of *Scheuchzeria palustris* is represented by a large vesicular cell.

Hofmeister, 1858, 1861 • Stenar, 1935.

SCHISANDRACEAE

The anther is tetrasporangiate with a persistent epidermis whose cells, in *Schisandra grandiflora*, become papillate and filled with tannin. Wall development conforms to the Dicotyledonous type. The endothecium develops fibrous thickenings and may become irregularly 2-layered, the 1–3 middle layers are ephemeral, and the cells of the glandular tapetum become 2-nucleate. In *S. grandiflora*, owing to an occasional periclinal division, the tapetum may be irregularly 2-layered. Simultaneous cytokinesis in the microspore mother cells follows meiosis and the microspore tetrads are tetrahedral or decussate. Pollen grains are 2-celled when shed and in *S. grandiflora* they germinate by rupture of the exine at three furrows.

The ovule is anatropous, bitegmic, and crassinucellar, with the micropyle formed by both integuments. The archesporium is multicellular but only 1 cell is functional and cuts off a primary parietal cell which gives rise to 3–5 parietal layers. Cytokinesis in the megaspore mother cell accompanies meiosis, although it may be suppressed in the micropylar dyad cell, and the chalazal megaspore of a linear or T-shaped tetrad or "triad" develops into a Polygonum type embryo sac. In *Schisandra chinensis* two types of embryo sac formation have been described and these may occur in ovules of the same flower. Both result in the formation of a 4-nucleate embryo sac consisting of egg apparatus and upper polar nucleus, but whereas one has a monosporic origin, the other is bisporic. The synergids are pyriform, the polar nuclei fuse before fertilization, and the 3 antipodal cells are very ephemeral.

Endosperm formation is *ab initio* Cellular.

Embryogeny conforms either to the Asterad or the Onagrad type and a massive suspensor is formed. In *S. grandiflora* an interval of 4–5 weeks intervenes between fertilization and division of the zygote.

Hayashi, 1960, 1963b · Jalan and Bhandari, 1963 · Kapil, 1964 · Swamy, 1964b · Yoshida, 1962.

SCROPHULARIACEAE

The anther is tetrasporangiate with a persistent epidermis and its wall development follows the Dicotyledonous type. The endothecium develops fibrous thickenings and in *Chelone glabra* the primary endothecial layer undergoes several periclinal divisions to form 4–8 layers, all of which become fibrous. The middle layer is ephemeral and 2 such layers are formed in *C. glabra*. The cells of the glandular tapetum become at least 2-nucleate and nuclear fusions may occur. Simultaneous cytokinesis in the microspore mother cells follows meiosis and the microspore tetrads are tetrahedral, isobilateral, or decussate. Pollen grains are 2-celled when shed.

The ovule is anatropous to hemianatropous, but campylotropous in *Orthocarpus luteus* and *Torenia fournieri*, unitegmic, and tenuinucellar. The archesporial cell functions directly as the megaspore mother cell in which usually cytokinesis accompanies meiosis and the chalazal megaspore of a linear tetrad develops into a Polygonum type embryo sac. In *Linaria ramosissima*, however, the micropylar dyad cell degenerates and the chalazal dyad cell develops into an Allium type embryo sac. In *Melampyrum lineare*, cytokinesis in the megaspore mother cell is suppressed and embryo sac development is of a modified Drusa type in which all or some of the 3 chalazal megaspore nuclei fail to develop further ("strike") and degenerate. The synergids are pyriform and those of *Striga* are hooked, the polar nuclei fuse before fertilization, and the 3 small antipodal cells persist into early postfertilization stages in *Lindenbergia*, *Mazus*, and *Vandellia*. In *Mimulus rigens* only 2 antipodal cells are formed, one of which is 2-nucleate. Starch grains are present in the embryo sacs of *Alonsoa* and *Pentstemon*. The embryo sac is commonly swollen distally and only its tubular proximal portion is enclosed by the endothelium. In *Torenia cordifolia*, *T. fournieri*, *T. hirsuta*, *Vandellia crustacea*, and *V. hirsuta* the apex of the embryo sac grows through the micropyle and reaches the placenta. A hypostase may be differentiated.

Endosperm formation is *ab initio* Cellular with the development of terminal haustoria whose origin and form are specifically characteristic. In some instances, however, the primary chalazal chamber does not exhibit any haustorial activity and either remains 1-cellular (*Torenia fournieri*) or forms 4 juxtaposed cells (*Celsia coromandeliana*, *Nemesia floribunda*, *N. melissaefolia*), while the absence of a micropylar haustorium has been reported in *Chaenorrhinum minus* and *Linaria genistaefolia*. Failure to develop any endosperm haustoria occurs only in *Angelonia grandiflora*, *Mimulus cardinalis*, and *Scrophularia marylandica*, although, according to Balicka-Iwanowska (1899), an ephemeral micropylar haustorium in *A. grandiflora* is replaced by a secondary structure.

Embryogeny usually conforms to the Onagrad type and a slender uniseriate suspensor of up to 10 cells is formed. In *Ellisiophyllum pinnatum*, however, development follows the Solanad type and the suspensor consists of 40–50 cells which become swollen and exhibit haustorial activity.

Arekal, 1963a,b,c, 1964 • Arekal and Raju, 1964 • Bachmann, 1882 • Balicka-Iwanowska, 1899 • Banerji, 1961 • O. Berg, 1898 • R. Y. Berg, 1954 • Bernard, 1903 • S. P. Bhatnagar and Singh, 1964 • Buscalioni, 1893 • Chatin, 1874 • M. T. Cook, 1924a • Crété, 1948a, 1949b, 1950a,b,c,d, 1951d, 1952d, 1953d, 1954e,f, 1955f, 1958d, 1964b • Dahlgren, 1922, 1923 • Deecke, 1854, 1855a,b • Dop, 1913a, 1914 • Elfert, 1895 • Elfving, 1879 • Evans, 1919 • Glišić, 1933, 1937 • Gscheidle, 1924 • Guignard, 1882b, 1884 • Guilford and Fisk, 1952 • Habermann, 1906 • Håkansson, 1926 • Hallier, 1903 • Hartl, 1957 • Hofmeister, 1849, 1851, 1855a, 1858b, 1859 • C. V. K. Iyengar, 1929, 1931, 1933, 1934, 1937, 1939a,b,c, 1940a,b,c, 1941, 1942a,b,c, 1947 • Jönsson, 1879–1880, 1881 • M. C. Joshi and Varghese, 1962, 1963 • Junell, 1962 • Kumar and Abraham, 1941 • Lötscher, 1905 • Lundqvist,

1915 • P. Maheshwari and Navalakha, 1941 • Meunier, 1897 • Michell, 1915 • Millsaps, 1936 • Němec, 1910 • F. Noll, 1883 • N. Pal, 1959 • Persidsky, 1934 • Radlkafer, 1856 • Raghavan and Srinivasan, 1941b, 1941c • K. Y. Rudenko, 1961a • T. Rudenko, 1929 • Safeeulla, 1950 • Safeeulla and Govindu, 1949, 1950 • Sampathkumaran and Iyengar, 1929 • Samuelsson, 1913 • Schacht, 1850, 1955a,b,c, 1863 • Schertz, 1919 • Schlotterbeck, 1896, 1898 • E. Schmid, 1906 • Schnarf, 1925 • Soltwedel, 1882 • Souèges, 1921a, 1935f, 1948d • Srinath, 1934, 1938-1939, 1940 • A. R. Srinivasan, 1946 • V. K. Srinivasan, 1940 • Steffen, 1956 • Strasburger, 1877, 1884b • H. G. Svensson, 1928 • Tiagi, 1956 • Tischler, 1899 • Tulasne, 1849, 1855 • Varghese, 1963 • Vesque, 1878, 1879b • Ward, 1880b • Warming, 1873, 1878 • Weiss, 1932 • Wilcke, 1930 • Westermaier, 1890 • Wurdinger, 1910 • Yamaha, 1926 • Yamazaki, 1953, 1954, 1957a,b.

SCYPHOSTEGIACEAE

Embryologically unknown.

SCYTOPETALACEAE

Embryologically unknown.

SELAGINACEAE

The number of sporangia comprising the anther has not been reported, but during their development 3 parietal cell layers are formed. It is not clear whether the hypodermal layer differentiates as a fibrous endothecium but the middle layer is ephemeral and the cells of the glandular (?) tapetum become 2-4-nucleate and nuclear fusions occur. Microsporogenesis has not been described but the microspore tetrads are tetrahedral. The nature of the mature pollen grains has not been reported.

The ovule is anatropous, unitegmic, and tenuinucellar. The archesporial cell functions directly as the megaspore mother cell in which cytokinesis accompanies meiosis and the chalazal megaspore of a linear tetrad develops into a Polygonum type embryo sac. The synergids are slender and pyriform, the polar nuclei fuse before fertilization, and the 3 antipodal cells persist sometimes during early endosperm formation. An endothelium encloses the embryo sac.

Endosperm formation is *ab initio* Cellular with the development of terminal 2-celled haustoria in *Dischisma ciliatum, Hebenstreitia dentata,* and *Selago spuria* but in *Lagotis glauca* the 1-celled chalazal haustorium is 2-nucleate.

Embryogeny in *Lagotis* conforms to the Onagrad type and a long, uniseriate suspensor is formed.

Jönsson, 1879–1880 • Kapil and Masand, 1964 • V. K. Sharma, 1962 • Vos, 1945.

SIMAROUBACEAE

The anther is tetrasporangiate with a persistent epidermis. The endothecium develops fibrous thickenings, the 2 or 3 middle layers are ephemeral, and the cells of the glandular tapetum become 2-multinucleate. In *Samadera indica* nuclear fusions occur and the tapetum becomes irregularly 2-layered. Simultaneous cytokinesis in the microspore mother cells follows meiosis and the microspore tetrads are tetrahedral, decussate, isobilateral, or, rarely, T-shaped. Pollen grains are 2-celled when shed.

The ovule is anatropous to hemianatropous, bitegmic, and crassinucellar, with the micropyle formed by the inner integument. A group of 2–4 archesporial cells differentiates but only one cuts off a primary parietal cell, which forms 6–17 parietal layers. The apical cells of the nucellar epidermis divide periclinally and give rise to a nucellar cap 2 cells in thickness in *Suriana maritima* but 9 cells thick in *Brucea amarissima*. Cytokinesis in the megaspore mother cell accompanies meiosis and the chalazal megaspore of a linear or T-shaped tetrad develops into a Polygonum type embryo sac. The synergids are broadly pyriform and those of *Ailanthus malabarica* and *Suriana maritima* exhibit the filiform apparatus. The polar nuclei fuse before fertilization and the 3 antipodal cells are ephemeral. A hypostase is differentiated.

Endosperm formation is Nuclear with an aggregation of nuclei at the chalazal end of the embryo sac which elongates as a haustorium. Following wall formation at the periphery, the tissue becomes cellular throughout.

Embryogeny conforms to the Onagrad type and polyembryony has been reported in *Brucea amarissima*.

Mauritzon, 1935e • Nair and Joseph, 1957 • Nair and Joshi, 1958 • Nair and Sukumaran, 1960 • L. L. Narayana, 1957a • M. A. Rau, 1940b • Schürhoff, 1924b, 1926b • Wiger, 1935, 1936.

SMILACACEAE

The structure of the anther has not been described. In *Smilax herbacea* successive cytokinesis in the microspore mother cells accompanies meiosis and the microspore tetrads are isobilateral. There is no record of the number of cells in the mature pollen grains.

Development of the embryo sac, endosperm, and embryo have not been investigated.

Elkins, 1914 • L. E. Humphrey, 1914 • Ono, 1926.

SOLANACEAE

The anther is tetrasporangiate and its wall development conforms to the Dicotyledonous type except in *Withania somnifera* where it follows the Basic type. The endothecium develops fibrous thickenings except in those genera with pore dehiscence, the 1 or 2 middle layers are ephemeral, and the tapetal cells become 2-nucleate. An amoeboid tapetum has been reported in *Datura stramonium* but a glandular one in *Capsicum frutescens, Lycium europaeum, Solanum tuberosum,* and *Withania somnifera.* Simultaneous cytokinesis in the microspore mother cells follows meiosis and the microspore tetrads are tetrahedral, isobilateral, or decussate. Pollen grains are usually 2-celled when shed but those of *Capsicum frutescens* may be 3-celled and starch occurs in the pollen grains of *Duboisia.*

The ovule is anatropous to hemianatropous, unitegmic, and tenuinucellar. The archesporial cell functions directly as the megaspore mother cell in which usually cytokinesis accompanies meiosis and the chalazal megaspore of a linear tetrad develops into a Polygonum type embryo sac. However, suppression of cytokinesis after the homotypic division and the development of the chalazal dyad cell into an Allium type embryo sac occurs in *Capsicum frutescens* var. Japanese Ornamental, *Cestrum elegans, Nicotiana ditagla,* and *N. rustica,* while the tetrasporic Adoxa type has been reported in *Solanum muricatum* and *S. tuberosum.* The synergids are elongated and pyriform, with hooks present in *S. phureja,* and those of *Lycopersicum esculentum* and *S. tuberosum* exhibit the filiform apparatus. The polar nuclei fuse before fertilization and, although the 3 antipodal cells are usually ephemeral, they enlarge and persist during endosperm formation in *Atropa belladonna, Datura metel,* and *S. phureja.* Starch grains occur in the embryo sacs of *Cestrum diurnum* and *S. tuberarium,* and an endothelium is differentiated.

Endosperm formation may be *ab initio* Cellular (*Atropa, Datura, Nicandra, Nicotiana, Petunia, Physochlaena, Salpiglossus variabilis, Scopolia, Solanum withania*), Nuclear (*Capsicum, Lycium, Salpiglossus picta, Schizanthus*) or Helobial (*Hyoscyamus,* and probably *Du-*

boisia). The antipodal end of the embryo sac usually elongates and forms a nonaggressive haustorium.

Embryogeny conforms to the Solanad type except in *Capsicum annum* where the Onagrad type is followed.

Arnason, 1943 • Balicka-Iwanowska, 1899 • C. Barnard, 1949 • Beamish, 1955 • P. N. Bhaduri, 1932, 1933, 1935, 1936 • Brown, 1949 • Buchholz and Blakeslee, 1922, 1927 • Campin, 1924 • Chatin, 1870, 1874 • A. E. Clarke, 1940 • Cochran, 1938 • D. C. Cooper, 1931b, 1946 • Crété, 1954b, 1959d, 1960b, 1961a,b,c,d • Cuchtmanówna, 1930 • Dahlgren, 1915a, 1923 • Danielyan, 1963 • Dnyansagar and Cooper, 1960 • Dorasamy and Gopinath, 1944 • Elfving, 1879 • Fagherazzi-Abgrall and Meyer, 1963 • Farr, 1916 • Ferguson, 1927 • Fruhwirth, 1914 • Glišić, 1928 • Glushchenko, 1962 • Goodspeed, 1915, 1923, 1947 • L. Guignard, 1882b, 1901d, 1902a • Haberlandt, 1922b • Hanstein, 1870 • Hegelmaier, 1886 • Hofmeister, 1855, 1858b • Howard and Ram, 1925 • Howlett, 1936 • K. V. Ivanova and Orel, 1963 • Jain, 1956 • G. W. Johnston, 1941 • Jönsson, 1879–1880 • Jostoff, 1926, 1937 • Krishnamurthy and Rao, 1958, 1960 • Krüger, 1932 • Lamm, 1937 • J. H. Lee, and Cooper, 1958 • Lengel, 1960 • Levan, 1937 • Lötscher, 1905 • Magtang, 1936 • Maryanovich, 1939 • Mascré, 1919a,b, 1921 • Meyer, Abgrall, and Hortin, 1962 • Modilewski, 1936, 1937a,b • Modilewski and Dzubenko, 1937, 1940 • Mohan Ram and Kamini, 1964 • Molliard, 1896 • Mutafjan, 1964 • Namakawa, 1919 • Nanetti, 1912 • O'Neal, 1920 • P. Palm, 1922 • Pavari, 1957 • Persidsky, 1935 • Persidsky and Modilewski, 1935 • Poddubnaja-Arnoldi, 1936 • R. Prakash and Chatterjee, 1953 • Rees-Leonard, 1935 • Rick, 1946 • Rietsema, Blondel, Satina, and Blakeslee, 1955 • Rybchenko, 1959, 1963, 1964 • Samuelsson, 1913 • Sansome, Satina, and Blakeslee, 1944 • Sanz, 1945 • Satina and Blakeslee, 1935a,b, 1941 • Satina, Rappaport, and Blakeslee, 1950 • Scarascia, 1953 • Schlotterbeck, 1896 • Shams-ul-Islam-Khan, 1951 • Smith, 1935 • Souèges, 1907, 1920f,g, 1922f, 1936h • Stow, 1927, 1936 • Svensson, 1925, 1926 • Swaminathan, 1954 • Tongnini, 1900 • Vasil, 1962 • Ventura, 1930a • Vesque, 1878, 1879 • Walker, 1955 • Wangenheim, 1957 • Warming, 1873 • Wellington, 1913 • E. J. Williams, 1955 • Yamaha, 1926 • Young, 1922, 1923.

SONNERATIACEAE

The anther is tetrasporangiate with a persistent epidermis and its wall development in *Sonneratia apetala* conforms to the Dicotyledonous type. The endothecium develops fibrous thickenings, the 2 or 3 middle layers are ephemeral, and the cells of the glandular tapetum become 2-nucleate. Pollen grains are 2-celled when shed.

The ovule is anatropous, bitegmic, and crassinucellar, with the micropyle formed by both integuments. A multicellular archesporium is common but only one cell is functional and cuts off a primary parietal cell which forms 4–6 parietal layers. In *Duabanga sonneratioides* the apical cells of the nucellar epidermis divide periclinally and form a nucellar cap 2 cells in thickness. Cytokinesis in the megaspore mother cell accompanies meiosis and the chalazal megaspore of a linear tetrad develops into a Polygonum type embryo sac. Fatty globules appear in the megaspore mother cell just prior to meiosis, and persist in the mature embryo sac. The synergids are hooked, the polar nuclei fuse before fertilization, and the 3 antipodal cells are very ephemeral.

Endosperm formation is Nuclear but the tissue later becomes cellular throughout after the initiation of walls at the micropylar pole.

Embryogeny conforms to the Onagrad type.

A. C. Joshi, 1939a • Karsten, 1891 • Mauritzon, 1939c • Venkateswarlu, 1936a,b, 1937b.

SPARGANIACEAE

The anther is tetrasporangiate but, apart from the record that the cells of the amoeboid tapetum become multinucleate, its wall structure and the development of the pollen grains have not been described.

The ovule is anatropous, bitegmic, and crassinucellar. The archesporial cell cuts off a primary parietal cell but no account of embryo sac development has been traced. The synergids are pyriform, the polar nuclei fuse before fertilization, and the secondary nucleus moves close to the 3 antipodal cells which undergo postfertilization secondary multiplication, and as many as 150 cells may be formed in *Sparganium simplex*.

Endosperm formation is reported to be Nuclear but the basal position of the primary endosperm nucleus suggests the possibility of Helobial endosperm with the formation of a small and easily overlooked chalazal chamber.

Embryogeny conforms to the Onagrad type.

Campbell, 1899c,d • P. Claussen, 1927 • Dietz, 1887 • Elfving, 1879 • Hegelmaier, 1874b • B. Palm, 1915 • Schacht, 1850 • Schürhoff, 1920b • Souèges, 1924e • Stenar, 1925b • Tischler, 1912, 1915.

SPHAEROSEPALACEAE

Embryologically unknown.

SPIGELIACEAE

Development of the anther and pollen grains has not been described, but the tapetum is amoeboid.

The ovule is anatropous to hemianatropous, unitegmic, and tenuinucellar. The archesporial cell functions directly as the megaspore mother cell in which cytokinesis accompanies meiosis and the chalazal megaspore of a linear tetrad develops into a Polygonum type embryo sac. The synergids are pyriform, the polar nuclei fuse just before fertilization, and the 3 antipodal cells degenerate soon after.

Endosperm formation in *Spigelia splendens* is Nuclear and later becomes cellular in a centripetal manner. In *Mitrasacme alsinoides*, however, there is a modified Helobial type of endosperm formation since a row of 4 cells is formed before free-nuclear division and a nonaggressive lateral haustorium develops, but finally the tissue becomes cellular throughout.

Embryogeny conforms to the Solanad type.

Dahlgren, 1922 • Juel, 1915 • Yamazaki, 1963.

STACHYURACEAE

Development of the anther and pollen grains has not been investigated but the latter are 2- or 3-celled when shed.

The ovule of *Stachyurus chinensis* is anatropous, bitegmic, and crassinucellar, with the micropyle formed by both integuments. The archesporial cell cuts off a primary parietal cell which gives rise to 3 parietal layers and the apical cells of the nucellar epidermis divide periclinally to form a nucellar cap 2 or 3 cells in thickness. Cytokinesis in the megaspore mother cell accompanies meiosis and the chalazal megaspore of a linear tetrad develops into a Polygonum type embryo sac. The synergids are pyriform, the polar nuclei fuse before fertilization, and the 3 antipodal cells are ephemeral. A caruncle is formed from the outer integument during postfertilization stages.

Endosperm formation is Nuclear but the tissue later becomes cellular throughout.

Embryogeny has not been described.

Mauritzon, 1936b.

STACKHOUSIACEAE

The anther is tetrasporangiate with a persistent epidermis which becomes cutinized at maturity. The endothecium develops fibrous thickenings, the middle layer is ephemeral, and the cells of the glandular tapetum become 2-nucleate. Simultaneous cytokinesis in the microspore mother cells follows meiosis and the microspore tetrads are isobilateral, tetrahedral, or decussate. Pollen grains are 3-celled when shed and contain starch grains.

The ovule is anatropous, bitegmic, and tenuinucellar, with the micropyle formed by both integuments. The archesporial cell functions directly as the megaspore mother cell in which cytokinesis accompanies meiosis and the chalazal megaspore of a linear or T-shaped tetrad develops into a Polygonum type embryo sac. The synergids are pyriform and those of *Stackhousia lineariaefolia* degenerate before fertilization. The polar nuclei fuse early and the 3 antipodal cells become multinucleate in *S. lineariaefolia* and those of *S. brunonis*, *S. monogyna* and *S. viminea* undergo secondary multiplication to form 10–15 cells. A hypostase is usually differentiated.

Endosperm formation is Nuclear but after the formation of about 128 nuclei the tissue become cellular throughout.

Embryogeny conforms to the Asterad type and the suspensor is very short.

Billings, 1901 • Hofmeister, 1858 • Mauritzon, 1936c,d • Narang, 1953.

STAPHYLEACEAE

The anther is tetrasporangiate with a persistent epidermis. The endothecium develops fibrous thickenings, the middle layer is ephemeral, and the cells of the glandular tapetum become 2-nucleate. Simultaneous cytokinesis in the microspore mother cells follows meiosis and the microspore tetrads are tetrahedral. Pollen grains are 2-celled when shed.

The ovule is anatropous, bitegmic, and crassinucellar, with the micropyle formed by both integuments. The archesporial cell cuts off a primary parietal cell which gives rise to 3–8 parietal layers and the apical cells of the nucellar epidermis divide periclinally to form a nucellar cap 2 or 3 cells in thickness. Cytokinesis in the megaspore mother cell accompanies meiosis and the chalazal megaspore of a linear tetrad develops into a Polygonum type embryo sac. The synergids of *Turpinia nepalensis* are hooked and exhibit the filiform apparatus, the polar nuclei fuse before fertilization, and the 3 antipodal cells are ephemeral.

Endosperm formation is Nuclear but embryogeny has not been described.

Guérin, 1901 • Jönsson, 1879–1880, 1881 • Mottier, 1914 • L. L. Narayana, 1960a • Riddle, 1905b • Soltwedel, 1882 • Strasburger, 1880b, 1884b.

STEGNOSPERMACEAE

Embryologically unknown.

STENOMERIDACEAE

Embryologically unknown.

STERCULIACEAE

The anther is tetrasporangiate with a persistent epidermis and its wall development conforms to the Dicotyledonous type, with the exception of *Pterospermum* and *Sterculia* where the Basic type is followed. The endothecium develops fibrous thickenings, the 1 or 2 middle layers are ephemeral, and the cells of the glandular tapetum become multinucleate. In *Guazuma tomentosa* and *Waltheria indica*, however, Venkata Rao (1949) has reported the development of a false periplasmodium following breakdown of the inner tangential tapetal walls. Simultaneous cytokinesis in the microspore mother cells follows meiosis and the microspore tetrads are tetrahedral. Pollen grains are 2-celled when shed and frequently contain starch grains.

The ovule is anatropous, bitegmic, and crassinucellar, usually with a zigzag micropyle formed by both integuments. However, in *Abroma augusta* and *Guazuma tomentosa* the nucellus protrudes beyond the poorly developed inner integument and only the outer integument forms the micropyle; an extension of this condition is seen in the naked nucelli of *Buettneria herbacea* and *Helicteres isora* where growth of both integuments is arrested. A multiple archesporium is common but usually only one cell undergoes further development and cuts off a primary parietal cell. In *Pterospermum acerifolium* and *P. heyneanum*, however, at least 10–15 archesporial cells start development, but, while the hypodermal cells each cut off a primary parietal cell, the subhypodermal ones function directly as megaspore mother cells and all may undergo meiosis. The primary parietal cell gives rise to 3–6 parietal layers and the apical cells of the nucellar epidermis divide periclinally to form a nucellar cap 2–6 cells in thickness. Cytokinesis in the megaspore mother cell accompanies meiosis and the chalazal megaspore of a linear tetrad develops into a Polygonum type embryo sac. The synergids are hooked, the polar nuclei remain closely applied but do not fuse until one is fertilized by a male gamete, the 3 antipodal cells commence degeneration before fertilization, and starch grains are present in the embryo sac. A hypostase is differentiated and may be cup-shaped.

Endosperm formation is Nuclear and according to Håkansson (1947) the primary endosperm nucleus in *Theobroma cacao* is not formed until 72 hours after pollination. The endosperm later becomes cellular throughout and Cheesman (1927) reported the appearance of the first cell walls 50 days after fertilization in *T. cacao*. Embryogeny conforms to the Asterad type and a 3-celled suspensor is formed. The zygote of *T. cacao* divides 40–50 days after fertilization.

Banerji, 1941 • Cheesman, 1927 • Håkansson, 1947 • Heyn, 1930 • Kuyjper, 1914 • Müntzing, 1947 • Y. M. L. Sharma, 1938 • Stahel, 1928 • Venkata Rao, 1948, 1949, 1950, 1951b, 1952c, 1953b • Warming, 1878 • Wright, 1907.

STILBEACEAE

Embryologically unknown.

STRASBURGERIACEAE

Embryologically unknown.

STRELITZIACEAE

Development of the anther and pollen grains has not been described but in *Heliconia bihai* successive cytokinesis in the microspore mother cells accompanies meiosis.

The ovule is anatropous, bitegmic, and crassinucellar, with the micropyle formed by both integuments. The archesporial cell cuts off a primary parietal cell which forms a single parietal layer and the apical cells of the nucellar epidermis become radially elongated. Cytokinesis in the megaspore mother cell accompanies meiosis and the chalazal megaspore of a linear or T-shaped tetrad develops into a Polygonum type embryo sac. The synergids are pyriform, the polar nuclei fuse before fertilization, and the 3 small antipodal cells soon degenerate.

Endosperm formation is Nuclear but embryogeny is unknown.

W. H. Brown and Sharp, 1911 • J. E. Humphrey, 1896 • Kracauer, 1930 • Mauritzon, 1936e • B. Palm, 1920.

STRYCHNACEAE

The number of sporangia comprising the anther has not been recorded. In *Strychnos* three parietal layers are formed and the cells of the glandular tapetum become 2-nucleate. Simultaneous cytokinesis in the microspore mother cells follows meiosis and the microspore tetrads are tetrahedral. Pollen grains are 3-celled when shed.

The ovule is anatropous, unitegmic, and tenuinucellar. The archesporial cell functions directly as the megaspore mother cell in which cytokinesis accompanies meiosis and the chalazal megaspore of a linear tetrad develops into a Polygonum type embryo sac. The synergids are pyriform, the polar nuclei fuse before fertilization, and the 3 antipodal cells are ephemeral.

Endosperm formation and embryogeny have not been investigated.

Mohrbutter, 1936.

STYLIDIACEAE

The anther is tetrasporangiate and its wall development conforms to the Dicotyledonous type. The endothecium develops fibrous thickenings, the middle layer is ephemeral, and the cells of the glandular tapetum become 2-nucleate. Simultaneous cytokinesis in the microspore mother cells follows meiosis and the microspore tetrads are tetrahedral. Pollen grains are 3-celled when shed and those of *Levenhookia dubia* and *Stylidium graminifolium* may germinate *in situ*.

The ovule is anatropous, unitegmic, and tenuinucellar. The archesporial cell functions directly as the megaspore mother cell in which cytokinesis accompanies meiosis and the chalazal megaspore of a linear tetrad develops into a Polygonum type embryo sac. The synergids are very elongated, hooked, and, in *Levenhookia*, they exhibit the filiform apparatus. The polar nuclei fuse before fertilization, the 3 antipodal cells persist into postfertilization stages, and starch grains are present in the embryo sac of *Stylidium*. A well-developed endothelium is formed.

Endosperm formation is *ab initio* Cellular with the development of terminal haustoria, each of which is 2-celled and gives off long, aggressive processes which invade the integument.

Embryogeny follows the Solanad type and a slender 5-6-celled suspensor is formed.

Burns, 1900 • Crété, 1951d • Dahlgren, 1920 • Rosén, 1935, 1949 • Subramanyam, 1950a,b, 1951b,d, 1953.

STYRACACEAE

The anther is tetrasporangiate and its wall development conforms to the Dicotyledonous type. The nature of the wall layers has not been described apart from the glandular tapetum whose cells become 2-nucleate. Simultaneous cytokinesis in the microspore mother cells follows meiosis and the microspore tetrads are tetrahedral or isobilateral. Pollen grains are 2-celled when shed.

The ovule is anatropous to hemianatropous, bitegmic, and tenuinucellar, with the micropyle formed by the inner integument. The archesporial cell functions directly as the megaspore mother cell in which cytokinesis accompanies meiosis and the chalazal megaspore of a linear or T-shaped tetrad develops into a Polygonum type embryo sac. The synergids are much elongated, the polar nuclei often fuse only in association with a male gamete, and the 3 antipodal cells are ephemeral. Starch grains are present in the embryo sac.

Endosperm formation is *ab initio* Cellular.

Embryogeny conforms to the Solanad type and a broad multiseriate suspensor is developed in *Styrax officinalis*.

Copeland, 1938a • Manshard, 1936 • Veillet-Bartoszewska, 1960.

SYMPLOCACEAE

Development and structure of the anther and pollen grains have not been investigated.

The ovule is anatropous, unitegmic, and tenuinucellar. The archesporial cell functions directly as the megaspore mother cell in which cytokinesis accompanies meiosis and the chalazal or subchalazal megaspore of a linear tetrad develops into a Polygonum type embryo sac. The synergids are elongated or beaked, the polar nuclei fuse just before fertilization, and the 3 antipodal cells remain uninucleate. Starch grains are present in the embryo sac which is enclosed by an endothelium.

Endosperm formation and embryogeny have not been described but adventive polyembryony has been reported in *Symplocos klotzschii*.

Chirtoiü, 1918 • Warming, 1913.

TACCACEAE

The anther is tetrasporangiate with a persistent epidermis and its wall development probably conforms to the Dicotyledonous type. The endothecial cells become much enlarged radially, the 2 middle layers are ephemeral, and the cells of the glandular tapetum become 2-nucleate. Simultaneous cytokinesis in the microspore mother cells follows meiosis and the microspore tetrads are tetrahedral. Pollen grains are 2-celled when shed.

The ovule is anatropous, bitegmic, and crassinucellar, with the micropyle formed by the inner integument. The archesporial cell cuts

off a primary parietal cell which forms a single parietal layer. Cyto-kinesis in the megaspore mother cell accompanies meiosis and the chalazal megaspore of a linear tetrad develops into a Polygonum type embryo sac. The synergids are pyriform, the polar nuclei fuse before fertilization, and the 3 antipodal cells are ephemeral. The devel-opment of an embryo sac by somatic apospory is of occasional occur-rence in *Schizocapsa plantaginea*.

Endosperm formation is Nuclear but later the tissue becomes cellular.

Embryogeny is unknown.

Håkansson, 1921 • Limpricht, 1902 • Paetow, 1931 • B. Palm, 1920 • Solms-Laubach, 1878 • Süssenguth, 1919, 1921a.

TAMARICACEAE

The anther is tetrasporangiate with a persistent epidermis. The endothecium develops fibrous thickenings, the 2 middle layers are ephemeral, and the cells of the glandular tapetum become 2- or 3-nu-cleate, followed by nuclear fusion and further division. Simultaneous cytokinesis in the microspore mother cells follows meiosis and the microspore tetrads are tetrahedral, decussate, or isobilateral. Pollen grains are 2-celled when shed in *Tamarix* spp., but 3-celled in *Myri-caria germanica*.

The ovule is anatropous, bitegmic, and crassinucellar, with the mi-cropyle formed by the inner integument. At ovule maturity the epider-mal cells of the chalaza grow out as long hairs. The archesporial cell cuts off a primary parietal cell which forms a single parietal layer. Cytokinesis in the megaspore mother cell does not accompany meiosis and the embryo sac is tetrasporic but its postmeiotic behavior is variable. Either the megaspore nuclei divide further to form embryo sacs of the Adoxa, Drusa, or Chrysanthemum cinarariaefolium types or, after assuming the 1 + 3 arrangement, the 3 chalazal nuclei fuse and a Fritillaria type of embryo sac results. *Myricaria germanica* consistently follows the Fritillaria type, but in *Tamarix* embryo sac formation is very variable and all four types may occur in the same species. The synergids are broad and may be shortly hooked but the filiform apparatus has been reported only in *M. germanica*. The polar nuclei become closely associated near the egg but only fuse in associa-tion with a male gamete, and the 3 antipodal cells degenerate at fertilization or shortly after.

Endosperm formation in *T. tetrandra* is *ab initio* Cellular but in the other members it is Nuclear and becomes cellular later.

Embryogeny conforms to the Solanad type and a broad massive suspensor is formed. Polyembryony is common.

Battaglia, 1941, 1943 • Frisendahl, 1912 • Hjelmqvist and Grazi, 1964 • B. M. Johri, 1954 • B. M. Johri and Kak, 1954 • A. C. Joshi and Kajale, 1936 • Mauritzon, 1936b • Pàroli, 1939 • Puri, 1939a • Y. M. L. Sharma, 1939, 1940 • Traub, 1939 • Zabban, 1936.

TECOPHILAEACEAE

Anther development and structure have not been investigated but the cells of the glandular (?) tapetum of *Odontostomum* become 2-nucleate. Simultaneous cytokinesis in the microspore mother cells follows meiosis and the microspore tetrads are tetrahedral. Pollen grains are 2-celled when shed.

The ovule is anatropous, bitegmic, and crassinucellar, with the micropyle formed by both integuments in *Odontostomum* but only the inner one in *Cyanella*. The archesporial cell cuts off a primary parietal cell which gives rise to 1 or 2 parietal layers and in *Odontostomum* the apical cells of the nucellar epidermis divide periclinally and form a nucellar cap 3–5 cells in thickness. Cytokinesis in the megaspore mother cell accompanies meiosis, although it is sometimes suppressed in the micropylar dyad cell, and the chalazal megaspore of a linear tetrad or "triad" develops into a Polygonum type embryo sac. The synergids are pyriform, the polar nuclei fuse before fertilization, and the 3 antipodal cells commence degeneration early although their remains may persist into early endosperm formation. In *Cyanella capensis*, and perhaps *Cyanastrum*, the mature embryo sac forms a tubular chalazal haustorium. A funicular obturator develops in *Cyanastrum* and *Odontostomum*.

Endosperm formation is Nuclear but later it becomes cellular except for the chalazal haustorium, which remains free-nuclear.

Embryogeny has not been described but adventive embryony leading to polyembryony has been reported in *Cyanella capensis*.

Cave, 1952 • Fries, 1919 • Nietsch, 1941 • Vos, 1950.

TETRACENTRACEAE

Embryologically unknown.

TETRAMERISTACEAE

Embryologically unknown.

THEACEAE

The anther is tetrasporangiate with a persistent epidermis which in *Cleyera integrifolia* and *Tutcheria shinkoensis* bears a thick cuticle. The endothecium develops fibrous thickenings, the 1–3 middle layers are ephemeral, and the cells of the glandular tapetum become 2-nucleate. Simultaneous cytokinesis in the microspore mother cells follows meiosis and the microspore tetrads are tetrahedral, isobilateral, or decussate. Pollen grains are 2-celled when shed.

The ovule is anatropous, bitegmic, and tenuinucellar, with the micropyle formed by the inner integument. The archesporial cell functions directly as the megaspore mother cell in which cytokinesis accompanies only the heterotypic division in *Thea sinensis* and the chalazal dyad cell develops into an Allium type embryo sac. The synergids are pyriform, the polar nuclei fuse before fertilization, and the 3 antipodal cells remain 1-nucleate. A hypostase is differentiated.

Endosperm formation is Nuclear but the tissue later becomes cellular.

Embryogeny conforms to the Solanad type and polyembryony has been reported in *Thea*.

Braun, 1960 • Buschmann, 1914 • Cavara, 1899 • Cohen-Stuart, 1916 • Fagerlind, 1939c • G. W. Johnston, 1941 • Kapil and Sethi, 1963 • Keng, 1962 • Tomo, Fuchinoue, and Fuchinoue, 1958 • Venkataramani, 1950 • Wu, 1960.

THEOPHRASTACEAE

Development of the anther and pollen grains has not been described but, according to Schnarf, the tapetum is multilayered.

The ovule is anatropous to hemianatropous or almost campylotropous, bitegmic, and tenuinucellar, with the micropyle formed by both integuments. The archesporial cell functions directly as the megaspore mother cell in which cytokinesis accompanies meiosis and the chalazal megaspore of a linear tetrad develops into a Polygonum type embryo sac. The synergids of *Theophrasta macrophylla* are hooked, the polar nuclei fuse before fertilization, and the 3 antipodal cells degenerate at embryo sac maturity.

Endosperm formation is Nuclear but embryogeny is unknown.

Dahlgren, 1916 • Mauritzon, 1935a • Schnarf, 1931a • Warming, 1913.

THISMIACEAE

The anther is tetrasporangiate with a persistent epidermis. The endothecium develops fibrous thickenings, the middle layer is ephemeral, and the tapetum is probably glandular. The development of the pollen grains has not been described but they are 2- or 3-celled when shed.

The ovule is anatropous, bitegmic, and tenuinucellar. The archesporial cell functions directly as the megaspore mother cell in which cytokinesis accompanies meiosis and the chalazal megaspore of a linear tetrad develops into a Polygonum type embryo sac. The synergids are pyriform, the polar nuclei fuse before fertilization, and in *Thismia americana* the 3 antipodal nuclei are not enclosed in cells. Somatic apospory has been reported in *Thismia* spp.

Endosperm formation is either *ab initio* Cellular (*T. leutzelburgii*) or Helobial (*T. clandestina, T. javanica, T. versteegii*) where the small primary chalazal chamber becomes haustorial and the primary micropylar chamber becomes coenocytic and finally cellular.

Embryogeny is little known but early cleavages indicate either the Asterad or the Onagrad type.

Bernard and Ernst, 1910, 1911 • Ernst, 1918 • Ernst and Bernard, 1909a,b, 1911 • Goebel and Süssenguth, 1924 • Johow, 1885 • K. Meyer, 1909, 1925b • Miers, 1866 • N. E. Pfeiffer, 1914, 1918 • Rosenberg, 1930 • Schnarf, 1929b • Treub, 1883d.

THURNIACEAE

Embryologically unknown.

THYMELAEACEAE

The anther is tetrasporangiate with a persistent epidermis and its wall development conforms to the Monocotyledonous type in *Lasiosiphon eriocephalus* but the Basic type in *Wikstroemia canescens*. The endothecium develops fibrous thickenings, the 1 or 2 middle layers are ephemeral, and the cells of the glandular tapetum become 2–6-nucleate with frequent nuclear fusions. Simultaneous cytokinesis in the microspore mother cells follows meiosis and the microspore tetrads are tetrahedral or isobilateral. Pollen grains are 3-celled when shed and often contain starch grains.

The ovule is anatropous to hemianatropous, bitegmic, and crassinucellar, with the micropyle formed by the inner integument. The archesporial cell cuts off a primary parietal cell which gives rise usually to 3–5 parietal layers, but in *Daphne* 8–10 layers are formed. The apical cells of the nucellar epidermis divide periclinally to form a nucellar cap 2 or 3 cells in thickness although in *Daphne cannabina* it becomes a much-elongated structure, up to 14 cells in length, which protrudes into the micropyle. Cytokinesis in the megaspore mother cell accompanies meiosis and the chalazal megaspore of a linear or T-shaped tetrad develops into a Polygonum type embryo sac. The synergids are hooked and those of *Daphne cannabina* exhibit the filiform apparatus, while the polar nuclei fuse immediately before fertilization. In *D. alpina*, *Gnidia carinata*, and *Wikstroemia indica* 3 antipodal cells are present, but some degree of secondary multiplication is usual and 30 or more cells may be formed in *Daphne* spp., *Dirca palustris*, *Passerina pectinata*, *Thymelaea arvensis*, and *T. passerina*. A hypostase is usually present and an obturator of elongated cells forms from the base of the style.

Endosperm formation is Nuclear but the tissue later becomes cellular throughout.

Embryogeny conforms to the Asterad type and the suspensor is either absent or short. Polyembryony has been reported in *Daphne cannabina* and *Wikstroemia indica*.

Balicka-Iwanowska, 1899 • Beauregard, 1877 • Dahlgren, 1915a • Fagerlind, 1940c • Fuchs, 1938 • Guérin, 1913, 1915 • Hofmeister, 1849 • Jönsson, 1879–1880, 1881 • A. C. Joshi, 1937a • Kausik, 1940c • Mauritzon, 1939c • Osawa, 1913a • Prohaska, 1883 • Souèges, 1942a • Strasburger, 1884a, 1885, 1909b • Venkateswarlu, 1945, 1946, 1947a,c • Vesque, 1879a • H. Winkler, 1904, 1906 • Yamaha, 1926.

TILIACEAE

The anther is tetrasporangiate and in *Muntingia calabura* its wall development conforms to the Basic type. The epidermis is persistent and its cells may become tannin-filled. In *Elaeocarpus* the cells of the subepidermal layer develop into stone cells but in other representatives a fibrous endothecium is formed. The 1 or 2 middle layers are ephemeral and the cells of the glandular tapetum become 2-nucleate. Simultaneous cytokinesis in the microspore mother cells follows meiosis and the microspore tetrads are tetrahedral. Pollen grains are 2-celled when shed.

The ovule is anatropous to hemianatropous, bitegmic, and crassinucellar, with the micropyle either formed by the outer integument (*Corchorus*), formed by the inner (*Entelea*), or zigzag and formed by both integuments (*Aristotelia, Elaeocarpus, Muntingia, Tilia*). Although a multicellular archesporium is common, only one cell cuts off a primary parietal cell which gives rise to 4–8 parietal layers, and in *Entelea palmata* and *Triumfetta rhomboidea*, the apical cells of the nucellar epidermis undergo a single periclinal division and form a nucellar cap 2 or 3 cells in thickness. Cytokinesis in the mega-spore mother cell accompanies meiosis and the chalazal megaspore of a linear or T-shaped tetrad develops into a Polygonum type embryo sac. In *Aristotelia manqui* and *A. racemosa* Mauritzon (1934a) reported that usually the subchalazal megaspore functions. The synergids of *Elaeocarpus* and *Muntingia* are hooked and those of *Corchorus, Sparrmania,* and *Triumfetta* extend almost half the length of the embryo sac. The polar nuclei fuse just before or at fertilization in the micropylar portion of the embryo sac, but in *Elaeocarpus* fusion occurs close to the 3 ephemeral antipodal cells. Starch grains are present in the mature embryo sac. An endothelium and a hypostase is differentiated in *Elaeocarpus*.

Endosperm formation is Nuclear, often with an accumulation of nuclei and cytoplasm at the chalazal end. Wall formation is initiated around the embryo and the tissue becomes cellular throughout.

Embryogeny conforms to the Onagrad type in *Muntingia* but otherwise it follows the Asterad type. Polyembryony has been reported in *Corchorus olitorius*.

Banerji, 1932, 1933 • Battacharya and Mitra, 1952 • Brandza, 1891 • M. R. Choudhury, 1961 • R. M. Datta, 1954, 1955, 1960 • Iyer, 1962 • Iyer, Sulbha, and Swaminathan, 1961 • Juel, 1915 • Mauritzon, 1934a • Panda, 1961 • Sommer, 1929 • Souèges, 1941c • Stenar, 1925b • Strasburger, 1884b • Sulbha and Swaminathan, 1959 • Venkata Rao, 1951a, 1952b, 1953a • Venkata Rao and K. V. S. Rao, 1952 • Warming, 1878.

TOVARIACEAE

The development and structure of the anther have not been described apart from the report of a glandular tapetum. Simultaneous cytokinesis in the microspore mother cells follows meiosis and the pollen grains are 2-celled when shed.

The ovule is bitegmic and crassinucellar with a zigzag micropyle formed by both integuments. The archesporial cell cuts off a primary parietal cell which undergoes many divisions. Cytokinesis in the megaspore mother cell accompanies meiosis and the chalazal megaspore of a linear tetrad develops into a Polygonum type embryo sac. The synergids are elongated and bear the filiform apparatus.

Endosperm formation is Nuclear but later the tissue becomes cellular.

Embryogeny has not been investigated.

Mauritzon, 1934 • Schürhoff, 1926b.

TRAPACEAE

The anther is tetrasporangiate with a persistent epidermis. The endothecium develops fibrous thickenings, the 2 or 3 middle layers are ephemeral, and the cells of the glandular tapetum become multinucleate with frequent nuclear fusions. The tapetum becomes irregularly 2-layered and Ubisch granules are present on its inner walls. Simultaneous cytokinesis in the microspore mother cells follows meiosis and the microspore tetrads are tetrahedral or decussate. Pollen grains are 2-celled when shed and those of *Trapa bispinosa* may germinate *in situ*.

The ovule is anatropous, bitegmic, and crassinucellar, but although the inner integument exceeds the outer in length, a true micropyle is not formed owing to the development of a long nucellar beak. The archesporial cell cuts off a primary parietal cell which gives rise to several parietal layers, and these, together with layers derived from periclinal divisions of the nucellar epidermis, form the nucellar beak which reaches the surface of the ovule. Cytokinesis in the megaspore mother cell accompanies meiosis and the chalazal megaspore of a linear tetrad develops into a Polygonum type embryo sac. The synergids are pyriform and in *T. natans* the 3 antipodal nuclei are very ephemeral and may fuse to form a single large hypertrophied nucleus, while in *T. bispinosa* Ghosh (1954) and Ram (1956) were unable to detect any antipodal nuclei or lower polar nucleus. A hypostase is differentiated and the nucellar beak persists during early embryogeny.

Endosperm formation does not occur. The primary endosperm nucleus assumes an irregular outline and moves to the base of the embryo sac where it degenerates.

Embryogeny conforms to the Solanad type. The haustorial suspensor is long, coiled, and multiseriate, its upper portion forming a collar around the embryo proper, one of whose cotyledons is suppressed in development.

Ghosh, 1954 • Gibelli and Ferrero, 1891a,b, 1895 • Hofmeister, 1858 • Ishikawa, 1918 • Nagl, 1962 • Ram, 1956 • Tison, 1919.

TREMANDRACEAE

Development and structure of the anther and pollen grains have not been described.

The ovule is anatropous, bitegmic, and crassinucellar, with the micropyle formed by both integuments. The presence of a parietal layer in *Tetratheca* spp. presupposes the cutting off of a primary parietal cell, but there is no information on the development of the embryo sac. According to Mauritzon (1936d) 3 antipodal cells are present.

Endosperm formation and embryogeny have not been investigated.

Chatin, 1870 • Mauritzon, 1936d.

TRICHOPODACEAE

The anther is tetrasporangiate with a persistent epidermis. The endothecium develops fibrous thickenings, the middle layer is ephemeral, and the cells of the glandular tapetum become 2-nucleate. Successive cytokinesis in the microspore mother cells accompanies meiosis and the microspore tetrads are tetrahedral, decussate, isobilateral, or linear. Pollen grains are 2-celled when shed and sometimes germinate *in situ*.

The ovule of *Trichopus zeylanicus* is anatropous, bitegmic and tenuinucellar, with the zigzag micropyle formed by both integuments. The archesporial cell functions directly as the megaspore mother cell in which cytokinesis accompanies meiosis and the chalazal megaspore of a linear or T-shaped tetrad develops into a Polygonum type embryo sac. The synergids are hooked, the polar nuclei fuse at fertilization, and the 3 antipodal cells degenerate soon after. A hypostase is differentiated.

Endosperm formation is Nuclear but after a large number of nuclei have formed the tissue becomes cellular.

Embryogeny has not been described in detail, but the figures of Rao (1955e) suggest the Solanad type.

A. N. Rao, 1955e.

TRIGONIACEAE

Development and structure of the anther and pollen grains have not been investigated.

The ovule is anatropous, bitegmic, and crassinucellar, with the micropyle formed by both integuments. Since a parietal layer is present between the megaspore mother cell and the nucellar epidermis in *Trigonia parviflora*, presumably it was preceded by the cutting off of a primary parietal cell from an archesporial cell. Development of the embryo sac has not been described.

Endosperm formation and embryogeny are unknown.

Mauritzon, 1936d.

TRILLIACEAE

Development and structure of the anther and pollen grains have not been described.

The ovule is anatropous, bitegmic, and crassinucellar, with the micropyle formed by the inner integument. The archesporial cell cuts off a primary parietal cell which forms usually a single parietal layer, but in *Trillium undulatum* there are sometimes 2 such layers. In *T. recurvatum* the apical cells of the nucellar epidermis divide periclinally to form a nucellar cap 2–3 cells in thickness. Usually cytokinesis in the megaspore mother cell follows only the heterotypic meiotic division and the chalazal dyad cell develops into an Allium type embryo sac. In *T. recurvatum*, however, Chamberlain (1898) reported the formation of a linear megaspore tetrad and the development of the chalazal megaspore into a Polygonum type embryo sac, while according to McAllister (1914) cytokinesis is suppressed in *Medeola virginica* and the embryo sac is of the Adoxa type. The synergids are pyriform, the polar nuclei fuse only in association with a male gamete, and the 3 antipodal cells are usually ephemeral but in *T. undulatum* they persist into early embryogeny.

Endosperm formation is Helobial in *T. undulatum* and after a period of free-nuclear division both chambers become cellular. In the earlier reports of Nuclear endosperm in several species of *Trillium* it is possible that the formation of the small primary chalazal chamber was overlooked.

Embryogeny has not been described but adventive embryony is common.

Atkinson, 1899 • Brandt, 1916 • Chamberlain, 1898 • Coulter and Chamberlain, 1903 • Ernst, 1902 • Heatley, 1916 • Howe, 1940 • Jeffrey and Haertl, 1939a,b • B. M. Johri and Eunus, 1950 • McAllister, 1914 • Nothnagel, 1918 • Ono, 1928b • A. Smith, 1896 • Spangler, 1925 • Stenar, 1951a • Swamy, 1948c.

TRIMENIACEAE

Embryologically unknown.

TRIURIDACEAE

The anther of *Sciaphila* is tetrasporangiate with a persistent epidermis. The endothecium develops fibrous thickenings, the middle layer is ephemeral, and the tapetum is probably glandular. Successive cytokinesis in the microspore mother cells accompanies meiosis and the microspore tetrads are tetrahedral or isobilateral. Pollen grains are 3-celled when shed.

The ovule is anatropous, bitegmic, and tenuinucellar, with the micropyle formed by the inner integument. The archesporial cell functions directly as the megaspore mother cell in which cytokinesis accompanies meiosis and the chalazal megaspore of a linear tetrad develops into a Polygonum type embryo sac. The synergids are pyriform, the polar nuclei fuse before fertilization, and the 3 small antipodal cells are ephemeral.

Endosperm formation is Nuclear but the tissue later becomes cellular.

Embryogeny has not been investigated.

Johow, 1889 • Ohga and Sinotô, 1924, 1932 • Poulsen, 1886, 1905 • Wirz, 1910.

TROCHODENDRACEAE

The anther of *Euptelea* is tetrasporangiate with a persistent epidermis and the endothecium develops fibrous thickenings, but otherwise there is no information on its wall structure. Development of the pollen grains has not been described.

The ovule of *Euptelea* and *Trochodendron* is anatropous, bitegmic, and crassinucellar but the development of the embryo sac has not been investigated.

Endosperm formation is *ab initio* Cellular, but embryogeny is unknown.

Harms, 1897 • A. C. Martin, 1946 • Nast and Bailey, 1945, 1946 • Subramanyam, 1962.

TROPAEOLACEAE

The anther of *Tropaeolum* is tetrasporangiate but neither its wall development nor that of the microspores has been investigated. The pollen grains are 2-celled when shed.

The ovule is anatropous, bitegmic, and tenuinucellar, with the micropyle formed by the inner integument. The archesporial cell functions directly as the megaspore mother cell in which cytokinesis accompanies meiosis and the chalazal megaspore of a linear tetrad develops into a Polygonum type embryo sac. The synergids are pyriform, the polar nuclei fuse before fertilization, and the 3 antipodal cells degenerate at about the same time.

Endosperm formation is Nuclear.

Embryogeny has not been described in detail but possibly conforms to the Solanad type. Aggressive suspensor haustoria are formed which invade the integuments, the funicle, and the placenta.

Bersier, 1960 • Bolenbach, 1928 • Braun, 1860 • Brunotte, 1900 • Dickson, 1876 • Hegelmaier, 1876, 1878 • Hofmeister, 1849, 1858 • Hubert, 1896 • Kayser, 1893 • Leidicke, 1903 • Nagl, 1962 • Sachs, 1874 • Schacht, 1950, 1955d • Schürhoff, 1924b • Strasburger, 1875 • Suguira, 1925 • Walker, 1947 • Warming, 1873 • Wilson, 1843 • Wóycicki, 1907a,b.

TURNERACEAE

Development and structure of the anther and pollen grains have not been investigated.

The ovule of *Turnera ulmifolia* is anatropous, bitegmic, and crassinucellar, with the micropyle formed by both integuments. The archesporium is multicellular and several cells may each cut off a primary parietal cell, giving rise to about 3 parietal layers. Cytokinesis in the functional megaspore mother cell accompanies meiosis and the chalazal megaspore of a linear tetrad develops into a Polygonum type embryo sac. The synergids are hooked, the polar nuclei fuse before fertilization, and the 3 antipodal cells are ephemeral. An aril develops from the funicle, which, after fertilization, encloses the seed unequally.

Endosperm formation is Nuclear but the tissue becomes cellular later.

Embryogeny conforms to the Onagrad type and a short 2-celled suspensor is formed.

Dahlgren, 1928b • Hofmeister, 1858b • Mauritzon, 1933c, 1936b • Raju, 1956b.

TYPHACEAE

The anther of *Typha latifolia* is tetrasporangiate with a persistent epidermis. The endothecium develops fibrous thickenings, the middle layer is ephemeral, and the cells of the glandular tapetum become 2-nucleate. Successive cytokinesis in the microspore mother cells accompanies meiosis and the microspore tetrads are tetrahedral or isobilateral. Pollen grains are shed singly or in tetrads and are individually 2-celled.

The ovule is anatropous, bitegmic, and crassinucellar, with the micropyle formed by the inner integument. The archesporial cell cuts

off a primary parietal cell which gives rise to 1 or 2 parietal layers and the apical cells of the nucellar epidermis occasionally undergo a periclinal division. Cytokinesis in the megaspore mother cell accompanies meiosis and the chalazal megaspore of a linear or T-shaped tetrad develops into a Polygonum type embryo sac. The synergids are pyriform, the polar nuclei fuse before fertilization, and the 3 antipodal cells degenerate soon after.

Endosperm formation is Nuclear and embryogeny conforms to the Asterad type.

Čelakovský, 1885 • Claussen, 1927 • Dahlgren, 1918 • Dietz, 1886, 1887 • Goebel, 1923 • Graef, 1955 • Guttenberg, 1960 • Kronfeld, 1886 • Morong, 1888 • Rohrbach, 1869 • Roscoe, 1927b • J. H. Schaffner, 1897d • Schoenebeck, 1924 • Skvarla and Larson, 1963.

ULMACEAE

The anther is tetrasporangiate. The endothecium develops fibrous thickenings, the 2 middle layers of *Ulmus americana* are ephemeral, but in *Holoptelea integrifolia* where 3 or 4 layers are formed, the outermost persists. The cells of the glandular tapetum become 2–4-nucleate. Simultaneous cytokinesis in the microspore mother cells follows meiosis and the microspore tetrads are tetrahedral or decussate. Pollen grains are 2-celled when shed in *Holoptelea* but 3-celled in *Ulmus*.

The ovule is anatropous to hemianatropous, bitegmic, and usually crassinucellar, with the micropyle formed of both integuments (*Celtis*) or only the inner (*Holoptelea, Ulmus*). The archesporial cell usually cuts off a primary parietal cell which forms 2–5 parietal layers, but Walker (1950) reported the direct development of the archesporial cell into the megaspore mother cell and a tenuinucellar ovule in *U. glabra, U. pumila,* and *U. racemosa*. The apical cells of the nucellar epidermis undergo a single periclinal division to form a nucellar cap 2 cells in thickness in *U. americana* and *U. glabra*. In the megaspore mother cell of *Holoptelea integrifolia* cytokinesis accompanies meiosis and the chalazal megaspore of a linear tetrad develops into a Polygonum type embryo sac. In *Ulmus*, however, the embryo sac is tetrasporic and of either the Adoxa or Drusa types, both of which occur with varying frequencies in the same species. The synergids are pyriform, the polar nuclei fuse before fertilization, and although 3 antipodal cells are present in the Adoxa type embryo sac, the number in one of the Drusa type varies with the degree of "strike." Secondary multiplication of antipodals occurs in *Holoptelea* and up to 10 cells may be formed. A hypostase is differentiated and a funicular obturator is formed in *Holoptelea*. The pollen tube enters the ovule either through the chalaza or the integuments.

Endosperm formation is Nuclear and the tissue later becomes cellular.

Embryogeny conforms to the Solanad type in *Ulmus* and the Onagrad type in *Holoptelea*. Polyembryony is of common occurrence.

Amato, 1940a • Asanova, 1964 • Capoor, 1937b • Dahlgren, 1915a • Ekdahl, 1941 • Hofmeister, 1858 • Jönsson, 1879–1880 • Lagerberg, 1909 • Leliveld, 1935 • Modilewski, 1908b • Nawaschin, 1898a • Poddubnaja-Arnoldi, 1936 • Shuttuck, 1905 • Walker, 1938a, 1950.

UMBELLIFERAE

The anther is tetrasporangiate and its wall development conforms to the Dicotyledonous type. The endothecium develops fibrous thickenings, the middle layer is ephemeral, and the cells of the glandular tapetum become 2-nucleate. Simultaneous cytokinesis in the microspore mother cells follows meiosis and the microspore tetrads are tetrahedral, isobilateral, or decussate. Pollen grains are 3-celled when shed.

The ovule is anatropous, unitegmic, and usually tenuinucellar, with a very long micropyle formed by the combination of massive integument and small nucellus. In *Foeniculum vulgare* the ovule is pseudocrassinucellar through periclinal divisions of the apical nucellar epidermal cells, forming a nucellar cap 5–8 cells in thickness. A multicellular archesporium is common and several cells may function directly as megaspore mother cells, but usually only one develops further. In the subfamilies Apioideae and Saniculoideae, and the tribe Hydrocotyleae, cytokinesis in the megaspore mother cell usually accompanies meiosis and the chalazal megaspore of a linear tetrad develops into a Polygonum type embryo sac. In *Bupleurum aureum*, however, there is no cytokinesis after the homotypic division and the embryo sac is of the Allium type, although it is monosporic in other species of *Bupleurum*. Suppression of cytokinesis in connection with meiosis results in tetrasporic embryo sac formation, and in the tribe Mulineae, the Drusa type showing usually some degree of "strike" is characteristic. The only record of the Penaea type of embryo sac is in *Azorella trifurcata*. The synergids are short and broad and the polar nuclei fuse before or at fertilization, while in *Azorella* the secondary nucleus is formed from the fusion of 4 nuclei, one of which is derived from each quadrant of nuclei. The antipodal cells persist into early postfertilization stages but their number varies with the type of embryo sac development. In the Polygonum type 3 cells are formed which, in *Astrantia* and *Sanicula,* undergo secondary multiplication, but in the Drusa type their number is 11 or less, depending on the degree of "strike." An endothelium is always differentiated, and a hypostase is present in *Bupleurum tenue.*

Endosperm formation is Nuclear but the tissue later becomes cellular.

Embryogeny conforms to the Solanad type and a long suspensor is common.

Adatia and Shah, 1952 • J. S. Agrawal, 1950 • Bartsch, 1882 • Beghtel, 1925 • Borthwick, 1931 • Braak and Kho, 1958 • Cammerloher, 1910 • Cheignon, 1962 • Coulter and Chamberlain, 1903 • Denisova, 1962 • Elfving, 1879 • Familler, 1896 • Flemion and Henrickson, 1949 • Flemion and Waterbury, 1941 • S. C. Gupta, 1962a,b, 1964 • S. C. Gupta and M. Gupta, 1964 • S. C. Gupta and Kumari, 1959 • Håkansson, 1923, 1927, 1928, 1952a • Hegelmaier, 1878, 1885 • Hofmeister, 1858 • Juel, 1915 • Jurica, 1922 • Liehr, 1927 • Lietz, 1929 • Lindenbein, 1932 • Marano, 1954a,b • Mez, 1887 • Nordheim, 1930 • Paliwal, 1950a, 1951 • Petersen, 1911 • Rubashevskaia, 1931 • Schulz-Gaebel, 1930 • Schürhoff, 1929 • G. L. Shah, 1953 • D. Singh and Gupta, 1956 • Souèges, 1926a, 1930, 1945a, 1952e, 1954d,e,f,g,h, 1955a,b,e, 1958c • Strasburger, 1884b • Tanfani, 1888 • Welch and Grimball, 1947 • Zenkteler, 1962.

URTICACEAE

The development and structure of the anther have not been described, but simultaneous cytokinesis in the microspore mother cells follows meiosis and the microspore tetrads are tetrahedral or decussate. The pollen grains are 2-celled when shed.

The ovule is anatropous to hemianatropous, bitegmic, and crassinucellar, with the micropyle formed by the inner integument except in *Parietaria* where both integuments are involved. The archesporial cell cuts off a primary parietal cell which gives rise to 2–6 parietal layers and the apical cells of the nucellar epidermis divide periclinally to form a nucellar cap 2–5 cells in thickness. Cytokinesis in the megaspore mother cell accompanies meiosis and the chalazal megaspore of a linear tetrad develops into a Polygonum type embryo sac. Gonial apospory has been reported in several species of *Elatostemma* and the triploid form of *Boehmeria spicata.* The synergids are pyriform, the polar nuclei fuse before fertilization, and in *Urtica cannabina* the 3 antipodal cells undergo secondary multiplication. A hypostase is formed in *Urtica.*

Endosperm formation is Nuclear and the tissue later becomes cellular, with the development of a short chalazal haustorium in *Urtica.*

Embryogeny conforms to the Asterad type. Adventive embryony and polyembryony have been reported in *Elatostemma acuminatum.*

Beghtel, 1925 • Fagerlind, 1944a • Grossbard, 1924 • Hofmeister, 1858 • Lebègue, 1956a,b,c • Modilewski, 1908b • Negodi, 1930 • Nicolas, 1915 • Okabe, 1963 • Souèges, 1920j, 1921f • Strasburger, 1910a • Treub, 1906.

VACCINIACEAE

The anther is tetrasporangiate and its wall development in *Oxycoccus* conforms to the Dicotyledonous type, but with no differentiation of mechanical tissue. The innermost of the 2 or 3 hypodermal cell layers is ephemeral and the tapetum is glandular. Pollen grains are shed as permanent tetrads and individually they are 2- or 3-celled.

The ovule is anatropous, unitegmic, and tenuinucellar. The archesporial cell functions directly as the megaspore mother cell in which cytokinesis accompanies meiosis and the chalazal megaspore of a linear tetrad develops into a Polygonum type embryo sac. The synergids are pyriform, the polar nuclei fuse only in association with a male gamete in *Vaccinium angustifolium,* and the 3 antipodal cells are usually ephemeral. An endothelium encloses the embryo sac.

Endosperm formation is Nuclear in *V. angustifolia* with a linear arrangement of 4 nuclei before transverse walls are laid down. In *V. myrtillus,* however, the endosperm is *ab initio* Cellular, and according to Stevens (1919) either condition may occur in *V. corymbosa.* Terminal coenocytic endosperm haustoria are formed in all species.

Embryogeny conforms to the Solanad type.

Artopoeus, 1903 • Batygina, Teriokhin, Alimova, and Yakovlev, 1963 • Bell, 1957 • Bell and Burchill, 1955a,b • Chatin, 1870 • Hagerup, 1954 • Hofmeister, 1858b, 1859 • Matthews and Knox, 1926 • Peltrisot, 1904 • Safijowska, 1960 • Samuelsson, 1913 • N. E. Stevens, 1919 • Veillet-Bartoszewska, 1958a.

VAHLIACEAE

The anther of *Vahlia viscosa* is tetrasporangiate but its wall development has not been described except for the report that the cells of the glandular (?) tapetum become 2-nucleate. Simultaneous cytokinesis in the microspore mother cells follows meiosis and the microspore tetrads are tetrahedral or isobilateral. Pollen grains are 2-celled when shed.

The ovule is anatropous, bitegmic, and tenuinucellar, with the micropyle formed by the inner integument. The archesporial cell functions directly as the megaspore mother cell in which cytokinesis accompanies meiosis and the chalazal megaspore of a linear tetrad develops into a Polygonum type embryo sac. The synergids are hooked, the polar nuclei fuse before fertilization, and the 3 antipodal cells persist into early postfertilization stages. An endothelium encloses the embryo sac.

Endosperm formation is *ab initio* Cellular with the development of a nonaggressive 4-celled chalazal haustorium.

Embryogeny conforms to the Caryophyllad type.

Mauritzon, 1933a • Raghavan and Srinivasan 1942c.

VALERIANACEAE

The anther is tetrasporangiate and its wall development conforms to the Dicotyledonous type. The endothecium develops fibrous thickenings, the middle layer is ephemeral, and the tapetum is amoeboid. Simultaneous cytokinesis in the microspore mother cells follows meiosis and the pollen grains are 3-celled when shed.

The ovule is anatropous, unitegmic, and tenuinucellar. The archesporial cell functions directly as the megaspore mother cell in which cytokinesis accompanies meiosis and the chalazal megaspore of a linear tetrad develops into a Polygonum type embryo sac. The synergids are pyriform and commonly become hooked, the polar nuclei fuse before fertilization, and the 3 antipodal cells persist during early postfertilization stages. An endothelium encloses the embryo sac.

Endosperm formation is *ab initio* Cellular and embryogeny of *Centranthus* and *Valerianella* conforms to the Asterad type.

Asplund, 1920 • Elfving, 1879 • Guignard, 1893 • Hofmeister, 1858 • Jönsson, 1879–1880, 1881 • Juel, 1915 • Schürhoff, 1926b • Souèges, 1923a, 1941b • Vesque, 1878 • Yamaha, 1926.

VELLOZIACEAE

The development and structure of the anther have not been described except for the report of a glandular tapetum. Successive cytokinesis in the microspore mother cells accompanies meiosis, but there is no information on the constituents of the pollen grains.

The ovule of *Vellozia* is anatropous and pseudocrassinucellar. The apical cells of the nucellar epidermis divide periclinally and the archesporial cell functions directly as the megaspore mother cell. No information has been traced on the development of the embryo sac.

Endosperm formation and embryogeny have not been investigated.

Schnarf, 1931a • Stenar, 1925b • Süssenguth, 1919.

VERBENACEAE

The anther is tetrasporangiate with a persistent epidermis and its wall development follows the Dicotyledonous type in *Congea villosa* and *Stachytarpheta dichotoma,* although the Monocotyledonous type has been reported in *Lippia nodiflora.* The endothecium develops fibrous thickenings, and while a single ephemeral middle layer is usual, up to 3 may be present in *Avicennia officinalis.* The cells of the glandular tapetum become 2–4-nucleate and Ubisch granules are present on the inner tangential walls. Simultaneous cytokinesis in the microspore mother cells follows meiosis and the microspore tetrads are tetrahedral, decussate or isobilateral. Pollen grains are usually 2-celled when shed but in *Caryopteris wallichiana* and *Stachytarpheta dichotoma* they are 3-celled, and those of *Verbena* contain starch grains.

The ovule is anatropous, unitegmic, and tenuinucellar. In *Avicennia officinalis* ovule curvature is arrested at an early stage so that it remains almost orthotropous and, because of the incomplete growth of the integument, a micropyle is not formed. The archesporial cell functions directly as the megaspore mother cell in which cytokinesis accompanies meiosis and the chalazal megaspore of a linear tetrad develops into a Polygonum type embryo sac. The synergids are hooked and beaked except in *Tectona grandis,* the polar nuclei fuse before or at fertilization, and the 3 antipodal nuclei of *Avicennia* degenerate soon after their formation, although usually they are enclosed in 3 ephemeral cells. In *Lantana camara,* however, the antipodal cells become multinucleate and occupy almost half the embryo sac before they degenerate during early postfertilization stages. In *Avicennia* the upper portion of the embryo sac protrudes into the loculus and no endothelium is differentiated as in other members. Starch grains have been reported in the embryo sacs of several genera.

Endosperm formation is *ab initio* Cellular with terminal haustoria. The chalazal haustorium is 2–4-nucleate in *Canadea, Lippia, Stachytarpheta, Tectona, Verbena,* and others but in *Callicarpa* and *Lantana* it consists of 4 uninucleate cells and in *Avicennia* it is 1-celled. The micropylar haustorium is more variable and usually less developed than the chalazal one and is frequently 4-celled, although in *Avicennia marina* and *Clerodendron fallax* only 2 cells are formed which become much enlarged and give off processes which penetrate the micropyle. In *Avicennia officinalis* the endosperm develops in the extra-ovular portion of the embryo sac and a haustorium penetrates the placenta directly. According to Swamy and Padmanabhan (1961a) the endosperm of *Avicennia* does not contain food reserves and functions as conducting tissue between the haustorium and the embryo.

Embryogeny conforms to the Onagrad type and in *Avicennia* the seed is viviparous.

Crété, 1942, 1951d • Dahlgren, 1923 • Duffas, 1930 • Hofmeister, 1858b • Jönsson, 1879–1880 • Junell, 1934 • Kanda, 1920 • Karsten, 1891 • Koorders, 1896 • J. K. Maheshwari, 1954 • K. C. Misra, 1937, 1939 • Padmanabhan, 1959, 1960, 1962a,b, 1964 • N. Pal, 1951b,c • Patermann, 1935 • Roever, 1935 • Schnarf, 1923, 1925 • Schwencke, 1931 • Souèges, 1935c,d • Swamy and Padmanabhan, 1961a • Tandon and Bali, 1955 • Tatachar, 1940 • Treub, 1883b,c • Warming, 1873.

VIOLACEAE

The anther is tetrasporangiate with a persistent epidermis. The endothecium develops fibrous thickenings, the 2–4 middle layers are ephemeral, and the cells of the glandular tapetum become 2-nucleate, with Ubisch granules on their inner walls in *Ionidium*. Simultaneous cytokinesis in the microspore mother cells follows meiosis and the microspore tetrads are tetrahedral, decussate, and isobilateral. Pollen grains are 2-celled when shed and those of the cleistogamous flowers of *Viola odorata* germinate *in situ*, the pollen tubes growing directly to the stigma through the anther wall.

The ovule is anatropous, bitegmic, and crassinucellar, with the micropyle formed by both integuments in *Ionidium* and *Viola*, but only the inner one in *Hybanthus*. The archesporial cell cuts off a primary parietal cell which gives rise to 2–4 parietal layers and in *Hybanthus* and *Ionidium* the apical cells of the nucellar epidermis divide periclinally to form a nucellar cap 2 cells in thickness. Cytokinesis in the megaspore mother cell accompanies meiosis and the chalazal megaspore of a linear tetrad develops into a Polygonum type embryo sac. The synergids are elongated and frequently hooked but a filiform apparatus has been reported only in *V. odorata* var. *praecox* and *V. riviniana*. The polar nuclei fuse in association with a male gamete and the 3 antipodal cells are ephemeral except in *H. concolor*, where Andrews (1910) reported them to be much enlarged and to extend almost to the center of the embryo sac. A fleshy aril arises from the lower part of the raphe.

Endosperm formation is Nuclear but later the tissue becomes cellular.

Embryogeny conforms to the Asterad type but no suspensor is formed.

Andrews, 1910 • Bliss, 1912 • Dahlgren, 1915a • Elfving, 1879 • Gershoy, 1940 • Gorczyński, 1929 • Greene, 1898 • Guignard, 1884 • Hofmeister, 1858 • Lagerberg, 1909 • Madge, 1929 • Mauritzon, 1936b • Mukherjee and Venugopalan, 1957 • D. Müller, 1857 • Raju, 1958 • Sachs, 1874 • Schacht, 1850, 1858 • Schnarf, 1922a • D. Singh, 1956b, 1961a, 1962a, 1963b • D. Singh and S. Gupta, 1963 • Souèges, 1937e • Strasburger, 1877 • Tulasne, 1855 • Vesque, 1879 • Warming, 1878 • West, 1930 • Westermaier, 1890.

VITACEAE

The anther is usually tetrasporangiate but in *Vitis himalayana* and *V. latifolia* it is bisporangiate, and in *V. pedata* its wall development follows the Basic type. The endothecium develops fibrous thickenings, the 2 middle layers are ephemeral, and the cells of the glandular tapetum become multinucleate, followed by nuclear fusions. In *V. trifolia*, Adatia, Mulay, and Hingorani (1950) reported an amoeboid tapetum. Simultaneous cytokinesis in the microspore mother cells follows meiosis and the microspore tetrads are tetrahedral, isobilateral, and decussate. Pollen grains are 2- or 3-celled when shed.

The ovule is anatropous, bitegmic, and crassinucellar, with the micropyle formed by the inner integument. The archesporial cell cuts off a primary parietal cell which gives rise to 4–18 parietal layers, and usually the apical cells of the nucellar epidermis divide periclinally to form a nucellar cap 2–11 cells in thickness. Cytokinesis in the megaspore mother cell accompanies meiosis and the chalazal megaspore of a linear tetrad develops into a Polygonum type embryo sac. The synergids are hooked, the polar nuclei fuse before fertilization and the 3 antipodal cells are ephemeral. According to Kashyap (1955) a varying number of nucellar cells or nuclei migrate into the antipodal extremity of the embryo sac of *V. trifolia*, where they degenerate. In *V. pallida* the apex of the embryo sac passes through the micropyle into the loculus, where it may become embedded in the ovary wall. Abortion of the egg apparatus is common in *Vitis* and is followed by parthenocarpic development of the fruit. A hypostase is differentiated and an obturator has been reported in *V. latifolia* and *V. trifolia*.

Endosperm formation is Nuclear but later the tissue becomes cellular and ruminate, following the development of ingrowths from the inner integument.

Embryogeny conforms to the Asterad type.

Adatia, Mulay, and Hingorani, 1950, 1953 • Baranov, 1927 • Berlese, 1882 • Dorsey, 1914 • Elfving, 1879 • Kashyap, 1955, 1958 • Mulay, Nair, and Sastry,

1953 • Nair and Nambisan, 1957 • Nair and Parasuraman, 1954, 1962 • Nair and Suri, 1957 • H. M. Pearson, 1932 • Periasamy, 1962a,b • Pfeffer, 1872 • Tischler, 1913 • Tkachenko, 1958.

VIVIANIACEAE

Embryologically unknown.

VOCHYSIACEAE

Development and structure of the anther and pollen grains have not been described.

The ovule of *Vochysia* is hemianatropous, bitegmic, and crassinucellar, with the micropyle formed by both integuments. The archesporial cell cuts off a primary parietal cell which gives rise to about 40 parietal layers. Development of the embryo sac, endosperm formation, and embryogeny have not been investigated.

Mauritzon, 1936d.

WINTERACEAE

The anther is tetrasporangiate and in *Degeneria* its wall development follows the Basic type. The endothecium develops fibrous thickenings and the 2–4 middle layers are usually ephemeral, although in *Zygogynum* the persistent outermost layer becomes fibrous and is indistinguishable from the endothecium. The cells of the glandular (*Degeneria, Zygogynum*) or amoeboid (*Drimys, Pseudowintera*) tapetum become 2-nucleate or finally 1-nucleate by fusion. Simultaneous cytokinesis in the microspore mother cells follows meiosis and the microspore tetrads are tetrahedral, decussate, or isobilateral. In *Degeneria* the pollen grains are shed singly but usually they adhere in permanent tetrads, and individually they are 2-celled.

The ovule is anatropous, bitegmic, and crassinucellar, with the micropyle formed by the inner integument. The archesporial cell cuts off a primary parietal cell which gives rise to 4–10 parietal layers and in *Pseudowintera* the apical cells of the nucellar epidermis divide periclinally and form a nucellar cap 2 cells in thickness. Cytokinesis in the megaspore mother cell accompanies meiosis and the chalazal megaspore of a linear tetrad develops into a Polygonum type embryo sac. The synergids of *Pseudowintera* are shortly hooked and exhibit the filiform apparatus, the polar nuclei fuse before fertilization, and the 3 antipodal cells may persist into early postfertilization stages.

Endosperm formation is *ab initio* Cellular although Strasburger (1905) reported the Nuclear type in *Drimys winteri*. Ruminate endosperm is formed in *Degeneria vitiensis*.

Embryogeny has not been investigated but the zygote of *Degeneria* divides transversely after about 300 endosperm cells have formed.

Bailey and Nast, 1943a,b, 1945 • Bhagavathi, 1938 • Bhandari, 1963a • Strasburger, 1905a • Swamy, 1949c, 1952 • Tucker, 1959 • Wille, 1886.

XANTHORRHOEACEAE

The development and structure of the anther and pollen grains have not been investigated.

The ovule is anatropous, bitegmic, and crassinucellar, with the micropyle formed by the inner integument. In *Lomandra rigida* the archesporial cell cuts off a primary parietal cell which gives rise to 3 parietal layers, and the apical cells of the nucellar epidermis divide periclinally to form a nucellar cap 3 cells in thickness. Cytokinesis in the megaspore mother cell accompanies meiosis and the chalazal megaspore of a linear tetrad develops into a Polygonum type embryo sac. The synergids are pyriform and exhibit the filiform apparatus, the polar nuclei fuse before fertilization, and 3 large antipodal cells are formed. The mature embryo sac of *Lomandra* is as broad as it is long and occupies the apex of long column of nucellar tissue.

Endosperm formation and embryogeny have not been described.

Schnarf and Wunderlich, 1939.

XYRIDACEAE

The anther is tetrasporangiate with a persistent epidermis. The cells of the endothecium do not develop fibrous thickenings, the middle layer is ephemeral, and the cells of the glandular tapetum become 2-nucleate and sometimes 1-nucleate by fusion. Successive cytokinesis in the microspore mother cells accompanies meiosis and the microspore tetrads are isobilateral or occasionally decussate. In *Xyris pauciflora* the pollen grains are 2-celled when shed, but those of *X. indica* are 3-celled.

The ovule is orthotropous, bitegmic, and tenuinucellar, with the micropyle formed by both integuments. The archesporial cell functions directly as the megaspore mother cell in which cytokinesis accompanies meiosis in *X. indica*, and although the micropylar dyad cell may often remain undivided, the chalazal megaspore of a linear tetrad or "triad" develops into a Polygonum type embryo sac. In *X. pauciflora*, however, the micropylar dyad cell degenerates soon after its formation and the chalazal dyad cell develops into an Allium type embryo sac. The synergids may be shortly hooked, the polar nuclei fuse before fertilization, and in *X. pauciflora* the 3 antipodal nuclei show signs of degeneration soon after their formation, but in *X. indica* they are enclosed in cells before they break down.

Endosperm formation is Nuclear, with an accumulation of nuclei and cytoplasm at the chalazal end of the embryo sac. Wall formation is initiated at the micropylar pole and the first cells are 1-nucleate, but toward the base of the embryo sac larger portions of cytoplasm containing several nuclei are enclosed and the cells are coenocytic. Some evidence of nuclear fusion and the secondarily uninucleate condition was reported in *X. pauciflora*.

Embryogeny is of the Asterad type but no suspensor is formed and the embryo is undifferentiated in the mature seed.

Govindappa, 1953, 1955 • Weinzieher, 1914.

ZANNICHELLIACEAE

The anther of *Zannichellia palustris* is tetrasporangiate, but apart from the report of an amoeboid tapetum its wall structure has not been described. Successive cytokinesis in the microspore mother cells accompanies meiosis and the pollen grains of *Zannichellia palustris* are 3-celled when shed.

The ovule is anatropous, bitegmic, and crassinucellar. The archesporial cell cuts off a primary parietal cell which forms several parietal layers below the nucellar epidermis. According to Campbell (1897) the embryo sac develops from the micropylar megaspore, but as he found a row of only 3 cells the possibility exists that the functional so-called megaspore is really the micropylar dyad cell and that the embryo sac is of the Scilla type. The polar nuclei fuse before fertilization and the 3 antipodal cells may undergo secondary multiplication to form 4 or 5 cells.

Endosperm formation is Helobial and embryogeny conforms to the Caryophyllad type. The basal cell of the 3-celled uniseriate suspensor is large and vesicular.

Campbell, 1897 • Hofmeister, 1858, 1861 • Jönsson, 1881 • B. Palm, 1915 • Souèges, 1954a • Venkatesh, 1952 • Warming, 1873 • Wille, 1882b.

ZINGIBERACEAE

The anther is tetrasporangiate with a persistent epidermis which in *Amomum, Elettaria,* and *Zingiber* develops fibrous thickenings and resembles the underlying endothecium. Of the 4–6 middle layers, the inner ones are ephemeral, and the outer 1 or 2 layers may develop fibrous thickenings and persist. The tapetum is usually glandular and its cells become 2-nucleate, but an amoeboid tapetum has been reported in *Amomum dealbatum* and *Nicolaia atropurpurea.* In *Amomum* and *Costus* nuclear divisions may be accompanied by periclinal cell divisions so that the tapetum becomes irregularly 2- or 3-layered. Successive cytokinesis in the microspore mother cells accompanies meiosis and the microspore tetrads are usually isobilateral, but tetrahedral, linear, and T-shaped tetrads are of occasional occurrence. Pollen grains are 2-celled when shed and frequently contain starch grains.

The ovule is anatropous, bitegmic, and crassinucellar, with the micropyle formed by the inner integument. The archesporial cell cuts off a primary parietal cell which forms a single parietal layer, and the apical cells of the nucellar epidermis become much elongated radially, while the lateral nucellar epidermal cells may undergo several periclinal divisions. Cytokinesis in the megaspore mother cell accompanies meiosis and the chalazal megaspore of a linear tetrad develops into a Polygonum type embryo sac. Suppression of cytokinesis and the development of a tetrasporic Adoxa type embryo sac has been reported in *Costus* spp. The synergids are usually hooked in *Costus* and *Hedychium,* the polar nuclei fuse before fertilization, and the secondary nucleus moves close to the 3 ephemeral antipodal nuclei. Several authors have reported the occurrence of supernumerary nuclei at the antipodal pole, which may be of nucellar origin. A hypostase is always differentiated. A caruncle is formed from the lip of the outer integument and varies in its development from a swollen pad of tissue (*Alpinia, Costus*) to a sheath which extends proximally over the ovule (*Elettaria, Hedychium*). In *Hitchenia* this sheath is lobed and in *Zingiber* its margin is fringed.

Endosperm formation is Helobial and the small chalazal chamber usually remains 2-nucleate, but in *Costus speciosus* and *Hitchenia caulina* up to 24 nuclei occur. The behavior of this chamber in *Hedychium acuminatum* is very variable in that it may remain 1-nucleate or, if the nucleus divides, a transverse wall may form and the upper cell becomes coenocytic. In the micropylar chamber nuclear divisions continue during early embryogeny and cell formation takes place when the embryo reaches the globular stage.

Embryogeny in *Costus speciosus* conforms to the Caryophyllad type, but in other representatives it follows the Asterad type and a suspensor is not developed. Polyembryony has been reported in *H. acuminatum*.

Banerji, 1940a • Banerji and Venkateswarlu, 1935 • F. Berger, 1958 • Boehm, 1931 • Elfving, 1879 • P. J. Gregory, 1936 • Harling, 1949 • J. E. Humphrey, 1896 • Lötscher, 1905 • Madge, 1934, 1936 • Mauritzon, 1936e • B. Palm, 1915, 1920 • Panchaksharappa, 1959, 1962a,b • Raghavan and Venkatasubban, 1941c • Sachar and Arora, 1963 • Schachner, 1924 • Süssenguth, 1919, 1921a.

ZOSTERACEAE

The development and structure of the anther have not been described in detail, but in *Zostera marina* 3 or 4 parietal layers are formed, of which the innermost is the amoeboid tapetum. Most of the sporogenous cells divide longitudinally to form elongated microspore mother cells but a few divide transversely and their daughter cells are sterile. Successive cytokinesis in the microspore mother cells accompanies meiosis but is always parallel to the long axis of the cell and the filiform microspores elongate up to 2000 μ. The pollen grains are filamentous and 2-nucleate when shed.

The ovule is orthotropous, bitegmic, and pseudocrassinucellar, with the micropyle formed by the inner integument. The apical cells of the nucellar epidermis divide periclinally and form a nucellar cap 3 cells in thickness. The archesporial cell functions directly as the megaspore mother cell in which cytokinesis accompanies meiosis and the chalazal megaspore of a linear tetrad develops into a Polygonum type embryo sac. The synergids are pyriform, the polar nuclei fuse before fertilization, and the 3 antipodal cells persist into early embryogeny. A hypostase is differentiated following active division of the chalazal cells.

Endosperm formation is Nuclear and during early postfertilization stages the base of the embryo sac extends into the chalaza around the hypostase.

Embryogeny conforms to the Caryophyllad type and the basal cell of the suspensor becomes much enlarged.

Clavaud, 1878 • Dahlgren, 1939b • Grönland, 1851 • Hofmeister, 1852, 1858, 1861 • Jönsson, 1881 • Rosenberg, 1901a,b • Souèges, 1954a • A. R. A. Taylor, 1957.

ZYGOPHYLLACEAE

The anther is tetrasporangiate with a persistent epidermis and its wall development follows the Dicotyledonous type. The cells of the endothecium develop fibrous thickenings, and the 2 or 3 middle layers are ephemeral except in *Guaiacum* and *Seetzenia* where the 1 or 2 layers persist and some cells may develop fibrous thickenings similar to those of the endothecium. The cells of the glandular tapetum usually become 2- or 3-nucleate and in *Peganum* and *Seetzenia* fusion may restore the 1-nucleate condition, whereas in *P. harmala* the tapetum is irregularly 2-layered. Simultaneous cytokinesis in the microspore mother cells follows meiosis and the microspore tetrads are tetrahedral, decussate, or isobilateral. Pollen grains are 2-celled when shed in *Peganum*, *Seetzenia*, and *Zygophyllum*, but 3-celled in *Fagonia*, while those of *P. harmala* occasionally germinate *in situ*.

The ovule is anatropous, bitegmic, and crassinucellar, with the micropyle formed either by the inner integument (*Fagonia, Tribulus, Zygophyllum*) or both (*Guaiacum, Peganum, Seetzenia*). A multicellular archesporium is common, each cell cutting off a primary parietal cell and 1–4 parietal layers are formed below the nucellar epidermis. Cytokinesis in the megaspore mother cell accompanies meiosis, and although more than one linear tetrad may form, only one chalazal megaspore is functional and this gives rise to a Polygonum type embryo sac. The synergids are pyriform, the polar nuclei fuse before fertilization, and the 3 antipodal cells are usually ephemeral, but in *P. harmala* they persist into early endosperm formation. An endothelium is differentiated in all representatives except *P. harmala* and *S. orientalis*, and a hypostase is usually present.

Endosperm formation is Nuclear and several hundred free nuclei may be formed before the first walls appear at the micropylar pole and the tissue ultimately becomes cellular throughout. In *Fagonia cretica* and *Seetzenia orientalis*, the chalazal endosperm cells are at first coenocytic and nuclear fusions occur, but in *S. orientalis* the basal cell remains multinucleate and is caecum-like.

Embryogeny conforms to the Solanad type and polyembryony has been reported in *P. harmala* and *Z. fabago*.

Kapil and Ahluwalia, 1963 • Masand, 1963b • Mauritzon, 1934c,d • Nair and Gupta, 1961 • H. S. Narayana and Rao, 1962, 1963 • M. A. Rau, 1962 • Reese, 1958 • Schürhoff, 1924b • R. D. Shukla, 1960, 1962 • Souèges, 1952c, 1953a,b,e.

BIBLIOGRAPHY

Abbe, E. C., 1935. Studies in the phylogeny of the Betulaceae. 1. Floral and inflorescence anatomy. Bot. Gaz. 97:1–67.

Abele, K., 1923. Entwicklungsgeschichtliche Untersuchungen über die Piperaceen *Peperomia verschaffeltii* und *P. metallica*. Acta Univ. Latviensis 8:371–398.

Abele, K., 1924. Untersuchungen an Gametophyten von *Peperomia incana*. Bot. Arch. 7:321–324.

Abraham, A., 1935. Studies on the morphology of *Tinospora cordifolia*. Madras Pres. Coll. Bot. Mag. 2:9–16.

Abraham, A. and P. M. Mathew, 1963. Cytology of coconut endosperm. Ann. Bot. 27:505–512.

Abraham, P., 1934. Occurrence of extracarpellary ovules on the floral axis in cotton. J. Indian bot. Soc. 14:291.

Adatia, R. D., 1946. The occurrence of entire pollen grains inside the carpels of some Anonaceae. J. Univ. Bombay B 14:47–68.

Adatia, R. D. and S. G. Gavde, 1962. Embryology of the Celastraceae. *In* Plant Embryology—A Symposium. CSIR. New Delhi: 1–11.

Adatia, R. D., B. N. Mulay, and G. R. Hingorani, 1950. A contribution to the embryology of *Vitis trifolia*. 1. J. Univ. Bombay B 19:1–10.

Adatia, R. D., B. N. Mulay, and G. R. Hingorani, 1953. A contribution to the embryology of *Vitis trifolia*. 2. J. Univ. Bombay B 21:51–60.

Adatia, R. D. and G. L. Shah, 1952. A contribution to the life history of *Coriandrum sativum*. J. Univ. Bombay B 20:34–46.

Admiral'skaya, S. A., 1960. (Fertilization and development of the embryo and endosperm of the allopolyploid variety of peppermint, *Mentha piperita*.) Dokl. Akad. Nauk SSSR 130:919–921.

Adriance, G., 1931. Factors influencing fruit setting in the pecan. Bot. Gaz. 91:144–166.

Afanas'eva, N. G., 1962. (A morphological and embryological study of corn embryogenesis.) Nauk Dokl. Vysshei Shkoly Biol. Nauk 4:107–112.

Afanas'eva, N. G., 1964. (An experiment in a comparative and embryological study of the *Zea mays* hybrid "Tatarskaya 6" and its parental forms.) Nauk Dokl. Vyssh. Shkoly. Biol. Nauk 6:126–130.

Afzelius, K., 1916. Zur Embryosackentwicklung der Orchideen. Svensk bot. Tidskr. 10:183–227.

Afzelius, K., 1918. Zur Entwicklungsgeschichte der Gattung *Gloriosa*. Acta hort. Berg. 6:3–12.

Afzelius, K., 1920. Einige Beobachtungen über die Samenentwicklung der Aponogetonaceae. Svensk bot. Tidskr. 14:168–175.

Afzelius, K., 1922. Embryosackentwicklung und Chromosomenzahl bei einigen *Platanthera*-Arten. Svensk bot. Tidskr. 16:370–382.

Afzelius, K., 1924. Embryologische und zytologische Studien in *Senecio* und verwandten Gattungen. Acta hort. Berg. 8:123–219.

Afzelius, K., 1928. Die Embryobildung bei *Nigritella nigra*. Svensk bot. Tidskr. 22:82–91.

Afzelius, K., 1932. Zur Kenntnis der Fortpflanzungsverhältnisse und Chromosomenzahlen bei *Nigritella nigra.* Svensk. bot. Tidskr. 26:365–369.

Afzelius, K., 1936. Apomixis in der Gattung *Arnica.* Svensk bot. Tidskr. 30:572–679.

Afzelius, K., 1954. Embryo sac development in *Epipogium aphyllum.* Svensk bot. Tidskr. 48:513–520.

Afzelius, K., 1959. Apomixis and polyembryony in *Zygopetalum mackayi.* Acta Hort. Berg. 19:7–13.

Agarwal, S., 1961a. Synergid haustoria of *Quinchamalium chilense.* Nature 192:1313–1314.

Agarwal, S., 1961b. The embryology of *Strombosia.* Phytomorphology 11:269–272.

Agarwal, S., 1962. Embryology of *Quinchamalium chilense.* In Plant Embryology—A Symposium. CSIR. New Delhi: 162–169.

Agarwal, S., 1963a. Morphological and embryological studies in the family Olacaceae. 1. *Olax.* Phytomorphology 13:185–196.

Agarwal, S., 1963b. Morphological and embryological studies in the family Olacaceae. 2. *Stombosia.* Phytomorphology 13:348–356.

Agrawal, J. S., 1950a. The embryo sac of *Fritillaria liliacea.* Proc. 37th. Indian Sci. Congr.

Agrawal, J. S., 1950b. Studies in Umbelliferae. 1. *Foeniculum vulgare.* Proc. 37th. Indian Sci. Congr. 3:46–47.

Agrawal, J. S., 1952. The embryology of *Lilaea subulata,* with a discussion on its systematic position. Phytomorphology 2:15–29.

Agrawal, J. S., 1954. Female gametophyte, endosperm and embryo of *Scurrula.* Proc. 41st. Indian Sci. Congr. 3:137.

Ahuja, Y. R., 1955. Environment and rate of growth of embryo in *Brassica campestris* var. *toria.* Current Sci. 24:205–206.

Ahuja, Y. R. and P. N. Bhaduri, 1956. The embryology of *Brassica campestris* var. *toria.* Phytomorphology 6:63–67.

Åkerberg, E., 1936. Studien über die Samenbildung bei *Poa pratensis.* Bot. Notiser 1936: 213–280.

Åkerberg, E., 1939. Apomictic and sexual seed formation in *Poa pratensis.* Hereditas 25:359–370.

Åkerberg, E., 1942. Cytogenetic studies in *Poa pratensis* and in hybrid with *Poa alpina.* Hereditas 28:1–126.

Åkerberg, E., 1943. Further studies of the embryo and endosperm development in *Poa pratensis.* Hereditas 29:199–201.

Åkerberg, E. and S. Bingefors, 1953. Progeny studies in the hybrid *Poa pratensis* x *Poa alpina.* Hereditas 39:125–136.

Albanese, M., 1904. Ein neuer Fall von Endotropismus des Pollenschlauches und abnormer Embryosackentwicklung bei *Sibbaldia procumbens.* S. B. Akad. Wiss. Wien 113:1.

Alden, I., 1912. A contribution to the life history of *Uvularia sessilifolia.* Bull. Torrey bot. Cl. 39:439–446.

Aleksandrov, V. G. and O. G. Aleksandrova, 1938. (On the endosperm nucleus and its role in the filling and ripening of the grains of cereals.) Dokl. Akad. Nauk SSSR 20:613–616.

Aleksandrov, V. G. and A. V. Dobrotvorskaya, 1957. (The formation of stamens and of a fibrous layer in anthers.) Bot. Zhur. 42:1473–1490.

Alicja, H. and M. Marja, 1934. (The development and degeneration of the antipodal apparatus in *Triticum durum* and *T. vulgare.*) Acta Soc. bot. Polon. 11:409–421.

Allan, P., 1963a. Pollen studies in *Carica papaya*. 1. Formation, development, morphology and production of pollen. S. Afr. J. Agr. Sci. 6:517–530.

Allan, P., 1963b. Pollen studies in *Carica papaya*. 2. Germination and storage of pollen. S. Afr. J. Agr. Sci. 6:613–624.

Almeida, J. L. F. de and T. M. Sampayo, 1950. Sobre a differenciacao nuclear dos micrósporos de *Luzula purpurea*. Bol. Soc. Broteriana 24:323–334.

Amato, F. di, 1939. Ricerche embryologiche e caryologiche sul genere *Euphorbia*. N. G. bot. Ital. 46:470–509.

Amato, F. di, 1940a. Embriologia di *Ulmus campestris*. N. G. bot. Ital. 47:247–263.

Amato, F. di, 1940b. Contributo all'embriologia della Plumbaginaceae. N. G. bot. Ital. 47:349–382.

Amato, F. di, 1940c. Apomissia in *Statice oleaefolia* var. *confusa*. N. G. bot. Ital. 47:504.

Amato, F. di, 1943. Nuovo contributo alla embriologia delle Plumbaginaceae. N. G. bot. Ital. 50:79–99.

Amato, F. di, 1946a. Osservazioni cito-embryologiche su *Cornus mas*, con particolare riguardo allo sterilità di un biotipo triploide. N. G. bot. Ital. 53:170–210.

Amato, F. di, 1946b. Nuovo ricerche embriologiche e cariologiche sul genere *Euphorbia*. N. G. bot. Ital. 53:405–436.

Amato, F. di, 1948–1949. Risultati di una analisi cario-embriologica in una popolazione di *Nothoscordum fragrans*. Caryologia 1:194–200.

Amato, F. di, 1949a. Studio citologico ed embriologico di *Bowiea volubilis*. Caryologia 2:60–70.

Amato, F. di, 1949b. Triploidia e apomissia in *Statice oleaefolia* var. *confusa*. Caryologia 2:71–84.

Amici, G. B., 1824. Observations microscopiques sur diverses espèces des plantes. Ann. Sci. nat. Bot. 2:41–70; 211; 248.

Amici, G. B., 1847. Sur la fécondation des Orchidées. Ann. Sci. nat. Bot. (3) 7:193–205.

Anderson, A. M., 1927. Development of the female gametophyte and caryopsis of *Poa pratensis* and *Poa compressa*. J. Agr. Res. 34:1001–1018.

Anderson, E. and K. Sax, 1934. A cytological study of self-sterility in *Tradescantia*. Bot. Gaz. 95:609–621.

Anderson, F., 1922. The development of the flower and embryology of *Martynia louisiana*. Bull. Torrey. bot. Cl. 49:141–157.

Anderson, L. E., 1939. Cytoplasmic inclusions in the male gametes of *Lilium*. Amer. J. Bot. 26:761–766.

Anderson-Kotto, I., 1932. Observations on the inheritance of apospory and alternation of generations. Svensk bot. Tidskr. 26:99–106.

Andersson, A., 1931. Studien über die Embryologie der Familien Celastraceae, Oleaceae und Apocynaceae. Lunds Univ. Årsskr. (2). 27:1–112.

Andrews, F. M., 1895. Development of the embryo sac of *Jeffersonia diphylla*. Bot. Gaz. 20:423–424.

Andrews, F. M., 1902. Karyokinesis in *Magnolia* and *Liriodendron*, with special reference to the behavior of the chromosomes. Beih. bot. Ztbl. 11:134–142.

Andrews, F. M., 1910. The development of the embryo sac of *Hybanthus concolor*. Bull. Torrey bot. Cl. 37:477–478.

Angremont, A. de, 1912. Parthenokarpie und Samenentwicklung bei Bananen. Ber. dtsch. bot. Ges. 30:686–691.

Angremont, A. de, 1915. Parthenokarpie und Samenbildung bei Bananen. Flora 107:57–110.

Anikiev, V. V., 1963. (Some specific characteristics in the formation of the male gametophyte of barley under dry soil conditions.) Dokl. Akad. Nauk SSSR 152:1250–1252.

Annen, E., 1945. Die Embryosack- und Pollenentwicklung bei einigen polyploiden Garten-Astern im Vergleich mit der wildwachsenden *Aster amellus*. Ber. schweiz. bot. Ges. 55:81.

Anzalone, B., 1949. Osservazioni citoembryologiche in *Taraxacum megalorrhizon*. Ann. di Bot. (Roma) 23:31–41.

Arcangeli, G., 1876. Studi sul *Cytinus hypocistis*. Atti Congr. int. Bot. Firenze 1874. Firenze 1876.

Arcangeli, G., 1897. Studi sul germogliamento del grani pollinici. Bull. Soc. bot. Ital. 4:262–266.

Archibald, E. E. A., 1939. The development of the ovule and seed of jointed cactus, *Opuntia aurantiaca*. S. Afr. J. Sci. 36:195–211.

Arekal, G. D., 1961a. Contribution to the embryology of *Hoppea dichotoma*. Canad. J. Bot. 39:1001–1006.

Arekal, G. D., 1961b. Embryology of *Klugia notoniana*. Bot. Gaz. 123:144–150.

Arekal, G. D., 1963a. Contribution to the embryology of *Chelone glabra*. Phytomorphology 13:376–388.

Arekal, G. D., 1963b. Contribution to the embryology of *Chaenorrhinum minus*. Proc. Indian Acad. Sci. B. 58:375–385.

Arekal, G. D., 1963c. Embryological studies in the Canadian representatives of the tribe Rhinantheae, Scrophulariaceae. Canad. J. Bot. 41:267–302.

Arekal, G. D., 1964. Contribution to the embryology of *Gerardia pedicularia*. J. Indian bot. Soc. 43:409–423.

Arekal, G. D., 1965. Embryology of *Mimulus ringens*. Bot. Gaz. 126:58–66.

Arekal, G. D. and D. Raju, 1964. The female gametophyte of *Linaria ramosissima*. Current Sci. 33:591–592.

Armand, L., 1912. Fécondation et développement de l'embryon chez les Lobéliacées. C. R. Acad. Sci. Paris 155:1534–1536.

Armand, L., 1913. Les phénomènes cinétiques de la prophase hétérotypique chez le *Lobelia erinus*. C. R. Acad. Sci. Paris 156:1089–1090.

Armand, L., 1921. Les phénomènes nucléaires de la cinèse hétérotypique chez le *Lobelia urens* et chez quelques Campanulacées. C. R. Acad. Sci. Paris 172:762–764.

Armour, H., 1906. On the morphology of *Chloranthus*. New Phytol. 5:49–55.

Armstrong, J. M., 1937. A cytological study of the genus *Poa*. Canad. J. Res. C. 15:281–297.

Arnason, T. J., 1943. Female sterility in potatoes. Canad. J. Res. C. 21:41–56.

Arndt, C. H., 1935. Notes on polyembryony and multiple shoots from the seeds in *Mangifera indica*. Amer. J. Bot. 22:26–30.

Arnoldi, V., 1911. Zur Embryologie einiger Euphorbiaceen. Bull. Acad. Imp. Sci. St. Pétersb. (6), 5:966.

Arnoldi, V., 1912. Zur Embryologie einiger Euphorbiaceen. Trav. Mus. Bot. Acad. St. Pétersb. 9:136–154.

Arnoldi, V. and V. Dianova, 1934. Eine zytoembryologische Untersuchung einiger Arten der Gattung *Taraxacum*. Planta 23:19–46.

Arnott, H. J. 1959a. Vivipary in *Cordyline australis*. Madroño 15:71–73.

Arnott, H. J., 1959b. The cotyledon of *Yucca.* Congr. Internatl. Bot. 9th. 2:9–10.

Arnott, H. J., 1961. The morphology and anatomy of *Yucca* seeds. Amer. J. Bot. 48:531.

Arnott, H. J., 1962. The seed, germination and seedling of *Yucca.* Univ. Calif. Publ. Bot. 35:1–144.

Arora, N., 1953. The embryology of *Zizyphus rotundifolia.* Phytomorphology 3:88–98.

Artopoeus, A., 1903. Über den Bau und die Öffnungsweise der Antheren und die Entwicklung der Samen der Erikaceen. Flora 92:309–345.

Artschwager, E., 1927a. Development of flowers and seed in the sugar beet. J. Agr. Res. 34:1–25.

Artschwager, E., 1927b. Micro- and macrosporogenesis in sugar beet with special reference to the problem of incompatibility. Mem. Hort. Soc. N.Y. 3:295–297.

Artschwager, E., 1943. Contribution to the morphology and anatomy of guayule, *Parthenium argentatum.* U.S. Dept. Agr. Tech. Bull. 842:1–33.

Artschwager, E., 1946. Pollen degeneration in male-sterile sugar beets, with special reference to the tapetal plasmodium. Amer. J. Bot. 33:817.

Artschwager, E., 1947. Pollen degeneration in male-sterile sugar beets, with special reference to the tapetal plasmodium. J. Agr. Res. 75:191–197.

Artschwager, E., E. W. Brandes, and R. C. Starrett, 1929. Development of flower and seed of some varieties of sugar cane. J. Agr. Res. 39:1–30.

Artschwager, E. and R. C. McGuire, 1949. Cytology of reproduction in *Sorghum vulgare.* J. Agr. Res. 78:659–673.

Artschwager, E. and R. C. Starrett, 1933. The time factor in fertilization and embryo development in the sugar beet. J. Agr. Res. 47:823–843.

Artz, T., 1933. Über die Embryobildung von Pseudomonokotylen, *Podophyllum emodi* und *Eranthis hiemalis.* Beih. bot. Ztbl. 50:671–696.

Asana, J. J. and R. D. Adatia, 1947. Contributions to the embryology of the Anonaceae. 1. *Artabotrys odoratissimus.* J. Univ. Bombay B 16:7–21.

Asana, J. J. and R. N. Sutaria, 1929. A cytological study of pollen development in *Carica papaya.* J. Indian bot. Soc. 8:235–244.

Asana, J. J. and R. N. Sutaria, 1932. Microsporogenesis in *Luffa aegyptiaca.* J. Indian bot. Soc. 11:181–187.

Asanova. V. K., 1964. (*Zelkova carpinifolia* and its ability for reproduction.) Bot. Zhur. 49:436–438.

Asplund, E., 1920. Studien über die Entwicklungsgeschichte der Blüten einiger Valerianaceen. Kgl. Svenska Vet.-Akad. Handl. 61:1–66.

Atabekova, A. I., 1957. (Polyembryony, supernumerary cotyledons and fasciation in leguminous plants.) Bull. Glavnogo. Bot. Sad. Moskva-Leningrad 28:65–70.

Atabekova, A. I. and C.-H. Ling, 1962. (The embryology of lupin.); *In* Lupin. Moscow:97–113.

Atabekova, A. I. and C.-H. Ling, 1963. (Comparative embryology of *Lupinus.*) Izv. Timiry. Sel'sk. Akad. 2:219–221.

Atkinson, G. F., 1899. Studies on reduction in plants. Bot. Gaz. 28:1–28.

Avanzi, H. G., 1948. Ozzervazioni cita-embriologiche su *Ammobium alatum.* Caryologia 1:83–91.

Avery, G. S., 1930. Comparative anatomy and morphology of embryos and seedlings of maize, oats and wheat. Bot. Gaz. 89:1–39.

Ayres, J. A., 1915. Flower of *Adenocaulon bicolor.* Bot. Gaz. 59:154–157.

Ayyangar, G. N. R., 1930. Polyembryony in *Eleusine coracana.* Madras Agr. J. 18:393–395.

Ayyangar, G. N. R. and V. P. Rao, 1935. Dummy pollen. Current Sci. 4:315.

Ayyangar, G. S., 1948. Some observations on stomata found on cotton ovules. Indian Cotton Gr. Rev. 2:187–192.

Babcock, E. B. and G. L. Stebbins, 1938. The American species of *Crepis*. Publ. Carnegie Inst. Washington 504:1–199.

Bacchi, O., 1943. Cytological observations in *Citrus*. 2. Megasporogenesis, fertilization, endosperm and polyembryony. Bot. Gaz. 105:221–225.

Bachmann, E., 1882. Darstellung der Entwicklungsgeschichte und des Baues der Samenschalen der Scrophulariaceen. Verh. Ksl. Leop.-Carol. dtsch. Akad. Nat.-forsch. 43:1–179.

Bağda, H., 1948. Morphologische und biologische Untersuchungen über Valonea-Eichen, *Quercus macrolepis,* im Haci-Kadin-Tal bei Ankara. Comm. Fac. Sci. Univ. Ankara 1:89–125.

Bağda, H., 1952. Untersuchungen über den weiblichen Gametophyten der Valonea-Eichen, *Quercus macrolepis*. Rev. Fac. Sci. Univ. Instanbul 17:77–94.

Bailey, I. W. and C. G. Nast, 1943a. The comparative morphology of the Winteraceae. 1. Pollen and stamens. J. Arnold Arbor. 24:340–346.

Bailey, I. W. and C. G. Nast, 1943b. The comparative morphology of the Winteraceae. 2. Carpels. J. Arnold Arbor. 24:472–481.

Bailey, I. W. and C. G. Nast, 1945. The comparative morphology of the Winteraceae. 7. Summary and conclusions. J. Arnold Arbor. 26:37–47.

Baillon, H., 1858a. Etude générale du grupe des Euphorbiacées. Paris.

Baillon, H., 1858b. Recherches sur l'organogenie du *Callitriche* et sur ses rapports naturels. Bull. Soc. bot. France 5:337.

Baillon, H., 1867–1895. Histoire des Plantes. Paris.

Baillon, H., 1875. Traité du développement de la fleur et du fruit. Adansonia 11:163.

Baillon, H., 1882. La polyembryonie du Dompte-Venin. Bull. mens. Soc. Linn. Paris 1:336.

Bajpai, P. N. and A. N. Maurya, 1963. Studies on blossom bud differentiation and male gametophyte in *Limonia acidissima*. Agra Univ. J. Res. (Sci.) 12:97–104.

Baker, H. G., 1959. Adventitious embryony in *Pachira* and its taxonomic consequences. Congr. Internat. Bot. 9th. 2:14.

Baker, H. G., 1960. Apomixis and polyembryony in *Pachira oleaginea*. Amer. J. Bot. 47:296–302.

Bakshi, T. S., 1952. Floral morphology and embryology of *Psilostachys sericea*. Phytomorphology 2:151–161.

Bakshi, T. S., 1959. Ecology and morphology of *Pterospora andromeda*. Bot. Gaz. 120:203–217.

Balesubramanian, R., 1932. Parthenogenesis in cotton. Madras Agr. J. 12:509–517.

Balfour, E., 1957. The development of the vascular systems in *Macropiper excelsa*. 1. The embryo and seedling. Phytomorphology 7:354–364.

Balicka-Iwanowska, G. P., 1899. Contribution à l'étude du sac embryonnaire chez certaines Gamopétales. Flora 86:47–71.

Ballantine, A. J., 1909. A preliminary note on the embryo sac of *Protea lepidocarpon*. Ann. Bot. 23:161–162.

Balls, W. L., 1905. The sexuality of cotton. Year-book Khedival Agr. Soc., Cairo.

Balls, W. L., 1906. The cytology of cotton. New Phytol. 4:222.

Bally, W., 1916. Zwei Fälle von Polyembryonie und Parthenokarpie. Verh. schweiz. Nat. Ges. 98:169–170.

Bambacioni, V., 1928a. Come avviene in *Fritillaria persica,* lo sviluppo del gametofito femminile e l'aumento dei cromosomi nella regione chalazale. C. R. Accad. Lincei Roma (6) 6:544–546.

Bambacioni, V., 1928b. Ricerche sulla ecologia e sulla embriologia di *Fritillaria persica.* Ann. di Bot. (Roma) 18:7–37.

Bambacioni, V., 1928c. Contributo alla embriologia di *Lilium candidum.* C. R. Accad. Lincei Roma (6) 8:612–618.

Bambacioni, V. and A. Giombini, 1930. Sullo sviluppo del gametofito femminile in *Tulipa gesneriana.* Ann. di Bot. (Roma) 18:373–386.

Bambacioni-Mezzetti, V., 1931a. Sullo sviluppo dell' embrione in *Tulipa gesneriana.* Ann. di Bot. (Roma) 19:145–155.

Bambacioni-Mezzetti, V., 1931b. Nuove ricerche sull' embriologia delle Giliacee. Ann. di Bot. (Roma) 19:365–382.

Bambacioni-Mezzetti, V., 1932. Sullo sviluppo dell'embrione in *Tulipa gesneriana.* Ann. di Bot. (Roma) 19:145.

Bambacioni-Mezzetti, V., 1935. Ricerche morfologiche sulle Lauraceae. Lo sviluppo dell'ovulo e dei sacchi pollinici nel *Laurus nobilis.* Ann. di Bot. (Roma) 21:1–19.

Bambacioni-Mezzetti, V., 1937. Gimnoovulia in *Persea gratissima* e considerazioni sulla monomeria del pistillo di questa pianta. Ann. di Bot. (Roma) 21:1–7.

Bambacioni-Mezzetti, V., 1938. Ricerche morfologiche sulle Lauraceae. Lo sviluppo dell'ovulo e dei sacchi pollinica nel *Laurus nobilis.* Ann. di Bot. (Roma) 21:186–204.

Bambacioni-Mezzetti, V., 1941. Ricerche morfologiche sulle Lauraceae. Embriologia della *Umbellaria californica* e del *Laurus canariensis.* Ann. di Bot. (Roma) 22:99–116.

Bambacioni-Mezzetti, V., 1947. Sull'embriologia della *Fritillaria messanensis* e sull'opportunità di distinguere una serie *Fritillaria* nel tipo *Euphorbia dulcis.* Ann. di Bot. (Roma) 23:1–23.

Banchetti, C., 1961. (The development of the female gametophyte of *Senecio leucanthemifolia* var. *pinnatifidus.*) Caryologia 14:303–311.

Banerji, I., 1932. The development of the embryo sac and fertilization in jute. J. Indian bot. Soc. 11:228–240.

Banerji, I., 1933. The development of the flower and pollen in jute. Indian J. agr. Sci. 3:116–126.

Banerji, I., 1934. Sterility of the female gametophyte of *Colocasia antiquorum.* Current Sci. 2:432.

Banerji, I., 1937. Sterility in *Colocasia antiquorum.* J. Indian bot. Soc. 16:159–164.

Banerji, I., 1938. A note on the embryology of groundnut, *Arachis hypogaea.* J. Bombay nat. hist. Soc. 40:539–543.

Banerji, I., 1940a. A contribution to the life history of *Costus speciosus.* J. Indian bot. Soc. 19:181–196.

Banerji, I., 1940b. A contribution to the life history of *Tridax procumbens.* J. Bombay nat. hist. Soc. 42:89–99.

Banerji, I., 1940c. A contribution to the morphology and cytology of *Carthamus tinctorius.* Proc. Nat. Inst. Sci. India. 6:73–86.

Banerji, I., 1940d. A contribution to the life history of *Tridax procumbens.* Proc. Indian Acad. Sci. B 1:325–336.

Banerji, I., 1941. A note on the development of the female gametophyte in *Abroma angusta* and *Pentapetes phoenicea*. Current Sci. 10:30.

Banerji, I., 1942a. A contribution to the life history of *Blumea laciniata*. J. Indian bot. Soc. 21:295–307.

Banerji, I., 1942b. The development of the female gametophyte and floss in *Bombax malabaricum*. Proc. Indian Acad. Sci. B. 16:205–211.

Banerji, I., 1947. Life history of *Typhonium trilobatum*. Proc. Nat. Inst. Sci. India B. 13:207–230.

Banerji, I., 1949. A contribution to the life history of *Acalypha fallax*. Bull. bot. Soc. Bengal 3:29–32.

Banerji, I., 1951. Pollen and embryo sac of two Euphorbiaceae. Proc. Indian Acad. Sci. B. 34:172–181.

Banerji, I., 1954. Morphological and cytological studies on *Citrus grandis*. Phytomorphology 4:390–396.

Banerji, I., 1961. The endosperm in Scrophulariaceae. J. Indian bot. Soc. 40:1–11.

Banerji, I. and P. N. Bhaduri, 1933. Polyembryony in Solanaceae. Current Sci. 1:310.

Banerji, I. and K. L. Chaudhuri, 1944. A contribution to the life history of *Litchi chinensis*. Proc. Indian Acad. Sci. B. 19:19–27.

Banerji, I. and K. L. Das, 1937. A note on the development of the embryo sac in *Trichosanthes dioica*. Current Sci. 5:427–428.

Banerji, I. and M. K. Dutt, 1944. The development of the female gametophyte in some members of the Euphorbiaceae. Proc. Indian Acad. Sci. B. 20:51–60.

Banerji, I. and H. C. Gangulee, 1937. Spermatogenesis in *Eichhornia crassipes*. J. Indian bot. Soc. 16:289–295.

Banerji, I. and A. Hakim, 1954. A contribution to the life history of *Artocarpus lakoocha*. Proc. Indian Acad. Sci. B. 39:128–132.

Banerji, I. and S. Haldar, 1942. A contribution to the morphology and cytology of *Monochoria hastaefolia*. Proc. Indian Acad. Sci. B. 16:91–106.

Banerji, I. and S. Pal, 1959. A contribution to the life history of *Synedrella nodiflora*. J. Linn. Soc. Lond. Bot. 55:810–817.

Banerji, I. and K. K. Samal, 1936. Microsporogenesis in *Crotalaria juncea*. Indian J. agr. Sci. 6:116–126.

Banerji, I. and V. Venkateswarlu, 1935. A preliminary note on the development of the female gametophyte in *Costus speciosus*. Current Sci. 4:414.

Bannerjee, N. S. and R. M. Datta, 1960. Genesis of the embryo sac in *Vigna catjang*. Indian Agr. 4:90–94.

Bannier, J. P., 1923. Untersuchungen über apogame Fortpflanzung bei einigen elementaren Arten von *Erophila verna*. Rec. trav. bot. Néerl. 20:1–106. Proc. Kon. Akad. Wet. Amsterdam 26:349–356.

Bannikova, V. P., 1963. (Cytoembryology of distant hybrids. 1. Embryogenesis on crossing durum wheat and rye.) Ukrain. bot. Zhur. 20:3–13.

Bannikova, V. P. and O. K. Ostapenko, 1964. (Specific features of the embryogenesis of the Khmelevka variety of tobacco, *Nicotiana rustica*.) Ukrain. bot. Zhur. 21:20–26.

Baranetzky, J., 1880. Die Kernteilung in den Pollenmutterzellen einiger Tradescantien. Bot. Zeit. 38:241–248, 265–274, 281–296.

Baranov, P. A., 1915. (Study of the development of the embryo sac in *Spiranthes australis* and *Serapias pseudocardigera*.) Bull. Soc. Imp. nat. Moscow 29:74–92.

Baranov, P. A., 1916. Materials on the embryology of the Orchids. J. Russian bot. Soc. 2:20–29.

Baranov, P. A., 1918. (Contributions to the study of the embryology of the orchids.) J. Russian bot. Soc. 2:20–29.

Baranov, P. A., 1925a. On the reduction of the female generation in the Orchidaceae. Bull. Univ. Asie cent. Tashkent 10:181–195.

Baranov, P. A., 1925b. (Contribution to the embryology of the orchids. 2. *Herminium monorchis.*) J. Russian bot. Soc. 9:5–9.

Baranov, P. A., 1926. Zytologische und embryologische Untersuchungen an *Drimiopsis maculata.* Ztschr. f. Zellforsch. und Micros. Anat. 3:131–148.

Baranov, P. A., 1927. Zur Morphologie und Embryologie der Weinrebe. Ber. dtsch. bot. Ges. 45:97–114.

Baranov, P. A., 1955. (History of plant embryology in connection with the development of ideas on the origin of organisms.) Moscow.

Baranov, P. A., 1959. The progress of investigations in plant fertilization, apomixis and polyembryony in the USSR. Congr. Internat. Bot. 9th. 2:19.

Baranov, P. A., E. A. Baranova, and N. N. Polunina, 1955. (An interesting feature of embryogenesis of Eucalyptus). Bot. Zhur. 40:99–102.

Baranov, P. and V. Poddubnaja, 1925. (On the embryology of the Amaryllidaceae of Turkestan: *Ungernia severzovii* and *Ixiolirion tartaricum.*) Bull. Univ. Asie cent. Tashkent 10:1–14.

Barber, H. N., 1940. The suppression of meiosis and the origin of diplochromosomes. Proc. Roy. Soc. London B. 128:170–185.

Barber, H. N., 1942. The pollen grain division in the Orchidaceae. J. Genet. 43:97–103.

Barber, K. G., 1909. Comparative histology of fruits and seeds of certain species of Cucurbitaceae. Bot. Gaz. 47:263–310.

Barlow, B. A., 1958. Heteroploid twins and apomixis in *Casuarina nana.* Aust. J. Bot. 6:204–219.

Barlow, B. A., 1964. Classification of the Loranthaceae and Viscaceae. Proc. Linn. Soc. N.S.W. 89:254–267.

Barnard, C., 1949. Microsporogenesis, macrosporogenesis and development of the macrogametophyte and seeds of *Duboisia leichhardtii* and *D. myoporoides.* Aust. J. Sci. Res. B. 2:241–248.

Barnéoud, M., 1844. Recherches sur le développement, la structure générale et la classification des Plantaginées et des Plumbaginées. Diss. Paris.

Barnes, C. R., 1885. The process of fertilization in *Campanula americana.* Bot. Gaz. 10:349–354.

Bartels, F., 1956. Zur Entwicklung der Keimpflanze von *Epilobium hirsutum.* 1. Die im Proembryo ablaufenden Zellteilungen bis zum beginnenden "herzformigen Embryo." Flora 144:105–120.

Bartsch, E., 1882. Beiträge zur Anatomie und Entwicklungsgeschichte der Umbelliferen-Früchte. Diss. Breslau.

Bary, A. de, 1868. *Prosopanche burmeisteri,* eine neue Hydnoree aus Südamerika. Abh. nat. Ges. Halle 10.

Bashaw, E. C., 1962. Apomixis and sexuality in buffel grass, *Pennisetum ciliare.* Crop Sci. 2:412–415.

Bashaw, E. C. and E. C. Hoit, 1958. Megasporogenesis, embryo sac development and embryogenesis in dalligrass, *Paspalum dilatatum.* Agron. J. (U.S.A.) 50:753–756.

Batikyan, G. G. and D. P. Cholakhyan, 1962. (Embryological study of fertilization in corn in the Kamo region of the Armenian SSR.) Izvest. Akad. Nauk Armyansk. SSR. Biol. 15:27–37.

Battacharya, S. S. and J. N. Mitra, 1952. The development of the female gametophyte in *Triumfetta rhomboidea*. Sci. and Cult. 17:343–344.

Battaglia, E., 1940. Embriologia di *Ligularia kaempferi*. N. G. Bot. Ital. 47:271–286.

Battaglia, E., 1941. Contributo all'embriologia delle Tamaricaceae. N. G. Bot. Ital. 48:575–612.

Battaglia, E., 1943. Alcune osservazione sullo sviluppo del gametofito femmineo della *Myricaria germanica*. N. G. Bot. Ital. 49:464–467.

Battaglia, E., 1945a. Fenomeni citologici nuovi nella embriogenesi ("semigamia") e nella microsporogenesi ("doppio nucleo di restituzione") di *Rudbeckia laciniata*. N. G. Bot. Ital. 52:34–38.

Battaglia, E., 1945b. Sulla terminologia dei processi meiotici. N. G. Bot. Ital. 52:42–57.

Battaglia, E., 1946a. Ricerche cariologiche ed embriologiche sul genere *Rudbeckia*. 1–5. Il gametofito femminile e maschile di *R. bicolor, R. hirta, R. hirta var. meine freude, R. amplexicaule* e *R. purpurea (Echinacea purpurea)*. N. G. Bot. Ital. 53:1–26.

Battaglia, E., 1946b. Ricerche cariologiche ed embriologiche sul genere *Rudbeckia*. 6. Apomissia in *R. speciosa*. N. G. Bot. Ital. 53:27–69.

Battaglia, E., 1946c. Ricerche cariologiche ed embriologiche sul genere *Rudbeckia*. 7. Apomissia in *R. laciniata,* ed amfimissia nella sua varietà a fiori doppi. N. G. Bot. Ital. 53:437–482.

Battaglia, E., 1946d. Ricerche cariologiche ed embriologiche sul genere *Rudbeckia*. 8. Semigamia in *R. laciniata*. N. G. Bot. Ital. 53:483–511.

Battaglia, E., 1947a. Meiosi anormale nella microsporogenesi di *Laurus nobilis*. Atti Soc. Tosc. Sci. nat. B. 54:1–22.

Battaglia, E., 1947b. Ricerche cariologiche ed embriologiche sul genere *Rudbeckia*. 9. Le anomalie del gametofito femminile cellularizzato di *R. laciniata*. N. G. Bot. Ital. 54:377–405.

Battaglia, E., 1947c. Ricerche cariologiche ed embriologiche sul genere *Rudbeckia*. 10. Le anomalie della meiosi durante la microsporogenesi di *R. laciniata* con particolare riguardo alla formazione del nucleo di restituzione. N. G. Bot. Ital. 54:406–431.

Battaglia, E., 1947d. Ricerche cariologiche ed embriologiche sul genere *Rudbeckia*. 11. Semigamia in *R. speciosa*. N. G. Bot. Ital. 54:531–559.

Battaglia, E., 1947e. Ricerche cariologiche e embriologiche sul genere *Rudbeckia*. 12. Gametofito femminile e maschile di *R. flava*. N. G. Bot. Ital. 54:560–567.

Battaglia, E., 1947f. Ricerche cariologiche e embriologiche sul genere *Rudbeckia*. La "semigamia" singolare comportamento del nucleo spermatico nelle uova diploidi delle specie apomittiche del genere *Rudbeckia* e conseguente embriogenesi di tipo chimerico. C. R. Accad. Lincei Roma (8) 2:63–67.

Battaglia, E., 1947g. Apomissia in *Hieracium ramosum*. Atti Soc. Tosc. Sci. nat. B. 54:50–69.

Battaglia, E., 1947h. Sulla terminologia dei processi mitotica. N. G. bot. Ital. 54:596–632.

Battaglia, E., 1947i. Sulla terminologia dei processi apomittici. N. G. bot. Ital. 54:674–696.

Battaglia, E., 1948a. Ricerche sulla parameiosi restituzionale nel genere *Taraxacum*. Caryologia 1:1–47.

Battaglia, E., 1948b. Agglutinazione cromosomica ("stickiness") quale causa di eccezionali condizioni nucleari nelle cellule del Tappeto di *Crepis zacintha*. Caryologia 1:248–268.

Battaglia, E., 1949. L'alterazione della meiosi nella riproduzione apomittica di *Chondrilla juncea*. Caryologia 2:23–30.

Battaglia, E., 1950. L'alterazione della meiosi nella riproduzione apomittica di *Erigeron karwinskianus* var. *mucronatus*. Caryologia 2:165–204.

Battaglia, E., 1951a. The male and female gametophytes of angiosperms—an interpretation. Phytomorphology 1:87–116.

Battaglia, E., 1951b. Development of angiosperm embryo sacs with non-haploid eggs. Amer. J. Bot. 38:718–724.

Battaglia, E., 1951c. Development of the tetrasporic embryo sac of *Chrysanthemum viscosum*. Bot. Gaz. 112:490–494.

Battaglia, E., 1952a. Ricerche embriologiche sul *Rudbeckia columnaris*. Atti Soc. Tosc. Sci. nat. B. 59:172–197.

Battaglia, E., 1952b. Nuovi reperti di apomissia e di amfimissia nel genere *Rudbeckia*. Atti Soc. Tosc. Sci. nat. B. 59:205–209.

Battaglia, E., 1954. Semigamia chez *Rudbeckia sullivantia*. Congr. Internat. Bot. 8th.:245–247.

Battaglia, E., 1955a. New symbols in cytology. Phytomorphology 5:171–172.

Battaglia, E., 1955b. The concepts of spore, sporogenesis and apospory. Phytomorphology 5:173–177.

Battaglia, E., 1955c. Unusual cytological features in the apomictic *Rudbeckia sullivanti*. Caryologia 8:1–32.

Battaglia, E., 1956. Do new types of embryo sac development occur in *Antennaria carpatica?* Phytomorphology 6:119–123.

Battaglia, E., 1958a. L'evoluzione del gametofito maschile delle gimnosperme alle angiosperme sulla base di recenti osservazioni in *Gnetum*. Caryologia 11:217–228.

Battaglia, E., 1958b. L'abolizione del tipo embriologico *Scilla* e la creazione dei nuovi tipo *Endymion* ed *Allium*. Caryologia 11:247–252.

Battaglia, E., 1958c. Osservazioni critiche sul tipo di sviluppo del gametofito femminile attribuito a *Scilla hyacinthoides*. Caryologia 11:253–258.

Battaglia, E., 1958d. Ricerche embriologiche in *Scilla autumnalis* e *Scilla obtusifolia*. Nota preliminare. N. G. Bot. Ital 65:397–398.

Battaglia, E., 1959. New types of embryo sac development in *Scilla autumnalis*. Congr. Internat. Bot. 9th. 2:23–24.

Battaglia, E., 1963. Apomixis. *In* Maheshwari, P. (ed.): Recent Advances in the Embryology of Angiosperms. Delhi.:221–264.

Battaglia, E. and J. W. Boyes, 1955. Post-reductional meiosis: its mechanism and causes. Caryologia 8:87–134.

Battaglia, E. and N. Breviglieri, 1955. Microsporogenesi regolare e irregolare in *Olea europea*. Caryologia 8:45–68.

Battaglia, E. and E. Feeley, 1959. The embryo sac of *Scilla pratensis*. Caryologia 11:407–414.

Batygina, T. B., 1962a. (Microsporogenesis and pollen grain development in wheat, *Triticum vulgare* var. *diamant*). Dokl. Akad. Nauk SSSR Biol. Sci. 142:187–190.

294   BIBLIOGRAPHY

Batygina, T. B., 1962b. (Fertilization in wheat). Trud. bot. Inst. Akad. Nauk SSSR (7). 5:260–293.

Batygina, T. B., E. S. Teriokhin, G. K. Alimova, and M. S. Yakovlev, 1963. (Genesis of male sporangia in the families Gramineae and Ericaceae). Bot. Zhur. 48:1108–1120.

Bauch, K., 1911. Beiträge zur Entwicklungsgeschichte und physiologischen Anatomie der Palmenblüte. Diss. Berlin.

Baude, E., 1956. Die Embryoentwicklung von *Stratiodes aloides*. Planta 46:649–671.

Bauer, R., 1922. Entwicklungsgeschichtliche Untersuchungen an Polygonaceen-Blüten. Flora 115:272–292.

Baum, H., 1948a. Vergleichend morphologische, anatomische und entwicklungsgeschichtliche Untersuchungen über die *Astragalus*-Frucht. Ann. Nat. Mus. Wien 56:246–261.

Baum, H., 1948b. Die Stellung der Samenanlagen am Karpell bei *Asclepias syriaca, Cynanchum vincetoxicum* und *Erythraea centaurium*. Österr, bot. Zeit. 95:251–256.

Baur, E., 1912. Die Entstehung der elementaren Arten von *Erophila verna*. Zeit. ind. Abst. Vererb. Lehre 6:186.

Beal, J. M., 1939. Cytological studies in relation to the classification of the genus *Calochortus*. Bot. Gaz. 100:528–547.

Beamish, K. I., 1955. Seed failure following hybridization between the hexaploid *Solanum demissum* and four diploid *Solanum* spp. Amer. J. Bot. 42:297–304.

Beatty, A. V., 1940. Mitosis in the pollen tube of *Eschscholtzia*. Genetics 25:10.

Beatty, A. V., 1943. The division of the generative nucleus in *Eschscholtzia*. Amer. J. Bot. 30:378–382.

Beatty, J. W. and A. V. Beatty, 1953. Duration of the stages in microspore development and in the first microspore division of *Tradescantia paludosa*. Amer. J. Bot. 40:593–596.

Beaudry, J. R., 1951. Seed development following mating *Elymus virginicus* x *Agropyron repens*. Genetics 36:109–133.

Beaudry, J. R., 1959. Studies on *Solidago*. Megasporogenesis, development of the megagametophyte and mode of reproduction in *Solidago altissima*. Proc. Genet. Soc. Canada 3:7–14.

Beauregard, M., 1877. Structure et développement du fruit des *Daphne*. Bull. Soc. bot. France 24:385–387.

Bechtel, A., 1921. The floral anatomy of the Urticales. Amer. J. Bot. 8:386–410.

Beck, P. and J. S. Horton, 1932. Microsporogenesis and embryology in certain species of *Bromus*. Bot. Gaz. 93:42–54.

Beer, R., 1906. On the development of the pollen grain and anther of some Onagraceae. Beih. bot. Ztbl. A. 19:286–313.

Beer, R., 1907. The supernumerary pollen grains of *Fuchsia*. Ann. Bot. 21:305–307.

Beer, R., 1911. Studies in spore development. Ann. Bot. 25:199–214.

Beghtel, F. E., 1925. The embryology of *Pastinaca sativa*. Amer. J. Bot. 12:327–337.

Beijerinck, W., 1940. *Calluna:* a monograph of the Scotch heather. Kon. Ned. Akad. Wett. Verh. 38:1–180.

Belikova, N. L., 1952. (Polyembryony in beans, *Phaseolus*.) Bjul. Moskov Obsc. Ispyt. Prir. Biol. 57:65–66.

Belitser, N. V., 1963. (The embryology of *Zizania aquatica*). Zhur. Inst. bot. Acad. Sci. RSS Ukraine 20:7–15.

Bell, H. P., 1957. The development of the blueberry seed. Canad. J. Bot. 35:139–153.

Bell, H. P. and J. Burchill, 1955a. Flower development in the lowbush blueberry. Canad. J. Bot. 33:251–258.

Bell, H. P. and J. Burchill, 1955b. Winter resting stages of certain Ericaceae. Canad. J. Bot. 33:547–561.

Belling, J., 1908. Report of the Assistant in horticulture Mango. Ann. Rep. Fla. agric. Exp. Sta.: 110–125.

Bellows, J. M. and R. Bamford, 1941. Megagametophyte development in a triploid tulip. Bot. Gaz. 104:699–711.

Belyaeva, L. Y., 1964. (Cytoembryological study of seed development and the accumulation of ergastic substances in the seed of Crambe abyssinica.) Zhur. Inst. bot. Akad. Sci. RSS. Ukraine 21:58–60.

Benecke, W., 1906. Einige Bemerkungen über die Bedingungen des Blühens und Fruchtens der Gewächse. Bot. Zeit. 64:98–107.

Benetskaia, G. K., 1939. (In vivo observations of the male gametes in the pollen tubes of Asclepias cornutii, Vinca major and Vinca minor.) Bot. Zhur. 24:273–281.

Bennett, H. W., 1944. Embryology of Paspalum dilatatum. Bot. Gaz. 106:40–45.

Benson, M., 1894. Contribution to the embryology of the Amentiferae. 1. Trans. Linn. Soc. London (2) Bot. 3:409–424.

Benson, M., E. Sanday, and E. Berridge, 1906. Contribution to the embryology of the Amentiferae. 2. Carpinus betulus. Trans. Linn. Soc. London (2) Bot. 7:37–44.

Benson, M. and E. J. Welsford, 1909. The morphology of the ovule and female flower of Juglans regia and of a few allied genera. Ann. Bot. 23:623–633.

Berg, O., 1898. Beitrag zur Kenntnis der Entwicklung der Embryosackes der Angiospermen. Diss. Erlangen.

Berg, R. Y., 1954. Development and dispersal of the seed of Pedicularis silvatica. Nyutt Mag. Bot. 2:1–60.

Berger, C. A., E. J. Feeley, and E. R. Witkus, 1956. The cytology of Xanthisma texanum. 4. Megasporogenesis and embryo sac formation, pollen grain mitosis and embryo formation. Bull. Torrey bot. Cl. 83:428–434.

Berger, F., 1958. Zur Samenanatomie der Zingiberaceen-Gattungen Elettaria, Amomum und Aframomum. Sci. Pharm. 26:224–258.

Berger, X., 1953. Untersuchungen über die Embryologie partiell apomiktischer Rubus-bastarde. Ber. schweiz. bot. Ges. 63:224–266.

Berghs, J., 1905a. La microsporogénèse de Convallaria maialis. Cellule 21:383–396.

Berghs, J., 1905b. La microsporogénèse de Drosera rotundifolia, Narthecium ossifragum et Helleborous foetidus. Cellule 22:141–160.

Bergman, B., 1932. Aposporie bei Picris hieracioides und Leontodon hispidus. Svensk bot. Tidskr. 26:453–457.

Bergman, B., 1935a. Zytologiche Studien über die Fortpflanzung bei den Gattungen Leontodon und Picris. Svensk bot. Tidskr. 29:155–301.

Bergman, B., 1935b. Zytologiche Studien über sexuelle and asexuelle Hieracium umbellatum. Hereditas 20:47–64.

Bergman, B., 1935c. Zur Kenntnis der Zytologie der skandinavischen Antennaria-Arten. Hereditas 20:214–226.

Bergman, B., 1937. Eine neue apomiktische Antennaria. Svensk bot. Tidskr. 31:391–394.

Bergman, B., 1941. Studies on the embryo sac mother cell and its development in *Hieracium* subg. *Archieracium*. Svensk. bot. Tidskr. 35:1–42.

Bergman, B., 1942. Zur Embryologie der Gattung *Erigeron*. Svensk bot. Tidskr. 36:429–443.

Bergman, B., 1944. A contribution to the knowledge of the embryo sac mother cell and its development in two apomicts. Svensk bot. Tidskr. 38:249–259.

Bergman, B., 1950. Meiosis in two different clones of the apomictic *Chondrilla juncea*. Hereditas 36:297–320.

Bergman, B., 1951. On the formation of reduced and unreduced gametophytes in the females of *Antennaria carpatica*. Hereditas 37:501–518.

Berlese, A. N., 1882. Studi sulla forma, struttura e sviluppo del semenelle Ampelideae. Malpighia 6:293–324, 442–536.

Bernard, C., 1900. Recherches sur les sphères attractives chez *Lilium candidum*. Jour. de Bot. 14:118–124, 177–188, 206–212.

Bernard, C., 1903. Sur l'embryogénie de quelques plantes parasites. Jour. de Bot. 17:23–32, 62–68, 117–137, 168–197.

Bernard, C. and A. Ernst, 1910. Beiträge zur Kenntniss der Saprophyten Javas. 3. Embryologie von *Thismia javanica*. Ann. jard. bot. Buitenz. 23:48–61.

Bernard, C. and A. Ernst, 1911. Beiträge zur Kenntnis der Saprophyten Javas. 6. Embryologie von *Thismia clandestina* und *T. verstegii*. Ann. jard. bot. Buitenz. 24:70–77.

Bernard, C. and A. Ernst, 1914. Beiträge zur Kenntniss der Saprophyten Javas. Embryologie von *Burmannia tuberosa*. Ann. jard. bot. Buitenz. 28:121–124.

Bernhardi, J. J., 1832. Über die merkwürdigsten Verschiedenheiten des entwickelten Pflanzenembryos und ihren Werth für Systematik. Linnaea 7:561–613.

Berridge, E. M., 1914. The structure of the flower of Fagaceae, and its bearing on the affinities of the group. Ann. Bot. 28:509–526.

Bersier, J.-D., 1960. L'ovule et la placentation dans le genre *Tropaeolum*. Arch. Sci. Genève) 13:566–567.

Beruti, R., 1961. Lo sviluppo del gametofito femminile di *Hypochoeris aetnensis*. Caryologia 14:319–325.

Bessey, E. A., 1898. The comparative morphology of the pistils of the Ranunculaceae, Alismaceae and Rosaceae. Bot. Gaz. 26:297–314.

Bessey, E. A., 1908. The Florida strangling figs. 19th. Rep. Mo. bot. Gdn. 19:25–33.

Beth, K., 1938. Untersuchungen über die Ausflösung von Adventivembryonie durch Wundreiz. Planta 28:296–343.

Bhaduri, P. N., 1932. The development of ovule and embryo sac in *Solanum melongena*. J. Indian bot. Soc. 11:202–224.

Bhaduri, P. N., 1933. A note on the "new type of fertilization" in plants. Current Sci. 2:95.

Bhaduri, P. N., 1935. Studies on the female gametophyte in Solanaceae. J. Indian bot. Soc. 14:133–149.

Bhaduri, P. N., 1936. Studies in the embryology of the Solanaceae. 1. Bot. Gaz. 98:283–295.

Bhaduri, S., 1944. A contribution to the morphology of pollen grains of Acanthaceae and its bearing on taxonomy. J. Dep. Sci. Calcutta Univ. 1:25–38.

Bhagavathi, P. R., 1938. Microsporogenesis in *Drimys*. Presidency Coll. Bot. Mag. Madras 5:22–25.

Bhalla, V., 1941a. Life history of *Euphorbia helioscopia*. Proc. 28th. Indian Sci. Congr. 3:161.

Bhalla, V., 1941b. Sterility in *Euphorbia royleana*. Proc. 28th. Indian Sci. Congr. 3:162.

Bhandari, N. N., 1962. Studies in the family Ranunculaceae. 3. Development of the female gametophyte in *Adonis annua*. Phytomorphology 12:70–74.

Bhandari, N. N., 1963a. Embryology of *Pseudowintera colorata*: A vesselless dicotyledon. Phytomorphology 13:303–316.

Bhandari, N. N., 1963b. Studies in the family Ranunculaceae. 5. The female gametophyte of *Adonis aestivalis*: a reinvestigation. Phytomorphology 13: 317–320.

Bhargava, H. R., 1932. Contribution to the morphology of *Boerhaavia repandra*. J. Indian bot. Soc. 11:303–326.

Bhargava, H. R., 1934. Contribution to the morphology of *Mollugo nudicaulis*. Proc. Indian Acad. Sci. B. 1:271–278.

Bhargava, H. R., 1935a. Contribution to the morphology of *Eclipta erecta*. Proc. Indian Acad. Sci. B. 1:325–339.

Bhargava, H. R., 1935b. The life history of *Trianthema monogyna*. Proc. Indian Acad. Sci. B. 2:49–58.

Bhargava, H. R., 1936. The life history of *Chenopodium album*. Proc. Indian Acad. Sci. B. 4:179–200.

Bhargava, H. R. and R. H. Sawhney, 1958. Morphological studies in the Polygonaceae. 1. Contribution to the life history of *Rumex dentatus*. J. Univ. Saugar 7:21–28.

Bhatnagar, S. P., 1959a. Some observations on the post-fertilization development of the embryo sac of *Santalum*. Phytomorphology 9:87–91.

Bhatnagar, S. P., 1959b. The embryology of *Mida salicifolia*. Proc. 46th. Indian Sci. Congr. 3:281–282.

Bhatnagar, S. P., 1960. Morphological and embryological studies in the family Santalaceae. 4. *Mida salicifolia*. Phytomorphology 10:198–207.

Bhatnagar, S. P., 1964. Microsporogenesis and male gametophyte of *Santalum*. Symp. Palynology. Lucknow.

Bhatnagar, S. P., 1965a. Some observations on the embryology of *Holboellia latifolia*. Current Sci. 34:28–29.

Bhatnagar, S. P., 1965b. Studies on angiospermic parasites. 2. *Santalum album*. The Sandalwood tree. Bull. Nat. Bot. Gdns. Lucknow 112:1–90.

Bhatnagar, S. P. and S. Agarwal, 1961. Morphological and embryological studies in the family Santalaceae. 6. *Thesium*. Phytomorphology 11:273–282.

Bhatnagar, S. P. and N. S. Singh, 1964. Development and structure of angiosperm seed. 2. *Antirrhinum majus*. Bull. Nat. Bot. Gdns. Lucknow 92:1–10.

Bianchi, D. E., D. J. Schwemmin, and W. H. Wagner, 1959. Pollen release in the common ragweed, *Ambrosia artemisiifolia*. Bot. Gaz. 120:235–243.

Bianchi, R., 1946. Untersuchungen über die Fortpflanzungsverhaltnisse von *Gager fistulosa* und *Lloydia serotina*. Ber. schweiz. bot. Ges. 56:523–582. Diss. Zürich.

Biermann, M., 1896. Beiträge zur Kenntnis der Entwicklungsgeschichte der Früchte von *Citrus vulgaris* (*C. aurantium*) und anderer *Citrus* arten. Diss. Zürich.

Bijok, K., 1960. (Studies in the karyological differentiation of the anther tapetum in *Chrysanthemum subcorymbosum, C. segetum* and *C. corymbosum*.) Acta Biol. Cracov. Bot. 3:15–24.

Bijok, K., 1962. (Cytoembryological studies in species *Crambe abyssinica*.) Acta Soc. bot. Polon. 31:119–134.

BIBLIOGRAPHY

Billings, F. H., 1901. Beiträge zur Kenntnis der Samenentwicklung. Flora 88:253–318.

Billings, F. H., 1903. Chalazogamy in *Carya olivaeformis*. Bot. Gaz. 35:134–135.

Billings, F. H., 1904. A study of *Tillandsia usneoides*. Bot. Gaz. 38:99–121.

Billings, F. H., 1909. The nutrition of the embryo sac and embryo in certain Labiatae. Kansas Univ. Sci. Bull. 5:67–83.

Billings, F. H., 1932. Microsporogenesis in *Phoradendron*. Ann. Bot. 46:979–992.

Billings, F. H., 1933. Development of embryo sac in *Phoradendron*. Ann. Bot. 47:261–278.

Billings, F. H., 1934. Male gametophyte of *Atriplex hymenelytra*. Bot. Gaz. 95:477–484.

Billings, F. H., 1937. Some new features in the reproductive cytology of angiosperms, illustrated by *Isomeris arborea*. New Phytol. 36:301–326.

Birge, W. L., 1911. The anatomy and some biological aspects of the "ball moss," *Tillandsia recurvata*. Bull. Univ. Texas 194:13.

Bishop, J. B. and J. McGowan, 1953. The role of the vegetative nucleus in pollen tube growth and in the division of the generative cell in *Tradescantia paludosa*. Amer. J. Bot. 40:658–659.

Biswas, I. S., 1955. Cytological and embryological investigations in the Asclepiadaceae. Current Sci. 24:204–205.

Biswas, I. S., 1957. Embryological studies in *Daemia extensa*. J. Indian bot. Soc. 36:207–222.

Bitter, G., 1906. Parthenogenesis und Variabilität der *Bryonia dioica*. Abh. nat. Ver. Bremen 18:99–107.

Blackman, V. H. and E. J. Welsford, 1913. Fertilization in *Lilium*. Ann. Bot. 27:111–114.

Bley, F., 1925. Zur Embryologie von *Laurembergia javanica*. Diss. Zürich.

Bliss, M. C., 1912. A contribution to the life history of *Viola*. Ann. Bot. 26:155–163.

Blodgett, F. H., 1923. The embryo of *Lemna*. Amer. J. Bot. 10:336–342.

Bobde, P. L., 1963. Male and female gametophytes of *Operculina turpethum*. Bull. Soc. Coll. Sci. Nagpur 4:33–38.

Bocanzeva, Z. P., 1944. (An investigation into the biology of flowering and embryological development in *Haloxylon ammodendron*.) Bot. Zhur. 29:36–48.

Böcher, T. W., 1947. Cytological studies of *Arabis holboellii*. Hereditas 33:573.

Böcher, T. W., 1951. Cytological and embryological studies in the amphiapomict *Arabis holboellii* complex. Kl. Danske Vid. Selsk. Biol. 6:1–59.

Bochmann, F., 1901. Beiträge zur Entwicklungsgeschichte offizineller Samen und Früchte. Diss. Bern.

Bocquet, G., 1959. The campylotropous ovule. Phytomorphology 9:222–227.

Bocquet, G. and J. D. Bersier, 1960. (The systematic value of the ovule: Teratological developments.) Arch. Sci. (Genève) 13:475–496.

Bocsa, I. and G. Mandy, 1964. Investigations into the morphology, flowering and fertilization biology of wild *Medicago* species. Acta Bot. 10:13–26.

Boehm, K., 1931. Embryologische Untersuchungen an Zinziberaceen. Planta 14:411–440. Diss. Rostock.

Bohn, P. R., 1924. Sur le sac embryonnaire des Euphorbes. Bull. Soc. bot. France 71:576–579.

Bohutinsky, G., 1914. Entwicklungs-Abweichungen beim Mais. Ber. dtsch. bot. Ges. 32:222–248.

Bolenbach, A., 1928. Microsporogenesis in *Tropaeolum majus* with special reference to the cleavage process in tetrad formation. Bull. Torrey bot. Cl. 55:105–115.

Bonnet, J., 1912. Recherches sur l'evolution des cellules nourricières du pollen chez les Angiospermes. Arch. f. Zellf. 7:605–722.

Boodle, L. A. and A. W. Hill, 1929. *Typhonodorum lindleyanum*. The development of the embryo and germination of the seed. Ann. Bot. 43:437–450.

Böös, G., 1917. Über Parthenogenesis in der Gruppe *Aphanes* der Gattung *Alchemilla*, nebst einigen in Zusammenhang damit stehenden Fragen. Lunds Univ. Årsskr. (2). 13:1–37.

Böös, G., 1920. Der experimentelle Nachweis Parthenogenesis in der Gruppe *Aphanes* der Gattung *Alchemilla*. Bot. Notiser 1920:145–150.

Böös, G., 1924. Neue embryologische Studien über *Alchemilla arvensis*. Bot. Notiser 1924:209–250.

Borgenstam, E., 1922. Zur Zytologie der Gattung *Syringa* nebst Erörterungen über den Einfluss äusserer Faktoren auf die Kernteilungsvorgänge. Arkiv. f. Bot. 17(15).

Borthwick, H. A. and W. W. Robbins, 1928. Lettuce seed and its germination. Hilgardia 3:275–289.

Borthwick, R. A., 1931. Development of the macrogametophyte and embryo of *Daucus carota*. Bot. Gaz. 92:23–44.

Borwein, B., M. L. Coetsee, and S. Krupko, 1949. Development of the embryo sac of *Restio dodii* and *Elegia racemosa*. J. Sth. Afr. Bot. 15:1–11.

Bosch, E., 1947. Blütenmorphologie und zytologische Untersuchungen an Palmen. Ber. schweiz. bot. Ges. 57:37–100.

Bose, P. K., 1937. Cytological studies of *Argemone mexicana*. J. Indian bot. Soc. 16:197–206.

Bose, P. K. and I. Banerji, 1933. The development of the female gametophyte and chromosome number in *Argemone mexicana*. Current Sci. 2:94.

Botschanzeva, Z. P., 1937. Spermatogenesis bei *Tulipa* und seine Erlerung zwecks Kariosystematik. Bull. Univ. Asie Centrale (Tashkent) 22:329–338.

Bouharmont, J., 1961. Note sur la pollinisation naturelle de l'*Hévéa* à Yangambi. Agric. du Congo 52:245–264.

Bouharmont, J., 1962. Fécondation de l'ovule et développement de la graine après croisement et autopollinisation chez *Hevea brasiliensis*. Cellule 62:119–130.

Bouharmont, J., 1963. Evolution de l'ovule fécondé chez *Musa acuminata* subsp. *burmannica*. Cellule 63:259–279.

Boursnell, J. G., 1950. The symbiotic seed-borne fungus in the Cistaceae. 1. Distribution and function of the fungus in the seedling and in the tissues of the mature plant. Ann. Bot. 14:217–243.

Boveri, T., 1891. Befruchtung. Anat. Hefte Ergeb. 1:386–485.

Bower, F. O., 1922. The primitive spindle as a fundamental feature in the embryology of plants. Proc. Roy. Soc. Edinburgh 43:1–36.

Bowers, C. G., 1931. The development of pollen and viscid strands in *Rhododendron catawbiense*. Bull. Torrey bot. Cl. 57:285–313.

Boyes, J. W., 1939a. Development of the embryo sac of *Plumbagella micrantha*. Amer. J. Bot. 26:539–547.

Boyes, J. W., 1939b. Embryo sac development in *Plumbagella*. Proc. Nat. Acad. Sci. (Wash.) 25:141–145.

Boyes, J. W., 1959. Demonstration of embryo sac development of *Plumbagella micrantha*. Congr. Internat. Bot. 9th. 2:43–44.

Boyes, J. W. and E. Battaglia, 1951a. The tetrasporic embryo sacs of *Plumbago coccinea, P. scandens* and *Ceratostigma willmottianum*. Bot. Gaz. 112:485–489.

Boyes, J. W. and E. Battaglia, 1951b. Embryo sac development in the Plumbaginaceae. Caryologia 3:305–310.

Boyes, J. W. and W. P. Thompson, 1937. The development of the endosperm and embryo in reciprocal interspecific crosses in cereals. J. Genet. 34:203–227.

Braak, J. P. and Y. O. Kho, 1958. Some observations on the floral biology of the carrot, *Daucus carota*. Euphytica 7:131–139.

Bradbury, D., 1929. A comparative study of the developing and aborting fruits of *Prunus cerasus*. Amer. J. Bot. 16:525–542.

Brandt, R. P., 1916. Notes on the Californian species of *Trillium*. 3. Seasonal changes in *Trillium* spp. with special reference to the reproductive tissues. Univ. Calif. Publ. Bot. 7:39–68.

Brandza, M., 1891. Développement des téguments de la graine. Rev. gén. Bot. Paris 1:1–32, 71–84, 103–126, 150–165, 227–240.

Braun, A., 1857. Über Parthenogenesis bei Pflanzen. Abh. kon. Akad. wiss. Berlin, phys. Abt.:311–376.

Braun, A., 1860. Über Polyembryonie und Keimung von *Coelobogyne*. Ein Nachtrag zu der Abhandlung über Parthenogenesis der Pflanzen. Abh. kon. Akad. wiss. Berlin, phys. Abt. 1860:107–263.

Bremekamp, C. E. B., 1938. Notes on the Acanthaceae of Surinam. Rec. Trav. bot. Néerl. 35:130–174.

Bremekamp, C. E. B., 1942. The position of the genus *Thomandersia*. Rec. Trav. bot. Néerl. 39.

Bremekamp, C. E. B., 1944. Materials for a monograph of the Strobilanthinae (Acanthaceae). Rec. Trav. bot. Néerl. 41:1–306.

Bremekamp, C. E. B., 1953. The delimitation of the Acanthaceae. Proc. Kon. Nederl. Akad. Wet. Amst. C. 56:533–546.

Bremer, G., 1915. Reliquiae Treubianae. 2. The development of the ovule and embryo sac of *Pittosporum ramiflorum* and *Pittosporum timorense*. Ann. Jard. bot. Buitenz. 14:161–164.

Bremer, G., 1946. De cytologie van soortasbastaarden bij *Saccharum*. Vakblad Biologen 21:3–10.

Bremer, G., 1959. Increase of chromosome number in species hybrids of *Saccharum* in relation to the embryo sac development. Bibl. Genet. 18:1–99.

Bremner, P. M., R. N. Eckersall, and R. K. Scott, 1963. The relative importance of embryo size and endosperm size in causing the effects associated with seed size in wheat. J. Agr. Sci. 61:139–145.

Brenchley, W. E., 1909. On the strength and development of wheat, *Triticum vulgare*. Ann. Bot. 23:117–139.

Brenchley, W. E., 1912. The development of the grain of barley. Ann. Bot. 26:903–928.

Brenner, W., 1922. Zur Kenntnis der Blütenentwicklung einiger Juncaceen. Acta soc. sci. Fennicae 50:1–37.

Breslavetz, L., 1929. Zytologische Studien über *Melandrium album*. Planta 7:444–460.

Breslavetz, L., 1930. Spermatogenesis and fertilization process in some plants in connection with the question of heredity through the plasma. Proc. USSR Congr. Genetics 2:181–186.

Bretzler, E., 1924. Beiträge zur Kenntnis der Gattung *Platanus*. Bot. Arch. 7:388–417.

Briggs, B. G., 1964. The control of interspecific hybridization in *Darwinia*. Evolution 18:292–303.

Brink, R. A. and D. C. Cooper, 1936. The mechanism of pollination in alfalfa, *Medicago sativa*. Amer. J. Bot. 23:678–683.

Brink, R. A. and D. C. Cooper, 1940. Double fertilization and development of the seed in angiosperms. Bot. Gaz. 102:1–25.

Brink, R. A. and D. C. Cooper, 1944. The antipodals in relation to abnormal endosperm behaviour in *Hordeum jubatum* x *Secale cereale*. Genetics 29:370–390, 391–406.

Brink, R. A. and D. C. Cooper, 1947. The endosperm in seed development. Bot. Rev. 8:423–477. 9:479–541.

Briosi, G., 1882. Intorno un organo di alcuni vegetali. Mem. Accad. naz. Lincei (3) 12:215–219.

Briosi, G. and F. Tongnini, 1894. Intorno all'anatomia della canapa, *Cannabis sativa*. Atti Ist. bot. Univ. Pavia (2) 3:91–208.

Briquet, J., 1916. Etudes caryologiques sur les genres des Composées *Anthemis, Ormenis* et *Santolina* suivies de quelques conclusions anatomiques et physiologiques d'intérêt général. Ann. Conser. et Jard. bot. Genève 19.

Brisseau-Mirbel, C. F., 1815. Eléménts de physiologie végétale et de botanique. Paris.

Brizicky, G. K., 1964. Polyembryony in *Euonymus*. J. Arnold Arbor. 45:251–259.

Brock, R. D., 1955. Chromosome balance and endosperm failure in *Hyacinthus*. Heredity 9:199–222.

Brofferia, J., 1930. Osservazioni sulla sviluppo della Calycanthaceae. Ann. di Bot. (Roma) 18:387–394.

Brokschmidt, O., 1904. Morphologische, anatomische und biologische Untersuchungen über *Hottonia palustris*. Diss. Erlangen.

Brongniart, A., 1827. Mémoire sur la génération et développement de l'embryon dans les végétaux phanérogames. Ann. Sci. Nat. 12:14–53, 145–172, 225–296.

Brongniart, A., 1831. Observation sur le mode de fécondation des Orchidées et des Cistinées. Ann. Sci. Nat. (1) 24:113–130.

Brooks, A. E., 1960. A preliminary study of *Epifagus virginiana*. Proc. Indiana Acad. Sci. 70:73–78.

Brough, P., 1923. Preliminary note on the embryo sac of *Styphelia longifolia*. Proc. Linn. Soc. N. S. W. 48:674–680.

Brough, P., 1924. Studies in the Epacridaceae. 1. The life history of *Styphelia longifolia*. Proc. Linn. Soc. N. S. W. 49:162–178.

Brough, P., 1927. Studies in the Goodeniaceae. 1. The life history of *Dampiera stricta*. Proc. Linn. Soc. N. S. W. 52:471–498.

Brough, P., 1933. The life history of *Grevillea robusta*. Proc. Linn. Soc. N. S. W. 58:33–73.

Brouland, M., 1935. Recherches sur l'anatomie florale des Renonculacées. Botaniste 27:1–278.

Brouwer, J., 1923. Onderzoekingen over de Platanaceae. Proefschr. Utrecht.

Brouwer, J., 1924. Studies in Platanaceae. Rec. trav. bot. Neerl. 21:369–382.

Brown, C. M., 1964. Pollen tube growth and embryological development in *Avena strigosa* x *A. sativa*. Crop Sci. 4:475–477.

Brown, M. M., 1917. The development of the embryo sac and embryo of *Phaseolus vulgaris*. Bull. Torrey bot. Cl. 44:537–544.

Brown, S. W., 1949. Endomitosis in the tapetum of tomato. Amer. J. Bot. 36:703–716.

Brown, W. H., 1908. The nature of the embryo sac of *Peperomia*. Bot. Gaz. 46:445–460.

Brown, W. H., 1909. The embryo sac of *Habenaria*. Bot. Gaz. 48:241–250.

Brown, W. H. and L. W. Sharp, 1911. The embryo sac of *Epipactis*. Bot. Gaz. 52:439–452.

Brown, W. L., 1941. The cytogenetics of *Poa pratensis*. Ann. Miss. Bot. Gdns. 28:493–522.

Brown, W. V., 1949. A cytological study of cleistogamous *Stipa leucotricha*. Madroño 10:97–107.

Brown, W. V., 1951. Apomixis in *Zephyranthes texana*. Amer. J. Bot. 38:697–702.

Brown, W. V., 1955. A species of grass with liquid endosperm. Bull. Torrey bot. Cl. 82:284–285.

Brown, W. V., 1959. Apomixis in the grass subfamily Panicoideae. Congr. Internat. Bot. 9th. 2:49–50.

Brown, W. V., 1960. The morphology of the grass embryo. Phytomorphology 10:215–223.

Brown, W. V. and G. E. Coe, 1951. A study of sterility in *Hilaria belangeri* and *Hilaria mutica*. Amer. J. Bot. 38:823–830.

Brown, W. V. and W. H. P. Emery, 1957a. Apomixis in the Gramineae, Tribe Andropogoneae: *Themeda triandra* and *Bothriochloa ischaemum*. Bot. Gaz. 118:246–253.

Brown, W. V. and W. H. P. Emery, 1957b. Some South African apomictic grasses. J. Sth. Afr. Bot. 23:123–125.

Brown, W. V. and W. H. P. Emery, 1958. Apomixis in the Gramineae: Panicoideae. Amer. J. Bot. 45:253–263.

Browne, E. T., 1961. Morphological studies in *Aletris*. 1. Development of the ovule, megaspores and megagametophyte of *A. aurea* and their connection with the systematics of the genus. Amer. J. Bot. 48:143–147.

Brumfield, R. T., 1941. Asymmetrical spindles in the microspore division of certain angiosperms. Amer. J. Bot. 28:713–722.

Brunotte, C., 1900. Recherches embryogénique sur quelques espèces des genres *Impatiens* et *Tropaeolum*. Diss. Paris et Nancy.

Bruns, E., 1892. Das Grasembryo. Flora 76:1–33.

Bruyne, C. de, 1906. Le sac embryonnaire de *Phaseolus vulgaris*. Bull. Acad. Roy. Belg. Cl. Sciènces: 577–598.

Bryant, L. R., 1935. A study of the factors affecting the development of the embryo sac and the embryo in the McIntosh apple. New Hampshire Agr. Exp. Sta. Tech. Bull. 61:1–40.

Buchenau, F., 1857. Über die Blüthenentwicklung von *Alisma* und *Butomus*. Flora 15:241–256.

Buchenau, F., 1865. Morphologische Studien an deutschen Lentibulariaceen. Bot. Zeit. 23:61.

Buchenau, F., 1869. Über die Richtung der Samenknospe bei den Alismaceen. Jahrb. f. wiss. Bot. 7.

Buchenau, F., 1872. Über Blüthenentwicklung bei den Compositen. Bot. Zeit. 30:304.

Buchenau, F., 1882. Beiträge zur Kenntnis der Alismaceen, Butomaceen und Juncaginaceen. Engler's Bot. Jahrb. 2:465–510.

Buchet, S. and C. L. Gatin, 1908. Un cas de polyembryonie chez le *Triglochin palustre* et une germination anormale de *l'Arisarum vulgare*. Bull. Soc. bot. France 55:164–169.

Buchholz, J. T. and A. F. Blakeslee, 1922. Studies of the pollen tubes and abortive ovules of the Globe mutant of *Datura*. Science 55:597–599.

Buchholz, J. T. and A. F. Blakeslee, 1927. Pollen tube growth at various temperatures. Amer. J. Bot. 14:358–369.

Buchner, L., 1948. Vergleichende embryologische Studien an Scilloideae. Österr. bot. Zeit. 95:428–450.

Buell, K. M., 1952a. Developmental morphology in *Dianthus*. 1. Structure of the pistil and seed development. Amer. J. Bot. 39:194–210.

Buell, K. M., 1952b. Developmental morphology in *Dianthus*. 2. Starch accumulation in ovule. Amer. J. Bot. 39:458–467.

Buell, M. F., 1935. Seed and seedling of *Acorus calamus*. Bot. Gaz. 96:758–765.

Buell, M. F., 1938. Embryology of *Acorus calamus*. Bot. Gaz. 99:556–568.

Burns, G. P., 1900. Beiträge zur Kenntniss der Stylidiaceen. Flora 87:313–354.

Burr, H. G., 1903. The embryology of *Vallisneria spiralis*. Ohio Nat. 3:439–443.

Buscalioni, L., 1893. Sulla struttura e sulla sviluppo del seme della *Veronica hederaefolia*. Mem. R. Acc. Sci. Torino (2) 43:1–50.

Buscalioni, L., 1894. Contribuzione allo studio della membrana cellulare. 4. *Plantago lanceolata*. Malpighia 8:3–13.

Buscalioni, L., 1898. Osservazione et ricerche sulla vegetale. Ann. Ist. bot. Roma 7:255–346.

Buschmann, E., 1914. Zur Untersuchung der Entwicklungsgeschichte von *Thea chinensis*. Arch. Pharm. 252:412–420.

Bushnell, E. P., 1936. Development of the macrogametophyte in certain Labiatae. Bot. Gaz. 98:190–197.

Butters, F. K., 1909. The seeds and seedlings of *Caulophyllum thalictroides*. Minnesot. Bot. Stud. 4:11–33.

Buxbaum, F., 1937a. Die Entwicklungslinien der Lilioideae. 1. Die Wurmbeoidea. Bot. Arch. 38:213–293.

Buxbaum, F., 1937b. Die Entwicklungslinien der Lilioideae. 2. Die systematische Stellung der Gattung *Gagea*. Bot. Arch. 38:305–398.

Buxbaum, F., 1944. Untersuchungen zur Morphologie der Kakteenblüte. 1. Das Gynaecium. Bot. Arch. 45:190–247.

Buxbaum, F., 1948. Zur Klärung der phylogenetischen Stellung der Aizoaceae und Cactaceae im Pflanzenreich. Jahrb. schw. Kakt. Ges. 2:3–16.

Buxbaum, F., 1949. Vorläufer des kakteen-Habitus den Phytolacaceen. Österr. bot. Zeit. 96:5-14.

Buxbaum, F., 1955. Morphology of cacti. 3. Fruits and seeds. Pasadena.

Buxbaum, F., 1956. Das Gesetz der Verkürzung der vegetativen Phase in der Familie der Cactaceae. Österr. bot. Zeit. 103:353–362.

Buxbaum, F., 1958. Morphologie der Kakteen. 4. Samen. In F. Buxbaum and W. Andreae, "Die Kakteen" 9:79–97.

Byelyayeva, L. Y., 1936. (Development of the male and female gametophytes, pollination and fertilization in *Crambe abyssinica*). Ukrain. bot. Zhur. 20:24–31.

Byxbee, E., 1900. The development of the karyokinetic spindle in the pollen mother cell of *Lavatera*. Proc. Calif. Acad. Sci. (3) 2:63–82.

Caldwell, O. W., 1899. On the life history of *Lemna minor*. Bot. Gaz. 27:37–66.

Cammerloher, H., 1910. Studien über die Samenanlagen der Umbelliferen und Araliaceen. Österr. bot. Zeit. 60.

Camp, W. H. and M. M. Hubbard, 1963. Vascular supply and structure of the ovule and aril in peony and of the aril in nutmeg. Amer. J. Bot. 50:174–178.

Campbell, D. H., 1897. A morphological study of *Naias* and *Zannichellia*. Proc. Calif. Acad. Sci. (3). Bot. 1:1–71.

Campbell, D. H., 1898. The development of the flower and embryo in *Lilaea subulata*. Ann. Bot. 12:1–28.

Campbell, D. H., 1899a. A peculiar embryo sac in *Peperomia pellucida*. Ann. Bot. 13:626.

Campbell, D. H., 1899b. Die Entwicklung des Embryosackes von *Peperomia pellucida*. Ber. dtsch. bot. Ges. 17:452–456.

Campbell, D. H., 1899c. Studies on the flower and embryo of *Sparganium*. Proc. Calif. Acad. Sci. (3). Bot. 1:293–328.

Campbell, D. H., 1899d. Notes on the structure of the embryo sac in *Sparganium* and *Lysichiton*. Bot. Gaz. 27:153–166.

Campbell, D. H., 1900. Studies on the Araceae. 1. Ann. Bot. 14:1–25.

Campbell, D. H., 1901. The embryo sac of *Peperomia*. Ann. Bot. 15:103–118.

Campbell, D. H., 1902. Recent investigations upon the embryo sac of angiosperms. Amer. Nat. 36:7–12.

Campbell, D. H., 1903. Studies on the Araceae. 2. The embryo sac and embryo of *Aglaonema* and *Spathicarpa*. Ann. Bot. 17:665–687.

Campbell, D. H., 1905. Studies on the Araceae. 3. Ann. Bot. 19:329–349.

Campbell, D. H., 1908. The embryo sac of *Pandanus*. Preliminary note. Ann. Bot. 22:330.

Campbell, D. H., 1909. The embryo sac of *Pandanus*. Bull. Torrey bot. Cl. 36:205–220.

Campbell, D. H., 1910. The embryo sac of *Pandanus coronatus*. Bull. Torrey bot. Cl. 37:293–295.

Campbell, D. H., 1911. The embryo sac of *Pandanus*. Ann. Bot. 25:773–789.

Campbell, D. H., 1912. The embryo sac of *Aglaonema*. Scottish bot. Rev. 1:100–115.

Campin, M. G., 1924. An irregular method of pollen formation in *Solandra grandiflora*. New Phytol. 23:282–287.

Campin, M. G., 1925. A cytological study of pollen development in *Nolana*. New Phytol. 24:16–23.

Campo, E., 1963. (Flower morphogenesis and embryogeny in a bisexual *Populus deltoides*.) N. G. bot. Ital. 70:212–219.

Camus, A. and E.-G., 1904. Classification des Saules d'Europe et monographie des Saules de France. Jour. de Bot. 18:177–233.

Camus, A. and E.-G. 1905. Classification des Saules d'Europe et monographie des Saules de France. Jour. de Bot. 19:125–144.

Candolle, A. P. de, 1827. Organographie végétale. 2. Paris.

Candolle, C. de, 1862. Mémoire sur la famille des Juglandées. Ann. Sci. nat. Bot. (4). 18:5–48.

Cannon, W. A., 1900. A morphological study of the flower and embryo of the wild oat, *Avena fatua*. Proc. Calif. Acad. Sci. (3) 1:329–356.

Cannon, W. A., 1903. Studies in plant hybrids: spermatogenesis of a hybrid cotton. Bull. Torrey bot. Cl. 30:133–172.

Canright, J. E., 1953. The comparative morphology and relationships of the Magnoliaceae. 2. Significance of pollen. Phytomorphology 3:355–365.

Capoor, S. P., 1937a. Contribution to the morphology of some Indian Liliaceae. 2. The gametophytes of *Urginea indica*. Beih. bot. Ztbl. 56A:156–170.

Capoor, S. P., 1937b. The life history of *Holoptelea integrifolia*. Beih. bot. Ztbl. 57A:233–249.

Cappelletti, C., 1927. Processi degenerativi negli ovuli in seguito ad impedita fecondazione. N. G. bot. Ital. 34:409–490.

Cappelletti, C., 1929. Sterilita di origine meiotica nella *Ruta patavina*. Ann. di Bot. (Roma) 18:145–166.

Cappelletti, C., 1931. Sull'azione dei prodotti del ricambio di miceli microrizogeni sulle piante ospiti. Ann. di Bot. (Roma) 19:1–62.

Cappelletti, C., 1947. Il cemento pollinico di *Lilium* ha propri eta ormoniche? N. G. bot. Ital. 54:783–786.

Cappelletti, C. and G. Tappi, 1947. Sulla costizuzione chimica de cemento pollinico di *Lilium candidum*. Lav. Bot. 1947:53–56.

Cappelletti, C. and G. Tappi, 1948. Sulla composizione chimica del cemento pollinico di *Lilium candidum*. N. G. bot. Ital. 55:150–152.

Carano, E., 1911. Su la struttura di stami anomali nel *Papaver rhoeas*. Ann. di Bot. (Roma) 9:389–392.

Carano, E., 1913a. Alcune osservazioni sul embriogenesi dell Asteraceae. Ann. di Bot. (Roma) 11:313–315.

Carano, E., 1913b. Su particolari anomalie del sacco embrionale di *Bellis perennis*. Ann. di Bot. (Roma) 11:435–439.

Carano, E., 1914a. Sulla divisione cellulare che segue all'amitosi nelle antipodi di *Bellis perennis*. C. R. Accad. Lincei Roma (5) 23:514–516.

Carano, E., 1914b. Embriologia delle Podostemaceae. Ann. di Bot. (Roma) 12:163–164.

Carano, E., 1915a. Ricerche sull'embriogenesi delle Asteracee. Ann. di Bot. (Roma) 13:251–301.

Carano, E., 1915b. Sull'embriologia di *Poinsettia pulcherrima*. Ann. di Bot. (Roma) 13:343–350.

Carano, E., 1915c. Sull'embriologia di *Senecio vulgaris*. C. R. Accad. Lincei Roma (5) 24:1244–1248.

Carano, E., 1918. Contributo alla embriologia dei genere *Aster* e *Solidago*. C. R. Accad. Lincei Roma (5) 27:255–257.

Carano, E., 1919a. L'*Erigeron karwinokianus* var. *mucronatus* e apogamo. C. R. Accad. Lincei Roma (5) 28:94–96.

Carano, E., 1919b. Nuovo contributo alla embriologia delle Asteraceae. C. R. Accad. Lincei Roma (5) 28:412–415.

Carano, E., 1920a. Studi cito-embriologico sul genere *Erigeron*. C. R. Accad. Lincei Roma (5) 29:157–159.

Carano, E., 1920b. Il significato e la causa del'apogamia secondo le recenti ricerche. Riv. di Biol. 2:403–410, 633–647.

Carano, E., 1921a. Nuove ricerche sulla embriologia delle Asteracee. Ann. di Bot. (Roma) 15:97–196.

Carano, E., 1921b. Le nuove idee sulla parthenogenesi e l'apogamia. Riv. di Biol. 3:1–7.

Carano, E., 1924. Osservazioni sul meccanismo di divisione della cellula madre del sacco embrionale nelle piante apogame. C. R. Accad. Lincei Roma (5). 33:150–155.

Carano, E., 1925. Sul particolare sviluppa del gametofito O di *Euphorbia dulcis*. C. R. Accad. Lincei Roma (6). 1:633–635.

Carano, E., 1926. Ulteriori osservazioni su *Euphorbia dulcis* in rapporto col suo comportamento apomittico. Ann. di Bot. (Roma) 17:50–79.

Carey, G., 1934. Further investigations on the embryology of viviparous seeds. Proc. Linn. Soc. N. S. W. 59:392–410.

Carey, G. and L. Fraser, 1932. The embryology and seedling development of *Aegiceras majus*. Proc. Linn. Soc. N. S. W. 57:341–360.

Cario, R., 1881. Anatomische Untersuchungen von *Tristicha hypnoides*. Bot. Zeit. 1881:25–33, 41–48, 57–64, 73–82.

Carlson, E. M. and B. C. Stuart, 1936. Development of spores and gametophytes in certain New World species of *Salvia*. New Phytol. 35:68–91.

Carlson, M. C., 1940. Formation of the seed of *Cypripedium parviflorum*. Bot. Gaz. 102:295–301.

Carlson, M. C., 1945. Megasporogenesis and development of the embryo sac of *Cypripedium parviflorum*. Bot. Gaz. 107:107–114.

Carniel, K., 1961. Das Antherentapetum von *Zea mays*. Österr. bot. Zeit. 108:1.

Carniel, K., 1962a. Beiträge zur Entwicklungsgeschichte des sporogenen Gewebes der Gramineen und Cyperaceen. Österr. bot. Zeit. 109:81–95.

Carniel, K., 1962b. Die Entwicklung des Antherentapetums der Cyperaceen und Endomitoses an Kernen mit diffuscentromerischen Chromosomen. Österr. bot. Zeit. 109:168–173.

Carniel, K., 1963a. Das Antherentapetum. Österr. bot. Zeit. 110:145–176.

Carniel, K., 1963b. (Contributions to the developmental history of the sporogenous tissues and of the tapetum in some Dipsacaceae). Österr. bot. Zeit. 110:547–555.

Caroll, F. B., 1919. The development of the chasmogamous and the cleistogamous flowers of *Impatiens fulva*. Contr. bot. Lab. Univ. Pennsylv. 4:144–183.

Carter, K. M., 1928. A contribution to the cytology of *Orobanche minor*. J. Roy. Micros. Soc. 48:389–403.

Caruel, T., 1869. Sur la structure florale et les affinités des Eriocaulacées. Mem. Soc. Imp. Cherbourg 4.

Caspary, R., 1854. Über Samen, Keimung, Specien u. Nährpflanzen der Orobanchen. Flora 37:577–588, 593–603.

Caspary, R., 1867. Untersuchungen über den Samen und die Keimung von *Pinguicula vulgaris*. Schr. phys.-ökon. Ges. Königsberg 18:16.

Cassera, J. D., 1935. Origin and development of the female gametophyte, endosperm and embryo in *Orobanche uniflora*. Bull. Torrey bot. Cl. 62:455–466.

Cassini, A. H., 1828. L'analyse de l'embryon des Graminées. Jour. de Phys. 91:321–420.

Castetter, E. F., 1925. Studies in the comparative cytology of the annual and biennial varieties of *Melilotus alba*. Amer. J. Bot. 12:270–286.

Castetter, E. F., 1926. Cytological studies in the Cucurbitaceae. 1. Microsporogenesis in *Cucurbita maxima*. Amer. J. Bot. 13:1–10.

Catalano, G., 1928. Sulle anomalie negli organi di riproduzione di *Agave zapupe*, in rapporto alla probabile natura ibrida di questa pianta. Bull. Soc. Sci. Nat. Econ. Palermo 10:31–40.

Catalano, G., 1929. Megasporogenesi aberrante in *Agave sisalana*. N. G. bot. Ital. 36:317–324.

Catalano, G., 1930. Contributo alla conoscenza delle cause della sterilità in *Agave* e *Fourcroya*. Lav. R. Ist. Bot. Palermo 1:1–60.

Catalano, G., 1931. I rapporti genetici e la fruttificazione nelle *Agave* del gruppo Salmiane. Lav. R. Ist. Bot. Palermo 2:22–45.

Catalani, R., 1950–51. Cytoembryological studies on *Rudbeckia pinnata*. Caryologia 3:327–335.

Cavara, F. C., 1899. Studi sul The. Ricerche intorno allo sviluppo del frutto della *Thea chinensis*, cultivata nel r orto botanico di Pavia. Atti dell'Inst. bot. Pavia (2). 5:265–326.

Cave, M. S., 1939. Macrosporogenesis in *Leucocoryne ixioides*. Cytologia 9:407–411.

Cave, M. S., 1941. Megasporogenesis and embryo sac development in *Calochortus*. Amer. J. Bot. 28:390–394.

Cave, M. S., 1942a. Development of the macrogametophyte of *Miersia chilensis*. Bot. Gaz. 104:185–187.

Cave, M. S., 1942b. Development of the female gametophyte in *Erythronium helenae* and *Erythronium tuolumnense*. Madroño 6:177–181.

Cave, M. S., 1948. Sporogenesis and embryo sac development of *Hesperocallis* and *Leucocrinum* in relation to their systematic position. Amer. J. Bot. 35:343–349.

Cave, M. S., 1952. Sporogenesis and gametogenesis in *Odontostomum hartwegii*. Phytomorphology 2:210–214.

Cave, M. S., 1953. Cytology and embryology in the delimitation of genera. *In* Plant Genera, their nature and definition. Chronica Botanica 14:140–153.

Cave, M. S., 1955. Sporogenesis and the female gametophyte of *Phormium tenax*. Phytomorphology 5:247–253.

Cave, M. S., 1959. Embryological characters of taxonomic value. Congr. Internat. Bot. 9th. 2:62.

Cave, M. S., H. J. Arnott, and S. A. Cook, 1961. Embryogeny in the California Peonies with reference to their taxonomic position. Amer. J. Bot. 48:397–404.

Čelakovský, L., 1885. Über die Inflorescenz von *Typha*. Flora 35:617–630.

Čelakovský, L., 1897. Über die Homologien des Grasembryos. Bot. Zeit. 55:141–174.

Celarier, R. P. and J. R. Harlan, 1957. Apomixis in *Bothriochloa, Dichanthium* and *Capillipedium*. Phytomorphology 7:93–102.

Cesca, G., 1961a. Ricerche cariologiche ed embriologiche sulle Euphorbiaceae. 1. Su alcuni biotipi di *Euphorbia dulcis* della Toscana. Caryologia 14:79–96.

Cesca, G., 1961b. Ricerche embriologiche su *Rudbeckia missouriensis*. Caryologia 14:129–139.

Chadefaud, M., 1946. L'origine et l'evolution de l'ovule des Phanérogames. Rev. Sci. 46:502–509.

Chakravarty, H. L., 1944. Studies on the Indian medicinal plants. 1. Aristolochiaceae. Indian J. Pharm. 6:96–101.

Chakravarty, H. L. and P. Sensarma, 1960. Studies on the male inflorescence of *Trichosanthes bracteata*. Current Sci. 29:108–109.

Chakravarty, R. S., 1935. Polyembryony in *Murraya koenigii.* Current Sci. 3:361–362.

Chakravarty, R. S., 1936. Nucellar polyembryony in Rutaceae. Current Sci. 5:202–203.

Chakravorti, A. K., 1947. The development of female gametophytes and seed of *Coccinia indica.* J. Indian bot. Soc. 25:95–104.

Chamberlain, C. J., 1895. Contributions to the embryology of *Aster novae-anglica.* Bot. Gaz. 20:205–212.

Chamberlain, C. J., 1897a. Contribution to the life history of *Salix.* Bot. Gaz. 23:147–179.

Chamberlain, C. J., 1897b. Contribution to the life history of *Lilium philadelphicum.* 2. The pollen grain. Bot. Gaz. 23:423–430.

Chamberlain, C. J., 1898. Winter characteristics of certain sporangia. Bot. Gaz. 25:124–128.

Chamberlain, C. J., 1905. Alternation of generations in animals from a botanical standpoint. Bot. Gaz. 39:139–144.

Chamberlain, C. J., 1914a. Cytology and embryology of *Smilacina.* Bot. Gaz. 57:441–442.

Chamberlain, C. J., 1914b. The embryo of *Gyrostachys.* Bot. Gaz. 57:443.

Chamberlain, C. J., 1918. The embryo sac of *Aster* and *Solidago.* Bot. Gaz. 65:571–572.

Chandler, C., W. M. Porterfield, and A. B. Stout, 1937. Microsporogenesis in diploid and triploid types of *Lilium tigrinum,* with special reference to abortion. Cytologia (Fujii Jub. Vol.): 1025–1035.

Chandra, N., 1962. Morphological studies in the Gramineae. Agra Univ. J. Res. (Sci.) 11:91–92.

Chandra, N., 1963a. Morphological studies in the Gramineae. 4. Embryology of *Eleusine indica* and *Dactyloctenium aegyptium.* Proc. Indian Acad. Sci. B. 58:117–127.

Chandra, N., 1963b. Some ovule characters in the systematics of Gramineae. Current Sci. 32:277–279.

Chandravadana, P., 1963. A note on the embryology of *Erythrina indica.* Current Sci. 32:229–230.

Chandravadana, P., 1965. A note on the embryology of *Gliricidia sepium.* Current Sci. 34:185–186.

Chapman, M., 1933. The ovule and embryo sac of *Saxifraga virginiensis.* Amer. J. Bot. 20:151–158.

Chatin, J., 1870. De l'anthère. Paris.

Chatin, J., 1874. Etudes sur le développement de l'ovule et de la graine dans les Scrofularinées, les Solanacées, les Borraginées et les Labiées. Ann. Sci. nat. Bot. (5). 19:1–107.

Chaudhuri, K. L., 1940. A note on the morphology and chromosome number of *Litchi chinensis.* Current Sci. 9:416.

Chauveaud, G. L., 1892a. Sur la structure de l'ovule et de l'enveloppement du sac embryonnaire du Dompte-Venin, *Vincetoxicum.* C. R. Acad. Sci. Paris 114:313–315.

Chauveaud, G. L., 1892b. Sur la fécondation dans les cas de polyembryonie. C. R. Acad. Sci. Paris 114:504–506.

Chauveaud, G. L., 1902. De la réproduction chez le Dompte-Venin. Diss. Paris.

Cheesman, E. E., 1927. Fertilization and embryogeny in *Theobroma cacao*. Ann. Bot. 41:107–126.

Cheignon, M., 1962. La meiose, les associations chromosomiques supplementaires et le développement des ovules chez *Thapsia villosa*. Rev. Cytol. et Biol. Veg. 24:217–262.

Chennaveeraiah, M. S. and T. S. Mahabale, 1962. Morphological and embryological studies in *Dipcadi. In* Plant Embryology: A Symposium. CSIR. New Delhi:12–22.

Cherenky, I. M., 1962. (The embryology of secondary blooming of apple trees in the Zakarpat'e). Ukrain. bot. Zhur. 19:23–29.

Chhonkar, U. P. S., 1961. Seedcoat development in *Reseda odorata*. Proc. 48th. Indian Sci. Congr. 3:275.

Chiappini, M., 1954. Research on the embryonic development of some species of the genus *Centaurea*. Sassari Univ. Ist. Bot. B. 4:274–289.

Chiarugi, A., 1924. Embriologia delle Cistaceae. C. R. Accad. Lincei, Roma (5) 33:103–105.

Chiarugi, A., 1925. Embriologia delle Cistaceae. N. G. bot. Ital. 32:223–314.

Chiarugi, A., 1926a. Aposporia e apogamia in *Artemisia nitida*. N. G. bot. Ital. 33:501–626.

Chiarugi, A., 1926b. Fenomeni di aposporia e di apogamia in *Artemisia nitida*. C. R. Accad. Lincei, Roma (6) 3:281–284.

Chiarugi, A., 1927a. Il gametofito femmineo delle Angiospermae nei suoi yari tipo di construzione e di sviluppo. N. G. bot. Ital. 34:1–133.

Chiarugi, A., 1927b. Ricerche sulla embriologia delle Asteraceae. N. G. bot. Ital. 34:717–777.

Chiarugi, A., 1927c. L'evoluzione della cellule del tappeto e la formazione del periplasmodio in aleune Asteraceae. N. G. bot. Ital. 34:783–828.

Chiarugi, A., 1930. Parthenocarpia in *Zizyphus sativa*. N. G. bot. Ital. 37:287–312.

Chiarugi, A., 1933. Lo sviluppo del gametofito femmineo della *Weddelina squamulosa*. C. R. Accad. Lincei, Roma 17:1095–1100.

Chiarugi, A., 1934. La partenogenesi spermimentale nelle piante superiori e la sua importanza per le indagini sulla loro costituzione genetica. Boll. Soc. Ital. Biol. 9:1182–1207.

Chiarugi, A. and E. Francini, 1929. Apomissia in *Ochna serrulata*. Atti Soc. Ital. Prog. Sci. (18th. Riun) Firenze.

Chiarugi, A. and E. Francini, 1930. Apomissia in *Ochna serrulata*. N. G. bot. Ital. 37:1–250.

Chikkannaiah, P. S., 1954. The embryo sac of *Ochna squarrosa*. Current Sci. 23:232.

Chikkannaiah, P. S., 1961. The embryo sac of *Rhoeo discolor:* a reinvestigation. J. Karnatak Univ. 6:57–60.

Chikkannaiah, P. S., 1962. Embryological studies in Commelinaceae. *In* Plant Embryology: A Symposium. CSIR. New Delhi:23–36.

Chikkannaiah, P. S., 1963. Embryology of some members of the family Commelinaceae: *Commelina subulata*. Phytomorphology 13:174–184.

Chikkannaiah, P. S., 1964. An embryological study of *Murdannia simplex*. J. Indian bot. Soc. 43:239–248.

Chikkannaiah, P. S., 1965a. Studies in *Tinantia fugax*. J. Karnatak Univ. (Sci.) 9:2–16.

Chikkannaiah, P. S., 1965b. A contribution to the life history of *Floscopa scandens*. J. Karnatak Univ. (Sci.) 9:3–15.

Chirtoiü, M., 1918. Recherches sur les Lacistémacées et les Symplocacées. Thesis, Genève.

Cho, J., 1938. The anatomical observation of the embryo in the rice. Bot. Mag. Tokyo 52:520–531.

Chodat, R., 1891. Monographica Polygalacearum. Mém. Soc. phys. et d' hist. nat. Genève. Vol. suppl. 1890 (7).

Chodat, R., 1903. Possibilité physiologique de la double fécondation sur *Parnassia palustris*. Bull. herb. Boissier (2) 3:363–364.

Chodat, R., 1904. L'embryogénie de *Parnassia palustris*. C. R. Soc. phys. et d'hist. nat. Genève 21:69–70.

Chodat, R., 1907. Principes de botanique. Genève.

Chodat, R., 1913. L'*Ophrys botteroni*, est-il une éspèce en voie de formation? Bull. Soc. bot. Genève (2) 5:13–28.

Chodat, R., 1916. Hydnoraceae. Bull. Soc. Bot. gén. 8:186–201.

Chodat, R. and C. Bernard, 1900. Sur le sac embryonnaire de l'*Helosis guayanensis*. Jour. de Bot. 14:72–79.

Chodat, R. and C. Bernard, 1902a. Embryologie du *Cytinus hypocystis*. Arch. Sci. phys. et nat. Genève 13.

Chodat, R. and C. Bernard, 1902b. Le sac embryonnaire de *Juglans regia*. Arch. Sci. phys. et nat. Genève 13.

Cholakhyan, D. P. and S. A. Sogomonyan, 1961. (A cytoembryological study of the fertilization process in corn, *Zea mays*, under the conditions of the Stepanavansk region of the Armenian SSR). Izvest. Akad. Nauk Armiansk. SSR. Biol. 14:15–24.

Chopra, R. N., 1953a. The endosperm in some Cucurbitaceae. Current Sci. 22:383–384.

Chopra, R. N., 1953b. Endosperm haustoria in some Cucurbitaceae. Proc. 40th. Indian Sci. Congr.:97.

Chopra, R. N., 1954. Occurrence of endosperm haustoria in some Cucurbitaceae. Nature 173:352–353.

Chopra, R. N., 1955. Some observations on endosperm development in the Cucurbitaceae. Phytomorphology 5:219–230.

Chopra, R. N., 1957. The mode of embryo sac development in *Opuntia aurantiaca*: a reinvestigation. Phytomorphology 7:403–406.

Chopra, R. N. and S. Agarwal, 1958. Some further observations on the endosperm haustoria in the Cucurbitaceae. Phytomorphology 8:194–201.

Chopra, R. N. and S. Agarwal, 1960. The female gametophyte of *Benincasa cerifera*. Bot. Notiser 1960:192–202.

Chopra, R. N. and H. Kaur, 1965. Embryology of *Bixa orellana*. Phytomorphology 15:211–214.

Chopra, R. N. and R. C. Sachar, 1963. Endosperm. *In* Maheshwari, P. (ed.): Recent Advances in the Embryology of Angiosperms:135–170.

Chou, Y.-L., 1952. Floral morphology of three species of *Gaultheria*. Bot. Gaz. 114:198–221.

Chouard, P., 1931. Types de développement de l'appareil végétatif chez les Scillées. Ann. Sci. nat. Bot. 13:132–323.

Choudhury, H. C., 1942. Chromosome studies in some British species of *Limonium*. Ann. Bot. 6:183.

Choudhury, J. K. and J. N. Mitra, 1953. Abnormal tricotyledonous embryo and the morphological structure of normal fruit and seed of *Cinnamomum camphora*. Sci. and Cult. 19:159–160.

Choudhury, M. R., 1961. On the structure of the embryo sac in 4n *Corchorus capsularis*. Indian Agr. 5:29–31.

Christen, H. R., 1950. Untersuchungen über die Embryologie pseudogamer und sexueller *Rubus*-Arten. Ber. schweiz. bot. Ges. 60:153–198.

Christoff, M. A., 1940. Über die Fortpflanzungsverhältnisse bei einigen Arten der Gattung *Hieracium* nach einer experimentell induzierten Chromosomenvermehrung. Planta 31:73–90.

Christoff, M. A., 1942. Embryologische Studien über die Fortpflanzung einiger *Poa*-Arten. Jahrb. Fakult. Land. u. Forstw. Sofia 20:169–187.

Christoff, M. and G. Papasova, 1943. Die genetischen Grundlagen der apomiktischen Fortpflanzung in der Gattung *Potentilla*. Zeit. induk. Abst. und Verebung 81:1–27.

Chubirko, M. M., 1952. (Macrosporogenesis and development of the female gametophyte of *Lotus corniculatus*). Dokl. Soobsch. Uzhgorodsk. Univ. Biol. 5:17–19.

Chubirko, M. M., 1962. (Microsporogenesis and the development of the male gametophyte of *Vicia villosa*). Nauk Zap. Uzhgorods'k Univ. 49:10–17.

Chubirko, M. M., 1964. (Embryogenesis in bird's foot trefoil, *Lotus corniculatus*). Ukrain. bot. Zhur. 21:27–35.

Church, G. L., 1929a. Meiotic phenomena in certain Gramineae. 1. Festuceae, Aveneae, Agrostideae, Chlorideae and Phalarideae. Bot. Gaz. 87:608–629.

Church, G. L., 1929b. Meiotic phenomena in certain Gramineae. 2. Paniceae and Andropogoneae. Bot. Gaz. 88:63–84.

Church, M. B., 1916. The development of the embryo sac and embryo of *Cooperia drummondii*. Bull. Torrey bot. Cl. 43:397–405.

Chuvashina, N. P. and T. A. Gorshkova, 1962. (Characteristics of microsporogenesis in apple-pear hybrids.) Tr. Tsentr. Genet. Lab. im. I. V. Michurina 8:15–18.

Clark, J., 1904. Beitrag zur Morphologie der Commelinaceae. Flora 93:483–513.

Clark, L., 1923. The embryogeny of *Podophyllum peltatum*. Minnesot. Stud. Pl. Sci. 4:111–126.

Clarke, A. E., 1940. Fertilization and early embryo development in the potato. Amer. Potato Jour. 17:20–25.

Clarke, B., 1858. Structure and affinities of Myricaceae and Chloranthaceae. Ann. and Mag. Nat. Hist. (3) 1.

Clarke, B., 1865. On the structure and affinities of Callitrichaceae. Jour. de Bot. 3.

Clarke, C. B., 1887. On *Acalypha indica*. Ann. Bot. 1:359–360.

Clausen, J., 1954. Partial apomixis as an equilibrium system in evolution. Caryologia 6 (Suppl.): 469–479.

Claussen, P., 1919. Bemerkungen zu der Arbeit Dahlgrens über den Embryosack von *Plumbagella*. Sitz. d. Ges. Naturf. Freunde, Berlin 8:341–345.

Claussen, P., 1927. Über das Verhalten des Antherentapetums bei einigen Monocotylen und Ranales. Bot. Arch. 18:1–27.

Clavaud, A., 1878. Sur le véritable mode de fécondation du *Zostera marina*. Act. Soc. Linn. Bordeaux 32.

Cleland, R. E., 1924. Meiosis in pollen mother cells of *Oenothera franciscana*. Bot. Gaz. 77:149–170.

Cochran, H. L., 1938. A morphological study of flower and seed development in pepper. J. Agric. Res. 56:395–419.

Cocucci, A. E., 1961. Embriologià de *Trianthema argentina*. Kurtziana 1:105–122.

Cocucci, A. E., 1964. The life history of *Aa achalensis*. Phytomorphology 14:588–597.

Coe, G. E., 1953. Cytology of reproduction in *Cooperia pedunculata*. Amer. J. Bot. 40:335–343.

Coe, H. S. and J. N. Martin, 1920. Sweet clover seed. U.S. Dept. Agr. Bull. 1:844.

Cohen, L. I., 1962. Studies on the ontogeny of the dwarf mistletoes, *Arceuthobium*. 1. Embryogeny and histogenesis. Amer. J. Bot. 50:400–407.

Cohen-Stuart, C. P., 1916. Sur le développement des cellules génératrices de *Camellia theifera*. Ann. jard. bot. Buitenz. 30:1–22.

Cohn, F. M., 1914. Beiträge zur Kenntnis der Chenopodiaceen. Flora 106:51–89.

Coker, W. C., 1907. The developemnt of the seed in the Pontederiaceae. Bot. Gaz. 44:293–301.

Cole, J. F., 1895. Polyembryony. Nature 51:558.

Cole, R. D., 1917. Imperfection of pollen and mutability of *Rosa*. Bot. Gaz. 63:110–123.

Collins, G. N., 1909. Apogamy in the maize plant. Contr. N. St. Nat. Herb. 12.

Compton, R. H., 1912. Note on a case of doubling of embryo sac, pollen tube and embryo. Ann. Bot. 26:243–244.

Conant, G. H. and C. W. Haquist, 1944. Gametophyte development in *Lilium michiganensis*. Cardina Biol. Suppl. Co., Elon College, N.C.

Condit, I. J., 1926. Fruit, bud and flower development in *Ficus carica*. Amer. Soc. Hort. Sci. Proc. 23:259–263.

Condit, I. J., 1928. Cytological and morphological studies in the genus *Ficus*. 1. Chromosome number and morphology in seven species. Univ. Calif. Pubs. Bot. 11:233–244.

Condit, I. J., 1932. The structure and development of flowers in *Ficus carica*. Hilgardia 6:443–481.

Condit, I. J., 1938. Parthenocarpy in the fig. Proc. Amer. Soc. Hort. Sci. 36:401–404.

Conrad, A. H., 1900. A contribution to the life history of *Quercus*. Bot. Gaz. 29:408–418.

Conrad, H. S., 1902. Note on the embryo of *Nymphaea*. Science 15:316.

Conrad, H. S., 1905. The Waterlilies: a monograph of the genus *Nymphaea*. Carnegie Inst. Publ., Wash. 4.

Constance, L., 1957. Plant taxonomy in an age of experiment. Amer. J. Bot. 44:88–92.

Constantin, M. J., 1964. Fertilization and embryogenesis in *Gossypium hirsutum* x *G. barbadense* hybrids. Cotton Impr. Conf. Proc. 16th.: 4–7.

Cook, M. T., 1902. Development of the embryo sacs and embryos of *Castalia odorata* and *Nymphaea advena*. Bull. Torrey bot. Cl. 29:211–220.

Cook, M. T., 1903a. The development of the embryo sac and embryo of *Claytonia virginiana*. Ohio Nat. 3:349–353.

Cook, M. T., 1903b. The development of the embryo sac and embryo of *Agrostemma githago*. Ohio Nat. 3:365–369.

Cook, M. T., 1906. The embryogeny of some Cuban Nymphaceae. Bot. Gaz. 42:376–392.

Cook, M. T., 1907a. The embryology of *Rhytidophyllum crenulatum*. Bull. Torrey bot. Cl. 34:179–184.

Cook, M. T., 1907b. The embryology of *Rhizophora mangle*. Bull. Torrey bot. Cl. 34:271–277.

Cook, M. T., 1907c. The embryology of *Sagittaria lancifolia*. Ohio Nat. 7:97–101.

Cook, M. T., 1907d. Notes on polyembryony. Torreya 7:113–117.

Cook, M. T., 1908. The development of the embryo sac and embryo of *Potamogeton lucens*. Bull. Torrey bot. Cl. 35:209–218.

Cook, M. T., 1909a. Notes on the embryology of the Nymphaceae. Bot. Gaz. 48:56–60.

Cook, M. T., 1909b. Notes on the embryo sac of *Passiflora adenophylla*. Bull. Torrey bot. Cl. 36:373–374.

Cook, M. T., 1909c. Notes on the embryology of the Caryophyllaceae. Ohio Nat. 9:477–479.

Cook, M. T., 1924a. Development of the seed of *Linaria vulgaris*. Bot. Gaz. 77:225–227.

Cook, M. T., 1924b. Development of seed of *Crotalaria sagittalis*. Bot. Gaz. 77:440–445.

Cook, R., 1938. A note on embryo rejuvenation. Amer. Nat. 63:279–322. J. Hered. 29:419–422.

Cooke, E. and A. Shively, 1904. Observations on the structure and development of *Epiphegus virginiana*. Contrib. Bot. Lab. Univ. Pennsylv. 2:352–398.

Cooper, D. C., 1931a. Microsporogenesis in *Bougainvillaea glabra*. Amer. J. Bot. 18:337–358.

Cooper, D. C., 1931b. Macrosporogenesis and development of the macrogametophyte of *Lycopersicum esculentum*. Amer. J. Bot. 18:739–748.

Cooper, D. C., 1932. The anatomy and development of the floral organs of *Bougainvillaea glabra*. Amer. J. Bot. 19:814–822.

Cooper, D. C., 1933a. Macrosporogenesis and embryology of *Melilotus*. Bot. Gaz. 95:143–155.

Cooper, D. C., 1933b. Nuclear divisions in the tapetal cells of certain Angiosperms. Amer. J. Bot. 20:358–364.

Cooper, D. C., 1934. Development of the embryo sac of *Lilium henryi*. Proc. Nat. Acad. Sci. (Wash.) 20:163–166.

Cooper, D. C., 1935a. Macrosporogenesis and development of the embryo sac of *Lilium henryi*. Bot. Gaz. 97:346–355.

Cooper, D. C., 1935b. Macrosporogenesis and embryology of *Medicago*. J. Agr. Res. 51:471–477.

Cooper, D. C., 1935c. Microsporogenesis and the development of the male gametes in *Portulaca oleracea*. Amer. J. Bot. 22:453–459.

Cooper, D. C., 1936. Development of the male gametes in *Lilium*. Bot. Gaz. 98:169–177.

Cooper, D. C., 1937. Macrosporogenesis and embryo sac development in *Euchlaena mexicana* and *Zea mays*. J. Agr. Res. 55:539–551.

Cooper, D. C., 1938. Embryology of *Pisum sativum*. Bot. Gaz. 100:123–132.

Cooper, D. C., 1939. Development of megagametophyte in *Erythronium albidum*. Bot. Gaz. 100:862–867.

Cooper, D. C., 1940. Macrosporogenesis and embryology of *Portulaca oleracea*. Amer. J. Bot. 27:326–330.

Cooper, D. C., 1941. Macrosporogenesis and the development of the seed of *Phryma leptostachya*. Amer. J. Bot. 28:755–761.

Cooper, D. C., 1943. Haploid-diploid twin in *Lilium* and *Nicotiana*. Amer. J. Bot. 30:408–413.

Cooper, D. C., 1946. Double fertilization in *Petunia*. Amer. J. Bot. 33:54–57.

Cooper, D. C., 1949. Flower and seed development in *Oxybaphus nyctagineus*. Amer. J. Bot. 36:348–355.

Cooper, D. C., 1951. Caryopsis development following matings between diploid and tetraploid strains of *Zea mays*. Amer. J. Bot. 38:702–708.

Cooper, D. C., 1952. The transfer of desoxyribose nucleic acid from the tapetum to the microsporocytes at the onset of meiosis. Amer. Nat. 86:219–229.

Cooper, D. C., 1959. The embryo and endosperm in hybrids. Congr. Internatl. Bot. 9th. 2:80.

Cooper, D. C. and R. A. Brink, 1940. Partial self-incompatibility and the collapse of fertile ovules as factors affecting seed formation in alfalfa. J. Agr. Res. 60:453–472.

Cooper, D. C. and R. A. Brink, 1949. The endosperm-embryo relationship in an autonomous apomict, *Taraxacum officinale*. Bot. Gaz. 111:139–153.

Cooper, D. C., R. A. Brink, and H. R. Albrecht, 1937. Embryo mortality in relation to seed formation in alfalfa, *Medicago sativa*. Amer. J. Bot. 24:203–213.

Cooper, G. O., 1935. Cytological studies in the Chenopodiaceae. 1. Microsporogenesis and pollen development. Bot. Gaz. 97:169–178.

Cooper, G. O., 1936. Cytological investigations of *Erechtites hieracifolia*. Bot. Gaz. 98:348–355.

Cooper, G. O., 1942a. Development of the ovule and the formation of the seed in *Plantago lanceolata*. Amer. J. Bot. 29:577–581.

Cooper, G. O., 1942b. Microsporogenesis and seed development in *Lobelia cardinalis*. Bot. Gaz. 104:72–81.

Copeland, H. F., 1933. The development of seeds in certain Ericales. Amer. J. Bot. 20:513–517.

Copeland, H. F., 1934. The structure of the flower of *Newberrya*. Madroño 2:137–142.

Copeland, H. F., 1935a. On the genus *Pityopus*. Madroño 3:154–168.

Copeland, H. F., 1935b. The structure of the flower of *Pholisma arenarium*. Amer. J. Bot. 22:366–383.

Copeland, H. F., 1937. The reproductive structures of *Pleuricospora*. Madroño 4:1–16.

Copeland, H. F., 1938a. The Styrax of Northern California and the relationships of the Styracaceae. Amer. J. Bot. 25:771–780.

Copeland, H. F., 1938b. The structure of *Allotropa*. Madroño 4:137–153.

Copeland, H. F., 1939. The structure of *Monotropsis* and the classification of the Monotropoideae. Madroño 5:105–119.

Copeland, H. F., 1941. Further studies on Monotropoideae. Madroño 6:97–119.

Copeland, H. F., 1943. A study, anatomical and taxonomic, of the genera of Rhododendroideae. Amer. Midl. Nat. 30:533–625.

Copeland, H. F., 1947. Observations on the structure and classification of the Pyroleae. Madroño 9:65–102.

Copeland, H. F., 1953. Observations on the Cyrillaceae, particularly on the reproductive structures of the North American species. Phytomorphology 3:405–411.

Copeland, H. F., 1954. Observations on certain Epacridaceae. Amer. J. Bot. 41:215–222.

Copeland, H. F., 1955. The reproductive structures of *Pistacia chinensis.* Phytomorphology 5:440–449.

Copeland, H. F., 1959. The reproductive structures of *Schinus molle.* Madroño 15:14–25.

Copeland, H. F., 1960. The reproductive structures of *Fraxinus velutina.* Madroño 15:161–172.

Copeland, H. F., 1961. Observations on the reproductive structures of *Anacardium occidentale.* Phytomorphology 11:315–325.

Copeland, H. F., 1963. Structural notes on hollies, *Ilex aquifolium* and *I. cornuta.* Phytomorphology 13:455–464.

Copeland, H. F. and B. E. Doyel, 1940. Some features of the structure of *Toxicodendron diversiloba.* Amer. J. Bot. 27:932–939.

Corner, E. J. H., 1949a. The Annonaceous seed and its four integuments. New Phytol. 48:332–364.

Corner, E. J. H., 1949b. The Durian theory or the origin of the modern tree. Ann. Bot. 13:367–414.

Corner, E. J. H., 1953. The Durian theory extended. 1. Phytomorphology 3:465–472.

Corry, T. H., 1883. On the mode of development of the pollinium in *Asclepias cornuti.* Trans. Linn. Soc. London (2) Bot. 2:75–84.

Corry, T. H., 1884. On the structure and development of the gynostegium, and the mode of fertilization of *Asclepias cornuti.* Trans. Linn. Soc. London (2) Bot. 2:173–207.

Corti, R., 1930a. Primi resultati di ricerche sulla embriologia e la cariologia di alcune Leguminose, N. G. bot. Ital. 37:278–279.

Corti, R., 1930b. Embriologia del genere *Ionopsidum.* N. G. bot. Ital. 37:510–526.

Corti, R., 1946. Embriologia ed embriogenesi in *Genista monosperma.* N. G. bot. Ital. 53:284–320.

Corti, R., 1948. Sul dioicismo di *Idesia polycarpa.* N. G. bot Ital. 55:446–495.

Corti, R., 1950. Embriologia ed embriogenesi in *Cytisus canariensis.* N. G. bot. Ital. 57:170–185.

Cortini, C., 1958. Sviluppo del gametofito femminile in *Malpighia fuscata.* Caryologia 11:42–56.

Coulon, J. de, 1922. Développement parthénogénétique du *Nardus stricta.* Acta Soc. Helvét. Sci. nat. 2:242–243.

Coulon, J. de, 1923. *Nardus stricta:* étude physiologique, anatomique et embryologique. Mém. Soc. Vaudoise Sci. nat. 6:245–332.

Coulter, J. M., 1889. Contribution to the life history of *Ranunculus.* Bot. Gaz. 25:73–88.

Coulter, J. M., 1908. Relation of megaspores to embryo sacs in angiosperms. Bot. Gaz. 45:361–366.

Coulter, J. M., 1911. The endosperm of angiosperms. Bot. Gaz. 52:380–385.

Coulter, J. M. and C. J. Chamberlain, 1903, 1912. Morphology of the Angiosperms. New York.

Coulter, J. M., C. J. Chamberlain, and J. H. Schaffner, 1897. Contribution to the life history of *Lilium philadelphicum*. Bot. Gaz. 23:412–422.

Coulter, J. M. and W. J. G. Land, 1914. The origin of monocotyledony. Bot. Gaz. 57:509–519.

Coulter, J. M. and J. N. Rose, 1886. The pollen spore of *Tradescantia virginica*. Bot. Gaz. 11:10–14.

Coulter, T., 1823. Mémoire sur les Dipsacées. Mém. Soc. Phys. Hist. nat. Genève 2:13–60.

Covas, G. and B. Schnack, 1945. El valor taxonomico de la relacion "longitud del pistillo: volumen del grano de polen." Darwiniana 7:80–90.

Coy, G. V., 1928. Morphology of *Sassafras* in relation to phylogeny of Angiosperms. Bot. Gaz. 86:149–171.

Creasy, W. D., 1961. Development of the megaspore, megagametophyte and embryo of *Arenaria fendleri* var. *fendleri*. Castanea 26:140–146.

Creech, J. L., 1955. An embryological study in the *Rhododendron* subg. *Anthodendron*. Bot. Gaz. 116:234–243.

Crété, P., 1936. Transformation de l'ovule en grain chez l'*Androsaemum officinale*. Bull. bot. Soc. France 83:654–657.

Crété, P., 1938a. Embryogénie des Lobéliacées Développement de l'embryon chez le *Lobelia syphilitica*. C. R. Acad. Sci. Paris 207:177–179.

Crété, P., 1938b. La polyembryonie chez le *Lobelia syphilitica*. Bull. Soc. bot. France 85:580–583.

Crété, P., 1942. Recherches histologiques et physiologiques sur l'embryologie des Labiatiflores. Contribution à l'étude des formation haustoriales. Thèse. Paris.

Crété, P., 1943. Recherches histologiques et physiologiques sur l'embryologie des Labiatiflores. Embryologie du *Globularia vulgaris*. Bull. Soc. bot. France 90:36–39.

Crété, P., 1944. Polyembryonie chez l'*Actinidia chinensis*. Bull. Soc. bot. France 91:89–92.

Crété, P., 1946a. Développement de l'albumen chez le *Loasa lateritia*. C. R. Acad. Sci. Paris 222:509–511.

Crété, P., 1946b. Embryogénie des Loasacées. Développement de l'embryon chez le *Loasa lateritia*. C. R. Acad. Sci. Paris 222:920–921.

Crété, P., 1946c. Embryogénie des Crassulacées. Développement de l'embryon chez le *Cotyledon umbilicus*. C. R. Acad. Sci. Paris 222:1311–1313.

Crété, P., 1946d. Embryogénie des Crassulacées. Développement de l'albumen et formation des haustoriums chez le *Cotyledon umbilicus*. C. R. Acad. Sci. Paris 222:1454–1455.

Crété, P., 1946e. Embryogénie des Hydrophyllacées. Développement de l'embryon chez le *Phacelia tanacetifolia*. C. R. Acad. Sci. Paris 223:459–460.

Crété, P., 1947. Embryogénie des Hydrophyllacées. Développement de l'embryon chez le *Nemophila insignis*. C. R. Acad. Sci. Paris 224:749–751.

Crété, P., 1948a. Recherches embryologiques chez les Scrofulariacées. Développement de l'albumen et de l'embryon chez le *Chaenostoma foetidum*. Bull. Soc. bot. France 95:142–146.

Crété, P., 1948b. Embryogénie des Papilionacées. Développement de l'embryon chez le *Lens esculenta*. C. R. Acad. Sci. Paris 226:590–592.

Crété, P., 1948c. Embryogénie des Campanulacées. Développement de l'embryon chez le *Trachelium caeruleum*. C. R. Acad. Sci. Paris 226:1742–1744.

Crété, P., 1949a. Un cas de polyembryonie chez une Gentianacee l'*Erythraea centaurium*. Bull. Soc. bot. France 96:113–115.

Crété, P., 1949b. Recherches embryologiques chez les Scrofulariacées. Développement de l'albumen chez le *Lyperia violacea*. Bull. Soc. bot. France 96:186–188.

Crété, P., 1949c. Recherches embryologiques sur les Gesneracées. Développement de l'albumen et de l'embryon chez le *Chirita lavandulacea*. Bull. Soc. bot. France 96:234–235.

Crété, P., 1949d. Embryogénie des Gentianacées. Développement de l'embryon chez le *Gentiana asclepiadea*. C. R. Acad. Sci. Paris 228:768–770.

Crété, P., 1949e. Embryogénie des Gentianacées. Développement de l'embryon chez l'*Erythraea centaurium*. C. R. Acad. Sci. Paris 228:1448–1449.

Crété, P., 1950a. Embryologie des Scrofulariacées. Développement de l'albumen chez les *Nemesia*. C. R. Acad. Sci. Paris 231:711–713.

Crété, P., 1950b. Embryologie des Scrofulariacées. L'albumen chez les *Nemesia*. Bull. Soc. bot. France 97:177–179.

Crété, P., 1950c. Embryologie des Scrofulariacées. Développement de l'albumen chez l'*Alonsoa caulauliata*. Bull. Soc. bot. France 97:196–197.

Crété, P., 1950d. Embryogénie des Scrofulariacées. Développement de l'embryon chez l'*Alonsoa caulauliata*. Bull. Soc. bot. France 97:204–206.

Crété, P., 1950e. Embryogénie des Asclepiadacées. Développement de l'embryon chez l'*Asclepias curassavica*. C. R. Acad. Sci. Paris 230:772–773.

Crété, P., 1950f. Embryogénie des Boragacées. Développement de l'embryon chez l'*Anchusa officinalis*. C. R. Acad. Sci. Paris 230:1198–1199.

Crété, P., 1951a. Embryogénie des Papilionacées. Développement de l'embryon chez le *Colutea arborescens*. C. R. Acad. Sci. Paris 232:176–178.

Crété, P., 1951b. Embryogénie des Papilionacées. Développement de l'embryon chez l'*Astragalus glycophyllos*. C. R. Acad. Sci. Paris 232:1009–1011.

Crété, P., 1951c. Embryogénie des Boragacées. Développement de l'embryon chez l'*Alkanna lutea* (*Nonnea lutea*). C. R. Acad. Sci. Paris 232:1689–1691.

Crété, P., 1951d. Répartition et intérêt phylogénétique des albumens à formations haustoriales chez les Angiospermes et plus particulièrement chez Gamopétales. Ann. Sci. nat. (2) 12:131–191.

Crété, P., 1952a. Embryogénie des Liliacées. Développement de l'embryon chez le *Scilla autumnalis*. C. R. Acad. Sci. Paris 235:313–316.

Crété, P., 1952b. Embryogénie des Liliacées. Développement de l'embryon chez le *Gasteria verrucosa*. C. R. Acad. Sci. Paris 235:1421–1423.

Crété, P., 1952c. Contribution à l'étude embryologique des Datiscacées. L'origine du sac embryonnaire et la transformation de l'ovule en graine chez le *Datisca cannabina*. Bull. Soc. bot. France 99:152–156.

Crété, P., 1952d. Embryologie des Scrofulariacées. Développement de l'albumen et de l'embryon chez le *Teedie lucida*. Bull. Soc. bot. France 99:266–268.

Crété, P., 1952e. Embryologie des Bignoniacées. Les premiers stades du développement de l'albumen chez l'*Amphicome arguta*. Bull. Soc. bot. France 99:315–318.

Crété, P., 1953a. Embryogénie des Boragacées. Développement de l'embryon chez l'*Eritrichium strictum*. C. R. Acad. Sci. Paris 236:224–226.

Crété, P., 1953b. Embryogénie des Papilionacées. Développement de l'embryon chez le *Trigonella caerulea*. C. R. Acad. Sci. Paris 236:740–742.

Crété, P., 1953c. Embryogénie des Caprifoliacées. Développement de l'embryon chez le *Leycesteria formosa*. C. R. Acad. Sci. Paris 237:1432–1434.

Crété, P., 1953d. Embryologie des Scrofulariacées. Développement de l'albumen et de l'embryon chez le *Digitalis purpurea*. Phytomorphology 3:168–172.

Crété, P., 1954a. Embryogénie des Liliacées. Développement de l'embryon chez l'*Endymion nutans*. C. R. Acad. Sci. Paris 238:280–282.

Créte, P., 1954b. Embryogénie des Solanacées. Les premiers stades du développement de l'embryon chez le *Physalis peruviana*. C. R. Acad. Sci. Paris 239:552–554.

Crété, P., 1954c. Embryogénie des Hydrophyllacées. Développement de l'embryon chez l'*Ellisia nyctelea*. C. R. Acad. Sci. Paris 239:1671–1673.

Crété, P., 1954d. Origine et structure du sac embryonnaire, de l'albumen et du tégument séminal chez le *Leycesteria formosa*. Bull. Soc. bot. France 101:130–133.

Crété, P., 1954e. Les premiers stades du développement de l'albumen et de l'embryon chez le *Tetranema mexicana*. Bull. Soc. bot. France 101:232–235.

Crété, P., 1954f. Embryologie de l'*Erinus alpinus*. Les relations entre les genres *Erinus* et *Digitalis*. Phytomorphology 4:325–328.

Crété, P., 1955a. L'origine du sac embryonnaire et le développement de l'albumen chez l'*Alloplectus sanguineus*. Bull. Soc. bot. France 102:205–208.

Crété, P., 1955b. Recherches embryologiques sur le *Xanthium strumarium*. Les affinities du groupe des *Ambrosia*. Bull. Soc. bot. France 102:293–296.

Crété, P., 1955c. Embryogénie des Résédacées. Développement de l'embryon chez le *Reseda glauca*. C. R. Acad. Sci. Paris 240:645–647.

Crété, P., 1955d. Embryogénie des Boragacées. Développement de l'embryon chez le *Cynoglossum officinale*. C. R. Acad. Sci. Paris 241:660–662.

Crété, P., 1955e. Embryogénie des Gentianacées. Développement de l'embryon chez le *Chlora perfoliata*. C. R. Acad. Sci. Paris 241:1825–1828.

Crété, P., 1955f. L'application de certaines donneés embryologiques à la systématique des Orobanchacées et de quelques familles voisines. Phytomorphology 5:422–435.

Crété, P., 1956a. Embryogénie des Lentibulariacées. Développement de l'embryon chez le *Pinguicula leptoceras*. C. R. Acad. Sci. Paris 242:1063–1066.

Crété, P., 1956b. Embryogénie des Lentibulariacées. Développement de l'albumen chez les *Pinguicula*. C. R. Acad. Sci. Paris 242:1346–1349.

Crété, P., 1956c. Embryogénie des Menyanthacées. Développement de l'embryon chez le *Limnanthemum nymphoides*. C. R. Acad. Sci. Paris 242:3110–3113.

Crété, P., 1956d. Embryogénie des Rubiacées. Développement de l'embryon chez le *Diodia dasycephala*. C. R. Acad. Sci. Paris 243:861–863.

Crété, P., 1956e. Contribution à l'étude de l'albumen et de l'embryon chez les Campanulacées et les Lobeliacées. Bull. Soc. bot. France 103:446–454.

Crété, P., 1956f. A propos de l'embryogénie du *Sonerila wallichii*. Bull. Soc. bot. France 103:599–603.

Crété, P., 1956g. A propos de l'embryologie de l'*Argemone mexicana*. Phytomorphology 6:144–148.

Crété, P., 1957a. Embryogénie des Melastomacées. Développement de l'embryon chez le *Clidemia hirta*. C. R. Acad. Sci. Paris 244:374–376.

Crété, P., 1957b. Embryogénie des Papavéracées. Le développement de l'embryon chez le *Dicranostigma franchetianum*. C. R. Acad. Sci. Paris 245:720–722.

Crété, P., 1957c. Embryogénie des Nolanacées. Développement de l'embryon chez le *Nolana prostrata*. C. R. Acad. Sci. Paris 245:853–855.

Crété, P., 1957d. Embryogénie des Saururacées. Développement de l'embryon chez l'*Houttuynia cordata*. C. R. Acad. Sci. Paris 245:1331–1334.

Crété, P., 1957e. Embryogénie des Saururacées. La transformation de l'ovule en graine chez l'*Houttuynia cordata*. C. R. Acad. Sci. Paris 245:1652–1655.

Crété, P., 1957f. Précis de Botanique. 1. Paris.

Crété, P., 1958a. Embryogénie des Cucurbitacées. Développement de l'albumen et de l'embryon chez le *Sicyos angulata*. C. R. Acad. Sci. Paris 246:456–459.

Crété, P., 1958b. Embryogénie des Papilionacées. Développement de l'albumen et de l'embryon chez le *Cantharospermum barbatum* (*Atylosia barbata*). C. R. Acad. Sci. Paris 246:821–823.

Crété, P., 1958c. La Parthénogenèse chez le *Sicyos angulata*. Bull. Soc. bot. France 105:18–19.

Crété, P., 1958d. Développement de l'albumen et l'embryon chez le *Collinsia bicolor*. Phytomorphology 8:302–305.

Crété, P., 1959a. Embryogénie des Gentianacées. Développement de l'embryon chez le *Gentiana punctata*. C. R. Acad. Sci. Paris 248:3594–3596.

Crété, P., 1959b. Embryogénie des Boragacées. Développement de l'embryon chez le *Pulmonaria officinalis*. C. R. Acad. Sci. Paris 249:748–750.

Crété, P., 1959c. Embryogénie des Boragacées. Développement du proembryon chez le *Pulmonaria officinalis*. C. R. Acad. Sci. Paris 249:2095–2097.

Crété, P., 1959d. Embryogénie du *Nicandra physaloides*. Phytomorphology 9:163–167.

Crété, P., 1959e. Précis de Botanique. 2. Systematique des Angiospermes. Paris.

Crété, P., 1960a. Embryogénie du *Calvoa orientalis*. C. R. Acad. Sci. Paris 250:3710–3712.

Crété, P., 1960b. Embryogénie des Solanacées. Développement de l'embryon chez le *Saracha jaltomata*. C. R. Acad. Sci. Paris 250:4194–4196.

Crété, P., 1960c. Embryogénie des Cucurbitacées. Développement de l'embryon chez l'*Ecballium elaterium*. C. R. Acad. Sci. Paris 251:968–970.

Crété, P., 1960d. Embryogénie des Melastomacées. Développement de l'embryon chez le *Bertolonia maculata*. C. R. Acad. Sci. Paris 251:1907–1909.

Crété, P., 1961a. Embryogénie des Solanacées. Développement de l'embryon chez le *Datura tatula*. C. R. Acad. Sci. Paris 252:2128–2130.

Crété, P., 1961b. Embryogénie des Solanacées. Développement de l'embryon chez le *Browallia demissa*. C. R. Acad. Sci. Paris 252:2921–2923.

Crété, P., 1961c. Embryogénie des Solanacées. Développement de l'embryon chez le *Capsicum annuum*. C. R. Acad. Sci. Paris 252:3104–3106.

Crété, P., 1961d. Embryologie des Solanacées. Développement de l'embryon chez le *Salpiglossis sinuata*. C. R. Acad. Sci. Paris 253:3032–3034.

Crété, P., 1963a. Embryo. *In* Maheshwari, P. (Ed.): Recent Advances in the Embryology of Angiosperms: 171–222. Delhi.

Crété, P., 1963b. Développement de l'albumen et de l'embryon chez le *Bystropogon origanifolius*. Phytomorphology 13:364–367.

Crété, P., 1964a. L'embryogénie et son rôle dans les essais de classification phylogénétique. Phytomorphology 14:70–78.

Crété, P., 1964b. L'albumen et l'embryon du *Mimulus moschatus*. Phytomorphology 14:468–472.

Cruz, R. de, 1957. Seed abortion in *Elymus-Sitanion* allopolyploids. Proc. Indian Acad. Sci. B. 45:247–262.

Cuchtmanówna, S., 1930. Sur la structure de sac embryonnaire chez *Petunia violacea*. Acta Soc. bot. Polon. 7:197–204.

Cummins, M. P., 1929. Development of the integument and germination of the seed of *Eleusine indica*. Bull. Torrey bot. Cl. 56:155–162.

Cunningham, D. D., 1889. On the phenomena of fertilization in *Ficus roxburghii*. Ann. Roy. bot. Gdns. Calcutta 1:13–51.

Cutter, V. M. and B. Freeman, 1954. The development of syncytial endosperm of *Cocos nucifera*. Nature 173:827–828.

Cutter, V. M., S. Katherine, and B. Freeman, 1955. Nuclear behavior and cell formation in the development of endosperm of *Cocos nucifera*. Amer. J. Bot. 42:109–115.

Czapik, R., 1954. Cytological and embryological studies in *Centaurea scabiosa*. Acta Soc. bot. Polon. 23:175–194.

Czapik, R., 1961. (Binucleate pollen mother cells in *Potentilla alba*.) Acta Biol. Cracov. Bot. 4:43–47.

Czapik, R., 1962. Embryological studies in the genus *Potentilla*. 2. *Potentilla arenaria*. Acta Biol. Cracov. Bot. 5:29–42.

Dahlgren, K. V. O., 1914. Einige morphologische und biologische Studien über *Primula officinalis*. Bot. Notiser 1914:161–176.

Dahlgren, K. V. O., 1915a. Über die Überwinterungsstadien der Pollensäcke und der Samenanlagen bei einigen Angiospermen. Svensk bot. Tidskr. 9:1–12.

Dahlgren, K. V. O., 1915b. Über die Embryologie von *Acicarpha tribuloides*. Svensk bot. Tidskr. 9:184–191.

Dahlgren, K. V. O., 1915c. Der Embryosack von *Plumbagella*, ein neuer Typus unter den Angiospermen. Arkiv. f. Bot. 14:1–10.

Dahlgren, K. V. O., 1916. Zytologische und embryologische Studien über die Reihen Primulales und Plumbaginales. Kgl. Svensk. Vet.-Akad. Handl. 56:1–80.

Dahlgren, K. V. O., 1918. Die jüngeren Entwicklungsstadien der Samenanlagen von *Typha latifolia*. Svensk bot. Tidskr. 12:207–211.

Dahlgren, K. V. O., 1920. Zur Embryologie der Kompositen mit besonderer Berücksichtigung der Endospermbildung. Zeit. f. Bot. 12:481–516.

Dahlgren, K. V. O., 1922. Die Embryologie der Loganiazeen-Gattung *Spigelia*. Svensk bot. Tidskr. 16:77–87.

Dahlgren, K. V. O., 1923. Notes on the *ab initio* cellular endosperm. Bot. Notiser 1923:1–24.

Dahlgren, K. V. O., 1924. Studien über die Endospermbildung der Kompositen. Svensk bot. Tidskr. 18:177–203.

Dahlgren, K. V. O., 1927a. Die Morphologie des Nuzellus mit besonderer Berücksichtigung der deckzellosen Typen. Jahrb. f. wiss. Bot. 67:347–426.

Dahlgren, K. V. O., 1927b. Die Befruchtungserscheinung der Angiospermen. Hereditas 10:169–229.

Dahlgren, K. V. O., 1927c. Über das Vorkommen von Stärke in den Embryosäcken der Angiospermen. Ber. dtsch. bot. Ges. 45:374–384.

Dahlgren, K. V. O., 1927d. Några Alismataceers embriologi. Vortrag gehalten bei Sitzung in "Botaniska Secktionen av Naturvetenskapliga Student sällskapet i Uppsala" am 6. Dez. 1927. Svensk bot. Tidskr. 21.

Dahlgren, K. V. O., 1928a. Die Embryologie einiger Alismatazeen. Svensk bot. Tidskr. 22:1–17.

Dahlgren, K. V. O., 1928b. Hakenförmige Leistenbildungen bei Synergiden. Ber. dtsch. bot. Ges. 46:434–443.

Dahlgren, K. V. O., 1930. Zur Embryologie der Saxifragoideen. Svensk bot. Tidskr. 24:429–448.

Dahlgren, K. V. O., 1933. Embryologien hos *Impatiens roylei*. Vortrag gehalten bei Sitzung in Botaniska Sectionen av Naturvetenskapliga Studentsällskapet i Uppsala d.9. Mai 1933. Svensk bot. Tidskr. 27:289.

Dahlgren, K. V. O., 1934a. Die Embryosackentwicklung von *Echinodorus macrophyllus* und *Sagittaria sagittifolia*. Planta 21:602–612.

Dahlgren, K. V. O., 1934b. Die Embryologie von *Impatiens roylei*. Svensk bot. Tidskr. 28:103–125.

Dahlgren, K. V. O., 1937. Die Entwicklung des Embryosackes bei *Plumbago zeylanica*. Bot. Notiser 1937:487–498.

Dahlgren, K. V. O., 1938. Hakenbildungen bei Synergiden. Svensk bot. Tidskr. 32:221–237.

Dahlgren, K. V. O., 1939a. Sur la présence d'amidon dans le sac embryonnaire chez les Angiospermes. Bot. Notiser 1939:221–231.

Dahlgren, K. V. O., 1939b. Endosperm- und Embryobildung bei *Zostera marina*. Bot. Notiser 1939:607–615.

Dahlgren, K. V. O., 1940a. Über den Gynäzeumbau der Gattung *Scleranthus*. Bot. Notiser 1940:231–236.

Dahlgren, K. V. O., 1940b. Postamentbildungen in den Embryosäcken der Angiospermen. Bot. Notiser 1940:347–369.

Dahlgren, K. V. O., 1950. The development in Sweden of botanical cytology and embryology. A short history of botany in Sweden. Internat. Bot. Congr. 7th.:79–100.

Dalmer, M., 1880. Über die Leitung der Pollenschläuche bei den Angiospermen. Jena Zeit. f. Nat. 14:530–566.

Dambroise, R., 1947. Contribution à l'histoire de l'albumen vrai chez les Centrospermées. Diss. Paris.

Dang-Van-Liem, 1959. Embryogénie des Buxacées. Développement de l'embryon chez le *Buxus sempervirens*. C. R. Acad. Sci. Paris 248:1844–1847.

Dang-Van-Liem, 1962. Recherches sur l'embryogénie des Tricoques. Thèse. Paris.

Danielyan, A. K., 1963. (Megasporogenesis and microsporogenesis of tobacco under conditions in the Armenian SSSR). Izvest. Akad. Nauk Armyansk. SSR. Biol. Nauk 16:87–90.

Danilina, A. N., 1959. (The embryology of *Lathyrus annuus*). Nauch. Dokl. Visshei Shkoly. Biol. Nauk 4:108–113.

Dark, S. O. S., 1936. Meiosis in diploid and tetraploid *Paeonia* species. J. Genet. 32:353–372.

Darling, C. A., 1909. Sex in dioecious plants. Bull. Torrey bot. Cl. 36:177–199.

Darlington, C. D., 1936. The analysis of chromosome movements. 1. *Podophyllum versipella*. Cytologia 7:242–247.

Darrow, G. M. and G. F. Waldo, 1933. Pseudogamy in blackberry crosses. J. Hered. 24:313–315.

Das, B. C., 1953. Cytological and embryological basis for sterility in autotetraploid sweet clover, *Melilotus alba*. Iowa State Coll. J. Sci. 27:537–561.

Das, B. C., 1961. Polyembryony in mulberry. Current Sci. 30:203.

Dastur, R. H., 1922. Notes on the development of the ovule, embryo sac and embryo of *Hydnora africana*. Trans. Roy. Soc. South Afr. 10:27–31.

Datta, R. M., 1934. On the development of the embryo sac and the pollen grain in *Cassia tora*. J. Indian bot. Soc. 13:277–299.

Datta, R. M., 1941. Tricotyledony in *Morus multicaulis*. Current Sci. 10:440.

Datta, R. M., 1954. Tricotyledony in *Corchorus capsularis*. Sci. and Cult. 20:240–241.

Datta, R. M., 1955. Male gametophyte in cultivated jute. Current Sci. 24:104.

Datta, R. M., 1960. Polyembryony in *Corchorus olitorius*. Sci. and Cult. 25:642.

Datta, R. M. and A. K. Paul, 1951. Morphology of the ovary of *Oryza sativa*. var. *plena* ("Double Rice"). Science 113:491.

Datta, S., 1933. Embryological and cytological studies in *Nolana atriplicifolia* and *N. prostrata*. J. Indian bot. Soc. 12:131–152.

Dauphiné, A. and S. Rivière, 1940. Sur la présence de tubes cribles dans des embryons der graines non germées. C. R. Acad. Sci. Paris 211:359–361.

David, E., 1938. Embryologische Untersuchungen an Myoporaceen, Salvadoraceen, Sapindaceen und Hippocrateaceen. Planta 28:680–703.

Davis, B. M., 1909. Cytological studies on *Oenothera*. 1. Pollen development of *Oenothera grandiflora*. Ann. Bot. 23:551–571.

Davis, B. M., 1910. Cytological studies in *Oenothera*. 2. The reduction division of *Oenothera biennis*. Ann. Bot. 24:631–651.

Davis, G. L., 1961a. The life history of *Podolepis jaceoides*. 1. Microsporogenesis and male gametogenesis. Phytomorphology 11:86–97.

Davis, G. L., 1961b. The life history of *Podolepis jaceoides*. 2. Megasporogenesis, female gametophyte and embryogeny. Phytomorphology 11:206–219.

Davis, G. L., 1961c. Abnormal embryo sacs in *Calotis cuneifolia*. Aust. J. Sci. 23:413–414.

Davis, G. L., 1961d. The occurrence of synergid haustoria in *Cotula australis*. Aust. J. Sci. 24:296.

Davis, G. L., 1962a. Embryological studies in the Compositae. 1. Sporogenesis, gametogenesis and embryogeny in *Cotula australis*. Aust. J. Bot. 10:1–12.

Davis, G. L., 1962b. Embryological studies in Australian Compositae. 2. Sporogenesis, gametogenesis and embryogeny in *Ammobium alatum*. Aust. J. Bot. 10:65–75.

Davis, G. L., 1963a. Embryological studies in the Compositae. 3. Sporogenesis, gametogenesis and early embryogeny in *Minuria denticulata*. Proc. Linn. Soc. N. S. W. 88:35–40.

Davis, G. L., 1963b. Generative apospory and diploid parthenogenesis in *Brachycome ciliaris* var. *lanuginosa*. Aust. J. Sci. 26:90.

Davis, G. L., 1964a. Somatic apospory and polyembryony in *Minuria integerrima*. Nature 204:94.

Davis, G. L., 1964b. The embryology of *Minuria integerrima*: a somatic apomict. Phytomorphology 14:231–239.

Davis, G. L., 1964c. Embryological studies in the Compositae. 4. Sporogenesis, gametogenesis and embryogeny in *Brachycome ciliaris*. Aust. J. Bot. 12:142–151.

Davis, G. L., 1964d. Development of the female gametophyte of *Minuria cunninghamii*. Aust. J. Bot. 12:152–156.

Day, D. F., 1896. Parthenogenesis in *Thalictrum fendleri*. Bot. Gaz. 22:241.

Decaisne, J., 1880. Examen des espèces des genres *Bombax* et *Pachira*. Fl. Serres et Jard. de l'Europe (2) 13:43–52.

Decrock, E., 1901. Anatomie des Primulacées. Ann. Sci. nat. Bot. (8) 13:1–199.

Deecke, T., 1854. Über die Entwicklung des Embryo der *Pedicularis palustris* und *sylvatica*. Abhandl. Nat. Ges. Halle 2:185–189.

Deecke, T., 1855a. Zur Entwicklungsgeschichte des Embryo der *Pedicularis sylvatica*. Bot. Zeit. 13:657–666.

Deecke, T., 1855b. Nouvelles recherches sur le développement de l'embryon du *Pedicularis sylvatica*. Ann. Sci. nat. Bot. 4:58–64.

Dellert, R., 1933. Zur systematischen Stellung von *Wachendorfia*. Österr. bot. Zeit. 82:335–345.

Demoor, V. P. G., 1853. Note sur l'embryon des Graminées. Bull. Acad. Roy. Sci. Belg. 20:358–369.

Denham, H. J., 1924. The cytology of the cotton plant. Microspore formation of Sea Island cotton. Ann. Bot. 38:407–438.

Denisova, G. A., 1962. (Specific characteristics of embryo development in seeds of certain Umbelliferae.) Dokl. Akad. Nauk SSSR 139:127–128.

Dermen, H., 1936. Aposporic parthenogenesis in a triploid apple, *Malus hupehensis*. J. Arnold Arbor. 17:90–105.

Derschau, M. V., 1918. Über disperme Befruchtung der Antipoden von *Nigella arvensis*. Ber. dtsch. bot. Ges. 36:260–262.

Desai, S., 1961. Studies on apospory in *Skimmia*. Rev. Internac. Bot. Exptl. 16:147–152.

Desai, S., 1962a. Cytology and embryology of the Rutaceae. Phytomorphology 12:178–184.

Desai, S., 1962b. Polyembryony in *Xanthoxylum*. Phytomorphology 12:184–189.

Deshpande, B. D. and P. Joneja, 1962. Studies in Asclepiadaceae. 1. Morphology and embryology of *Leptadenia pyrotechnica*. Rev. Internac. Bot. Exptl. 19:73–84.

Deshpande, P. K., 1959. Contribution to the embryology of *Kirganellia reticulata*. J. biol. Sci. 2:76–83.

Deshpande, P. K., 1960a. Morphology of the endosperm in *Caesulia axillaris*. Current Sci. 29:56–57.

Deshpande, P. K., 1960b. Studies in the family Compositae. Male and female gametophytes of *Parthenium hysterophorus*. J. biol. Sci. 3:26–29.

Deshpande, P. K., 1961. Fertilization and development of endosperm, embryo and seed coat in *Eclipta prostrata*. Bull. bot. Soc., Coll. Sci. Nagpur 2:1–8.

Deshpande, P. K., 1962a. Fertilization and development of endosperm, embryo and fruit in *Flaveria repanda*. J. Indian bot. Soc. 41:505–509.

Deshpande, P. K., 1962b. Contribution to the embryology of *Caesulia axillaris*. J. Indian bot. Soc. 41:540–549.

Deshpande, P. K., 1962c. A reinvestigation of the endosperm in *Tridax procumbens*. Current Sci. 31:113–114.

Deshpande, P. K., 1962d. Studies in the life history of *Glossocardia bosvallia*. Bull. bot. Soc., Coll. Sci. Nagpur 3:84–91.

Deshpande, P. K., 1964a. A contribution to the life history of *Volutarella ramosa* (*V. divaricata*). J. Indian bot. Soc. 43:141–148.

324   BIBLIOGRAPHY

Deshpande, P. K., 1964b. A contribution to the embryology of *Bidens triternata*. J. Indian bot. Soc. 43:149–157.

Desole, L., 1947. Studio embriologico di *Ornithogalum umbellatum*. Atti Soc. Toscana Sci. nat. 55:1–8.

Desole, L., 1951. First contribution to a knowledge of the embryological development of the genus *Centaurea*. N. G. bot. Ital. 58:162–168.

Dessiatoff, N., 1911. Zur Entwicklung des Embryosackes von *Euphorbia virgata*. Ber. dtsch. bot. Ges. 29:33–39.

Devine, V., 1950. Embryogeny of *Lychnis alba*. Amer. J. Bot. 37:197–208.

Diakonu, P., 1962. (A comparative study of microsporogenesis and gametogenesis of fertile and sterile forms of corn). Dokl. Mosk. Sel'skokhoz. Akad. im. K. A. Timiryaz. 77:143–151.

Dianova, V. J., A. A. Sosnovitz, and N. A. Steshina, 1934. (Comparative cytoembryological studies of *Parthenium argentatum* and *P. incanum*.) Bot. Zhur. 19:447–466.

Dianova, V. J., A. A. Sosnovitz, and N. A. Steshina, 1935. Vergleichende zytoembryologische Untersuchung der Varietaten von *Parthenium argentatum* und *P. incanum*. Beih. bot. Ztbl. 53A:293–308.

Dickey, R. D. and W. Reuther, 1940. Flowering, fruiting, yield and growth habits of tung trees. Fla. Agr. Expt. Sta. Bull. 343.

Dickson, A., 1876. On the embryogeny of *Tropaeolum peregrinum* and *T. speciosum*. Trans. Roy. Soc. Edinb. 27:223–235.

Diettert, R. A., 1938. The morphology of *Artemisia tridentata*. Lloydia 1:3–74.

Dietz, S., 1886. Die Blüten- und Fruchtenentwicklung bei den Gattungen *Typha* und *Sparganium*. Bot. Ztbl. 28:26–30, 56–60. Termész. Füzetek 10:254–262.

Dietz, S., 1887. Über die Entwicklung der Blüthen un Frucht von *Sparganium* und *Typha*. Biblioth. bot. 5.

Digby, L., 1912. The cytology of *Primula kewensis* and other related *Primula* hybrids. Ann. Bot. 26:357–388.

Digby, L., 1914. A critical study of the cytology of *Crepis virens*. Arch. f. Zellf. 12:97–146.

Dixit, S. N., 1954a. Occurrence of tracheids in the mamelon of *Amyema*. Sci. and Cult. 20:39–41.

Dixit, S. N., 1954b. The female gametophyte of *Amyema*. Proc. 41st. Indian Sci. Congr.: 138.

Dixit, S. N., 1955a. The female gametophyte of *Lepeostegeres gemmiflorus*. Proc. 42nd. Indian Sci. Congr.: 260–261.

Dixit, S. N., 1955b. The embryology of *Lepeostegeres gemmiflorus*. Current Sci. 24:278–279.

Dixit, S. N., 1956. The morphology and embryology of *Tolypanthus*. Proc. 43rd. Indian Sci. Congr.: 230.

Dixit, S. N., 1958a. Morphological and embryological studies in the family Loranthaceae. 4. *Amyema*. Phytomorphology 8:346–364.

Dixit, S. N., 1958b. Morphological and embryological studies in the family Loranthaceae. 5. *Lepeostegeres gemmiflorus*. Phytomorphology 8:365–376.

Dixit, S. N., 1961. Morphological and embryological studies in the family Loranthaceae. 8. *Tolypanthus*. Phytomorphology 11:335–345.

Dixon, H. H., 1895. Note on the nuclei of the endosperm of *Fritillaria imperialis*. Proc. Roy. Irish Acad. (3) 3:721–725.

Dixon, H. H., 1946. Evidence for a mitotic hormone: observations on the mitoses of the embryo sac of *Fritillaria imperialis*. Proc. Roy Soc. Dublin 24:119–124.

Dmitrieva, G. A. and S. V. Zhukova, 1961. (Organogenesis in *Agropyron glaucum*). *In* Morfogenez Rastenii: 592–596.

Dnyansagar, V. R., 1949. Embryological studies in the Leguminosae. 1. A contribution to the embryology of *Leucaena glauca*. J. Indian bot. Soc. 28:95–107.

Dnyansagar, V. R., 1951a. Embryological studies in the Leguminosae. 2. A. contribution to the embryology of *Mimosa hamata*. J. Indian bot. Soc. 30:100–107.

Dnyansagar, V. R., 1951b. Embryological studies in the Leguminosae. 3. A contribution to the embryology of *Pithecolobium saman* (*Enterolobium saman*). Proc. Indian Acad. Sci. B. 34:188–198.

Dnyansagar, V. R., 1952. Embryological studies in the Leguminosae. 4. A contribution to the embryology of *Neptunia triquetra*, Proc. Indian Acad. Sci. B. 34:1–11.

Dnyansagar, V. R., 1954a. Embryological studies in the Leguminosae. 6. Inflorescence, sporogenesis and gametophyte of *Vichrostachys cinerea* and *Parkia biglandulosa*. Lloydia 17:263–274.

Dnyansagar, V. R., 1954b. Embryological studies in the Leguminosae. 7. Endosperm and embryo development in *Neptunia triquetra* and *Prosopis spicigera*. J. Indian bot. Soc. 33:247–253.

Dnyansagar, V. R., 1954c. Embryological studies in the Leguminosae. 9. Development of endosperm and embryo in *Dichrostachys cinerea* and *Parkia biglandulosa*. J. Indian bot. Soc. 33:423–432.

Dnyansagar, V. R., 1954d. Embryological studies in the Leguminosae. 10. Supplementary observations on the development of the endosperm and embryo in *Leucaena glauca* and *Mimosa hamata*. J. Indian bot. Soc. 33:433–442.

Dnyansagar, V. R., 1954e. Behaviour of tapetal cells during microsporogenesis of *Adenanthera pavonina*. Current Sci. 23:131.

Dnyansagar, V. R., 1955. Embryological studies in the Leguminosae. 11. Embryological features and formulae and taxonomy of the Mimosaceae. J. Indian bot. Soc. 34:362–381.

Dnyansagar, V. R., 1956. Embryological studies in the Leguminosae. 12. Status of the Leguminosae. Saugar Univ. J. 1:39–53.

Dnyansagar, V. R., 1957. Embryological studies in the Leguminosae. 5. *Prosopis spicigera* and *Desmanthus virgatus*. Bot. Gaz. 118:180–186.

Dnyansagar, V. R., 1958. Embryological studies in the Leguminosae. 8. *Acacia auriculaeformis, Adenanthera pavonina, Calliandra hematocephala* and *Calliandra grandiflora*. Lloydia 21:1–25.

Dnyansagar, V. R. and D. C. Cooper, 1960. Development of the seed of *Solanum phureja*. Amer. J. Bot. 47:176–186.

Dnyansagar, V. R. and S. R. Malkhede, 1963. Development of the seed of *Trianthema portulacastrum*. Proc. Indian Acad. Sci. B. 57:343–355.

Dnyansagar, V. R. and D. K. Tiwary, 1956a. Microsporogenesis in *Fimbristylis quinquangularis*. Current Sci. 25:16.

Dnyansagar, V. R. and D. K. Tiwary, 1956b. Sporogenesis and gametophyte of *Fimbristylis quinquangularis*. Bull. bot. Soc. Univ. Saugar. 8:3–6.

Dodds, K. S., 1943. Genetical and cytological studies of *Musa*. 5. Certain edible diploids. J. Genet. 45:113–138.

Dodds, K. S., 1945. Genetical and cytological studies of *Musa*. 6. The development of female cells of certain edible diploids. J. Genet. 46:161–179.

Dodel, A., 1891. Beiträge zur Kenntnis der Befruchtungserscheinungen bei *Iris sibirica*. Fest. f. Nägeli und Köllicker. Zürich.

Doida, Y., 1960. Developmental studies in the genus *Polygonum*. 1. Microsporogenesis of *Polygonum persicaria*. Bot. Mag. (Tokyo) 73:278–282.

Dolcher, T., 1947. Ricerche embriologiche sulla femiglia delle Rhamnaceae. N. G. bot. Ital. 54:648–673.

Doll, W., 1927. Beiträge zur Kenntnis der Dipsaceen und Dipsaceenähnlicher Pflanzen. Bot. Arch. 17:107–146.

Don, D., 1827. On the affinities of the Empetraceae, a natural group of plants. Edinb. New Phil. Mag. 2:59–63.

Donati, G., 1912. Di alcune particolarità embriologiche in *Poinsettia pulcherrima*. C. R. Accad. Lincei, Roma 21:512–514.

Donati, G., 1913. Ricerche embriologiche sulle Euphorbiaceae. Ann. di Bot. (Roma) 11:395–399.

Dop, P., 1902a. Sur le pollen des Asclépiadées. C. R. Acad. Sci. Paris 135:710–712.

Dop, P., 1902b. Sur le développement de l'ovule des Asclépiadées. C. R. Acad. Sci. Paris 135:800–803.

Dop, P., 1903a. Recherches sur la structure et le développement de la fleur des Asclépiadées. Thesis. Paris. Toulouse.

Dop, P., 1903b. Sur l'ovule et la fécondation des Asclépiadées. C. R. Acad. Sci. Paris 136:250–252.

Dop, P., 1913a. Sur la cytologie des suçoirs micropylaires de l'albumen de *Veronica persica*. C. R. Acad. Sci. Paris 156:1922–1924.

Dop, P., 1913b. Recherches sur le développement et la nutrition du sac embryonnaire et de l'endosperme des *Buddleia*. Bull. Soc. bot. France 60:9–16, 45–50, 92–98.

Dop, P., 1914. Recherches sur le rôle des différenciations cytoplasmiques du suçoir micropylaire de l'albumen de *Veronica persica* dans la formation de cellulose. Rev. gén. bot. 25 (Fest. Bonnier): 167–177.

Dop, P., 1923. Remarques sur les Loganiacées. Bull. Soc. bot. France 70:136–139.

Dorasami, L. S. and D. M. Gopinath, 1944. Vine chilly: a comparative morphological and cytological study. Proc. Indian Acad. Sci. B. 20:40–42.

Dorasami, L. S. and D. M. Gopinath, 1945. An embryological study of *Linum mysorense*. Proc. Indian Acad. Sci. B. 22:6–9.

Dore, W. G., 1956. Some grass genera with liquid endosperm. Bull. Torrey bot. Cl. 83:335–337.

Dorsey, M. J., 1914. Pollen development in the grape with special reference to sterility. Univ. Minnesot. Agr. Exp. Bull. 144:1–60.

Dorsey, M. J., 1919. A study of sterility in the plum. Genetics 4:417–488.

Doumet, N., 1866. Le Pachira (*carolinea*) à fleurs blanches. Rev. hort. Paris 1866:208–211.

Dowding, E. S., 1931. Floral morphology of *Arceuthobium americanum*. Bot. Gaz. 91:42–54.

Doyel, B. E., 1942. Some features of the structure of *Arctostaphylos viscida*. Amer. J. Bot. 29:254–259.

Doyel, B. E. and L. M. Goss, 1941. Some details of the structure of *Sarcodes*. Madroño 6:1–7.

Doyle, J., 1953. Gynospore or megaspore: a restatement. Ann. Bot. 17:465–476.

Drahowzal, G., 1936. Beiträge zur Morphologie und Entwicklungsgeschichte der Pollenkörner. Österr. bot. Zeit. 85:241–269.

Drude, O., 1877a. Über den Bau und die systematische Stellung der Gattung *Carludovica*. Bot. Zeit. 35:591–593.

Drude, O., 1877b. Ausgewählte Beispiele zur Erläuterung der Fruchtbildung bei den Palmen. Bot. Zeit. 35:601–613, 617–631, 633–639.

Dube, V. P., 1962. Morphological and anatomical studies in Polygalaceae and its allied families. Agra Univ. J. Res. (Sci.) 11:109–112.

Ducamp, L., 1901a. Développement de l'embryon chez le Lierre, *Hedera helix*. C. R. Acad. Sci. Paris 133:651–653.

Ducamp, L., 1901b. Recherches sur la formation de l'ovule et du sac embryonnaire dans les Araliacées. C. R. Acad. Sci. Paris 133:753–756.

Ducamp, L., 1902. Recherches sur l'embryogénie des Araliacées. Ann. Sci. nat. Bot. (8). 15:311–402.

Dudgeon, W., 1918. Morphology of *Rumex crispus*. Bot. Gaz. 66:393–421.

Dudley, M. G., 1937. Morphological and cytological studies of *Calla palustris*. Bot. Gaz. 98:556–571.

Duffas, F., 1930. Sur l'évolution du sac embryonnaire de *Clerodendron arichotomum*. Bull. Soc. Hist. nat. Toulouse 59:177.

Duggar, B. M., 1899. On the development of the pollen grain and the embryo in *Bignonia venusta*. Bull. Torrey bot. Cl. 26:89–105.

Duggar, B. M., 1900. Studies in the development of the pollen grain in *Symplocarpus foetidus* and *Peltandra undulata*. Bot. Gaz. 29:81–98.

Dumée, P., 1910. Quelques observations sur l'embryon des Orchidées. Bull. Soc. bot. France 57:83–87.

Duncan, M., 1873. On the development of the gynoecium and the method of impregnation in *Primula vulgaris*. Bot. Jahrb.

Dunn, L. B., 1900. Morphology of the development of the ovule in *Delphinium exaltatum*. Proc. Amer. Assoc. Adv. Sci. 49:284.

Duthrie, A. V., 1915. Note on the apparent apogamy in *Pterygodium newdigatae*. Trans. Roy. Soc. Sth. Afr. 5:593–598.

Dutt, B. S. M., 1957a. Morphology of the ovule of *Crinum defixum*. Current Sci. 26:22–24.

Dutt, B. S. M., 1957b. Ovule and embryo sac of *Crinum asiaticum*. Sci. and Cult. 22:688–690.

Dutt, B. S. M., 1959. Ovule and embryo sac of *Crinum latifolium*: a reinvestigation. Current Sci. 28:293–294.

Dutt, B. S. M., 1962. A contribution to the life history of *Crinum defixum*. *In* Plant Embryology: A Symposium. CSIR New Delhi: 37–48.

Dutt, B. S. M., 1964. Ovule and embryo sac of *Pancratium maritimum*: a reinvestigation. Current Sci. 33:150–151.

Dutt, M., 1953. Dividing nuclei in coconut milk. Nature 171:799.

Dutt, M., 1955. The occurrence and division of free nuclei in the endospermal milk of some Palmae. Trans. Bose Res. Inst. Calcutta 19:117–125.

Dutt, M. K., 1943. Development of the microspores and the nuclear behavior in tapetal cells of *Putranjiva roxburghii*. Sci. and Cult. 8:309–310.

Dutt, N. L. and M. K. Krishnaswami, 1932. Observations on the cytology of the sugar cane. Indian J. Agric. Sci. 2:47–50.

Dutt, N. L. and K. S. Rao, 1933. Observations on the cytology of the sugar cane. Indian J. Agr. Sci. 3:37–56.

Dutta, S., 1939. A note on the development of the female gametophyte in some Indian Compositae. Current Sci. 8:471–472.

Duvick, D. N., 1955. Cytoplasmic inclusions of the developing and mature maize endosperm. Amer. J. Bot. 42:717–728.

D'Yakova, M. I., 1962. (The process of fertilization in *Mirabilis jalapa*.) Byull. Moskov. Obshch. Ispytat. Prirody. Otdel Biol. 67:145.

Dzevaltovs'kyi, A. K., 1961. (Specific morphological and cytoembryological characteristics of the development of normal varieties of cucumber and those with a tendency to parthenocarpy). Ukrain. bot. Zhur. 18:33–41.

Dzevaltovs'kyi, A. K., 1963a. (Development of the female gametophyte in *Benincasa hispida*.) *In* Questions of physiology, cytoembryology and the flora of the Ukraine). Akad. Nauk Ukrain. RSR:60–72.

Dzevaltovs'kyi, A. K., 1963b. (Cytoembryological studies of some Cucurbitaceae species.) Ukrain. bot. Zhur. 20:16–19.

Dzyubenko, L. K., 1959. (Cytoembryological investigation of the female generative zone in the sunflower ovule, *Helianthus*.) Ukrain. bot. Zhur. 16:8–19.

Dzyubenko, L. K., 1960. (Fertilization and early phases of development of embryo and endosperm in hybrid corn.) Ukrain. bot. Zhur. 17:6–24.

Eames, A. J., 1961. Morphology of the Angiosperms. New York.

Earle, T. T., 1938. Embryology of certain Ranales. Bot. Gaz. 100:257–275.

Eckardt, T., 1957. Zur systematischen Stellung von *Eucommia ulmoides*. Ber. dtsch. bot. Ges. 69:487–498.

Eckardt, T., 1963. Some observations on the morphology and embryology of *Eucommia ulmoides*. J. Indian bot. Soc., Maheshwari Commem. Vol. 42A:27–34.

Eckles, M. L., 1941. Megasporogenesis and development of the megagametophyte in *Nothoscordum bivalve*. Bot. Gaz. 102:806–809.

Edman, G., 1929. Zur Entwicklungsgeschichte der Gattung *Oxyris*, nebst zytologischen, embryologischen und systematischen Bemerkungen über einige andere Polygonaceen. Acta Hort. Berg. 9:165–291.

Edman, G., 1931. Apomeiosis und Apomixis bei *Atraphaxis frutescens*. Acta Hort. Berg. 11:13–66.

Edwards, J. G., 1920. Flower and seed of *Hedyosmum nutans*. Bot. Gaz. 70:409–424.

Edwards, T. I., 1934. Seed frequencies in *Cytisus* and *Peltandra*. Amer. Nat. 68:283–286.

Eichinger, A., 1907. Vergleichende Entwicklungsgeschichte von *Adoxa* und *Chrysosplenium*. Mitt. Bayer. bot. Ges. München 2:65–74, 81–93.

Eichinger, A., 1908. Beiträge zur Kenntnis und systematischen Stellung der Gattung *Parnassia*. Bot. Ztbl. 23:298–317.

Eichinger, A., 1910. Polyembryonie bei Pflanzen. Ein Fall von Polyembryonie beim Weizen. Naturw. Wochensch. 25:767–773.

Eichler, A. W., 1875–78. Blüthendiagramme. Leipzig.

Eichler, K., 1906. Über die doppelte Befruchtung bei *Tragopogon orientalis*. S. B. Acad. wiss. Wien 115:841–856.

Eigsti, O. J., 1937a. Pollen tube behavior in self-fertile and interspecific pollinated Resedaceae. Amer. Nat. 71:520–521.

Eigsti, O. J., 1937b. The morphology of pollen tubes in Angiosperms. Proc. Okla. Acad. Sci. 19:105–107.

Eigsti, O. J., 1941. The occurrence of a pollen tube with four sperms and two tube nuclei in *Polygonatum*. Proc. Okla. Acad. Sci. 21:134–136.

Einset, J., 1951. Apomixis in American polyploid blackberries. Amer. J. Bot. 38:768–772.

Ekambaram, T. and R. R. Panje, 1935. Contributions to our knowledge of *Balanophora*. 2. Life history of *B. dioica*. Proc. Indian Acad. Sci. B. 1:522–543.

Ekdahl, I., 1941. Die Entwicklung von Embryosack und Embryo bei *Ulmus glabra*. Svensk bot. Tidskr. 35:143–156.

Ekstrand, H., 1918. Zytologie und Embryologie der Gattung *Plantago*. Svensk bot. Tidskr. 12:202–206.

Elfert, W., 1895. Morphologie und Anatomie der *Limosella aquatica*. Diss. Erlangen.

Elfving, F., 1879. Studien über die Pollenkörner der Angiospermen. Jen. Zeit. f. Nat. 13:1–28; 1880. Quart. J. Micros. Sci. 20:19–35.

Elkins, M. G., 1914. The maturation phases in *Smilax herbacea*. Bot. Gaz. 57:32–53.

Elmore, C. J., 1898. Some results from the study of *Allium*. Bot. Gaz. 26:277–278.

Elssmann, E. and R. von Veh, 1931. Beiträge zur Frage nach den befruchtungsverhaltnissen de fur Deutschland wirtschaftlich wertvollsten Kern-, Stein- und Beerenobstsorten. 1. Nachweis der reduktionsteilung im weiblichen Archesp. von *Malus*, bei der Sorte "Schoner von Boskoop." Gartenbauwiss 6:1–54.

Elst, P. van der, 1909. Beitrage zur Kenntnis der Samenanlage der Saxifragaceae. Diss. Utrecht.

Emery, W. H. P., 1957. A study of reproduction in *Setaria macrostachya* and its relatives in the south-western United States and northern Mexico. Bull. Torrey bot. Cl. 84:106–121.

Emery, W. H. P. and W. V. Brown, 1957. Extra-ovular development of embryos in two grass species. Bull. Torrey bot. Cl. 84:361–365.

Emery, W. H. P. and W. V. Brown, 1958. Apomixis in the Gramineae, Tribe Andropogoneae: *Heteropogon contortus*. Madroño 14:238–246.

Endriss, W., 1902. Monographie von *Pilostyles ingae*. Flora 91:209–236.

Engelbert, V., 1940. Reproduction in some *Poa* species. Canada. J. Res. C. 18:518–521.

Engelbert, V., 1941. The development of twin embryo sacs, embryos and endosperm in *Poa arctica*. Canad. J. Res. C. 19:135–144.

Engleman, E. M., 1960. Ovule and seed development in certain Cacti. Amer. J. Bot. 47:460–467.

Engler, A., 1876. Beiträge zur Kenntniss der Antherenbildung der Metaspermen. Jahrb. f. wiss. Bot. 10:275–316.

Engler, A., 1877. Vergleichende Untersuchungen über die morphologischen Verhältnisse der Araceae. Verh. Ksl. Leop.-Carol. deut. Akad. Nat. 39:159–232.

Engler, A., 1884. Beiträge zur Kenntniss der Araceae. 5. Bot. Jahrb. 5:141–188, 287–336.

Englar, A., 1900. Polyembryonie bei *Mangifera indica*. Dtsch. bot. Monatschr. 18:95.

Engler, A. and K. Prantl, 1899. 1935. Die natürlichen Pflanzenfamilien. Leipzig.

330 BIBLIOGRAPHY

Enzenberg, U., 1961. Beiträge zur Karyologie des Endosperms. Österr. bot. Zeit. 108:245–285.

Erdtman, G., 1945. Pollen morphology and plant taxonomy. 5. On the occurrence of tetrads and dyads. Svensk bot. Tidskr. 39:286–297.

Erdtman, G., 1952. Pollen Morphology and Plant Taxonomy. Stockholm.

Erickson, L. C. and H. M. Benedict, 1947. Origin of the seed coats in guayule. J. agr. Res. 74:329–335.

Erickson, R. O., 1948. Cytological and growth correlations in the flower bud and anther development of *Lilium longiflorum*. Amer. J. Bot. 35:729–739.

Erlanson, E. W. and F. J. Hermann, 1927. The morphology and cytology of perfect flowers in *Populus tremuloides*. Papers Michig. Acad. Sci. 8:97–110.

Ernst, A., 1886. A new case of parthenogenesis in the vegetable kingdom. Nature 34:549–552.

Ernst, A., 1901. Beiträge zur Kenntniss der Entwicklung des Embryosackes und des Embryos (Polyembryonie) von *Tulipa gesneriana*. Flora 88:37–77.

Ernst, A., 1902. Chromosomenreduktion, Entwicklung des Embryosackes und Befruchtung bei *Paris quadrifolia* und *Trillium grandiflorum*. Flora 91:1–46.

Ernst, A., 1908a. Zur Phylogenie des Embryosackes der Angiospermen. Ber dtsch. bot. Ges. 26:419–438.

Ernst, A., 1908b. Ergebnisse neueren Untersuchungen über den Embryosack der Angiospermen. Verh. schw. nat. Jahresv. Ges. (1) 91:230–263.

Ernst, A., 1909. Apogamie bei *Burmannia coelestis*. Ber. dtsch. bot. Ges. 27:157–168.

Ernst, A., 1910. Review of "the development of the embryo sac of *Smilacina stellata*. McAllister, F. in Bot. Gaz. 48." Zeit. f. Bot. 2:127.

Ernst, A., 1913. Zur Kenntnis von Parthenogenesis und Apogamie bei Angiospermen. Verh. schw. nat. Jahresv. Ges. (2) 96:1–13.

Ernst, A., 1914. Embryobildung bei *Balanophora*. Flora 106:129–159.

Ernst, A., 1918. Bastardierung als Ursache der Apogamie im Pflanzenreich. Eine Hypothese zur experimentellen Vererbungs- und Abstammungslehre. Jena.

Ernst, A., 1942. Materialien und Fragestellungen zu blüthenmorphologischen, i.b. embryologisch-zytologischen Untersuchungen an Loranthaceen. Vjschr. naturf. Ges. Zürich 87:269–300.

Ernst, A. and C. Bernard, 1909a. Beiträge zur Kenntniss der Saprophyten Javas. 2. Äussere u. innere Morphologie von *Thismia javanica*. Ann. Jard. bot. Buitenz. (2) 8:32–36.

Ernst, A. and C. Bernard, 1909b. Beiträge zur Kenntniss der Saprophyten Javas. 3. Embryologie von *Thismia javanica*. Ann. Jard. bot. Buitenz. (2). 8:48–61.

Ernst, A. and C. Bernard, 1911. Beiträge zur Kenntniss der Saprophyten Javas. 6. Beiträge zur Embryologie von *Thismia clandestina* und *T. versteegii*. Ann. Jard. bot. Buitenz. (2) 9:71–78.

Ernst, A. and C. Bernard, 1912a. Beiträge zur Kenntniss der Saprophyten Javas. 9. Entwicklungsgeschichte des Embryosackes und des Embryos von *Burmannia candida* und *B. championii*. Ann. Jard. bot. Buitenz. (2) 10:161–188.

Ernst, A. and C. Bernard, 1912b. Beiträge zur Kenntniss der Saprophyten Javas. 12. Entwicklungsgeschichte des Embryosackes, des Embryos und des Endosperms von *Burmannia coelestis*. Ann. Jard. bot. Buitenz. (2) 11:234–257.

Ernst, A. and E. Schmid, 1909. Embryosackentwicklung und Befruchtung bei *Rafflesia patma*. Ber. dtsch. bot. Ges. 27:176–186.

Ernst, A. and E. Schmid, 1913. Über Blüte und Frucht von *Rafflesia*. Morpho-

logische-biologische Beobachtungen und entwicklungsgeschichtlich-zytologische Untersuchungen, Ann. Jard. bot. Buitenz. (2) 12:1–58.

Ernst-Schwarzenbach, M., 1945a. Kreuzungsversuche an Hydrocharitaceen. Arch.
Julius Klaus-Stift. f. Vererb. 20:22–41.

Ernst-Schwarzenbach, M., 1945b. Zur Blütenbiologie einiger Hydrocharitaceen.
Ber. schweiz. bot. Ges. 55:33–69.

Ernst-Schwarzenbach, M., 1956. Kleistogamie und Antherenbau in der Hydro-
charitaceen-Gattung *Ottelia*. Phytomorphology 6:296–311.

Esau, K., 1944. Apomixis in guayule. Proc. Nat. Acad. Sci. (Wash.) 30:352–355.

Esau, K., 1946. Morphology of reproduction in guayule and certain other species
of *Parthenium*. Hilgardia 17:61–101.

Esaulova, I. N., 1958. (Development of male and female gametophytes in the
pear). Sb. Rabot Asp. Molodykh Nauch. Sotrud. Vses. Inst. Rast. 2:102–105.

Esaulova, I. N., 1963. (On the embryology of *Malus domestica*). Nauch Tr.
Melitopol'skoi Opytn. Sta. 17:81–86.

Eseltine, G. P. van, 1929. A preliminary study of the Unicorn plants. New
York State Agric. Exper. Sta. Tech. Bull. 149:1–41.

Eunus, A. M., 1949. Contributions to the embryology of the Liliaceae, *Gloriosa
superba*. Proc. 36th. Indian Sci. Congr.: 132–133.

Eunus, A. M., 1950a. Contributions to the embryology of the Liliaceae. 1. *Albuca
transvalensis*. J. Indian bot. Soc. 29:68–78.

Eunus, A. M., 1950b. Contributions to the embryology of the Liliaceae. 4.
Gametophytes of *Smilacina stellata*. New Phytol. 49:269–273.

Eunus, A. M., 1951a. Contributions to the embryology of the Liliaceae. 5. Life
history of *Amianthium muscaetoxicum*. Phytomorphology 1:73–79.

Eunus, A. M., 1951b. Contributions to the embryology of the Liliaceae. 2.
Development of the embryo sac and fertilization in *Fritillaria pudica*. Paki-
stan J. Sci. Res. 3:106–113.

Eunus, A. M., 1952. Contributions to the embryology of the Liliaceae. 3. Embryogeny and development of the seed of *Asphodelus tenuifolius*. Lloydia
15:149–155.

Evans, A. T., 1919. Embryo sac and embryo of *Pentstemon secundiflorus*. Bot.
Gaz. 67:426–437.

Eyde, R. H., 1964. Inferior ovary and generic affinities of *Garrya*. Amer. J.
Bot. 51:1083–1092.

Eysel, G. 1937. Die Embryosackentwicklung von *Limnanthes douglasii*. Diss.
Marlburg.

Eyster, W. H., 1931. Vivipary in maize. Genetics 16:574–590.

Faber, F. C. von, 1912. Morphologische-physiologische Untersuchungen an Blüten
von *Coffea*-Arten. Ann. Jard. bot. Buitenz. (2) 10:59–160.

Facchini, F., 1884. (Amici's results on a study of *Cucurbita pepo*). Flora
27:359–360.

Fagerlind, F., 1936a. Die Embryologie von *Putoria*. Svensk bot. Tidskr.
30:362–372.

Fagerlind, F., 1936b. Embryologische Beobachtungen über die Gattung *Phyllis*.
Bot. Notiser 1936:577–584.

Fagerlind, F., 1937. Embryologische, zytologische und bestäubungsexperimentelle
Studien in der Familie Rubiaceae nebst Bemerkungen über einige Poly-
ploiditäts-probleme. Acta Horti Berg. 11:195–470. Diss. Stockholm.

Fagerlind, F., 1938a. Embryosack von *Plumbagella* und *Plumbago*. Arkiv. f. Bot. 29A:1–8.

Fagerlind, F., 1938b. *Ditepalanthus,* eine neue Balanophoraceen Gattung aus Madagaskar. Arkiv. f. Bot. 29A:1–15.

Fagerlind, F., 1938c. Wo kommen Tetrasporiche durch drei Teilungsschritte vollentwickelte Embryosäcke unter den Angiospermen vor? Bot. Notiser 1938:461–498.

Fagerlind, F., 1938d. Bau und Entwicklung der floralen Organe von *Helosis cayennensis.* Svensk bot. Tidskr. 32:139–159.

Fagerlind, F., 1939a. Drei Beispiele des Fritillaria-Typus. Svensk bot. Tidskr. 33:188–204.

Fagerlind, F., 1939b. Perisperm oder Endosperm bei *Coffea?* Svensk bot. Tidskr. 33:303–309.

Fagerlind, F., 1939c. Kritische und revidierende Untersuchungen über das Vorkommen des Adoxa ("Lilium")-Typus. Acta Horti Berg. 13:1–49.

Fagerlind, F., 1939d. Die Entwicklung des Embryosackes bei *Peperomia pellucida.* Archiv. f. Bot. 29A:1–15.

Fagerlind, F., 1940a. Stempelbau und Embryosackentwicklung bei einigen Pandanazeen. Ann. Jard. bot. Buitenz. 49:55–78.

Fagerlind, F., 1940b. Die Terminologie der Apomixis Prozesse. Hereditas 26:1–22.

Fagerlind, F., 1940c. Zytologie und Gametophytenbildung in der Gattung *Wikstroemia.* Hereditas 26:23–50.

Fagerlind, F., 1941a. Der Bau der Samenanlage und des Makrogametophyten bei *Quisqualis indica.* Bot. Notiser 1941:217–222.

Fagerlind, F., 1941b. Die Embryosackentwicklung bei *Tanacetum vulgare* und einigen *Chrysanthemum*-Arten. Svensk bot. Tidskr. 35:157–176.

Fagerlind, F., 1941c. Die Embryosackbildung bei *Camassia.* Svensk bot. Tidskr. 35:258–260.

Fagerlind, F., 1943. Vorkommen und Entstehung von Hakenleisten an Synergiden und Eizellen. Svensk bot. Tidskr. 37:339–351.

Fagerlind, F., 1944a. Die Samenbildung und die Zytologie bei agamospermischen und sexuellen Arten von *Elatostema* und einigen nehestehenden Gattungen nebst Beleuchtung einiger damit zusammenhangender Probleme. Kgl. Svensk. Vet.-Akad. Handl. (3) 21:1–130.

Fagerlind, F., 1944b. Is my terminology of the apomictic phenomena of 1940 incorrect and inappropriate? Hereditas 30:590–596.

Fagerlind, F., 1944c. Der tetrasporische Angiospermen-Embryosack und dessen Bedeutung für das Verhältnis der Entwicklungsmeckanik und Phylogenie des Embryosackes. Arkiv. f. Bot. 31A:1–71.

Fagerlind, F., 1945a. Bildung und Entwicklung des Embryosacks bei sexuellen und agamospermischen *Balanophora*-Arten. Svensk bot. Tidskr. 39:65–82.

Fagerlind, F., 1945b. Bau der floralen Organe bei der Gattung *Langsdorffia.* Svensk bot. Tidskr. 39:197–210.

Fagerlind, F., 1945c. Bau des Gynöceums, des Samenanlage und des Embryosackes bei einigen Repräsentaten des Familie Icacinaceae. Svensk bot. Tidskr. 39:346–364.

Fagerlind, F., 1945d. Blüte und Blütenstand der Gattung *Balanophora.* Bot. Notiser 1945:330–350.

Fagerlind, F., 1946a. Sporogenesis, Embryosackentwicklung und pseudogame Samenbildung bei *Rudbeckia laciniata.* Acta Hort. Berg. 14:39–90.

Fagerlind, F., 1946b. Gynöceummmorphologie, Embryologie und systematische Stellung der Gattung *Erythropalum*. Svensk bot. Tidskr. 40:9–14.

Fagerlind, F., 1946c. Hormonale Substanzen als Ursache der Frucht- und Embryobildung bei pseudogamen *Hosta*-Biotypen. Svensk bot. Tidskr. 40:230–234.

Fagerlind, F., 1947d. Die Restitutions- und Kontraktionskerne der *Hieracium*-Mikrosporogenese. Svensk bot. Tidskr. 41:247–263.

Fagerlind, F., 1947e. Die systematische Stellung der Familie Grubbiaceae. Svensk bot. Tidskr. 41:315–320.

Fagerlind, F., 1947f. Macrosporogenesis und Embryosackbildung bei agamospermischen *Taraxacum*-Biotypen. Svensk bot. Tidskr. 41:365–390.

Fagerlind, F., 1947g. Macrogametophyte formation in two agamospermous *Erigeron* spp. Acta Hort. Berg. 14:221–247.

Fagerlind, F., 1947h. Gynöceummorphologische und embryologische Studien in der Familie Olacaceae. Bot. Notiser 1947:207–230.

Fagerlind, F., 1948a. Beiträge zur Kenntnis der Gynöceumorphologie und Phylogenie der Santalales-Familien. Svensk bot. Tidskr. 42:195–229.

Fagerlind, F., 1948b. Compatibility, eu- and pseudoincompatibility in the genus *Rosa*. Acta Horti Berg. 15:1–38.

Fagerlind, F., 1959. Development and structure of the flower and gametophytes in the genus *Exocarpus*. Svensk bot. Tidskr. 53:257–282.

Fagherazzi-Abgrall, M. and J. Meyer, 1963. Développement de l'albumen avec différenciation d'un tissu chalazien d'aspect haustorial chez deux *Schizanthus*. Phytomorphology 13:22–29.

Familler, J., 1896. Biogenetische Untersuchungen über verkümmerte oder umgebildete Sexualorgane. Flora 82:133–168.

Famintzin, A., 1879. Embryologische Studien. Mém. Acad. Imp. Sci. St. Pétersb. (7) 26:1–19.

Farley, H. M. and A. H. Hutchinson, 1941. Seed development in *Medicago* (alfalfa) hybrids. 1. The normal ovule. Canad. J. Res. C. 19:421–437.

Farooq, M., 1952a. An exceptional gynoecium of *Citrus medica* var. *limon*, showing adherent pollen chambers and extra-ovarian ovules. Current Sci. 21:72–73.

Farooq, M., 1952b. The embryology of *Borreria hispida* (*Spermacoce hispida*): a reinvestigation. Current Sci. 21:252–253.

Farooq, M., 1953. Endosperm and seed structure of *Oldenlandia corymbosa*. Current Sci. 22:280–282.

Farooq, M., 1958a. The development of the embryo in *Utricularia stellaris* var. *inflexa*. Sci. and Cult. 23:479–480.

Farooq, M., 1958b. The embryology of *Oldenlandia corymbosa*. J. Indian bot. Soc. 37:358–364.

Farooq, M., 1959. The embryology of *Borreria hispida* (*Spermacoce hispida*): a reinvestigation. J. Indian bot. Soc. 38:280–287.

Farooq, M., 1960a. The embryology of *Galium asperifolium*. J. Indian bot. Soc. 39:171–175.

Farooq, M., 1960b. The embryology of some species of *Utricularia*. Sci. and Cult. 25:428–430.

Farooq, M., 1965. Studies in the Lentibulariaceae. 3: The embryology of *Utricularia uliginosa*. Phytomorphology 15:123–131.

Farooq, M. and S. A. Siddiqui, 1964a. The embryology of *Utricularia stellaris*. Sci. and Cult. 30:394–395.

Farooq, M. and S. A. Siddiqui, 1964b. The development of endosperm in *Utricularia vulgaris americana*. A reinvestigation. Proc. 51st. Indian Sci. Congr. 3:338.

Farquharson, L. I., 1955. Apomixis and polyembryony in *Tripsacum dactyloides*. Amer. J. Bot. 42:737–743.

Farr, C. H., 1916. Cytokinesis of the pollen mother cells of certain dicotyledons. Mem. N.Y. Bot. Gdns. 6:253–317.

Farr, C. H., 1918. Cell division by furrowing in *Magnolia*. Amer. J. Bot. 5:379–395.

Farr, C. H., 1922a. The meiotic cytokinesis of *Nelumbo*. Amer. J. Bot. 9:296–306.

Farr, C. H., 1922b. Quadripartition by furrowing in *Sisyrinchium*. Bull. Torrey bot. Cl. 49:51–61.

Farr, W. K., 1920. Cell division of the pollen mother cell of *Cobaea scandens alba*. Bull. Torrey bot. Cl. 47:325–338.

Farrell, M. E., 1914. The ovary and embryo of *Cyrtanthes sanguineus*. Bot. Gaz. 57:428–436.

Fauth, A., 1903. Beiträge zur Anatomie und Biologie der Früchte und Samen einiger einheimische Wasser- und Sumpfpflanzen. Beih. bot. Ztbl. 14.

Favarger, C., 1954. Sur une fonction curieuse de l'albumen pendant la germination. Ber. schweiz. bot. Ges. 64:84–93.

Favorsky, N., 1928. Materialen zur Biologie und Embryologie der Zuckerrübe. Trudy Nauch. Inst. Selek. 2:1–18.

Fedortschuk, V. F., 1931. Embryologische Untersuchung von *Cuscuta monogyna* und *Cuscuta epithymum*. Planta 14:94–111.

Fedorschuk, V. F., 1932. Entwicklung und Bau des männlichen Gametophyten bei den Arten der Convolvulaceen-Gattung *Quamoclit*. Planta 16:554–574.

Fedortschuk, V. F., 1935. (Polyembryony in red clover, *Trifolium pratense*.) Bull. Mosc. Provinc. agric. Expt. Plt. 4:1–38.

Fedortschuk, V. F., 1944. (Development and structure of ovules and seeds in red clover, *Trifolium pratense*.) Moskov. Ordene Lenina Sel'sk. Akad. Im. K. A. Timiriazeva Trud. 25:1–39.

Feng, Y.-A., 1934. Recherches cytologiques sur la caryocinèse, la spermatogénèse et la fécundation chez les Caprifoliacées, en particulier sur la présence de centrosomes présidant à la caryocinèse dans les *Lonicera*. Botaniste 26:3–84.

Ferguson, M. C., 1907. Two embryo sac mother cells in *Lilium longiflorum*. Bot. Gaz. 43:418–419.

Ferguson, M. C., 1927. A cytological and genetical study of *Petunia*. 1. Bull. Torrey bot. Cl. 54:657–664.

Ferraris, T., 1902. Ricerche biologiche sulle Iridacee. 1. Embriologia del g. *Romulea maratti*. Ann. R. Ist. Bot. Roma 9:221–241.

Ferri, S., 1961. Ricerche sullo sviluppo embriologico di *Erigeron speciosus*. N. G. bot. Ital. 68:269–284.

Fickel, J., 1876. Über die Anatomie und Entwicklungsgeschichte der Samenschalen einiger Cucurbitaceen. Bot. Zeit. 34:737–744, 753–760, 769–776, 785–792.

Fiedler, H., 1910. Beiträge zur Kenntnis der Nyctaginaceae. Diss. Halle.

Figdor, W., 1897. Über *Cotylanthera*. Ann. Jard. bot. Buitenz. 14:213–247.

Filimonova, G. A., 1962. (Specific embryological features of flower buds in some cherry varieties.) Nauch. Dokl. Vyssh. Shkoly. Biol. Nauk 2:115–117.

Fink, B., 1899. Contribution to the life history of *Rumex*. Minn. bot. Stud. 2:137–153.

Finn, W. W., 1921. On the sexual process in *Asclepias cornuti*. Ukrain. bot. Mag. Kiew 1.

Finn, W. W., 1925. Male cells in angiosperms: spermatogenesis and fertilization in *Asclepias cornuti*. Bot. Gaz. 80:1–25.

Finn, W. W., 1926. Spermazellen bei *Vincetoxicum nigrum* und *V. officinalis*. Ber. dtsch. bot. Ges. 44:133–137.

Finn, W. W., 1928a. Über den Pollenschlauch bei *Fagus sylvatica*. Nawaschin Festsch.: 63–66.

Finn, W. W., 1928b. Spermazellen bei *Vinca minor* und *V. herbacea*. Ber. dtsch. bot. Ges. 46:235–246.

Finn, W. W., 1931. Zur Geschichte der Entdeckung der doppelten Befruchtung. Ber. dtsch. bot. Ges. 49:153–157.

Finn, W. W., 1935. Einige Bemerkungen über den männlichen Gametophyten der Angiospermen. Ber. dtsch. bot. Ges. 53:679–686.

Finn, W. W., 1936. Zur Entwicklungsgeschichte der Chalazogamen, *Ostrya carpinifolia*. Zhur. Inst. bot. Acad. Sci. RSS. Ukraine 8:15–25.

Finn, W. W., 1937a. Vergleichende Embryologie und Karyologie einiger *Cuscuta*-Arten. Zhur. Inst. bot. Acad. Sci. RSS. Ukraine 12:83–99.

Finn, W. W., 1937b. Entwicklungsgeschwindigkeit des männlichen Gametophyten bei den Angiospermen. Trav. Inst. Res. Sci. biol., Univ. Kiew 1937:71–86.

Finn, W. W., 1939. On the history of the development of the male gametophyte in Labiatae. Zhur. Inst. bot. Acad. Sci. RSS Ukraine 20:77–96.

Finn, W. W., 1940. Spermazellen bei Angiospermen. Bot. Zhur. 25:155–175.

Finn, W. W., 1941. Männlichen Gameten bei Angiospermen. Dokl. Akad. Nauk SSSR 30:451–458.

Finn, W. W. and T. Rudenko, 1930. Spermatogenesis und Befruchtung bei einigen Orobanchaceae. Bull. Jard. bot. Kieff 11:69–82.

Fischer, A., 1880. Zur Kenntnis der Embryosackentwicklung einiger Angiospermen. Jen. Zeit. f. Nat. (7) 14:9–132.

Fischer, H., 1890. Beiträge zur vergleichenden Morphologie der Pollenkörner. Diss. Breslau.

Fischer, H. E., 1962. Gigaspollen infolge ausbleibender Zytokinese bei *Beta vulgaris*. Züchter. Dtsch. 32:307–311.

Fisher, G. C., 1914. Seed development in the genus *Peperomia*. Bull. Torrey bot. Cl. 41:137–156, 221–241.

Fisher, J. R. and J. R. Wells, 1962. Heteromorphic pollen grains in *Polymnia*. Rhodora 64:336–340.

Fisher, M. J., 1928. The morphology and the anatomy of the flowers of the Salicaceae. Amer. J. Bot. 15:307–326, 372–394.

Fisher, W. D., E. C. Bashaw, and E. C. Holt, 1954. Evidence for apomixis in *Pennisetum ciliare* and *Cenchrus setigerus*. J. Amer. Soc. Agron. 46:401–404.

Fitting, H., 1913. Folgen der Bestäubung und Befruchtung. Handw. d. Natur. 4:261–265.

Fleischer, E., 1874. Beiträge zur Embryologie der Monocotylen und Dicotylen. Flora 57:369–375, 384–394, 401–411, 417–448.

Flemion, F. and E. Henrickson, 1949. Further studies on the occurrence of the embryoless seeds in the Umbelliferae. Contr. Boyce Thompson Inst. 15:291–297.

Flemion, F. and E. Waterbury, 1941. Embryoless dill seeds. Contr. Boyce Thompson Inst. 12:157–161.

Flint, F. F., 1957a. Megasporogenesis and megagametogenesis in *Fothergilla gardeni* and *Fothergilla major*. Trans. Amer. Micros. Soc. 76:307–311.

Flint, F. F., 1957b. Megasporogenesis and megagametogenesis in *Hamamelis virginiana*. Virginia J. Sci. 8:185–189.

Flint, F. F., 1959a. Development of the megagametrophyte in *Liquidambar styraciflua*. Madroño 15:25–29.

Flint, F. F., 1959b. Relationships of the female gametophyte and the megasporangium. Proc. Congr. Internatl. Bot. 9th. 2:115.

Flint, F. F. and D. A. Johansen, 1958. Nucleocytoplasmic relationships in the Fritillaria-type of megagametogenesis. Amer. J. Bot. 45:464–473.

Flint, L. H. and C. G. Moreland, 1943. Notes on the photosynthetic activity in seeds of the Spider Lily. Amer. J. Bot. 30:315–317.

Fohn, M., 1935. Zur Entstehung und Weiterbildung der Extreteraume von *Citrus medica* und *Eucalyptus globulus*. Österr. bot. Zeit. 84:198–209.

Folsom, D., 1916. Studies in the morphology of *Yucca glauca*. Minn. bot. Stud. 4:427–435.

Forenbacher, A., 1913. Die Fortpflanzungsverhältnisse bei der Gattung *Potentilla*. Acad. Sci. et A. slav. sud. Zagreb. 55:132–160.

Foster, A. S., 1961. The floral morphology and relationships of *Kingdonia uniflora*. J. Arnold Arbor. 42:397–415.

Foster, L. T., 1943. Morphological and cytological studies on *Carica papaya*. Bot. Gaz. 105:116–126.

Fotidar, A. N., 1939. An example of a naked ovule in *Galphimia gracilis*. J. Indian bot. Soc. 18:59–63.

Franchino, A., 1951. Osservazioni embriologiche in *Calodendron capense*. Ann. di Bot. (Roma) 23:505–512.

Francini, E., 1927a. L'embriologia del *Cynanchum acutum*. N. G. bot. Ital. 34:381–396.

Francini, F., 1927b. L'embriologia del genere *Stapelia*. N. G. bot. Ital. 34:403–408.

Francini, E., 1928. Fenomeni di aposporia somatica, di aposporia goniale e di embrionia avventizia in *Ochna multiflora*. C. R. Accad. Lincei, Roma 7:92–94.

Francini, E., 1930. Primi dati di una revisione critica della sviluppo del gametofito femmineo del genere *Cypripedium*. N. G. bot. Ital. 37:277–278.

Francini, E., 1931. Ricerche embriologiche cariologiche sul genere *Cypripedium*. N. G. bot. Ital. 38:154–212.

Francini, E., 1945. Ibridazioni interspecifica nel genere *Papiopedilum*. N. G. bot. Ital. 52:21–29.

Francini, E., 1951. Osservazioni sulla essualtià di *Ceratonia siliqua*. N. G. bot. Ital. 58:423–440.

Fridriksson, S. and J. L. Bolton, 1963. Development of the embryo of *Medicago sativa* after normal fertilization and after pollination by other species of *Medicago*. Canad. J. Bot. 41:23–33.

Friemann, W., 1910. Über die Entwicklung der generativen Zelle im Pollenkorn der monokotylen Pflanzen. Diss. Bonn.

Fries, T. C. E., 1919. Der Samenbau bei *Cyanastrum*. Svensk bot. Tidskr. 13:295–304.

Frisendahl, A., 1912. Cytologische und entwicklungsgeschichtliche Studien über *Myricaria germanica*. Kgl. Svensk. Vet.-Akad. Handl. 48:1–62.

Frisendahl, A., 1927. Über die Entwicklung chasmogamer und kleistogamer Blüten bei der Gattung *Elatine*. Acta Hort. Götheb. 3:99–142.

Fritzsche, J., 1832. Beiträge zur Kenntnis der Pollen. Berlin.

Frost, H. B., 1926. Polyembryony, heterozygosis and chimeras in *Citrus*. Hilgardia 1:365–402.

Frost, H. B., 1938. Nucellar embryony and juvenile characters in clonal varieties of *Citrus*. J. Hered. 29:423–432.

Fruhwirth, C., 1914. Parthenogenesis bei Tabak. Zeit. f. Pflanz. 2:95–97.

Frye, T. C., 1901. Development of the pollen in some Asclepiadaceae. Bot. Gaz. 32:325–331.

Frye, T. C., 1902. A morphological study of certain Asclepiadaceae. Bot. Gaz. 34:389–413.

Frye, T. C., 1903. The embryo sac of *Casuarina stricta*. Bot. Gaz. 36:101–113.

Frye, T. C. and E. B. Blodgett, 1905. A contribution to the life history of *Apocynum androsaemifolium*. Bot. Gaz. 40:49–53.

Fryxell, P. A., 1957. Mode of reproduction of higher plants. Bot. Rev. 23:135–233.

Fuchs, A., 1936. Untersuchungen über den männlichen Gametophyten von *Elaeagnus angustifolia*. Österr. bot. Zeit. 85:1–16.

Fuchs, A., 1938. Beiträge zur Embryologie der Thymelaeaceae. Österr. Bot. Zeit. 87:1–41.

Fuchs, A. and H. Ziegenspeck, 1924. Aus der Monographie der *Orchis traunsteineri*. 4. Bot. Arch. Mez. 5:457–470.

Fuchs, A. and H. Ziegenspeck, 1927. Die Dactylorchisgruppe der Ophrydeen. Bot. Arch. Mez. 19:163–274.

Fullmer, E. L., 1899. The development of the microsporangia and microspores of *Hemerocallis fulva*. Bot. Gaz. 28:80–88.

Fulvio, T. E. di and M. S. Cave, 1964. Embryology of *Blandfordia nobilis*, with special reference to its taxonomic position. Phytomorphology 14:487–499.

Furlani, J., 1904. Zur Embryologie von *Colchicum autumnale*. Österr. bot. Zeit. 54:318–324, 373–379.

Furusato, K., 1951. (Studies on polyembryony in *Citrus*.). Jap. J. Genet. 26:223–224.

Furusato, K., 1953. Studies on polyembryony in *Citrus*. Ann. Rep. nat. Inst. Genet. Japan 4:56.

Furusato, K., Y. Ohta, and K. Ishibashi, 1957. Studies on polyembryony in *Citrus*. Rep. Kihara Inst. biol. Res. 8:40–48.

Gaétner, J., 1791. De fructibus et seminibus plantarum. 2. Tubingae.

Gaértner, J., 1849. Versuche und Beobachtungen über die Bastard-Erzeugungen im Pflanzenreich. Stuttgart.

Gager, C. S., 1902. The development of the pollinium and sperm cells in *Asclepias cornuti*. Ann. Bot. 16:123–148.

Gaines, E. F., and H. C. Aase, 1926. A haploid wheat plant. Amer. J. Bot. 13:373–385.

Gaiser, L. O., M. Sutherland, and R. Moore, 1943. Cytological studies in *Martynia louisiana*. Amer. J. Bot. 30:543–551.

Galimberti, Z., 1963. Embriologia di *Codiaeum variegatum* var. *pictum*. N. G. Bot. Ital. 70:21–32.

Ganapathy, P. M., 1956a. Floral morphology and embryology of *Hydrophylax maritima*. J. Madras Univ. B. 26:263–275.

Ganapathy, P. M. 1956b. Female gametophyte and endosperm of *Ophiorrhiza mungos*. J. Madras Univ. B. 26:589–592.

Ganapathy, P. S. and B. F. Palser, 1964. Studies of floral morphology in the Ericales. 7. Embryology in the Phyllodoceae. Bot. Gaz. 125:280–297.

Ganguli, J. K., 1948. Studies in the embryology of *Anisomeles indica* and *Leonurus sibiricus*. Proc. nat. Inst. Sci. India 14:181–212.

Ganong, W. F., 1898a. Contribution to a knowledge of the morphology and ecology of the Cactaceae. 2. The comparative morphology of the embryos and seedlings. Ann. Bot. 12:423–474.

Ganong, W. F., 1898b. Upon polyembryony and its morphology in *Opuntia vulgaris*. Bot. Gaz. 25:221–228.

Garcia, V., 1962a. Embryological studies in the Loasaceae. Development of endosperm in *Blumenbachia hieronymi*. Phytomorphology 12:307–312.

Garcia, V., 1962b. Embryological studies in the Loasaceae, with special reference to the endosperm haustoria. *In* Plant Embryology: A Symposium. CSIR. New Delhi: 157–161.

Gardner, F. E. and E. J. Kraus, 1937. Histological comparison of fruits developing parthenocarpically and following pollination. Bot. Gaz. 99:355–376.

Garg, S., 1958. Embryology of *Atkinsonia lingustrina*. Nature 182:1615–1616.

Garside, S., 1946. The developmental morphology of the pollen of Proteaceae. J. Sth. Afr. Bot. 12:27–34.

Gärtner, K. F., 1849. Versüche und Beobachtungen über die Bastard-Erzeugungen im Pflanzenreich. Stuttgart.

Garudamma, G. K., 1956. Studies in Meliaceae. 1. Development of embryo in *Azadirachta indica*. J. Indian bot. Soc. 35:222–225.

Garudamma, G. K., 1957. Studies in Meliaceae. 2. Gametogenesis in *Melia azadirachta*. J. Indian bot. Soc. 36:227–231.

Gassner, G. G., 1941. Über Bau der männlichen Blüten und Pollenentwicklung einiger Palmen der Unterfamilie der Ceroxylinae. Beih. bot. Ztbl. 61A:237.

Gates, R. R., 1909. Apogamy in *Oenothera*. Science B. 30:691–694.

Gates, R. R., 1911. Pollen formation in *Oenothera gigas*. Ann. Bot. 25:909–940.

Gates, R. R., 1914. On the apparent absence of apogamy in *Oenothera*. Science B. 39:37–38.

Gates, R. R., 1920. A preliminary account of the meiotic phenomena in pollen mother cells and tapetum of lettuce, *Lactuca sativa*. Proc. Roy. Soc. London B. 91:216–223.

Gates, R. R., 1925. Pollen tetrad wall formation in *Lathraea*. Cellule 35:47–60.

Gates, R. R., 1928. The cytology of *Oenothera*. Bibl. Genet. 4:401–492.

Gates, R. R., 1932. Heterospory and the angiosperms. Nature 129:793.

Gates, R. R. and J. Latter, 1927. Observations on the pollen development of two species of *Lathraea*. J. Roy. Micros. Soc. 1927:209–224.

Gates, R. R. and E. M. Rees, 1921. A cytological study of pollen development in *Lactuca*. Ann. Bot. 35:365–398.

Gates, R. R. and F. M. L. Sheffield, 1929. Megaspore development in *Oenothera rubicalyx*, with a note on chromosome linkage in *Oenotheraangustissima*. Proc. Roy. Soc. Lond. B. 105:499–516.

Gatin, C. L. 1905a. Un cas de polyembryonie chez le *Musa ensete*. Bull. Soc. bot. France 52:277–278.

Gatin, C. L., 1905b. Sur la radicule embryonnaire du *Musa ensete* Bull. Soc. bot. France 52:638–640.

Gatin, C. L., 1905c. Quelques cas de polyembryonie chez plusieurs éspèces de Palmiers. Rev. gén. Bot. 17:60–66.

Gatin, C. L., 1906. Recherches anatomiques et chimiques sur la germination des Palmiers. Ann. Sci. nat. Bot. (9) 3:191–315.

Gatin, C. L., 1908. Recherches anatomiques de l'embryon et la germination des Cannacées et des Musacées. Ann. Sci. nat. Bot. (9) 8:117–146.

Gatin, C. L., 1921. Première contribution à l'étude de l'embryon et de la germination des Aracées. Ann. Sci. nat. Bot. (10) 3.

Gäumann, E., 1918. Über die Entwicklungsgeschichte einiger Saxifragazeen. Vorläufige Mitteilung. Svensk bot. Tidskr. 12:268–269.

Gäumann, E., 1919. Studien über die Entwicklungsgeschichte einiger Saxifragales. Rec. trav. bot. Néerl. 16:285–322.

Gavde, S. G., 1963. A note on post-fertilization in *Cipadessa baccifera*. J. biol. Sci. India 6:11–13.

Geerts, T. H., 1908. Beiträge zur Kenntnis der cytologischen Entwicklung von *Oenothera lamarckiana*. Ber. dtsch. bot. Ges. 26:608–614.

Geerts, T. H., 1909. Beiträge zur Kenntniss der Cytologie und der partiellen Sterilität von *Oenothera lamarckiana*. Rec. trav. bot. Néerl. 5:91–206.

Geitler, L., 1935. Beobachtungen über die erste Teilung im Pollenkorn der Angiospermen. Planta 24:361–386.

Geitler, L., 1941. Embryosäcke aus Pollenkornern bei *Ornithogalum*. Ber. dtsch. bot. Ges. 59:419–423.

Geitler, L., 1942. Über die Struktur des generativen Kerns im zweikernigen Angiospermenpollen. Planta 32:187–195.

Geitler, L., 1948. Ergebnisse und Probleme der Endomitoseforschung. Österr. bot. Zeit. 95.

Geitler, L., 1955. Riesenkerne im Endosperm von *Allium ursinum*. Österr. bot. Zeit. 102:460–475.

Geitler, L., 1956. Zur Fortpflanzungsbiologie, Embryologie und mechanistischen Deutung der Embryogenese von *Epipogium aphyllum*. Österr. bot. Zeit. 103: 312–335.

Gelin, O. E. V., 1934. Embryologische und cytologische Studien in Heliantheae-Coreopsidinae. Acta Hort. Berg. 11:99–128.

Gelin, O. E. V., 1936. Zur Embryologie und Zytologie von *Berkheya bergiana* und *B. aldami*. Svensk bot. Tidskr. 30:324–328.

Gentry, H. S., 1955. Apomixis in black pepper and jojoba? J. Hered. 46:8.

Gentscheff, G., 1937. Zytologische und embryologische Studien über einige *Hieracium*-Arten. Planta 27:165–195.

Gentscheff, G., 1939. Über die pseudogame Fortpflanzung bei *Potentilla*. Genetica 20:398–404.

Gentscheff, G. and Å Gustafsson, 1940. Parthenogenesis and pseudogamy in *Potentilla*. Bot. Notiser 1940:109–132.

George, P. C., 1938. Observations on the megasporogenesis and embryogeny in *Sonerila speciosa*. Presid. Coll. bot. Mag. 5:26–29.

Gerassimov, J. J., 1890. Einige Bemerkungen über die Funktion des Zellkerns. Bull. Soc. Imp. nat. Mosc. 4:548–554.

Gerassimova, H., 1933. Fertilization in *Crepis capillaris*. Cellule 42:101–144.

Gerassimova, H., 1958. (On the gametophyte and on the principle features of the development and functioning of the reproductive elements in Angiosperms.) Trud. bot. Inst. Akad. Nauk SSSR.

Gerassimova-Navashina, H., 1947a. (Morphological observations on cytoplasm of the male gametophyte in *Crepis*.) Dokl. Akad. Nauk SSSR 56:415–418.

Gerassimova-Navashina, H., 1947b. (On the development and structure of sperms in *Crepis*.) Dokl. Akad. Nauk SSSR 56:643–646.

Gerassimova-Navashina, H., 1947c. (On the behaviour of sperms within the pollen tube in *Crepis*.) Dokl. Akad. Nauk SSSR 57:285–288.

Gerassimova-Navashina, H., 1947d. (The mitotic hypothesis of double fertilization.) Dokl. Akad. Nauk SSSR 57:395–398.

Gerassimova-Navashina, H., 1951. (Pollen grain, gametes and sexual reproduction in Angiosperms.) Trud. bot. Inst. Akad. Nauk SSSR (7) 2:294–355.

Gerassimova-Navashina, H., 1952. (A contribution to the cytological and embryological treatment of the pollination process.) Trud. bot. Inst. Akad. Nauk SSSR 3:165–211.

Gerassimova-Navashina, H., 1954a. (Double fertilization in Angiosperms, its nature and origin.) Diss. Leningrad.

Gerassimova-Navashina, H., 1954b. (The development of the embryo sac and the origin of Angiosperms.) Dokl. Akad. Nauk SSSR 95:877–880.

Gerassimova-Navashina, H., 1954c. (Development of the embryo sac, double fertilization and the origin of Angiosperms.) Bot. Zhur. 39:655–680.

Gerassimova-Navashina, H., 1957. On some cytological principles underlying double fertilization. Phytomorphology 7:150–167.

Gerassimova-Navashina, H., 1959a. The cytology of fertilization in flowering plants. Proc. Congr. Internatl. Bot. 9th. 2:132.

Gerassimova-Navashina, H., 1959b. (Embryological observations on *Arachis hypogaea*.) Bot. Zhur. 44:1453–1466.

Gerassimova-Navashina, H., 1960a. (The effect of temperature conditions on the course of embryological processes in plants.) Dokl. Akad. Nauk SSSR 131:688–691.

Gerassimova-Navashina, H., 1960b. A contribution to the cytology of fertilization in flowering plants. Nucleus 3:111–120.

Gerassimova-Navashina, H., 1961. Fertilization and events leading up to fertilization and their bearing on the origin of Angiosperms. Phytomorphology 11:139–146.

Gerassimova-Navashina, H., 1962. (Cytological data on stimulation to development of embryo sac cells.) Trud. bot. Inst. Akad. Nauk SSSR. (7) 5:238–249.

Gerassimova-Navashina, H. and T. B. Batygina, 1958. (Fertilization in *Scilla sibirica*.) Bot. Zhur. 43:959–988.

Gerassimova-Navashina, H. and S. N. Korobava, 1959. (The rôle of synergids in the process of fertilization.) Bjull. Mosk. Obshch. Ispyt. Prirody Otd. Biol. 64:69–76.

Gerdts, C. L., 1905. Bau und Entwicklung der Kompositenfrucht. Diss. Bonn.

Gerhard, K., 1929. Genetische und zytologische Untersuchungen an *Oenothera grandiflora*. Jen. Zeit. f. Med. Nat. 64:283–338.

Gering, K. and T. K. Zorina, 1961. (Effect of temperature on the process of fertilization and seed development following self-pollination in corn.) Dokl. Akad. Nauk SSSR 133:158–159.

Gershoy, A., 1940. The male gametophyte in some species of violets. Amer. J. Bot. 27:4 (Suppl.).

Gerstel, D. U. and W. Mishanec, 1950. On the inheritance of apomixis in *Parthenium argentatum*. Bot. Gaz. 112:96–106.

Ghatak, J., 1956. A contribution to the life history of *Oroxylum indicum*. Proc. Indian Acad. Sci. B. 43:72–87.

Ghose, S. L. and R. Alagh, 1933. Micro- and megasporogenesis in *Cassia purpurea*. Proc. 20th. Indian Sci. Congr.: 315–316.

Ghosh, M., 1954. The embryology and systematic position of *Trapa bispinosa*. Current Sci. 23:24–26.

Ghosh, M., 1955. The embryology of *Comandra umbellata*. Current Sci. 24:280–281.

Ghosh, R. B., 1962a. A note on nucellar polyembryony in *Aphanamixis polystachya*. Current Sci. 31:165.

Ghosh, R. B., 1962b. A contribution to the life history of *Wedelia calendulacea*. J. Indian bot. Soc. 41:197–206.

Ghosh, R. B., 1964. Supernumerary archesporial cell in *Ochna atropurpurea*. Current Sci. 33:116–117.

Gibbs, L. S., 1907. Notes on the development and structure of the seed in the Alsinoideae. Ann. Bot. 21:25–55.

Gibelli, G. and F. Ferrero, 1891a. Ricerche di anatomia e morfologia allo sviluppo dell'ovolo e del seme della *Trapa natans*. Malpighia 5:1–64.

Gibelli, G. and F. Ferrero, 1891b. Intorno allo sviluppo dell'ovolo e del seme della *Trapa natans*. Malpighia 5:156–218.

Gibelli, G. and F. Ferrero, 1895. Ricerche di anatomia e morfologia intorno allo sviluppo del fiore e del frutto della *Trapa natans*. Malpighia 9:379–437.

Giganti, R., 1929. Embriologia dell'*Acanthus molle*. N. G. bot. Ital. 36:1–33.

Giger, E., 1912. *Linnaea borealis*, eine monographische Studie. Beih. bot. Ztbl. 30:1–78. Diss. Zürich.

Gill, L. S., 1935. *Arceuthobium* in the United States. Trans. Conn. Acad. Arts and Sci. 32:111–245.

Gilliland, H. B., 1960. On the symmetry of the orchid embryo. *In* Proc. Cent. and Bicent. Congr. Biol., Singapore, 1958:277–279.

Giltay, E., 1893. Über den direkten Einfluss des Pollens auf Fruchtund Samenbildung. Jahrb. f. wiss. Bot. 25:489–509.

Gioelli, F., 1930. Ricerche sullo sviluppo del gametofito femmineo e del polline nel genero *Aloe*. Lav. R. Ist. Bot. Palermo 1:61–84.

Gioelli, F., 1933. Polimorfismo sessuale e sviluppo del gametofito femmineo e del polline in *Nolina longifolia*. Lav. R. Ist. Bot. Palermo 4:17.

Gioelli, F., 1935. Ricerche embriologiche sulla *Phyllostachya nigra*. Ann. di Bot. (Roma) 21:51–60.

Giroux, M., 1930. Sur la carpologie de quelques Composée nord-africaines. Bull. Soc. Hist. nat. Afr. Nord. 21.

Giroux, M., 1933. Note sur la position systématique du *Chrysanthemum cinerariifolium*, suivi de quelques remarques sur les caractères carpologiques des *Tanacetum*. Bull. Soc. Hist. nat. Afr. Nord. 24.

Glišić, L. M., 1924. (Development of the female x-generation and embryo in *Ramondia*.) Diss. Belgrade.

Glišić, L. M., 1927. (Development of the female gametophyte and endosperm in *Haberlea rhodopensis*.) Bull. Inst. Jard. bot. Univ. Belgrade 1:1–13.

Glišić, L. M., 1928. Zur Entwicklungsgeschichte der Solanaceen. Die Endospermbildung von *Datura metel*. Bull. Inst. Jard. bot. Univ. Belgrade 1:75–85.

Glišić, L. M., 1929. Über die Endosperm- und Haustorienbildung bei *Orobanche hederae* und *O. gracilis* (Zugleich ein Beitrag zur Phylogenie der Orobanchaceae). Bull. Inst. Jard. bot. Univ. Belgrade 2:106–141.

Glišić, L. M., 1931–32. Zur Entwicklungsgeschichte von *Lathraea squamaria*. Bull. Inst. Jard. bot. Univ. Belgrade 2:20–56.

Glišić, L. M., 1933. Zur Entwicklungsgeschichte von *Gratiola officinale*. Bull. Inst. Jard. bot. Univ. Belgrade 2:129–152.

Glišić, L. M., 1934. Zur Kenntnis der Samenentwicklung der Gesneriaceen. Über die Endosperm- und Haustorienbildung von *Roettlera*. Bull. Inst. Jard. bot. Univ. Belgrade 3:94–111.

Glišić, L. M., 1937. Ein Versuch der Verwertung der Endospermmerkmale für typologische und phylogenetische Zwecke innerhalb der Scrophulariaceen. Bull. Inst. Jard. bot. Univ. Belgrade 4:42–73.

Glück, H., 1940. Die Gattung *Trapella*. Jahrb. f. wiss. Bot. 71:267–336.

Glushchenko, G. I., 1962. (On the biology of flowering and the embryology of *Scopolia carniolica*.) Bot. Zhur. 47:1017–1025.

Godfrin, J., 1884. Recherches sur l'anatomie comparée des cotylédones et de l'albumen. Ann. Sci. nat. Bot. (6) 19:5–158.

Goebel, K., 1880. Zur Embryologie der Archegoniaten. Arch. bot. Inst. Würzburg 2:436–451.

Goebel, K., 1886. Beiträge zur Kenntnis gefüllter Blüten. Jahrb. f. wiss. Bot. 17.

Goebel, K., 1887. Outlines of Classification and Special Morphology. (English translation.) Oxford.

Goebel, K., 1900. Bemerkung zu vorstehende Mitteilung. Biol. Ztbl. 20:571–572.

Goebel, K., 1904. Die kleistogamen Blüten und Anpassungtheorie. Biol. Ztbl. 24:673–697, 737–753, 769–787.

Goebel, K., 1933a. Organographie der Pflanzen. München.

Goebel, K., 1933b. Organographie. Samenpflanzen. Jena.

Goebel, K. and K. Süssenguth, 1924. Beiträge zur Kenntnis der Burmanniaceae. Flora 117:55–90.

Golaszewska, Z., 1934a. (La formation du pollen et la garniture des chromosomes chez l'*Aspidistra elatior*.) Acta Soc. bot. Polon. 11:85–102.

Golaszewska, Z., 1934b. Die Entwicklung des Embryosackes bei *Aspidistra elatior*. Acta Soc. bot. Polon. 11:399–407.

Goldberg, B., 1941. Life history of *Peltandra virginica*. Bot. Gaz. 102:641–662.

Goldflus, M., 1898–1899. Sur la structure et les fonctions de l'assise épithéliale et des antipodes chez les Composées. Jour. de Bot. 12:374–384; 13:9–17, 49–59, 87–96. Thesis. Genève.

Golinski, S. J., 1893. Ein Beitrag zur Entwicklungsgeschichte des Androeceum und des Gynaeceum der Graser. Bot. Ztbl. 55:1–17, 65–72, 129–135.

Goodspeed, T. H., 1915. Parthenogenesis, parthenocarpy and phenospermy in *Nicotiana*. Univ. Calif. Publs. Bot. 5:249–272.

Goodspeed, T. H., 1923. A preliminary note on the cytology of *Nicotiana* sp. and hybrids. Svensk bot. Tidskr. 17:472–478.

Goodspeed, T. H., 1947. Maturation of the gametes and fertilization in *Nicotiana*. Madroño 9:110–120.

Gopinath, D. M., 1942. Preliminary note on the sterility in flax. *Linum usitatissimum.* Current Sci. 11:286.

Gopinath, D. M., 1943a. Reversed polarity in the embryo sac of *Heptapleurum venulosum.* Current Sci. 12:58–59.

Gopinath, D. M., 1943b. Cases of antipodal polyembryony in *Alangium lamarckii.* Current Sci. 12:329–330.

Gopinath, D. M., 1944. Gametogenesis and embryology in a few members of the Araliaceae. Proc. Indian Acad. Sci. B. 20:175–186.

Gopinath, D. M., 1945. A contribution to the embryology of *Alangium lamarckii,* with a discussion of the systematic position of the family Alangiaceae. Proc. Indian Acad. Sci. B. 22:225–231.

Gopinath, D. M., 1946. Development of the female gametophyte in *Flacourtia cataphracta* and *F. ramontchili.* Proc. 33rd Indian Sci. Congr. 3:109.

Gopinath, D. M. and K. S. Gopalkrishnan, 1949. The ovule and the development of the female gametophyte in *Homonia retusa* and *Euphorbia oreophylla.* Amer. Midl. Nat. 41:759–764.

Gorczyński, T., 1929. Recherches histo-cytologiques sur les fleurs cléistogames chez *Lamium amplexicaule, Oxalis acetosella* et *Viola odorata.* Acta Soc. bot. Polon. 6:248–295.

Gorczyński, T., 1930. Continuation des recherches sur la cléistogamie. 2. *Cardamine chenopodifolia.* Acta Soc. bot. Polon. 12:257–274.

Gorczyński, T., 1934. Untersuchungen über die Entwicklung der Samenanlage und des Embryosackes bei der Apfelsorte "Schoner von Boskoop." Acta Soc. bot. Polon. 11:87–108.

Gorczyński, T., 1935. Untersuchungen über Kleistogamie. 4. Entwicklung der Archesporgewebe und der Befruchtungsvorgang bei *Cardamine chenopodiifolia.* Acta Soc. bot. Polon. 12:257–274.

Gordon, N., 1922. The development of endosperm in cereals. Proc. Roy. Soc. Victoria 34:105–106.

Gore, U. R., 1932. The development of the female gametophyte and embryo in cotton. Amer. J. Bot. 19:795–807.

Gorham, A. L., 1953. The question of fertilization in *Smilacina racemosa.* Phytomorphology 3:44–50.

Gori, C., 1957. Sull'embriologia e citologia di alcune specie del genere *Reseda.* Caryologia 10:391–401.

Gourgenov, M., 1928. Fertilization in *Phelypaea ramosa.* Festsch. f. Nawaschin: 157–168.

Goursat, M.-J., 1961a. Développement de l'embryon chez le *Lathyrus latifolius.* C. R. Acad. Sci. Paris 252:3858–3860.

Goursat, M.-J., 1961b. Embryogénie des Légumineuses. Développement de l'embryon chez le *Scorpiurus vermiculate.* C. R. Acad. Sci. Paris 253:307–309.

Goursat, M.-J., 1961c. Embryogénie des Légumineuses. Développement de l'embryon chez le *Pocockia cretica.* C. R. Acad. Sci. Paris 253:960–962.

Govindappa, D. A., 1953. The embryo sac of *Xyris pauciflora.* Current Sci. 22:386.

Govindappa, D. A., 1955. Embryological studies in *Xyris pauciflora.* Proc. Indian Acad. Sci. B. 42:47–57.

Govindappa, D. A., 1956a. The development of endosperm in *Scilla indica.* Current Sci. 25:198–199.

Govindappa, D. A., 1956b. Morphological study of *Hypericum japonicum*. J. Mysore Univ. B. 15:69–79.

Govindappa, D. A. and G. Boriah, 1956. The development of female gametophyte in *Biophytum sensitivum*. Current Sci. 25:403–404.

Govindappa, D. A. and T. R. B. Naidu, 1956. The embryo sac and endosperm of *Blyxa oryzetorum*. J. Indian bot. Soc. 35:417–422.

Govindappa, D. A. and A. Sheriff, 1951. Contribution to the life history of *Scilla indica*. J. Mysore Univ. B. 12:15–21.

Govindu, H. C., 1950. Studies in the embryology of some members of the Bignoniaceae. Proc. Indian Acad. Sci. B. 32:164–178.

Gow, J. E., 1907. Morphology of *Spathyema foetida*. Bot. Gaz. 43:131–136.

Gow, J. E., 1908a. Embryogeny of *Arisaema triphyllum*. Bot. Gaz. 45:38–44.

Gow, J. E., 1908b. Studies in Araceae. Bot. Gaz. 46:35–42.

Gow, J. E., 1913. Observations on the morphology of the Aroids. Bot. Gaz. 56:127–142.

Graef, P. E., 1955. Ovule and embryo sac development in *Typha latifolia* and *Typha angustifolia*. Amer. J. Bot. 42:806–809.

Graef, P. E., 1958. The ovule and embryo sac of *Galax aphylla*. Virginia J. Sci. 9:319–322.

Graf, J., 1921. Beiträge zur Kenntnis der Gattung *Populus*. Ber. dtsch. bot. Ges. 39:193–194. Beih. bot. Ztbl. 38 A:405–454. Diss. Frankfurt.

Grafl, I., 1941. Über das Wachstum der Antipodenkerne von *Caltha palustris*. Chromosoma 2:1–11.

Graham, R. J. D., 1927. Studies in wild rice, *Oryza sativa*. Trans. and Proc. bot. Soc. Edinb. 29:349–351.

Gramuglio, G., 1962. Osservazioni sul comportamento sessuale del *Populus tremula* in Italia. N. G. bot. Ital. 69:78–90.

Graner, E. A., 1936. Megasporogenesis in *Coffea arabica*. Arquiv. Inst. Biol. veget. Rio de Jan. 3:69.

Graner, E. A., 1938. Embriogenese de *Coffea*. 1. Desenvolvimento do óvulo em *Coffea arabica*. Ann. la. Reun. Sulamer. Bot. 3:193–202.

Graves, A. H., 1908. The morphology of *Ruppia maritima*. Trans. Conn. Acad. Arts and Sci. 14:59–170.

Gray, A., 1857. Structure of ovule and seed coats of *Magnolia*. J. Linn. Soc. Lond. (Bot.). 2:106.

Grebel, 1829. Über die Samen des *Evonymus latifolius*. Flora 3:321–336.

Greco, R., 1929. Notizie preliminari sull' embriologia e la cariologia del *Mytrus communis*. N. G. bot. Ital. 36:57–59.

Greco, R., 1930. Embriologia del *Myrtus communis*. N. G. bot. Ital. 38:609–630.

Greene, E. S., 1898. Parthenogenesis in common plants. Plant World 1:102–103.

Greenshields, J. E. R., 1951. Polyembryony in alfalfa. Sci. Agric. Ottawa 31:212–222.

Greenshields, J. E. R., 1954. Embryology of interspecific crosses in *Melilotus*. Canad. J. Bot. 32:447–465.

Gregory, P. J., 1936. The floral morphology and cytology of *Elettaria cardamomum*. J. Linn. Soc. Lond. (Bot.). 50:363–387.

Gregory, R. P., 1905. The abortive development of the pollen in certain sweet peas, *Lathyrus odoratus*. Proc. Cambridge Phil. Soc. 13:148–157.

Gregory, R. P., 1912. The chromosomes of a giant form of *Primula sinensis*. Proc. Cambridge Phil. Soc. 16:560.

Gregory, R. P., 1914. On the genetics of tetraploid plants in *Primula sinensis*. Proc. Roy. Soc. London B. 87:484–492.

Grevtsova, N. A., 1962. (Microsporogenesis and male gametophyte in Ussurian pear, *Pyrus ussuriensis*.) Nauch. Dokl. Vysshei Shkoly Biol. Nauk 2:109–114.

Griesinger, R., 1935. Zytologische und experimentelle Untersuchungen an *Erophila verna*. Flora 129:363–379.

Griffith, W., 1836. On the ovulum of *Santalum album*. Trans. Linn. Soc. Lond. (Bot.) 18:59–70.

Griffith, W., 1838. Notes on the development of the ovule of *Loranthus* and *Viscum*. Trans. Linn. Soc. Lond. (Bot.) 18:71–91.

Griffith, W., 1843. On the ovulum of *Santalum, Osyris, Loranthus* and *Viscum*. Trans. Linn. Soc. Lond. (Bot.) 19:171–214.

Grimm, J., 1912. Entwicklungsgeschichtliche Untersuchungen an *Rhus* und *Coriaria*. Flora 104:309–334.

Grönland, J., 1851. Beitrag zur Kenntniss der *Zostera marina*. Bot. Zeit. 9:185–192.

Grosbard, S., 1924. Développement du pistil chez l'Urticée *Girardinia zeylanica*. Bull. Acad. Polon. B 1924:437–443.

Grove, A. R., 1941. Morphological study of *Agave lechuguilla*. Bot. Gaz. 103:354–365.

Grun, P., 1951. *Poa nervosa*, an extreme in asexual reproduction. Carnegie Inst. Wash. 50:112–115.

Grun, P., 1952. Apomixis and variation in *Poa nervosa*. Carnegie Inst. Wash. 51:117–119.

Grun, P., 1955. Cytogenetic studies of *Poa*. 3. Variation within *Poa nervosa*, an obligate apomict. Amer. J. Bot. 42:778–784.

Gscheidle, A., 1924. Über Haustorienbildung in der Gattung *Veronica* und ihre systematische Wertung. Flora 117:144–172.

Guard, A. T., 1943. The development of the seed of *Liriodendron tulipifera*. Proc. Indiana Acad. Sci. 53:75–77.

Guérin, P., 1899. Recherches sur le développement du tégument séminal et du péricarpe des Graminées. Ann. Sci. nat. Bot. (8) 9:1–59.

Guérin, P., 1901. Développement de la graine et en particulier, du tégument séminal de quelques Sapindacées. Jour. de Bot. 15:336–362.

Guérin, P., 1903. Sur le sac embryonnaire et en particulier les antipodes des Gentianacées. Jour. de Bot. 17:101–108.

Guérin, P., 1904. Recherches sur le développement et la structure anatomique du tégument séminal des Gentianacées. Jour. de Bot. 18:33–52, 83.

Guérin, P., 1913. Le tégument séminal et les trachées nucellaires des Thymelaeacées. C. R. Acad. Sci. Paris 156:398–400.

Guérin, P., 1915. Reliquiae Treubianae. 1. Recherches sur la structure anatomique de l'ovule et de la graine des Thymeleacées. Ann. Jard. bot. Buitenz. (2). 29:1–35.

Guérin, P., 1917. Sur l'étamine et le développement du pollen des Sauges. C. R. Acad. Sci. Paris 165:1009–1012.

Guérin, P., 1919. Développement de l'anthère et du pollen des Labiées. C. R. Acad. Sci. Paris 168:182–185.

Guérin, P., 1924. Le développement de l'anthère et du pollen chez Gentianacées. C. R. Acad. Sci. Paris 179:1620–1622.

Guérin, P., 1925. L'anthère des Gentianacées. Développement du sac polliniques. C. R. Acad. Sci. Paris 180:852–854.

Guérin, P., 1926. Le développement de l'anthère chez les Gentianacées. Bull. Soc. bot. France 73:5–18.

Guérin, P., 1927. Le développement de l'anthère et du pollen chez les Liliacées (*Sansevieria, Liriope, Ophiopogon, Peliosanthes*). Bull. Soc. bot. France 74:102–107.

Guérin, P., 1930. Le développement de l'oeuf et la polyembryonie chez l'*Erythronium dens-canis*. C. R. Acad. Sci. Paris 191:1369–1372.

Guérin, P., 1931. L'ovule et la graine de l'*Erythronium dens-canis*. Botaniste 23:185–195.

Guérin, P., 1937. L'ovule et la graine des *Erythronium* et des *Calochortus*. Ann. Sci. nat. Bot. (10) 19:255–265.

Guevara, V. F., 1961. The occurrence of twin embryos in *Cocos nucifera*. Philippine Agric. 44:520–522.

Guignard, J.-L., 1961a. Cypéracées. Développement de l'embryon chez le *Cyperus vegetus*. C. R. Acad. Sci. Paris 252:2125–2127.

Guignard, J.-L., 1961b. Embryogénie des Palmiers. Développement de l'embryon chez le *Chamaerops humilis*. C. R. Acad. Sci. Paris 253:1834–1836.

Guignard, J.-L., 1961c. Embryogénie des Graminées. Développement de l'embryon chez le *Setaria verticillata*. Bull. Soc. bot. France 108:212–217.

Guignard, J.-L., 1962a. Recherches sur l'embryogénie des Graminées; rapports des Graminées avec les autres Monocotylédones. Thèse. Paris.

Guignard, J.-L., 1962b. Embryogénie des Iridacées. Développement de l'embryon chez l'*Iris pseudacorus*. C. R. Acad. Sci. Paris 255:2161–2163.

Guignard, J.-L., 1963a. Embryogénie des Dioscoréacées. Développement de l'embryon chez le *Tamus communis*. C. R. Acad. Sci. Paris 256:3172–3175.

Guignard, J.-L., 1963b. Développement de l'embryon chez le *Mibora minima*. Bull. Soc. bot. France 110:193–194.

Guignard, J.-L., 1963c. Embryogénie des Aracées. Développement de l'embryon chez le *Pistia stratiotes*. C. R. Acad. Sci. Paris 257:1139–1142.

Guignard, J.-L., 1963d. Développement de l'embryon chez le *Moehringia pentandra*. C. R. Acad. Sci. Paris 257:2694–2697.

Guignard, J.-L., 1965. Embryogénie des Caryophyllacées. Développement de l'embryon chez le *Lychnis viscaria*. C. R. Acad. Sci. Paris 260:3144–3147.

Guignard, L., 1880a. Sur la pluralité des noyaux dans le suspenseur embryonnaire de quelques plantes. Bull. Soc. bot. France 27:191–193.

Guignard, L., 1880b. Note sur la structure et les fonctions du suspenseur chez quelques Légumineuses. Bull. Soc. bot. France 27:253–257.

Guignard, L., 1881a. Sur la polyembryonie chez quelques Mimosées. Bull. Soc. bot. France 28:177–179.

Guignard, L., 1881b. Sur l'origine du sac embryonnaire et le rôle des antipodes. Bull. Soc. bot. France 28:197–201.

Guignard, L., 1881c. Recherches d'embryogénie végétale comparée. 1. Légumineuses. Ann. Sci. nat. Bot. (6) 12:5–166.

Guignard, L., 1881d. Note sur l'embryogénie du genre *Lupinus*. Bull. Soc. bot. France 28:231–235.

Guignard, L., 1882a. Recherches anatomiques et physiologiques sur les Légumineuses. Diss. Paris.

Guignard, L., 1882b. Recherches sur le sac embryonnaire des phanérogames angiospermes. Ann. Sci. nat. Bot. (6) 13:136–199.

Guignard, L., 1882c. Recherches sur le développement de l'anthère et du pollen chez les Orchidées. Ann. Sci. nat. Bot. (6) 14:26–45.

Guignard, L., 1884. Recherches sur la structure et la division du noyan cellulaires chez les végétaux, Ann. Sci. nat. Bot. (6) 17:5–59.

Guignard, L., 1885. Observations sur les Santalacées. Ann. Sci. nat. Bot. (7) 2:181–202, 310–392.

Guignard, L., 1886a. Quelques observations sur les ovules et la fécondation des Cactées. Bull. Soc. bot. Lyon (2) 4:18–22.

Guignard, L., 1886b. Observations sur les ovules et la fécondation des Cactées. Bull. Soc. bot. France 33:276–280.

Guignard, L., 1886c. Sur la pollinisation et ses effets chez les Orchidées. Ann. Sci. nat. Bot. (7) 4:202–240.

Guignard, L., 1886d. Sur les effets de la pollinisation chez les Orchidées. C. R. Acad. Sci. Paris 103:219–221.

Guignard, L., 1889. Etudes sur les phénomènes morphologiques de la fécondation. Bull. Soc. bot. France 36:100–146.

Guignard, L., 1890a. Sur la formation et la différenciation des éléments sexuels qui interviennent dans la fécondation. C. R. Acad. Sci. Paris 110:590–592.

Guignard, L., 1890b. Sur la mode d'union des noyaux sexuels dans l'acte de la fécondation. C. R. Acad. Sci. Paris 110:726–728.

Guignard, L., 1891. Nouvelles études sur la fécondation. Ann. Sci. nat. Bot. (7) 14:163–296.

Guignard, L., 1893a. Note sur l'origine et la structure du tégument séminal chez les Capparidées, Resedacées. Hypericacées, Balsaminées et Linacées. Bull. Soc. bot. France (2) 40:56.

Guignard, L., 1893b. Recherches sur le développement de la graine et en particulier du tégument séminal. Jour. de Bot. 7:1–14, 21–34, 57–106, 140–153, 205–214, 241–250, 282–296, 303–311.

Guignard, L., 1897. Sur le mode particulier de formation du pollen chez le *Magnolia*. C. R. Acad. Sci. Paris 127:594–596.

Guignard, L., 1898. Les centres cinétiques chez les végétaux. Ann. Sci. nat. Bot. (8) 6:177–220.

Guignard, L., 1899a. Sur la formation du pollen et la réduction chromatique dans le *Najas major*. C. R. Acad. Sci. Paris 128:202–207.

Guignard, L., 1899b. Les découvertes récentes sur la fécondation chez les végétaux angiospermes. Vol. Jubil. Soc. Biol. Paris: 189–198.

Guignard, L., 1899c. Sur les anthérozoides et la double copulation sexuelle chez les végétaux angiospermes. C. R. Acad. Sci. Paris 128:864–871. Rev. gén. Bot. 11:129–135.

Guignard, L., 1899d. Etudes sur les phénomènes morphologiques de la fécondation. Bull. Soc. bot. France 36:100–146.

Guignard, L., 1899e. Le développement du pollen et la reduction chromatique dans le *Naias major*. Arch. Anat. microsc. 2:455–509.

Guignard, L., 1900a. L'appareil sexuel et la double fécondation dans les Tulipes. Ann. Sci. nat. Bot. (7) 11:365–387.

Guignard, L., 1900b. Nouvelles recherches sur la double fécondation chez les végétaux angiospermes. C. R. Acad. Sci. Paris 131:153–160.

Guignard, L., 1901a. La double fécondation dans le mais. Jour. de Bot. 15:37–50.

Guignard, L., 1901b. La double fécondation dans le *Naias major*. Jour. de Bot. 15:205–213.

Guignard, L., 1901c. La double fécondation chez les Rénonculacées. Jour. de Bot. 15:394–408.

Guignard, L., 1901d. Sur la double fécondation chez les Solanées et les Gentianées. C. R. Acad. Sci. Paris 133:1268–1272.

Guignard, L., 1902a. La double fécondation chez les Solanées. Jour. de Bot. 16:145–167.

Guignard, L., 1902b. La double fécondation chez les Crucifères. Jour. de Bot. 16:361–368. C. R. Acad. Sci. Paris 135:497–499.

Guignard, L., 1903a. Remarques sur la formation du pollen chez les Asclepiadacées. C. R. Acad. Sci. Paris 137:19–24.

Guignard, L., 1903b. La formation et le développement de l'embryon chez l'*Hypecoum*. Jour. de Bot. 17:33–44.

Guignard, L., 1904. La double fécondation chez les Malvacées. Jour. de Bot. 18:296–308.

Guignard, L., 1915a. Sur la formation du pollen. C. R. Acad. Sci. Paris 160:428–433.

Guignard, L., 1915b. Nouvelles observations sur la formation du pollen chez certaines Monocotylédones. C. R. Acad. Sci. Paris 161:623–625.

Guignard, L., 1917a. Sur le développement et la structure de l'ovule chez les Apocynacées et les Asclepiadacées. C. R. Acad. Sci. Paris 165:981–987.

Guignard, L., 1917b. L'ovule chez les Apocynacées et les Asclepiadacées. Mém. Acad. Sci. Inst. France 55:1–34.

Guignard, L., 1921. La fécondation et la polyembryonie chez les *Vincetoxicum*. Mém. Acad. Sci. Inst. France (2) 57:1–25.

Guignard, L., 1922. Sur l'existence de corps protéiques dans le pollen de diverses Asclepiadacées. C. R. Acad. Sci. Paris 175:1015–1020.

Guilford, V. B. and E. L. Fisk, 1952. Megasporogenesis and seed development in *Mimulus trigrinus* and *Torenia fournieri*. Bull. Torrey bot. Cl. 79:6–24.

Guliayev, V. A., 1961. (Notes on fertilization in *Citrullus vulgaris*). Byull. Vsesoyuz. Inst. Rastenievodstva 9:27–30.

Guliayev, V. A., 1963. (Comparative embryology of Cucurbitaceae and its significance for the taxonomy of this family.) Bot. Zhur. 48:80–85.

Gupta, B. L., 1934. Contribution to the life history of *Potamogeton crispus*. J. Indian bot. Soc. 13:51–65.

Gupta, B. L., 1935. Studies in the development of the pollen grain and embryo sac of *Wolffia arrhiza*. Current Sci. 4:104–105.

Gupta, M. N., 1958. Development of ovule and gametophytes in *Fimbristylis tenera*. Proc. 45th. Indian Sci. Congr. 3:289.

Gupta, M. N., 1959. Structure of the flowers and the development of gametophytes in *Kyllinga triceps*. Proc. 46th. Indian Sci. Congr. 3:283–284.

Gupta, M. N., 1962. Morphological studies in Cyperaceae. 1. Development of the ovule and the gametophytes in *Fimbristylis dichotoma*. Agra Univ. J. Res. (Sci.) 11:59–67.

Gupta, S. C., 1962a. Occurrence of exembryonate seeds in the Umbelliferae. Current Sci. 31:203–205.

Gupta, S. C., 1962b. Development of exembryonate seeds in *Foeniculum vulgare*. *In* Plant Embryology: A Symposium. CSIR. New Delhi: 188–191.

Gupta, S. C., 1964. The embryology of *Coriandrum sativum* and *Foeniculum vulgare*. Phytomorphology 14:530–547.

Gupta, S. C. and M. Gupta, 1964. Some observations on the embryology of *Foeniculum* and *Coriandum*. Proc. 46th. Indian Sci. Congr. 3:281.

Gurbel, J. J. A., 1952. Polyembryionia e embryiogenia adventica em *Citrus, Mangifera* e *Eugenia*. Rev. Lit. Duserica 3:443–450.

Gustafson, F. G., 1938. Induced parthenocarpy. Bot. Gaz. 99:840–844.

Gustafson, F. G., 1939. The cause of natural parthenocarpy. Amer. J. Bot. 26:135–138.

Gustafson, F. G., 1942. Parthenocarpy: natural and artificial. Bot. Rev. 8:599–654.

Gustafsson, Å., 1930. Kastrierungen und Pseudogamie bei *Rubus*. Bot. Notiser 1930:477–494.

Gustafsson, Å., 1931. Sind die *Canina*-Rosen apomiktisch? Bot. Nat. 21–30.

Gustafsson, Å., 1932. Zytologische und experimentelle Studien in der Gattung *Taraxacum*. Hereditas 16:41–62.

Gustafsson, Å., 1933a. Cytological studies in the genus *Hieracium*. Bot. Gaz. 94:512–533.

Gustafsson, Å., 1933b. Über die Teilung der Embryosackmutterzelle bei *Taraxacum*. Bot. Notiser 1933:531–534.

Gustafsson, Å., 1934a. Entwicklungswege der parthenogenetischen Embryosackmutterzelle. Bot. Notiser 1934:333–338.

Gustafsson, Å., 1934b. Die Formenbildung der Totalapomikten. Hereditas 19:259–283.

Gustafsson, Å., 1935. Studies on the mechanism of parthenogenesis. Hereditas 21:1–112.

Gustafsson, Å., 1939. The interrelation of meiosis and mitosis. 1. The mechanism of agamospermy. Hereditas 25:289–322.

Gustafsson, Å., 1942. Meiosis und Mitosis. Eine erklärung der meiotischen erscheinungen bei *Hieracium*. Chromosoma 2:367–387.

Gustafsson, Å., 1944. The terminology of the apomictic phenomena. Hereditas 30:145–151.

Gustafsson, Å., 1946. Apomixis in higher plants. 1. The mechanism of apomixis. Lunds Univ. Årsskr. (2). 42:1–66.

Gustafsson, Å., 1947a. Apomixis in higher plants. 2. The causal agent of apomixis. Lunds Univ. Årsskr. (2). 43:71–178.

Gustafsson, Å., 1947b. Apomixis in higher plants. 3. Biotype and species formation. Lunds Univ. Årsskr. (2). 43:183–370.

Gustafsson, Å. and A. Nygren, 1946. The temperature effect on pollen formation and meiosis in *Hieracium robustum*. Hereditas 32:1–14.

Guttenberg, H. von, 1960. Embryologische Studien an Monokotyledonen. 3. Die Embryogenese von *Triglochin maritimum, Arum maculatum* und *Typha latifolia*. Flora 149:243–281.

Guttenberg, H. von and H. Heydel, 1957. Vergleichende Studien über die Entwicklung von Primär-, Seiten- und sprossburtigen Wurzeln bei einigen Liliaceen. Bot. Stud. Jena 7:40–90.

Guttenberg, H. von, H. Heydel, and H. Pankow, 1954a. Embryologische Studien von Monokotyledonen. 1. Die Entstehung der Primärwurzel bei *Poa annua*. Flora 141:298–311.

Guttenberg, H. von, H. Heydel, and H. Pankow, 1954b. Embryologische Studien an Monokotyledonen. 2. Die Entwicklung des Embryos von *Allium giganteum*. Flora 141:476–500.

Guttenberg, H. von and C. Jakuszeit, 1957. Die Entwicklung des Embryos und der Primärwurzel von *Galtonia candidans* nebst Untersuchungen über die Differenzierung des Wurzelvegetationspunktes von *Alisma plantago*. Bot. Stud. Jena 7:91–126.

Guttenberg, H. von and H. Pankow, 1957. Vergleichende Studien über die Entwicklung monokotyler Embryonen und Keimpflanzen. Bot. Stud. Jena 7:1–39.

Guttenberg, H. von and A. Semlow, 1957. Die Entwicklung des Embryos und der Keimpflanze von Cyperaceen. Bot. Stud. Jena 7:127–141.

Guzowska, I., 1960. (Development and structure of the pollen grain in the Mexican plant, *Beschorneria decosteriana,* Cultivated in the Union of South Africa.) Poz. Towar. Przy. Nauk. Wydz. Mat.-Przy. Komis Biol. Prace 22:25–35.

Guzowska, I., 1964. Reinvestigation of embryo sac development, fertilization and early embryogeny in *Cytinus hypocistis.* Acta Soc. bot. Polon. 33:157–166.

Gvaladze, G. E., 1961. (The embryology of the genus *Allium*). Soobshch. Akad. Nauk. Gruzinsk. SSR 26:193–200.

Haber, J. M., 1959. The comparative anatomy and morphology of the flowers and inflorescences of the Proteaceae. 1. Some Australian taxa. Phytomorphology 9:325–357.

Haberlandt, G., 1895. Über die Ernährung der Keimlange und die Bedeutung des Endosperms bei viviparen Mangrovepflanzen. Ann. Jard. bot. Buitenz. 12:105–114.

Haberlandt, G., 1921a. Über experimentelle Erzeugung von Adventivembryonen bei *Oenothera lamarckiana.* S. B. Akad. Berlin 40:695–725.

Haberlandt, G., 1921b. Die Entwicklungserregung der Eizellen einiger parthenogenetischen Kompositen. S. B. Preuss. Akad. wiss. Wien 51:861–881.

Haberlandt, G., 1922a. Über Zellteilungshormone und Beziehungen zur Wundheilung, Befruchtung, Parthenogenesis und Adventivembryonie. Biol. Ztbl. 42:145–172.

Haberlandt, G., 1922b. Die Vorstufen und Ursachen der Adventivembryonie. S. B. Preuss. Akad. wiss. Berlin 25:386–406.

Haberlandt, G., 1923a. Über die Ursache des Ausbleibens der Reduktionsteilung in den Samenanlagen einiger parthenogenetischer Angiospermen. S. B. Preuss. Akad. wiss. Berlin 25:283–294.

Haberlandt, G., 1923b. Zur Embryologie von *Allium odorum.* Ber dtsch. bot. Ges. 41:174–179.

Haberlandt, G., 1925. Zur Embryologie und Cytologie von *Allium odorum.* Ber. dtsch. bot. Ges. 43:559–564.

Haberlandt, G., 1927. Zur Zytologie und Physiologie des weiblichen Gametophyten von *Oenothera.* Sitz. preuss. Akad. 1927:33–47.

Haberlandt, G., 1928. Die Lage des Zellkerns in der Eizelle der Angiospermen und ihre physiologische Bedeutung. S. B. Preuss. Akad. wiss. Berlin 24:450–456.

Haberlandt, G., 1938a. Über experimentelle Adventivembryonie. S. B. Preuss. Akad. wiss. Berlin 24:243–248.

Haberlandt, G., 1938b. Zur Entwicklungsphysiologie des Embryosackes von *Senecio vulgaris.* S. B. Preuss. Akad. wiss. Berlin 2:24–31.

Habermann, A., 1906. Der Fadenapparat in den Synergiden der Angiospermen. Beih. bot. Ztbl. 20:300–317.

Haccius, B., 1952. Die Embryoentwicklung bei *Ottelia alismoides* und das Problem des terminalen Monokotylen. Planta 40:443–460.

Haccius, B., 1954. Embryologische und histogenetische Studien an "monokotylen Dikotylen." 1. *Claytonia virginica.* Österr. bot. Zeit. 101:285.

Haccius, B., 1955. Experimentally induced twinning in plants. Nature 176:355–356.

Haccius, B. and E. Hartl-Baude, 1956. Embryologische und histogenetische Studien an "monokotylen Dikotylen." 2. *Pinguicula vulgaris* und *Pinguicula alpina.* Österr. bot. Zeit. 103:567–587.

Haeckel, I., 1930. Über Iridaceen. Flora 125:1–82.

Haenlein, F. H., 1874. Beiträge zur Entwicklungsgeschichte der Compositen. Bluethe 37.

Häfliger, E., 1943. Zytologisch-embryologische Untersuchungen pseudogamer Ranunkeln der *Auricomus*-Gruppe. Ber. scheweiz. bot. Ges. 53:317–382.

Hagedoorn, A. C. and A. L., 1924. Parthenogenesis in *Cucurbita.* Zeit. Ind. Abst. Vererb.-Lehre 34:186–213.

Hagerup, O., 1922. Om *Empetrum nigrum.* Bot. Tidsskr. 37:253–304.

Hagerup, O., 1926. Könsdelenes bygning og udvikling hos *Koenigia islandica.* Meddel. om Grönland 58:199–204.

Hagerup, O., 1928. Morphological and cytological studies of the Bicornes. Dansk. bot. Arkiv. 6:1–26.

Hagerup, O., 1934. Zur Abstammung einiger Angiospermen durch Gnetales und Coniferae. Kgl. Danske Vidensk. Selsk., Biol. Medd. 11.

Hagerup, O., 1942. The morphology and biology of the *Corylus* fruit. Kl. Danske Vidensk. Selsk., Biol. Medd. 17:1–32.

Hagerup, O., 1944. On fertilization, polyploidy and haploidy in *Orchis maculatus.* Dansk. bot. Arkiv. 11:1–26.

Hagerup, O., 1945. Facultative parthenogenesis and haploidy in *Epipactis latifolia.* Kl. Danske Vidensk Selsk., Biol. Medd. 19:1–13.

Hagerup, O., 1946. Studies on the Empetraceae. Kl. Danske Vidensk Selsk., Biol. Medd. 20:1–49.

Hagerup, O., 1947. The spontaneous formation of haploid, polyploid and aneuploid embryos in some orchids. Kl. Danske Vidensk Selsk., Biol. Medd. 20:1–22.

Hagerup, O., 1954. Autogamy in some drooping Bicornes flowers. Bot. Tidsskr. 51:103–116.

Hague, S. M., 1911. A morphological study of *Diospyros virginiana.* Bot. Gaz. 52:34–44.

Hair, J. B., 1956. Subsexual reproduction in *Agropyron.* Heredity 10:129–160.

Håkansson, Å., 1921. Beiträge zur Entwicklungsgeschichte der Taccaceen. Bot. Notiser 1921:189–268, 257–268.

Håkansson, Å., 1923. Studien über die Entwicklungsgeschichte der Umbelliferen. Lunds Univ. Årssk. (2). 18:1–20.

Håkansson, Å., 1924. Beiträge zur Zytologie eines *Epilobium*-Bastardes. Bot. Notiser 1924:269–278.

Håkansson, Å., 1925. Zur Zytologie der Gattung *Godetia.* Hereditas 6: 257–274.

Håkansson, Å, 1926. Zur Zytologie von *Celsia* und *Verbascum.* Lunds Univ. Årssk. (2). 21:1–47.

352 BIBLIOGRAPHY

Håkansson, Å., 1927. Der sechzehnkernige Embryosack von *Azorella trifurcata*. Ber. dtsch. bot. Ges. 45:654–664.

Håkansson, Å., 1929. Die Chromosomen in der Kreuzung *Salix viminalis* x *caprea*. Hereditas 13:1–52.

Håkansson, Å., 1943. Die Entwicklung des Embryosacks und die Befruchtung bei *Poa alpina*. Hereditas 29:25–61.

Håkansson, Å., 1944. Ergänzende Beiträge zur Embryologie von *Poa alpina*. Bot. Notiser 1944:299–311.

Håkansson, Å., 1946. Untersuchungen über die Embryologie einiger *Potentilla*-Formen. Lunds Univ. Årssk. (2) 42:1–70.

Håkansson, Å., 1947. Some observations on the seed development in Ecuadorian Cacao. Hereditas 33:526–538.

Håkansson, Å., 1948. Embryology of *Poa alpina* plants with accessory chromosomes. Hereditas 34:233–247.

Håkansson, Å., 1951. Parthenogenesis in *Allium*. Bot. Notiser 1951:143–179.

Håkansson, Å., 1952a. Seed development in *Bowlesia tenera*. Bot. Notiser 1952: 33–45.

Håkansson, Å., 1952b. Seed development after 2x, 4x crosses in *Galeopsis pubescens*. Hereditas 38:425–448.

Håkansson, Å., 1953a. Endosperm formation after 2x, 4x crosses in certain cereals, especially in *Hordeum vulgare*. Hereditas 39:57–64.

Håkansson, Å., 1953b. Die Samenbildung bei *Nothoscordum fragrans*. Bot. Notiser 1953:129–139.

Håkansson, Å., 1954. Endosperm formation in *Salix*. Bot. Notiser 1954:326–332.

Håkansson, Å., 1955. Endosperm formation in *Myrica gale*. Bot. Notiser 1955: 6–16.

Håkansson, Å., 1956. Seed development of *Brassica oleracea* and *B. rapa*. after certain reciprocal pollinations. Hereditas 42:373–396.

Håkansson, Å., 1957a. Notes on the giant chromosomes of *Allium nutans*. Bot. Notiser 1957:196–200.

Håkansson, Å., 1957b. Notes on endosperm formation in *Betula*. Bot. Notiser 1957:201–202.

Håkansson, Å. and S. Ellerström, 1950. Seed development after reciprocal crosses between diploid and tetraploid rye. Hereditas 36:256–296.

Håkansson, Å. and A. Levan, 1947. Endoduplicational meiosis in *Allium odorum*. Hereditas 43:179–200.

Hall, J. G., 1902. An embryological study of *Limnocharis emarginata*. Bot. Gaz. 33:214–219.

Hallier, H., 1903. Über die Abgrenzung und Verwandtschaft der einzelnen Sippen bei den Scrophulariaceae. Bull. Herb. Boiss. (3) 3:181.

Hallock, F. A., 1930. The relationship of *Garrya*. The development of the flower and seeds of *Garrya* and its bearing on the phylogenetic position of the genus. Ann. Bot. 44:771–812.

Halsted, B. D., 1887. Three nuclei in pollen grains. Bot. Gaz. 12:285–288.

Halsted, B. D., 1890. Observations upon doubling of flowers. Popular Science Monthly 38:374–381.

Hamann, U., 1962. Über Bau und Entwicklung des Endosperms der Philydraceae und über die Begriffe "mehliges Nährgewebe" und "Farinosae". Jahrb. f. wiss. Bot. 81:397–404.

Hamann, U., 1963. Die Embryologie von *Philydrum lanuginosum.* Ber. dtsch. bot. Ges. 76:203–208.

Hamilton, A. G., 1885. On the fertilization of *Goodenia hederacea.* Proc. Linn. Soc. N.S.W. 10:157–160.

Hamilton, A. G., 1894. Notes on the methods of fertilization of the Goodeniaceae. Proc. Linn. Soc. N.S.W., 19:201–212.

Hamilton, A. G., 1930. Note on the sterility in the Proteaceae. Proc. Linn. Soc. N.S.W. 55:39.

Hammond, B. L., 1937. Development of *Podostemon ceratophyllum.* Bull. Torrey bot. Cl. 64:17–36.

Hammond, H. S., 1908. The embryology of *Oxalis corniculata.* Ohio Nat. 8:261–264.

Hanausek, T. F., 1895. Über symmetrische und polyembryonische Samen von *Coffea arabica.* Ber. dtsch. bot. Ges. 13:73–78.

Hanawa, J., 1953. The embryo sac formation and the embryology of *Sesamum indicum* in 2x and 4x strains. Bot. Mag. Tokyo 66:98–102.

Hance, R. T., 1915. Pollen development and degeneration in *Zebrina pendula,* with special reference to the chromosomes. Bull. Torrey bot. Cl. 42:63–70.

Hanf, M., 1935. Vergleichende und entwicklungsgeschichtliche Untersuchungen über Morphologie und Anatomie der Griffel und Griffeläste. Beih. bot. Ztbl. 54A:99–141.

Hannig, E., 1909. Über den Öffnungsmechanismus der Antheren. Jahrb. f. wiss. Bot. 47:186–218.

Hansen, H. W., 1953. Developmental morphology of *Lotus corniculatus.* Iowa State Coll. J. Sci. 27:563–600.

Hansen, W., 1920. Die Doppelkeimigheit der Getreidekörner. Dtsch. Landw. Presse. 47:674.

Hanson, C. H., 1943. Cleistogamy and the development of the embryo sac in *Lespedeza stipulacea.* J. Agr. Res. 67:265–272.

Hanson, C. H., 1953. *Lespedeza stipulacea:* stamen morphology, meiosis, microgametogenesis and fertilization. Agron. Jour. 45:200–203.

Hanson, C. H. and W. A. Cope, 1955. Reproduction in the cleistogamous flowers of ten perennial species of *Lespedeza.* Amer. J. Bot. 42:624–627.

Hanstein, J., 1870. Die Entwicklungsgeschichte des Keimes der Monocotylen und Dikotylen. Bot. Abhandl. Bonn 1:1–112.

Hanstein, J., 1877. Die Parthenogenesis von *Coelobogyne ilicifolia.* Bot. Abhandl. Bonn 3:1–56.

Haque, A., 1946. Haploid-haploid polyembryony in *Sesbania aculeata.* Current Sci. 15:287.

Haque, A., 1951. The embryo sac of *Erythronium americanum.* Bot. Gaz. 112:495–500.

Haran, N., 1952. Apomixis in *Taraxacum cyprium.* Palestine J. Bot. 5:237–247.

Harlan, H. V., 1920. Daily development of kernels of Hannchen barley from flowering to maturity at Aberdeen, Idaho. J. Agr. Res. 19:393–430.

Harlan, H. V. and M. N. Pope, 1925. Some cases of apparent single fertilization in barley. Amer. J. Bot. 12:50–53.

Harlan, J. R., 1949. Apomixis in side-oats gramma. Amer. J. Bot. 36:495–499.

Harlan, J. R., H. M. Brooks, D. S. Borgaonkar, and J. M. J. de Wet, 1964. Nature and inheritance of apomixis in *Bothriochloa* and *Dichanthium.* Bot. Gaz. 125:41–46.

354 BIBLIOGRAPHY

Harland, S. C., 1936. Haploids in polyembryonic seeds of Sea Island cotton. J. Hered. 27:229–231.

Harling, G., 1946. Studien über den Blütenbau und die Embryologie der Familie Cyclanthaceae. Svensk bot. Tidskr. 40:257–272.

Harling, G., 1949. Zur Embryologie der Gattung *Hedychium*. Svensk bot. Tidskr. 43:357–364.

Harling, G., 1950. Embryological studies in the Compositae. 1. Anthemideae-Anthemidinae. Acta Hort. Berg. 15:135–168.

Harling, G., 1951a. Embryological studies in the Compositae. 2. Anthemideae—Chrysantheminae. Acta Hort. Berg. 16:1–56.

Harling, G., 1951b. Embryological studies in the Compositae. 3. Astereae. Acta Hort. Berg. 16:73–120.

Harling, G., 1954. The embryo sac development of *Vittadinia triloba*. Svensk bot. Tidsk. 48:489–496.

Harling, G., 1958. Monograph of the Cyclanthaceae. Acta Hort. Berg. 18:1–428.

Harling, G., 1960. Further embryological and taxonomical studies in *Anthemis* and some related genera. Svensk bot. Tidsk. 54:571–590.

Harms, H., 1897. Über die Stellung der Gattung *Tetracentron* und die Familie der Trochodendraceen. Ber. dtsch. bot. Ges. 15:350–360.

Harms, H., 1916. Über die Blüthenverhältnisse und die systematische Stellung der Gattung *Cercidiphyllum*. Ber. dtsch. bot. Ges. 34:272–283.

Harms, H., 1918. Zur Kenntnis der Gattung *Cercidiphyllum*. Mitteil. dtsch. dendrol. Ges. 26:71–87.

Harms, H., 1933. Zur Kenntnis von *Eucommia ulmoides*. Mitteil. dtsch. dendrol. Ges. 45:10–14.

Harrington, G. T. and W. Croker, 1923. Structure, physical characteristics and composition of the pericarp and integument of Johnson grass seed in relation to its physiology. J. agr. Res. 23:193–222.

Harris, B. J. and H. G. Baker, 1959. Pollination in *Kigelia africana*. J. West. Afr. Sci. Assn. 4:25–30.

Harris, C. J., 1935. The development of the flower and seed in *Galinsoga ciliata*. Univ. Pittsb. Bull. 32:131–137.

Harrold, T. J., 1935. Comparative study of the developing and aborting fruits of *Prunus persica*. Bot. Gaz. 96:505–520.

Hartl, D., 1957. Die Stellung von *Lindenbergia* im System der Scrophulariaceen. Beitr. Biol. Pfl. 33:265–277.

Hartman, A., 1923. Zur Entwicklungsgeschichte und Biologie der Acanthaceen. Flora 116:216–258.

Hartmann, M., 1929. Fortpflanzung und Befruchtung als Grundlage der Vererbung. Handl. Vererbungsw. 1.

Harvey, L. H., 1917. Polyembryony in *Quercus alba*. Ann. Rep. Mich. Acad. Sci. 19:329–331.

Hasitschka-Jenschke, G., 1959a. Bemerkenswerte Kernstrukturen im Endosperm und im Suspensor zweier Helobiae. Österr. bot. Zeit. 106:301–314.

Hasitschka-Jenschke, G., 1959b. Vergleichende karyologische Untersuchungen an Antipoden. Chromosoma 10:229–267.

Haupt, A. W., 1934. Ovule and embryo sac of *Plumbago capensis*. Bot. Gaz. 95:649–659.

Häuser, R., 1916. Untersuchungen an Macrogametophyten der Piperaceen. Beit. z. allg. Bot. 1:115–149. Diss. Berlin.

Hauss, H., 1927. Beiträge zur Kenntnis der Entwicklungsgeschichte von Flugein-richtungen bei höheren Samen. Bot. Archiv. 20:74.

Haviland, E., 1885. Some remarks on the fertilization of the genus *Goodenia.* Proc. Linn. Soc. N.S.W. 10:237–240.

Haviland, F. E., 1914. The pollination of *Goodenia cycloptera.* Proc. Linn. Soc. N.S.W. 39:851–854.

Hawksworth, F. G., 1961. Abnormal fruits and seeds in *Arceuthobium.* Madroño 16:96–101.

Hayashi, Y., 1960. On the microsporogenesis and pollen morphology in the family Magnoliaceae. Sci. Rpts. Tôhoku Univ. (4) Biol. 26:45–52.

Hayashi, Y., 1963a. The embryology of the family Magnoliaceae. 1. Megasporo-genesis, female gametophyte and embryogeny of *Illicium anisatum.* Sci. Rpts. Tôhoku Univ. (4) Biol. 29:27–33.

Hayashi, Y., 1963b. The embryology of the family Magnoliaceae. 2. Mega-sporogenesis, female gametophyte and embryogeny of *Schizandra repandra* and *Kadsura japonica.* Sci. Rpts. Tôhoku Univ. (4) Biol. 29:403–411.

Hayashi, Y., 1964. Megasporogenesis, female gametophyte and embryogeny of *Magnolia liliflora* and *Michelia fuscata.* Sci. Rpts. Tôhoku Univ. (4) Biol. 30:89–98.

Hayashi, Y., 1965. The comparative embryology of the Magnoliaceae in relation to the systematic consideration of the family. Sci. Rpts. Tôhoku Univ. (4) Biol. 31:29–44.

Hayman, D. L., 1956. Apomixis in Australian *Paspalum dilatatum.* Aust. Inst. agr. Sci. J. 22:292–293.

Heatley, M., 1916. A study of the life history of *Trillium cernum.* Bot. Gaz. 61:425–429.

Hedayetullah, S., 1935a. Embryo sac formation in *Capparis horrida.* Proc. 22nd. Indian Sci. Congr.: 258.

Hedayetullah, S., 1935b. The development of female gametophyte in *Moringa pterygosperma.* Proc. 22nd. Indian Sci. Congr.: 258.

Hedemann, E., 1931. Über experimentelle Erzeugung von Adventivembryonen bei *Mirabilis uniflora* und *Mirabilis froebellii.* Biol. Ztbl. 51:647–652.

Heel, J. P. van, 1925. Onderzoekringen over de ontwikkeling van de anthere, van der zaadknop en van het zaad bij *Beta vulgaris.* Thesis. Delph.

Hegelmaier, F., 1864. Monographie der Gattung *Callitriche.* Stuttgart.

Hegelmaier, F., 1867. Zur Systematik von *Callitriche.* Verh. Bot. Ver. Brandenb. 9:1.

Hegelmaier, F., 1868. Die Lemnaceen, eine monographische Untersuchung. Leipzig.

Hegelmaier, F., 1870. Über einige Samenknospen. Bot. Zeit. 28:489–495.

Hegelmaier, F., 1871. Über die Fruktifikationstheile von *Spirodela.* Bot. Zeit. 29: 621–630, 645–666.

Hegelmaier, F., 1874a. Zur Entwicklungsgeschichte monokotyledoner Keime nebst Bemerkungen über die Bildung des Samendeckel. 3. *Triticum vulgare.* Bot. Zeit. 32:657–671.

Hegelmaier, F., 1874b. Zur Entwicklungsgeschichte monokotyledoner Keime nebst Bemerkungen über die Bildung der Samendeckel. Bot. Zeit. 32:631–639, 648–671, 673–686, 688–700, 705–719.

Hegelmaier, F., 1875. Vergleichende Untersuchungen. Stuttgart.

Hegelmaier, F., 1878. "Vergleichende Untersuchungen über die Entwicklung dikotyledoner Keime und Berücksichtigung der pseudomonokotyledonen." Stuttgart.

Hegelmaier, F., 1880a. Zur Embryogenie und Endospermentwicklung von Lupinus. Bot. Zeit. 38:65-73, 81-91, 97-104, 121-137, 145-151.

Hegelmaier, F., 1880b. Über aus mehrkernigen Zellen aufgebaute Dikotyledonen-Keimträger. Bot. Zeit. 38:497-506, 513-522.

Hegelmaier, F., 1885. Untersuchungen über die Morphologie des Dikotyledonen-Endosperms. Nova Acta Leop. Car. Akad. Nat. 49:1-104.

Hegelmaier, F., 1886. Zur Entwicklungsgeschichte endospermatischer Gewebekörper. Bot. Zeit. 44:529-539, 545-555, 561-578, 585-596.

Hegelmaier, F., 1889. Über den Keimsack einiger Compositen und dessen Umhüllung. Bot. Zeit. 47:805-812, 821-826, 837-842.

Hegelmaier, F., 1897. Zur Kenntnis der Polyembryonie von Allium odorum. Bot. Zeit. 55:133-140.

Hegelmaier, F., 1901. Über einen neuen Fall von habitueller Polyembryonie. Ber. dtsch. bot. Ges. 19:489-499.

Hegelmaier, F., 1903. Zur Kenntnis der Polyembryonie von Euphorbia dulcis (purpurata). Ber. dtsch. bot. Ges. 21:6-19.

Heil, H., 1927. Vergleichend-anatomisch Studien an Samen von Chamaegigas und verwandten Gattungen. Ber. dtsch. bot. Ges. 45:555-561.

Heilborn, O., 1918. Zur Embryologie und Zytologie einiger Carex-Arten. Svensk bot. Tidsk. 12:212-224.

Heilborn, O., 1921. Taxonomical and cytological studies on cultivated Ecuadorian species of Carica. Ark. f. Bot. 17:1-16.

Heilborn, O., 1928. Taxonomical and embryological notes on Carica. Acta Hort. Berg. 9:105-108.

Heilborn, O., 1931. Studies on the taxonomy, geographical distribution and embryology of the genus Siparuna. Svensk bot. Tidsk. 25:202-228.

Heilscher, T., 1879. Anatomie und Biologie der Gattung Streptocarpus. Beitr. Biol. Pflanzen. 3:1-24.

Heimann-Winawer, P., 1919. Beiträge zur Embryologie von Colchicum autumnale. Diss. Freiburg.

Heimans, J., 1928. Chromosomen und Befruchtung bei Lilium martagon. Rec. Trav. bot. Néerl. 25:138-167.

Heimerl, A., 1887. Beiträge zur Anatomie der Nyctagineen. 1. Zur Kenntnis der Blütenbaues und der Fruchtentwicklung einiger Nyctagineen (Mirabilis jalapa und longiflora, Oxybaphus nyctagineus). Denkschr. Akad. wiss. Wien. 33.2:61-78.

Heimlich, L. F., 1927a. Microsporogenesis in the cucumber. Proc. nat. Acad. Sci. (Wash.) 13:113-115.

Heimlich, L. F., 1927b. The development and anatomy of the staminate flower of the cucumber. Amer. J. Bot. 14:227-237.

Heimlich, L. F., 1929. Microsporogenesis in Cucumis sativus. Cellule 39:7-24.

Heinricher, E., 1888. Zur Biologie der Gattung Impatiens. Flora 71:163-179.

Heinricher, E., 1896. Anatomischer Bau und Leistung der Saugorgane der Schuppenwurz-Arten (Lathraea clandestina und L. squamaria). Beitr. z. Biol. Pflanz. (7) 2:315.

Heinricher, E., 1915a. Beiträge zur Biologie der Zwergmistel, Arceuthobium oxycedri, besonders zur Kenntnis des anatomisches Baues und der Mechanik ihrer explosiven Beeren. S. B. Akad. wiss. Wien. (1) 124.

Heinricher, E., 1915b. Über Bau und Biologie der Blüten von *Arceuthobium oxycedri*. S. B. Akad. wiss. Wien. 124:181–230.

Heinricher, E., 1917. Zur Kenntnis der Blüte von *Cytinus hypocistis*. Ber. dtsch. bot. Ges. 35:513–517.

Heinricher, E., 1931. Monographie der Gattung *Lathraea*. Jena.

Heinricher, E., 1934. Zur Frage der Artbildung bei *Cytinus hypocistis* nebst anderen Bemerkungen. Ber. dtsch. bot. Ges. 52:48–53.

Heitz, E., 1951. Embryologischer Nachweis von Agamospermie mittels Simultanmethode. Experementia 7:456.

Heitz, E., 1953. Embryologische Mitteilungen. 1. Ein neues Objekt zur Untersuchung des Embryosacks an Totalpräparaten der Samenanlage. Ber. schweiz. bot. Ges. 63:194–200.

Heitz, E. and F. Resende, 1936. Zur Methodik der Pollenkorn und Pollenschlauchuntersuchung. Bol. Soc. Broteriana 11:5–15.

Heizmann, D. and C. A. Shull, 1944. The inflorescences of the cotton-wood poplar. Chicago Nat. 7:26–29.

Helm, F., 1895. Sur la polyembryonic d'une Apocynacée de genre *Kopsia*. Assoc. Fr. Av. Sci. 24th (Bordeaux): 638–640.

Henfrey, A., 1856. On the development of the ovule of *Santalum album*. Trans. Linn. Soc. Lond. (Bot.) 22:67–79.

Hennig, L., 1929. Beiträge zur Kenntnis der Resedaceen-Blüte und Frucht. Planta 9:507–563.

Henry, M. P., 1956. Etude cytologique du lait des cocos au cours du développement de la noix. C. R. Acad. Sci. Paris 245:401–404.

Hérail, J., 1889. Organes reproducteurs et formation de l'oeuf chez les Phanérogames. Paris.

Herms, W. B., 1907. Contributions to the life history of *Asimina triloba*. Ohio Nat. 8:211–216.

Hermsen, L., 1939. Studies in the embryology and cytology of *Saxifraga*. Medd. om Grønland 125:1–15.

Herr, J. M., 1954. The development of the ovule and female gametophyte in *Tiarella cordifolia*. Amer. J. Bot. 41:333–338.

Herr, J. M., 1959a. Notes on the structures and origin of the ovule in the genus *Ilex*. J. Elisha Mitchell Sci. Soc. 75:67.

Herr, J. M., 1959b. The development of the ovule and the megagametophyte in the genus *Ilex*. J. Elisha Mitchell Sci. Soc. 75:107–128.

Herr, J. M., 1959c. Embryological evidence for the relationship of Aquifoliaceae to Celastraceae. Virginia J. Sci. 10:259.

Herr, J. M., 1961. Endosperm development and associated ovule modifications in the genus *Ilex*. J. Elisha Mitchell Sci. Soc. 77:26–32.

Herrig, Fr., 1919. Über Spermazellen im Pollenschlauch der Angiospermen. Ber. dtsch. bot. Ges. 37:450–453.

Herrig, Fr., 1922. Über Fragmentation und Teilung der Pollenschlauchkerne von *Lilium candidum*. Beitr. allg. Bot. 2:403–411.

Heusser, C., 1919. Over de voortplantingsorganen van *Hevea brasiliensis*. Arch. v. Rubberkult. Ned.-Ind. 3:455–514.

Heusser, K., 1914. Die Entwicklung der generativen Organe von *Himantoglossum hircinum (Loroglossum hircinum)*. Thesis. Zürich.

Heusser, K., 1915. Die Entwicklung der generativen Organe von *Himantoglossum hircinum (Loroglossum hircinum)*. Beih. bot. Ztbl 32:218–277.

Hewitt, W. C., 1939. Seed development of *Lobelia amoena*. J. Elisha Mitchell Sci. Soc. 55:63–82.

Heyn, A. N. J., 1930. Die Befruchtung bei *Theobroma cacao*. Kon. Akad. Wet. Amsterdam 33:533–541.

Hieronymus, G., 1873. Beiträge zur Kenntnis der Centrolepidaceen. Abh. nat. Ges. Halle 12:115–222.

Hildebrand, F., 1863. Die Fruchtbildung der Orchideen, ein Beweis Für die doppelte Wirkung des Pollens. Bot. Zeit. 21:329.

Hill, T. G., 1900. The structure and development of *Triglochin maritimum*. Ann. Bot. 14:83–107.

Hille Ris Lambers, M., 1930. Polyembryonie en polyspermie bij Koffie. Med. Profstation Malang 74.

Himmelbaur, W., 1909. Eine blütenmorphologie Studie über *Datisca cannabina*. S. B. Akad. wiss. Wien 118:92–113.

Himmelbaur, W., 1911. Einige Abschnitte aus der Lebensgeschichte von *Ribes pallidum*. Jb. Hamburg wiss. Anstalen 29.

Himmelbaur, W., 1926. Zur Entwicklungsgeschichte von *Crocus sativus*. Leipzig.

Hindmarsh, G. J., 1964. Gametophyte development in *Trifolium pratense*. Aust. J. Bot. 12:1–14.

Hindmarsh, G. J., 1965. An embryological study of five species of *Bassia*. Proc. Linn. Soc. N.S.W. 90:274–289.

Hiorth, G., 1926. Zur Kenntnis der Homozygoten und der Pollenschlauchkonkurrens bei *Oenothera*. Abst. U. Vererb. 43:171–237.

Hiorth, G., 1927. Zur Kenntnis der Homozygoten-Eliminierung und der Pollenschlauch-Konkurrenz bei *Oenothera*. Abst. U. Vererb. 43:171–237.

Hjelmqvist, H., 1948. Studies on the floral morphology and phylogeny of the Amentiferae. Bot. Notiser (Suppl.) 1948: 147–166.

Hjelmqvist, H., 1951. The embryo sac development of *Tridax trilobata*. Bot. Notiser 1951: 180–187.

Hjelmqvist, H., 1953. The embryo sac development of *Quercus robur*. Phytomorphology 3:377–384.

Hjelmqvist, H., 1956a. The embryology of some South African *Alchemilla* species. Bot. Notiser 1956: 21–32.

Hjelmqvist, H., 1956b. Some notes on the endosperm and embryo development in Fagales and related orders. Bot. Notiser 1957: 173–195.

Hjelmqvist, H., 1957. The apomictic development in *Malus sieboldii*. Bot. Notiser 1957: 455–467.

Hjelmqvist, H., 1959a. Studien über Embryologie und Variabilität bei einigen *Aphanes*-Arten. Bot. Notiser 1959: 17–64.

Hjelmqvist, H., 1959b. On the embryology of two *Malus* hybrids. Bot. Notiser 1959: 453–464.

Hjelmqvist, H., 1962. The embryo sac development of some *Cotoneaster* species. Bot. Notiser 1962: 208–236.

Hjelmqvist, H., 1964. Variations in embryo sac development. Phytomorphology 14:186–196.

Hjelmqvist, H. and F. Grazi, 1964. Studies on variation in embryo sac development. Bot. Notiser 1964: 141–166.

Hjelmqvist. H., and U. Holmberg, 1961. The development of the embryo sac in *Sanvitalia procumbens*. Bot. Notiser 1961: 353–360.

Ho, M. Y., 1963. Embryological studies of soybeans. 1. The development of the embryo and albumen. Acta Bot. Sinica 11:318–328.

Hoar, C. S., 1916. Sterility as the result of hybridization and the condition of pollen in *Rubus*. Bot. Gaz. 62:370–388.

Hoar, C. S. and E. J. Haertl, 1932. Meiosis in the genus *Hypericum*. Bot. Gaz. 93:197–204.

Hoare, G., 1934. Gametogenesis and fertilization in *Scilla nonscripta*. Cellule 42:269–292.

Hoeppener, E. and O. Renner, 1929. Genetische und zytologische Oenotheren-Studien. Bot. Abh. Goebel 15:1–66.

Hoffman, C. A., 1933. Developmental morphology of *Allium cepa*. Bot. Gaz. 95:279–299.

Hoffmann, K., 1929. Cytologische Studien bei den Orchidaceen. Ber. dtsch. bot. Ges. 47:321–326.

Hoffmann, K., 1930. Beiträge zur Cytologie der Orchidaceen. Planta 10:523–595.

Hofmeister, W., 1847. Untersuchungen des Vorganges bei der Befruchtung der Oenotheren. Bot. Zeit. 5:785–792.

Hofmeister, W., 1848. Über die Entwicklung des Pollens. Bot. Zeit. 6:425–434, 649–658, 670–674.

Hofmeister, W., 1849. Die Entstehung des Embryo der Phanerogamen, eine Reihe mikroskopischer Untersuchungen. Leipzig.

Hofmeister, W., 1851. Zur Entwicklungsgeschichte des Embryo der Personaten. Flora 9:449–457.

Hofmeister, W., 1852. Zur Entwicklungsgeschichte der *Zostera*. Bot. Zeit. 10:121–131, 137–149, 157–158.

Hofmeister, W., 1855a. Notes embryologiques. Ann. Sci. nat. Bot. 3:209–219.

Hofmeister, W., 1855b. Embryologisches. Flora 13:257–266.

Hofmeister, W., 1858a. Embryobildung der Phanerogamen. Jahrb. f. wiss. Bot. 1:101–103.

Hofmeister, W., 1858b. Neuere Beobachtungen über die Embryobildung der Phanerogamen. Jahrb. f. wiss. Bot. 1:82–190.

Hofmeister, W., 1859. Neue Beiträge zur Kenntnis der Embryobildung der Phanerogamen. 1. Dikotyledonen mit ursprünglich einzelligem, nur durch Zellenteilung wachsendem Endosperm. Abh. Köngl. Sächs. Ges. (Akad.) wiss. 6:535–672.

Hofmeister, W., 1861. Neue Beiträge zur Kenntnis der Embryobildung der Phanerogramen. 2. Monokotyledon. Abh. Köngl. Sächs. Ges. Wiss. 7:629–760.

Höhnel, F. von, 1876. Morphologische Untersuchungen über die Samenschalen der Cucurbitaceen und einiger verwandten Familien. S. B. Akad. wiss. Wein. 73:297–337.

Holferty, G. M., 1901. Ovule and embryo of *Potamogeton natans*. Bot. Gaz. 31:339–346.

Holm, T., 1897. *Obolaria virginica:* a morphological and anatomical study. Ann. Bot. 11:369–383.

Holm, T., 1898. *Podophyllum peltatum:* a morphological study. Bot. Gaz. 27:419–433.

Holm, T., 1921. Morphological study of *Carya alba* and *Juglans nigra*. Bot. Gaz. 72:375–389.

Holmgren, I., 1913. Zur Entwicklungsgeschichte von *Butomus umbellata*. Svensk bot. Tidsk. 7:58–77.

Holmgren, I., 1915. Die Entwicklung des Embryosackes bei *Anthemis tinctoria*. Svensk bot. Tidsk. 9:171–183.

Holmgren, I., 1916. Apogamie in der Gattung *Eupatorium*. Svensk bot. Tidsk. 10:263–269.

Holmgren, I., 1919. Zytologische Studien über die Fortpflanzung bei den Gattungen *Erigeron* und *Eupatorium*. Kgl. Svensk. Vet.-Akad. Hendl. 59:1–118. Diss. Stockholm.

Homedes, J., 1928. Datos para una interpretación endocrina de las células de tapiz de los sacos polinicos. Bol. soc. española hist. nat. 28:315–320.

Honsell, E., 1954. Osservazioni sulla struttura dell'ovolo e sulla cariologia di *Calodendrum capense* e *Philocarpus pennatifolius*. Ann. di Bot. (Roma) 24:438–448.

Horn, C. L., 1940. Existence of only one variety of cultivated mangosteen explained by asexually formed "seed." Science 92:237–238.

Horn, C. L., 1943. The frequency of polyembryony in twenty varieties of mango. Proc. Amer. Soc. hort. Sci. 42:318–320.

Horne, A. S., 1909. The structure and affinities of *Davidia involucrata*. Trans. Linn. Soc. Lond. (2) (Bot.) 7:303–326.

Horne, A. S., 1914. A contribution to the study of evolution of the flower, with special reference to the Hamamelidaceae, Caprifoliaceae and Cornaceae. Trans. Linn. Soc. Lond. (2) (Bot.) 8:239–309.

Hoshikawa, K., 1961a. (Studies on the ripening of wheat grain. 1. Embryological observations of the early development of the endosperm.) Proc. crop sci. Soc. Japan 29:253–257.

Hoshikawa, K., 1961b. (Studies on the ripening of wheat grain. 2. Development of the endosperm tissue. 3. Development of the starch grain and reserve protein particle in the endosperm.) Proc. crop sci. Soc. Japan 29:415–420.

Hosriukova, K. J., 1951. (A contribution to the biological interpretation of the sexual generation in Angiosperms.) Tez. Vses. Sov. bot. Obsch. Akad. Nauk SSSR: 41–44.

Hotchkiss, A. T., 1958. Pollen and pollination in the Eupomatiaceae. Proc. Linn. Soc. N.S.W. 83:86–91.

Houk, W. G., 1936. The ovule and seed of *Coffea arabica*. Science 83:464–465.

Houk, W. G., 1938. Endosperm and perisperm of coffee with notes on the morphology of the ovule and seed development. Amer. J. Bot. 25:56–61.

Howard, G. and K. Ram, 1925. Studies in Indian tabaccos. 4. Parthenocarpy and parthenogenesis in two varieties of *N. tabacum* var. *cuba* and var. *mirodato*. Mem. Dept. Agr. Ind. Bot. 13:1–16.

Howe, T. D., 1922. A preliminary notice concerning the development of the embryo sac in *Grindelia squarossa*. Proc. Nebraska Acad. Sci. 5.

Howe, T. D., 1926. Development of the embryo sac in *Grindelia squarossa*. Bot. Gaz. 81:280–296.

Howe, T. D., 1940. Development of the embryo sac in *Trillium grandiflorum*. Amer. J. Bot. 27(Suppl.):11.

Howe, T. D., 1959. Recent studies of the female gametophyte in the Compositae, especially in the tribe Astereae. Congr. Internatl. Bot. 9th. 2:171–172.

Howe, T. D., 1964. Development of the embryo sac in *Ratibida tagetes*. Amer. J. Bot. 51:678.

Howlett, F. S., 1931. Factors affecting fruit setting. 1. Stayman Winesap. Ohio Agric. Exp. Sta. Bull. 483.

Howlett, F. S., 1936. The effect of carbohydrate and nitrogen deficiency upon microsporogenesis and the development of the male gametophyte in the tomato, *Lycopersicum esculentum*. Ann. Bot. 50:767–804.

Howlett, F. S., 1938. Factors affecting the rate and course of development of the female gametophyte in apple varieties. Proc. Amer. Soc. hort. Sci. 35:105–110.

Hrubý, C., 1934. A contribution to the cytology and embryology of *Erythronium dens-canis*. Bull. Internat. Acad. Sci. Bohème. 35:124–132.

Hrubý, C., 1938. Embryo sac development in *Erythronium dens-canis*. Chron. Bot. 4:20–21.

Hu, S. Y., 1963. Studies in the polyembryony of *Hosta caerulea*. 2. Observations on the development of adventure embryos under hormone treatments. Acta Bot. Sineca 11:21–25.

Huber, J. A., 1924. Zur Morphologie von *Mesembrianthemum*. Bot. Archiv. 5:7–25.

Huber, J. A., 1929. Blüten und Samenentwicklung der Kakteen und ihre Bedeutung für deren systematische Stellung. Mschr. dtsch. Kakt. Ges. 1:175–190.

Huber, J. A., 1937. Die Entwicklung der Samen bei den Kakteen. Cactaceae. (Mai):9–12.

Hubert, E. de, 1896. Recherches sur le sac embryonnaire des plantes grasses. Ann. Sci. nat. Bot. (8) 2:37–128.

Hulbary, R. L. and A. N. Rao, 1959. Flower development and gametogenesis in *Oenothera laciniata*. Proc. Iowa Acad. Sci. 66:91–97.

Hull, E. D., 1915. Polyembryony in *Opuntia rafinesquii*. Amer. Botanist 21:56–57.

Humphrey, J. E., 1896. The development of the seed in the Scitamineae. Ann. Bot. 10:1–40.

Humphrey, L. E., 1914. A cytological study of the stamens of *Smilax herbacea*. Ohio Nat. 15:357–369.

Hunzicker, H. R., 1954. Beiträge zur Aposporie und ihrer Genetik bei *Potentilla*. Arch. Klaus-Stift. Vererb. Forsch. 29:135–222. Diss. Zürich.

Hurey-Py, G., 1934. Recherches sur les conditions du pH nécessaires pour obtenir la germination des grains de pollen et la coloration vitale de leurs vacuoles. C. R. Acad. Sci. Paris 198:195–197.

Hurst, C. C., 1900. Notes on some experiments in hybridization and crossbreeding. J. Roy hort. Soc. 24.

Hurst, C. C., 1931. Embryo sac formation in diploid and polyploid species of Roseae. Proc. Roy. Soc. Lond. B. 109:126–148.

Huss, H. A., 1906. Beiträge zur Morphologie und Physiologie der Antipoden. Beih. bot. Ztbl. 20:77–174. Diss. Zürich.

Hutchinson, J., 1959. The Families of Flowering Plants. 2 vol. 2nd Ed. Oxford.

Hutchison, D. J. and E. C. Bashaw, 1964. Cytology and reproduction of *Panicum coloratum* and related species. Crop Sci. 4:151–153.

Iconomides, J., 1958. La formation de l'ovule et la Séminogenèse dans le *Clidemia hirta*. Bull. Soc. bot. France 105:230–234.

Ikeda, T., 1902. Studies in the physiological functions of the antipodals and related phenomena of the fertilization in Liliaceae. 1. *Tricyrtis hirta*. Bull. Coll. Agric. Imp. Univ. Tokyo 5:41–72.

Ikeno, S., 1910. Sind alle Arten der Gattung *Taraxacum* parthenogenetisch? Ber. dtsch. bot. Ges. 28:394–397.

Ikeno, S., 1916. Notes sur les résultats de l'hybridation artificielle de quelques espèces du genre *Salix*. Bot. Mag. Tokyo 30:316–320.

Ikeno, S., 1922. On hybridization of some species of *Salix*. Ann. Bot. 36:175–191.

Il'ina, G. M., 1961. (An embryological study of *Papaver somniferum*.) Byull. Moskov. Obshch. Ispytat. Prirody. Otdel Biol. 66:13–25.

Il'ina, G. M., 1962a. (The phenology of embryogenesis in *Papaver somniferum*). Nauchn. Dokl. Vysshei Shkoly. Biol. Nauk. 1:116–118.

Il'ina, G. M., 1962b. (Embryological study of mustard, *Brassica juncea*.) Vest. Mosk. Univ. Biol. (6) Pochvovedeniya 1:35–45.

Il'ina, G. M., 1964. (Development of pollen and the embryo sac in *Hypecoum procumbens*.) Bjull. Mosk. Obsh. Ispyt. Prirody. Biol. 69:130–134.

Inariyama, S., 1929. Karyological studies of *Iris kaempferi*. Jap. J. Bot. 4:405–426.

Irmisch, T., 1853. Beiträge zur Biologie und Morphologie der Orchideen. Leipzig.

Irmisch, T., 1854–55. Beiträge zur vergleichenden Morphologie der Pflanzen. Abh. Nat. Ges. 2:30–43; 3:63–102, 107–137.

Irmisch, T., 1876. Einige Beobachtungen an *Eucalyptus globulus*. Zeit. ges. Naturw. 14.

Isbell, C. L., 1928. Growth studies of the pecan. Ala. Agr. Expt. Sta. Bull. 226.

Ishii, K., 1964. (Embryo development in *Ipomoea* nil Choisy.) Tokyo Nihon Univ. Col. Agr. Vet. Med. Bull. 19:17–27.

Ishikawa, M., 1918. Studies on the embryo sac and fertilization in *Oenothera*. Ann. Bot. 32:279–317.

Islam, A. S., 1950. A contribution to the life history of *Ottelia alismoides*. J. Indian bot. Soc. 29:79–91.

Ivanova, K. V. and L. I. Orel, 1963. (Some biological peculiarities and an embryological characterization of *Solanum guineense*.) Trudy Priklad. bot. Genet. Selekt. 35:146–150.

Ivanovskaya, E. V., 1960. (Structure of the ovule and the nature of polyembryony of the Papirovka variety of apple.) Nauch. Dokl. Vyssh. Shkoly. Biol. Nauk. 1:99–102.

Ivanovskaya, E. V., 1962. (Concerning the embryology of apple trees. 1.) Nauch. Dokl. Vyssh. Shkoly. Biol. Nauk. 1:109–115.

Ivanovskaya, E. V., 1963. (The embryology of the apple tree, *Pyrus malus*. 2.) Nauch. Dokl. Vyssh. Shkoly. Biol. Nauk. 1:106–113.

Iwanami, Y., 1956. Protoplasmic movement in pollen grains and tubes. Phytomorphology 6:288–295.

Iyengar, C. V. K., 1929. Embryo sac and the development of haustorium in *Ilysanthes*. Proc. 16th Indian Sci. Congr.

Iyengar, C. V. K., 1931. Embryo sac and the development of haustorium in *Bonnaya* sp. Proc. 18th Indian Sci. Congr.

Iyengar, C. V. K., 1933. Embryo sac and development of endosperm haustorium in *Sopubia* sp. Proc. 20th. Indian Sci. Congr.

Iyengar, C. V. K., 1934. Embryo sac and the development of endosperm haustorium in *Alonsoa* sp. Proc. 21st Indian Sci. Congr.

Iyengar, C. V. K., 1937. Development of embryo sac and endosperm haustoria in some members of the Scrophularineae. 1. An account of *Sopubia delphinifolia*. J. Indian bot. Soc. 16:99–109.

Iyengar, C. V. K., 1939a. Development of the embryo sac and endosperm haustoria in some members of Scrophularineae. 2. *Isoplexis canariensis* and *Celsia coromandeliana*. J. Indian bot. Soc. 18:13–20.

Iyengar, C. V. K., 1939b. Development of the embryo sac and endosperm haustoria in some members of Scrophularineae. 3. *Limnophila heterophylla* and *Stemodia viscosa*. J. Indian bot. Soc. 18:35–42.

Iyengar, C. V. K., 1939c. A note on the embryo sac and endospern haustoria in some members of Scrophularineae. Current Sci. 8:261–263.

Iyengar, C. V. K., 1940a. Development of the embryo sac and endosperm haustoria in some members of Scrophularineae. 4. *Vandellia hirsuta* and *V. scabra*. J. Indian bot. Soc. 18:179–189.

Iyengar, C. V. K., 1940b. Development of the embryo sac and endosperm haustoria in some members of Scrophularineae. 5. *Ilysanthes hyssopioides* and *Bonnaya tenuifolia*. J. Indian bot. Soc. 19:5–17.

Iyengar, C. V. K., 1940c. Structure and development of seed in *Sopubia trifida*. J. Indian bot. Soc. 19:251–261.

Iyengar, C. V. K., 1941. Development of the embryo sac and endosperm haustoria in *Torenia cordifolia* and *T. hirsuta*. Proc. Nat. Inst. Sci. India 7:61–71.

Iyengar, C. V. K., 1942a. Development of seed and its nutritional mechanism in Scrophulariaceae. 1. *Rhamphicarpa longiflora*, *Centranthera hispida* and *Pedicularis zeylanica*. Proc. Natl. Inst. Sci. India 8:249–261.

Iyengar, C. V. K., 1942b. Development of embryo sac and endosperm haustoria in *Tetranema mexicana* and *Verbascum thapsus*. Proc. Nat. Inst. Sci. India 8:59–69.

Iyengar, C. V. K., 1942c. Development of embryo sac and endosperm haustoria in *Rehmannia angulata*. J. Indian bot. Soc. 21:51–57.

Iyengar, C. V. K., 1947. Development of seed and its nutritional mechanism in the Scrophulariaceae. 2. J. Mysore Univ. B. 7:82–98.

Iyengar, G. S., 1937. Life history of *Santalum album*. J. Indian bot. Soc. 16:175–195.

Iyengar, N. K., 1938. Pollen tube studies in *Gossypium*. J. Genet. 37:69–106.

Iyer, R. D., 1962. Embryological studies in relation to interspecific hybridization in jute. *In* Plant Embryology: A Symposium. C. S. I. R. New Delhi:49–54.

Iyer, R. D., K. Sulbha, and M. S. Swaminathan, 1961. Fertilization and seed development in crosses between *C. olitorius* and *C. capsularis*. Indian J. Genet. and Pl. Breeding 21:191–200.

Jacobson-Paley, R., 1920a. Sur le haustorium et la formation de l'albumen dans l'*Arum maculatum*. Bull. Soc. bot. Genève (2) 12:55–64.

Jacobson-Paley, R., 1920b. Etude sur la pollinisation et l'embryologie du *Swertia longifolia*. Bull. Soc. bot. Genève (2) 12:65–86.

Jacobson-Paley, R., 1920c. Sur le suçoir de l'*Arisarum vulgare*, et le rôle de la région chalazienne du sac embryonnaire. Bull. Soc. bot. Genève (2) 12:87–92.

Jacobson-Paley, R., 1920d. Le periplasmodium dans les anthères de l'*Arum maculatum*. Bull. Soc. bot. Genève (2) 12:306–318.

Jacobsson-Stiasny, E., 1913. Die spezielle Embryologie der Gattung *Sempervivum* im Vergleich zu den Befunden bei den anderen Rosales. Denkschr. Akad. wiss. Wien. 89:797–815.

Jacobsson-Stiasny, E., 1914a. Versuch einer embryologisch-phylogenetischen Bearbeitung der Rosaceae. S. B. Akad. wiss. Wien. 122:763–800.

Jacobsson-Stiasny, E., 1914b. Versuch einer phylogenetischen Werwertung der Endosperm- und Haustorialbildung bei den Angiospermen. S. B. Akad. wiss. Wien. 123:467–603.

Jacobsson-Stiasny, E., 1916. Fragen vergleichender Embryologie der Pflanzen. 1. Formenreihen mit sechzehnkernigen Embryosäcken. S. B. Akad. wiss. Wien. 125:593–732.

Jacobsson-Stiasny, E., 1918. Zur Embryologie der Aristolochiaceae. Denkschr. Akad. wiss. Wien 95:65–77.

Jacobsson-Stiasny, E., 1927. Versuch einer phylogenetischen Verwertung der Endosperm- und Haustorialbildung bei den Angiospermen. Hereditas 10:169–229.

Jaeger, G. F., 1814. Über die Missbildungen der Gewächse. Stuttgart.

Jaensch, O., 1905. Beitrag zur Embryologie von Ardisia crispa. Diss. Breslau.

Jagannathrao, C. and P. Subramanyam, 1934. A note on the occurrence of sterility in Bengal gram, Cicer varietinum. Madras agric. J. 22:187.

Jain, T. C., 1956. The gametophytes of Lycium europaeum. J. Indian bot. Soc. 35:181–188.

Jalan, S., 1960. The floral morphology and embryology of Caltha palustris. Symp. Pl. Embryol., Delhi (Abst.) :5–6.

Jalan, S., 1963. Studies in the family Ranunculaceae. 4. The embryology of Actaea spicata. Phytomorphology 13:338–347.

Jalan, S. and N. N. Bhandari, 1963. Extracarpellary ovules in some Ranales. Current Sci. 32:230–232.

Janczewski, E., 1903. La sexualité des Groseilliers, Ribes. Bull. Internat. Acad. Sci. Cracov.

Janczewski, E., 1907. Monographie des Groseilliers, Ribes. Mem. Soc. Phys. et d'Hist. nat. Genève 35.

Janczewski, E., 1908. Sur les anthères stériles des Groseilliers. Bull. Internat. Acad. Sci. Cracov.

Jaranowski, J., 1961. Haploid-diploid twin embryos in Melilotus. Genet. Polon. 2:129–137.

Jaranowski, J., 1962a. Fertilization and embryo development in the genus Lupinus. 1. Seed development in cases of autogamy. Genet. Polon. 3:209–246.

Jaranowski, J., 1962b. Fertilization and embryo development in the genus Lupinus. 2. Fertilization and embryo development following reciprocal species hybridization. Genet. Polon. 3:333–368.

Jaretzky, R., 1927. Die Degenerationserscheinungen in den Blüten von Rumex flexuosus. Jahrb. f. wiss. Bot. 66:301–320.

Jaretzky, R., 1928. Histologische und karyologische Studien an Polygonaceen. Jahrb. f. wiss. Bot. 69:357–490.

Jauch, B., 1918. Quelques points de l'anatomie et de la biologie des Polygalacées. Bull. Soc. bot. Genève 10:47–84. Thesis. Genève.

Jeffrey, E. C., 1895. Polyembryony in Erythronium americanum. Ann. Bot. 9:537–541.

Jeffrey, E. C. and E. J. Haertl, 1939a. The production of unfertilized seeds in Trillium. Science 90:81–82.

Jeffrey, E. C. and E. J. Haertl, 1939b. Apomixis in Trillium. Cellule 48:79–88.

Jennings, D. L., 1963. Variation in pollen and ovule fertility in varieties of cassava and the effects of interspecific crossing on fertility. Euphytica 12:69–76.

Jensen, G. H., 1918. Studies on the morphology of wheat. Washington Agr. Exp. Sta. Bull. 150.

Jensen, H. W., 1951. The normal and parthenogenetic forms of Orobanche uniflora in the eastern United States. Cellule 54:135–142.

Johansen, D. A., 1928a. The hypostase: its presence and function in the ovule of Onagraceae. Proc. nat. Acad. Sci. (Wash.) 14:710–713.

Johansen, D. A., 1928b. The hypostase and seed sterility in the Onagraceae. Madroño 1:165–167.

Johansen, D. A., 1929. Studies in the morphology of the Onagraceae. 1. *Hartmannia tetraptera*. Bull. Torrey bot. Cl. 56:285–298.

Johansen, D. A., 1930a. Studies in the morphology of the Onagraceae. 2. Embryonal manifestations of fasciation in *Clarkia elegans*. Bot. Gaz. 90:75–91.

Johansen, D. A., 1930b. Studies on the morphology of the Onagraceae. 4. *Stenosiphon linifolium*. Bull. Torrey bot. Cl. 57:315–326.

Johansen, D. A., 1931a. Studies on the morphology of the Onagraceae. 3. *Taraxia ovata*. Ann. Bot. 45:111–124.

Johansen, D. A., 1931b. Studies on the morphology of the Onagraceae. 5. *Zauschneria latifolia*, typical of a genus characterized by irregular embryology. Ann. N.Y. Acad. Sci. 33:1–26.

Johansen, D. A., 1931c. Studies on the morphology of the Onagraceae. 6. *Anogra pallida*. Amer. J. Bot. 18:854–864.

Johansen, D. A., 1933. Studies on the morphology of the Onagraceae. 7. *Gayophytum ramosissimum*. Bull. Torrey bot. Cl. 60:1–8.

Johansen, D. A., 1934. Studies on the morphology of the Onagraceae. 8. *Circaea pacifica*. Amer. J. Bot. 21:508–510.

Johansen, D. A., 1936. Morphology and embryology of *Fouquieria*. Amer. J. Bot. 23:95–99.

Johansen, D. A., 1945. A critical survey of the present status of plant embryology. Bot. Rev. 11:87–107.

Johansen, D. A., 1950. Plant Embryology. Waltham, Mass.

John, A., 1907. Mitteilungen über die Embryoentwicklung von *Caltha palustris*. Lotos, Prag. :41–47.

Johnson, A. M., 1936. Polyembryony in *Eugenia hookeri*. Amer. J. Bot. 23:83–88.

Johnson, D. S., 1900a. On the development of *Saururus cernuus*. Bull. Torrey bot. Cl. 27:365–372.

Johnson, D. S., 1900b. On the endosperm and embryo of *Peperomia pellucida*. Bot. Gaz. 30:1–11.

Johnson, D. S., 1902a. On the development of certain Piperaceae (*Piper adunca, P. medium, Heckeria umbellata*. Bot. Gaz. 34:321–340.

Johnson, D. S., 1902b. The embryology and germination of the genus *Peperomia*. Science 15:408–409.

Johnson, D. S., 1902c. The development of the embryo sac in *Piper* and *Heckeria*. Johns Hopkins Univ. Circ. 21:85–86.

Johnson, D. S., 1905. Seed development in the Piperales and its bearing on the relationships of the order. Johns Hopkins Univ. Circ. 178:28–31.

Johnson, D. S., 1907. A new type of embryo sac in *Peperomia*. Johns Hopkins Univ. Circ. 195:19–21.

Johnson, D. S., 1910. Studies in the development of Piperaceae. 1. The suppression and extension of sporogenous tissue in the flower of *Piper betel* var. *monoicum*. J. exptl. Zool. 9:715–749.

Johnson, D. S., 1914. Studies of the development of Piperaceae. 2. The structure and seed development of *Peperomia hispidula*. Amer. J. Bot. 1:323–339, 357–397.

Johnson, D. S., 1918. The fruit of *Opuntia fulgida*. A study of perennation and proliferation in the fruits of certain Cactaceae. Carnegie Inst. Wash.

Johnson, D. S., 1935. The development of the shoot, male flower and seedling of *Batis maritima*. Bull. Torrey bot. Cl. 62:19–31.

Johnson, T., 1888. *Arceuthobium oxycedri*. Ann. Bot. 2:137–160.

Johnson, T., 1889. The nursing of the embryo and some other points in *Myzodendron punctatum*. Ann. Bot. 3:179–206.

Johnston, G. W., 1941. Cytological studies of male gamete formation in certain Angiosperms. Amer. J. Bot. 28:306–319.

Johnston, G. W., 1953. Observation on twin embryo sacs in *Sorghum vulgare*, Phytomorphology 3:313–315.

Johnston, G. W., 1959a. Further evidence of some so-called abnormalities in the development of the male gametophyte of angiosperms. Phytomorphology 9:130–133.

Johnston, G. W., 1959b. Abnormal pollen of *Tulipa*. Phytomorphology 9:320–325.

Johnston, G. W., 1961. Microsporogenesis in *Exochorda racemosa*. Phytomorphology 11:41–45.

Johow, F., 1885. Die chlorophyllfreien Humusbewohner Westindiens, biologisch-morphologisch dargestellt. Jahrb. f. wiss. Bot. 16:415–449.

Johow F., 1889. Die chlorophyllfreien Humuspflanzen nach ihre biologischen und anatomisch-entwicklungsgeschichtlichen Verhältnissen. Jahrb. f. wiss. Bot. 20:475–525.

Johri, B. M., 1933. Contribution to the morphology of *Limnophyton obtusifolium*. Current Sci. 2:12–13.

Johri, B. M., 1934a. A note on the life history of *Sagittaria guayanensis*. Current Sci. 2:428–429.

Johri, B. M., 1934b. A note on the embryo sac of *Sagittaria sagittifolia*. Current Sci. 3:17–18.

Johri, B. M., 1935a. Life history of *Butomopsis lanceolata*. Nature 136:338.

Johri, B. M., 1935b. Studies in the family Alismaceae. 1. *Limnophyton obtusifolium*. J. Indian bot. Soc. 14:49–66.

Johri, B. M., 1935c. Studies in the family Alismaceae. 2. *Sagittaria sagittifolia*. Proc. Indian Acad. Sci. B. 1:340–348.

Johri, B. M., 1935d. The gametophytes of *Berberis nepalensis*. Proc. Indian Acad. Sci. B. 1:640–649.

Johri, B. M., 1935e. Studies in the family Alismaceae. 3. *Sagittaria guayanensis* and *S. latifolia*. Proc. Indian Acad. Sci. B. 2:33–48.

Johri, B. M., 1936a. Studies in the family Alismaceae. 4. *Alisma plantago, A. plantago-aquatica* and *Sagittaria graminea*. Proc. Indian Acad. Sci. B. 4:128–138.

Johri, B. M., 1936b. The life history of *Butomopsis lanceolata*. Proc. Indian Acad. Sci. B. 4:139–162.

Johri, B. M., 1938a. The embryo sac of *Limnocharis emarginata*. New Phytol. 37:279–285.

Johri, B. M., 1938b. The embryo sac of *Hydrocleis nymphoides*. Beih. bot. Ztbl. 48A:165–172.

Johri, B. M., 1951. Endosperm and embryo development in *Cuscuta reflexa*. Current Sci. 20:189–191.

Johri, B. M., 1952. Endosperm and embryo development in *Acalypha indica*. Proc. 39th. Indian Sci. Congr.

Johri, B. M., 1954. The endosperm of *Tamarix*. Proc. 41st. Indian Sci. Congr. 3:139–140.

Johri, B. M., 1956. Polyploid pollen grains in *Helixanthera ligustrina*. Proc. 43rd. Indian Sci. Congr. 3:258.

Johri, B. M., 1961. Recent work on angiosperm embryology. Mem. Indian bot. Soc. 3:165–172.

Johri, B. M., 1962a. Nutrition of the embryo sac. *In* P. Maheshwari, et al. (ed.), Proceedings of the Summer School of Botany, Darjeeling. New Delhi:106–118.

Johri, B. M., 1962b. Female gametophyte of the Santalales. *In* Plant Embryology: A Symposium. CSIR. New Delhi: 192–198.

Johri, B. M., 1963a. Female gametophyte. *In* P. Maheshwari (ed.), Recent Advances in the Embryology of Angiosperms. Delhi: 70–103.

Johri, B. M., 1963b. Embryology and taxonomy. *In* Maheshwari, P. (ed.): Recent Advances in the Embryology of Angiosperms. Delhi: 396–444.

Johri, B. M. and J. S. Agrawal, 1954. Embryology of *Helicanthes elastica*. Current Sci. 23:96–98.

Johri, B. M., J. S. Agrawal, and S. Garg, 1957. Morphological and embryological studies in the family Loranthaceae. 1. *Helixanthes elastica*. Phytomorphology 7:336–354.

Johri, B. M. and M. R. Ahuja, 1956. Development of endosperm and nucellar polyembryony in *Aegle marmelos*. Current Sci. 25:162–164.

Johri, B. M. and M. R. Ahuja, 1957. A contribution to the floral morphology and embryology of *Aegle marmelos*. Phytomorphology 7:10–24.

Johri, B. M. and S. P. Bhatnagar, 1955. A contribution to the morphology and the life history of *Aristolochia*. Phytomorphology 5: 123–137.

Johri, B. M. and S. P. Bhatnagar, 1957. Intra-carpellary pollen grains in Angiosperms. Phytomorphology 7:292–296.

Johri, B. M. and S. P. Bhatnagar, 1960. Embryology and taxonomy of the Santalales. 1. Proc. Nat. Inst. Sci. India B. 26:199–220.

Johri, B. M. and C. R. Chowdhury, 1957. A contribution to the embryology of *Citrullus colocynthis* and *Melothria maderaspatana*. New Phytol. 56:51–60.

Johri, B. M. and A. M. Eunus, 1950. The intracarpellary pollen grains in *Trillium*. Proc. 37th. Indian Sci. Congr. 3:44.

Johri, B. M. and S. Garg, 1956. Some observations on the development of endosperm in the Leguminosae. Proc. 43rd. Indian Sci. Congr. 3:228.

Johri, B. M. and S. Garg, 1959. Development of endosperm haustoria in some Leguminosae. Phytomorphology 9:34–46.

Johri, B. M. and D. Kak, 1954. The embryology of *Tamarix*. Phytomorphology 4:230–247.

Johri, B. M. and R. N. Kapil, 1953. Contribution to the embryology and life history of *Acalypha indica*. Phytomorphology 3:137–151.

Johri, B. M. and R. N. Konar, 1955. A contribution to the morphology and embryology of *Ficus religiosa*. Current Sci. 24:382–385.

Johri, B. M. and R. N. Konar, 1956. The floral morphology and embryology of *Ficus religiosa*. Phytomorphology 6:97–111.

Johri, B. M. and P. Maheshwari, 1951. The embryo sac of *Floerkea proserpinacoides*. Current Sci. 20:44–46.

Johri, B. M. and S. Nand, 1934. Development of gametophytes in *Cuscuta reflexa*. Proc. Indian Acad. Sci. B. 1:283–289.

Johri, B. M. and S. Prakash, 1965. Morphological and embryological studies in the family Loranthaceae. 11. *Tapinostemma acaciae*. Phytomorphology 15:150–158.

Johri, B. M. and B. Raj, 1965. Embryo sac development in *Moquiniella*. Nature 205:415–416.

Johri, B. M. and H. Singh, 1956. A contribution to the embryology of *Elytraria acaulis*. Proc. 43rd. Indian Sci. Congr. 3:228–229.

Johri, B. M. and H. Singh, 1959. The morphology, embryology and systematic position of *Elytraria acaulis*. Bot. Notiser 1959: 227–251.

Johri, B. M. and B. Tiagi, 1952. Floral morphology and seed formation in *Cuscuta reflexa*. Phytomorphology 2:162–180.

Johri, B. M. and I. K. Vasil, 1956. The embryology of *Ehretia laevis*. Phytomorphology 6:134–143.

Johri, B. M. and I. K. Vasil, 1960. The pollen and pollen tube. Ergebn. Biol. 23:1–13.

Johri, M. M., 1962. Intracarpellary pollen grains in *Fritillaria* and *Lilium*. Current Sci. 31:255–256.

Jones, B. L. and C. C. Gordon, 1965. Embryology and development of the endosperm haustorium of *Arceuthobium douglasi*. Amer. J. Bot. 52:127–132.

Jones, H. A., 1927a. Pollination and life history studies of lettuce, *L. sativa*. Calif. Agric. Expt. Sta. 2.

Jones, H. A., 1927b. Pollination and life history studies of lettuce, *L. sativa*. 1. Hilgardia 2:425–442.

Jones, H. A., 1929. Pollination and life history studies in lettuce, *L. sativa*. 2. Proc. Internatl. Cong. Plt. Sci. Ithaca, N.Y. 2:1045–1049.

Jones, H. A. and S. L. Emsweller, 1936. The development of the flower and megagametophyte of *Allium cepa*. Hilgardia 10:415–428.

Jones, J. W., 1928. Polyembryony in rice. J. Amer. Soc. Agron. 20:774.

Jones, K., 1964. Pollen structure and development in *Drosera*. J. Linn. Soc. London (Bot.) 59:81–87.

Jönsson, B., 1879–80. Om embryosäckens utveckling hos Angiospermerna. Lunds Univ. Årsskr. 16:1–86.

Jönsson, B., 1881. Ytterligare bidrag till kännedomen om Angiospermernas embryosäckutveckling. Bot. Notiser 1881:169–187.

Jönsson, B., 1883. Polyembryoni hos *Trifolium pratense*. Bot. Notiser 1883:135–137. Bot. Ztbl. 16:171.

Jordaan, P. G., 1946. Die Saadknop en Embriologie van *Brabejum stellatifolium*. J. Sth. Afr. Bot. 12:15–26.

Jørgensen, C. A., 1923. Studies on Callitrichaceae. Bot. Tidsskr. 38:81–126.

Jørgensen, C. A., 1925. Zur Frage der systematischen Stellung der Callitrichaceen. Jahrb. f. wiss. Bot. 64:440–442.

Jos, J. S., 1963. The structure and development of seeds in Convolvulaceae: *Ipomoea* spp. Agra Univ. J. Res. (Sci.) 12:247–260.

Joshi, A. C., 1933. Megaspore formation and embryo sac of *Argemone mexicana*. J. Indian bot. Soc. 12:83–91.

Joshi, A. C., 1936a. A contribution to the embryology and cytology of *Rivina humilis*. J. Indian bot. Soc. 15:91–103.

Joshi, A. C., 1936b. A note on the antipodals of *Digera arvensis*. Current Sci. 4:741–742.

Joshi A. C., 1937a. A study of pollen in the Thymelaeaceae. Proc. 24th. Indian Sci. Congr.

BIBLIOGRAPHY 369

Joshi, A. C., 1937b. Contributions to the embryology of the Menispermaceae. 1. *Cocculus villosus.* Proc. Indian Acad. Sci. B. 5:57–63.

Joshi, A. C., 1937c. Megasporogenesis in *Aloe vera.* J. Indian bot. Soc. 15:297–300.

Joshi, A. C., 1938a. A note on the morphology of the ovule of Rubiaceae, with special reference to *Cinchona* and coffee. Current Sci. 7:236–237.

Johsi, A. C., 1938b. Systematic distribution of the Fritillaria-type of embryo sac and the mono- or polyphyletic origin of Angiosperms. Chron. Bot. 4:507–508.

Joshi, A. C., 1938c. A note on the morphology of the gynaecium, ovule and embryo sac of *Psoralea corylifolia.* J. Indian bot. Soc. 17:169–172.

Joshi, A. C., 1939a. Embryological evidence for the relationships of the Lythraceae and related family. Current Sci. 8:112–113.

Joshi, A. C., 1939b. Structure and development of the embryo sac of *Iphigenia indica.* Proc. Nat. Inst. Sci. India 5:289–305.

Joshi, A. C., 1939c. Morphology of *Tinospora cordifolia,* with some observations on the origin of the single integument, nature of synergidae and affinities of the Menispermaceae. Amer. J. Bot. 26:433–439.

Joshi, A. C., 1940. Development of the embryo sac of *Gagea fascicularis.* Bull. Torrey bot. Cl. 67:155–158.

Joshi, A. C., 1943. The anatomy of the male flower of *Myristica fragrans* with special reference to the origin of the trimerous perianth. J. Indian bot. Soc. (Iyengar Commem. Vol.):91–95.

Joshi, A. C., 1944. Structure and development of the ovule and embryo sac of *Piper longum.* Proc. Nat. Inst. Sci. India 10:105–112.

Joshi, A. C., 1946. A note on the development of pollen of *Myristica fragrans,* and the affinities of the family Myristicaceae. J. Indian bot. Soc. 25:139–143.

Joshi, A. C. and L. B. Kajale, 1936. A note on the structure and development of the embryo sac, ovule and fruit of *Tamarix dioica.* Ann. Bot. 50:421–426.

Joshi, A. C. and L. B. Kajale, 1937. Fertilization and seed development in the Amarantaceae. Proc. Indian Acad. Sci. B. 5:91–100.

Joshi, A. C. and J. V. Pantulu, 1941. A morphological and cytological study of *Polianthes tuberosa.* J. Indian bot. Soc. 20:37–71.

Joshi, A. C. and B. V. R. Rao, 1934. Fruit and seed development in *Tinospora cordifolia* without fertilization and embryo formation inside. Current Sci. 3:62–63.

Joshi, A. C. and B. V. R. Rao, 1935. A study of microsporogenesis in two Menispermaceae. Cellule 44:219–234.

Joshi, A. C. and C. Venkata Rao, 1934. A contribution to the anatomy, morphology and cytology of the flower of *Digera arvensis.* J. Indian bot. Soc. 13:201–236.

Joshi, A. C. and V. R. Rao, 1936. The embryology of *Gisekia pharnaceoides.* Proc. Indian Acad. Sci. B. 3:71–92.

Joshi, A. C. and J. Venkateswarlu, 1933. Exceptional behaviour of the synergids in the embryo sac of Angiosperms. Nature 132:409.

Joshi, A. C. and J. Venkateswarlu, 1935a. Embryological studies in the Lythraceae. 1. *Lawsonia inermis.* Proc. Indian Acad. Sci. B. 2:481–493.

Joshi, A. C. and J. Venkateswarlu, 1935b. Embryological studies in the Lythraceae. 2. *Lagerstroemia.* Proc. Indian Acad. Sci. B. 2:523–534.

Joshi, A. C. and J. Venkateswarlu, 1935c. Structure and development of the synergids in *Ammannia baccifera.* New Phytol. 34:144–150.

Joshi, A. C. and J. Venkateswarlu, 1935d. A case of reversed polarity in the embryo sac. Ann. Bot. 49:841–843.

Joshi, A. C. and J. Venkateswarlu, 1936a. Structure and development of the synergids in *Ammannia baccifera:* a correction. New Phytol. 35:92.

Joshi, A. C. and J. Venkateswarlu, 1936b. Embryological studies in the Lythraceae. 3. Proc. Indian Acad. Sci. B. 3:377–400.

Joshi, M. C. and T. M. Varghese, 1962. Presence of twin embryos and twin ovules in *Anticharis linearis*. Sci. and Cult. 28:489.

Joshi, M. C. and T. M. Varghese, 1963. A contribution to the life history of *Anticharis linearis*. Proc. Indian Acad. Sci. B. 57:164–177.

Joshi, P. C., 1936a. Contribution to the life history of *Stellaria media*. Proc. Indian Acad. Sci. B. 3:8–22.

Joshi, P. C., 1936b. Some phases of the life history of two Tibetan Caryophyllaceae: *Arenaria musciormis* and *Thylacospermum rupifragum*. Proc. Indian Acad. Sci. B. 4:471–482.

Joshi, P. C., 1960. Morphological and embryological studies in the family Santalaceae. 5. *Osyris wightiana*. Phytomorphology 10:239–248.

Jost, L., 1888. Zur Kenntnis der Blütenentwicklung der Mistel. Bot. Zeit.

Jost, L., 1907. Über die Selbsterilität einiger Blüten. Bot. Zeit. 65:77–116.

Juel, H. O., 1887. Beiträge zur Anatomie der Marcgraviaceen. Kgl. Svensk. Vet.-Akad. Handl. 12:1–28.

Juel, H. O., 1897. Die Kerntheilungen in den Pollenmutterzellen von *Hemerocallis fulva* und die bei denselben auftretenden Unregelmässigkeiten. Jahrb. f. wiss. Bot. 30:205–226.

Juel, H. O., 1898. Parthenogenesis bei *Antennaria alpina*. Beih. bot. Ztbl. 74:369–372.

Juel, H. O., 1900a. Vergleichende Untersuchungen über typische und parthenogenetische Fortpflanzung bei der Gattung *Antennaria*. Kgl. Svensk. Vet.-Akad. Handl. 33:1–59.

Juel, H. O., 1900b. Beiträge zur Kenntnis der Tetradenbildung. Jahrb. f. wiss. Bot. 35:626–659.

Juel, H. O., 1902. Zur Entwicklungsgeschichte des Samens von *Cynomorium*. Beih. bot. Ztbl. 13:194–202.

Juel, H. O., 1903. Ein Beitrag zur Entwicklungsgeschichte der Samenanlage von *Casuarina*. Flora 92:284–293.

Juel, H. O., 1904. Die Tetradenteilung in der Samenanlagen von *Taraxacum*. Arkiv. f. Bot. 2:1–9.

Juel, H. O., 1906. Die Tetradenteilung bei *Taraxacum* und anderen Cichoraceen. Kgl. Svensk. Vet.-Akad. Handl. 39:1–21.

Juel, H. O., 1907. Studien über die Entwicklungsgeschichte von *Saxifraga granulata*. Nova Acta Reg. Soc. Sci. Upsal. (4) 1:1–41.

Juel, H. O., 1910. *Cynomorium* und *Hippuris*. Svensk bot. Tidskr. 4:151–159.

Juel, H. O., 1911. Studien über die Entwicklungsgeschichte von *Hippuris vulgaris*. Nov. Acta Reg. Soc. Sci. Upsal. (4) 2:1–26.

Juel, H. O., 1915. Untersuchungen über die Auflösung der Tapetenzellen in den Pollensäcken der Angiospermen. Jahrb. f. wiss. Bot. 56:337–364.

Juel, H. O., 1918. Beiträge zur Blütenanatomie und zur Systematik der Rosaceen. Kgl. Svensk. Vet.-Akad. Handl. 56:1–80.

Juel, H. O., 1927. Über die Blütenanatomie einiger Rosaceen. Nov. Acta Reg. Soc. Sci. Upsal. (Suppl.): 1–31.

Juel, H. O., 1929. Beiträge zur Morphologie und Entwicklungsgeschichte der Rhamnaceen. Kgl. Svensk. Vet.-Akad. Handl. 7:1–13.

Julén, U., 1950. Fertility conditions of tetraploid red clover. 1. Seed setting of tetraploid red clover in the presence of haploid pollen. Hereditas 36.

Juliano, J. B., 1931a. Floral morphology of Lyonothamnus floribundus. Bot. Gaz. 91:426–438.

Juliano, J. B., 1931b. Morphological study of the flower of Monochoria vaginalis. Philippine Agriculturalist 20:177–186.

Juliano, J. B., 1932. The cause of sterility in Spondias purpurea. Philippine Agriculturalist 21:15–24.

Juliano, J. B., 1934a. Studies on the morphology of Meliaceae. 1. Sandoricum koetjape. Philipp. J. Agr. 23:11–48.

Juliano, J. B., 1934b. Studies on the morphology of the Meliaceae. 2. Sterility in Santol, Sandoricum koetjape. Philipp. J. Agr. 23:49.

Juliano, J. B., 1934c. Origin of embryos in the strawberry mango. Philipp. J. Sci. 54:553–561.

Juliano, J. B., 1935a. Morphology of the sweet potato, Ipomoea batatus. Philipp. Agriculturalist 23:833–858.

Juliano, J. B., 1935b. Morphological contribution on the genus Anona. Philipp. Agriculturalist 23.

Juliano, J. B., 1935c. Anatomy and morphology of the Bunga, Aeginetia indica. Philipp. J. Sci. 56:405–451.

Juliano, J. B., 1937. Embryos of carabao mango, Mangifera indica. Philipp. Agriculturalist 25:749–760.

Juliano, J. B. and P. E. Alcala, 1933. Floral morphology of Musa errans var. botoan. Philipp. Agriculturalist 22:91–126.

Juliano, J. B. and M. J. Aldama, 1937. Morphology of Oryza sativa. Philipp. Agriculturalist 26:1–134.

Juliano, J. B. and N. L. Cuevas, 1932. Floral morphology of the mango (Mangifera indica) with special reference to the Pico variety from the Philippines. Philipp. Agriculturalist 26:449–472.

Juliano, J. B. and E. Quisumbing, 1931. Morphology of the male flower of Cocos nucifera. Philipp. J. Sci. 45:449–458.

Junell, S., 1930. Die Entwicklungsgeschichte von Circaeaster agrestis. Svensk. bot. Tidskr. 25:238–270.

Junell, S., 1934. Zur Gynaceummorphologie und Systematik der Verbenaceen und Labiaten nebst Bemerkungen über ihre Samenentwicklung. Symb. Bot. Upsala 4:1–219. Diss. Upsala.

Junell, S., 1937. Die Samenentwicklung bei einigen Labiaten. Svensk. bot. Tidskr. 31:67–110.

Junell, S., 1938. Über den Fruchtknotenbau der Borraginazeen mit pseudomonomeren Gynäzeen. Svensk bot. Tidskr. 32:261–273.

Junell, S., 1962. Embryology of Hebenstreitia, Dischisma, Sutera and Zaluzianskya. Acta Hort. Göteb. 25:91–101.

Jungers, V., 1931. Figures caryocinétiques et cloisonnement du protoplasme dans l'endosperme d'Iris. Cellule 40:293–354.

Jurica, H. S., 1922. A morphological study of the Umbelliferae. Bot. Gaz. 74:292–307.

Jüssen, F. J., 1928. Die Haploidgeneration der Araceen und ihre Verwertung für das System. In Engler's Bot. Jahrb. 62:155–283. Diss. Berlin.

Just, T., 1946. The use of embryological formulas in plant taxonomy. Bull. Torrey bot. Cl. 73:351–355.

Kabets'ka, H. O., 1964. (Development of the male gametophyte in the Persian walnut, *Juglans regia*). Zhur. Inst. bot. Acad. Sci. RSS Ukraine 21:52–57.

Kadry, A. E. R., 1946. Embryology of *Cardiospermum halicacabum*. Svensk bot. Tidskr. 40:111–126.

Kadry, A. E. R., 1950. Fruit development in *Cardiospermum halicacabum*, with special reference to the lacunae spaces. Svensk bot. Tidskr. 44:441–445.

Kadry, A. E. R., 1952. The development of microsporangium and pollen grains in *Cistanche tinctoria*. Bot. Notiser 1952: 46–47.

Kadry, A. E. R., 1953. The development of the female gametophyte in *Cistanche tinctoria*. Svensk bot. Tidsk. 47:488–508.

Kadry, A. E. R., 1955. The development of endosperm and embryo in *Cistanche tinctoria*. Bot. Notiser 1955: 231–243.

Kadry, A. E. R., 1960. The seed of *Cardiospermum halicacabum*: A criticism. Acta Bot. Néerl. 9:330–332.

Kaeiser, M. and S. G. Boyce, 1962. Embryology of *Liriodendron tulipifera*. Phytomorphology 12:103–109.

Kainradl, E., 1927. Beiträge zur Biologie von *Hydrolea spinosa*, mit besonderer Berücksichtigung von Fruchtwand und Samenentwicklung. S. B. Acad. wiss. Wien. 1. 136:167–194.

Kajale, L. B., 1935. The female gametophyte of *Alternanthera sessilis*. Proc. Indian Acad. Sci. B. 2:476–480.

Kajale, L. B., 1936. Embryo development in *Boerhaavia diffusa*. Current Sci. 4:743.

Kajale, L. B., 1937a. A case of polyembryony in the Nyctaginaceae. Current Sci. 5:429.

Kajale, L. B., 1937b. The antipodals of *Pupalia lappacea*. Current Sci. 6:222.

Kajale, L. B., 1937c. Embryology of *Achyranthes aspera*. Proc. Indian Acad. Sci. B. 5:195–205.

Kajale, L. B., 1938. Embryo and seed development in the Nyctaginaceae. 1. Studies in the genus *Boerhaavia*. J. Indian bot. Soc. 17:243–254.

Kajale, L. B., 1939. A contribution to the life history of *Bergia ammanioides*. J. Indian bot. Soc. 18:157–167.

Kajale, L. B., 1940a. A contribution to the embryology of the Amarantaceae. Proc. Nat. Inst. Sci. India 6:597–625.

Kajale, L. B., 1940b. Structure and development of male and female gametophytes of *Sesuvium portulacastrum*. Proc. Nat. Acad. Sci. India 10:82–89.

Kajale, L. B., 1942. A contribution to the embryology of the genus *Portulaca*. J. Indian bot. Soc. 21:1–19.

Kajale, L. B., 1944a. Development of the embryo sac of *Zizyphus jujuba*. Current Sci. 13:49.

Kajale, L. B., 1944b. A contribution to the life history of *Zizyphus jujuba*. Proc. Nat. Inst. Sci. India 10:387–391.

Kajale, L. B., 1944c. A contribution to the embryology of the Phytolaccaceae. 1. Studies in the genus *Phytolacca*. Patna Univ. J. 1:10–21.

Kajale, L. B., 1954a. A contribution to the embryology of the Phytolaccaceae. 2. Fertilization and the development of embryo, seed and fruit in *Rivina humilis* and *Phytolacca dioica*. J. Indian bot. Soc. 33:206–225.

Kajale, L. B., 1954b. Fertilization and the development of embryo and seed in *Euphorbia hirta.* Proc. Nat. Inst. Sci. India 20:353–360.

Kajale, L. B. and K. S. N. Murthy, 1954. The embryo sac of *Acalypha ciliata.* J. Indian bot. Soc. 33:417–422.

Kajale, L. B. and S. G. Ranade, 1952. Occurrence of four kinds of megaspore tetrads in *Elaeis guineensis.* Current Sci. 21:170.

Kajale, L. B. and S. G. Ranade, 1953. The embryo sac of *Elaeis guinensis.* J. Indian bot. Soc. 32:101–107.

Kajale, L. B. and G. V. Rao, 1943. Pollen and embryo sac of two Euphorbiaceae. J. Indian bot. Soc. 22:229–236.

Kalinina, L. V., 1959. (Development of the embryo in corn grains). Kukuruza 6:23–24.

Kamensky, K. W., 1928. Anatomische Strucktur der Samen von einigen *Cuscuta-*Arten und deren systematischer Wert. Angewante Bot. 10:387–406.

Kamerling, Z., 1930. La fécondation par traumatisme, c'est-à-dire après ablation du stigmate, pratiquée par Lucien Reychler. Bruxelles.

Kamiénsky, F., 1877. Vergleichende Untersuchungen über die Entwicklungsgeschichte der Utricularien. Bot. Zeit. 35:761–776.

Kamra, O. P., 1960. Occurrence of binucleate and multinucleate pollen mother cells in *Hordeum.* Hereditas 46:536–542.

Kanda, M., 1920. Field and laboratory studies in *Verbena.* Bot. Gaz. 69:54–71.

Kandelaki, G. V., 1961. (Studies of embryogenesis in Georgian wheat hybrids). *In* (Plant Morphogenesis). Moscow 2:362–365.

Kanta, K., 1961. Embryolessness in *Piper nigrum.* Phytomorphology 11:304–306.

Kanta, K., 1962. Morphology and embryology of *Piper nigrum.* Phytomorphology 12:207–221.

Kanta, K., N. S. Rangaswamy, and P. Maheshwari, 1962. Test tube fertilization in a flowering plant. Nature 194:1214–1217.

Kantor, T. S., 1957. (The embryology of cultivated flax). Byul. Gl. Bot. Sada Akad. Nauk SSSR 29:48–60.

Kapil, R. N., 1955. A contribution to the embryology of *Euphorbia esula* and *Chrozophora obliqua.* Proc. 42nd. Indian Sci. Congr. 3:234–235.

Kapil, R. N., 1956a. Development of embryo sac and endosperm in *Chrozophora rottleri:* a reinvestigation. Bot. Gaz. 117:242–247.

Kapil, R. N., 1956b. A further contribution to the morphology and life history of *Chrozophora.* Phytomorphology 6:278–288.

Kapil, R. N., 1960. Embryology of *Acalypha.* Phtomorphology 10:174–184.

Kapil, R. N., 1961. Some embryological aspects of *Euphorbia dulcis.* Phytomorphology 11:24–36.

Kapil, R. N. and K. Ahluwalia, 1963. Embryology of *Peganum harmala.* Phytomorphology 13:127–140.

Kapil, R. N. and S. Jalan, 1962. Studies in the family Ranunculaceae. 1. The embryology of *Caltha palustris. In* Plant Embryology: A Symposium. CSIR. New Delhi: 205–214.

Kapil, R. N. and S. Jalan, 1964. *Schisandra:* its embryology and systematic position. Bot. Notiser 1964: 285–306.

Kapil, R. N. and R. Maheshwari, 1964. Embryology of *Helianthemum vulgare.* Phytomorphology 14:547–557.

Kapil, R. N. and P. Masand, 1964. Embryology of *Hebenstreitia integrifolia.* Proc. Natl. Inst. Sci. India 30:99–113.

Kapil, R. N. and S. B. Sethi, 1962a. Gametogenesis and seed development in *Ainsliaea aptera*. Phytomorphology 12:222–234.

Kapil, R. N. and S. B. Sethi, 1962b. Development of seed in *Tridax trilobata*. Phytomorphology 12:235–239.

Kapil, R. N. and S. B. Sethi, 1963. Development of male and female gametophytes in *Camellia sinensis*. Proc. Nat. Inst. Sci. India B. 29:567–574.

Kapil, R. N. and I. K. Vasil, 1963. Ovule. *In* Maheshwari, P. (ed.). Recent Advances in the Embryology of Angiosperms. Delhi: 41–67.

Kapil, R. N. and M. R. Vijayaraghavan, 1962. Embryology and systematic position of *Pentaphragma horsfieldii*. Current Sci. 31:270–272.

Kapil, R. N. and M. R. Vijayaraghavan, 1965. Embryology of *Pentaphragma horsfieldii*, with a discussion on the systematic position of the genus. Phytomorphology 15:93–102.

Kapinos, G. E., 1960. (Flowering, pollination and embryology in *Sternbergia lutea* and *S. fischeriana*). Bot. Zhur. 45:1044–1055.

Kapinos, G. E., 1964. (Biology of blooming and embryology of the large flowered Sternbergias). *In* (Problems of Recent Embryology). Moskov. Univ.: 137–143.

Kapoor, B. M. and S. L. Tandon, 1963a. Contribution to the cytology of endosperm in some Angiosperms. 3. *Amaryllis belladonna*. Cytologia 28:399–408.

Kapoor, B. M. and S. L. Tandon, 1963b. Contributions to the cytology of endosperm in some Angiosperms. 4. *Zephyranthes grandiflora*. Genetica 34:102–112.

Kapoor, B. M. and S. L. Tandon, 1964. Contributions to the cytology of the endosperm in some Angiosperms. 5. *Zephyranthes lancasteri*. Phyton 21:37–43.

Kappert, H., 1933. Erbliche Polyembryonie bei *Linum usitatissimum*. Biol. Ztbl. 53:276–307.

Kapuskar, A. T., 1959. Studies in the embryology of the Leguminosae. 1. *Aeschynomene aspera*. J. biol. Sci. 2:120–121.

Kapuskar, A. T., 1964. Studies in the embryology of the Leguminosae. 2. Embryo development in *Aeschynomene aspera*. Proc. Indian Acad. Sci. B. 60:87–94.

Karag'ozova, M., 1963. (Embryological studies on *Iris pseudacorus*). Bulgar. Akad. Nauk. bot. Inst. Izv. 11:111–123.

Karsmark, K. A., 1933. Om gyneciemorfologien och embryologien hos *Polygala comosa*. Farmacev. Rev. 12:12.

Karsten, G., 1891. Über die Mangrove-Vegetation im malayischen Archipel. Eine morphologische-biologische Studie. Bibl. bot. Stuttgart 22:11–18, 31–41.

Karsten, G., 1902. Über die Entwicklung der weiblichen Blüthen bei einigen Juglandaceen. Flora 90:316–333.

Kasapligil, B., 1951. Morphological and ontogenetic studies of *Umbellaria californica* and *Laurus nobilis*. Univ. Calif. Publ. Bot. 25:115–240.

Kashyap, G., 1955. Studies in the family Vitaceae. 1. Floral morphology of *Vitis trifolia*. Agra Univ. J. Res. (Sci.) 4 (Suppl.): 777–783.

Kashyap, G., 1958. Studies in the family Vitaceae. 3. Floral morphology of *Vitis latifolia*, *V. himalayana* and *V. trifolia*. J. Indian bot. Soc. 37:240–248.

Kastikova, L. N., 1955. (Embryological researches on *Vicia faba*). Bjul. Moskov Obsc. Ispyt. Prir. Biol. B. 60:101–106.

Katz, E., 1926. Über die Funktion der Narbe bei der Keimung des Pollens. Flora 120:243–273.

Katz, E., 1943. Pollen tube development in *Taraxacum officinale*. Bot. Gaz. 104:650.

Kauffmann, N., 1869. Über die männlichen Blüthen von *Casuarina quadrivalvis*. Bjul. Moskov Obsc. Ispyt. Prir. 41:374–382.

Kausik, S. B., 1935a. The life history of *Utricularia coerulea*. Current Sci. 3:357–359.

Kausik, S. B., 1935b. The life history of *Lobelia trigona*, with special reference to the nutrition of the embryo sac. Proc. Indian Acad. Sci. B. 2:410–418.

Kausik, S. B., 1938a. The endosperm in *Grevillea robusta*. Current Sci. 6:332–333.

Kausik, S. B., 1938b. Studies in the Proteaceae. 1. Cytology and floral morphology of *Grevillea robusta*. Ann. Bot. 2:899–910.

Kausik, S. B., 1938c. Pollen development and seed formation in *Utricularia coerulea*. Beih. bot. Ztbl. 58A: 365–378.

Kausik, S. B., 1938d. Gametogenesis and embryogeny in *Lobelia nicotianaefolia*. J. Indian bot. Soc. 17:161–168.

Kausik, S. B., 1938e. Studies in the Proteaceae. 2. Floral anatomy and morphology of *Macadamia ternifolia*. Proc. Indian Acad. Sci. B. 8:45–62.

Kausik, S. B., 1939a. Studies in the Proteaceae. 3. Embryology of *Grevillea banksii*. Ann. Bot. 3:815–824.

Kausik, S. B., 1939b. Pollination and its influence on the behaviour of the pistillate flower in *Vallisneria spiralis*. Amer. J. Bot. 26:207–211.

Kausik, S. B., 1939c. A cytological study of *Scaevola lobelia*. Proc. Indian Acad. Sci. B. 9:39–48.

Kausik, S. B., 1940a. Studies in the Proteaceae. 4. Structure and development of the ovule of *Hakea saligna*. Ann. Bot. 4:73–80.

Kausik, S. B., 1940b. A contribution to the embryology of *Enalus acoroides*. Proc. Indian Acad. Sci. B. 11:83–99.

Kausik, S. B., 1940c. Structure and development of the ovule and embryo sac of *Lasiosiphon eriocephalus*. Proc. Nat. Inst. Sci. India 6:117–132.

Kausik, S. B., 1941a. Structure and development of the staminate flower and male gametophyte of *Enalus acoroides*. Proc. Indian Acad. Sci. B. 14:1–16.

Kausik, S. B., 1941b. Development of the vermiform appendage in *Grevillea robusta*. Proc. Indian Acad. Sci. B. 14:137–140.

Kausik, S. B., 1942. Studies in the Proteaceae. 7. The endosperm of *Grevillea robusta*, with special reference to the structure and development of the vermiform appendage. Proc. Indian Acad. Sci. B. 16:121–140.

Kausik, S. B. and M. V. S. Raju, 1955. A contribution to the floral morphology and embryology of *Utricularia reticulata*. Proc. Indian Acad. Sci. B. 41:155–166.

Kausik, S. B. and M. V. S. Raju, 1956. Variations in the development of the proembryo in *Utricularia coerulea*. Current Sci. 25:296–297.

Kausik, S. B. and P. V. K. Rao, 1942. The male gametophyte of *Halophila ovata*. J. Mysore Univ. B. 3:43–49.

Kausik, S. B. and K. Subramanyam, 1945a. A contribution to the embryology of *Lobelia trialata*. J. Indian bot. Soc. 24:175–181.

Kausik, S. B. and K. Subramanyam, 1945b. An embryological study of *Isotoma longiflora*. Proc. Indian Acad. Sci. B. 21:269–278.

Kausik, S. B. and K. Subramanyam, 1946a. Development of endosperm in *Lobelia nicotianaefolia*. Current Sci. 15:78–79.

Kausik, S. B. and K. Subramanyam, 1946b. A case of polyembryony in *Isotoma longiflora*. Current Sci. 15:257–258.

Kausik, S. B. and K. Subramanyam, 1946c. A contribution to the embryology of *Sphenoclea zeylanica*. Proc. Indian Acad. Sci. B. 23:274–280.

Kausik, S. B. and K. Subramanyam, 1947a. Embryology of *Cephalostigma schimperi*. Bot. Gaz. 109:85–90.

Kausik, S. B. and K. Subramanyam, 1947b. Embryogeny of *Isotoma longiflora*. Proc. Indian Acad. Sci. B. 26:164–167.

Kavaljian, L. G., 1952. The floral morphology of *Clethra alnifolia*, with some notes on *C. acuminata* and *C. arborea*. Bot. Gaz. 113:392–413.

Kayser, G., 1892. Beiträge zur Entwicklungsgeschichte der Samendecken bei den Euphorbiaceen mit besonderer Berücksichtigung von *Ricinus communis*. Ber. Pharmac. Ges. 2:5–19.

Kayser, G., 1893a. Untersuchungen über das eigenartige Verhalten des Nucellus der Samenanlagen von *Croton flaveus* var. *balsamifer*. Ber. dtsch. bot. Ges. 11:61.

Kayser, G., 1893b. Beiträge zur Kenntnis der Entwicklungsgeschichte der Samen mit besonderer Berücksichtigung des histogenetischen Aufbaues der Samenschalen. Jahrb. f. wiss. Bot. 25:79–148.

Kelkar, S. S., 1958a. A contribution to the embryology of *Lannea coromandelica*. J. Univ. Bombay 26:152–159.

Kelkar, S. S., 1958b. Embryology of *Rhus mysurensis*. J. Indian bot. Soc. 37:114–122.

Kelkar, S. S., 1960. The female gametophyte of *Euphorbia tirucalla*. Sci. and Cult. 25:633–635.

Kelkar, S. S., 1961. The development of endosperm and embryo in *Lannea coromandelica*. J. Univ. Bombay B. 29:1–5.

Kellermann, W. A., 1881. Die Entwicklungsgeschichte von *Gunnera chilensis*. Diss. Zürich.

Kempanna, C. and K. S. K. Sastry, 1958. Male sterility in *Crotalaria striata*. Current Sci. 27:181.

Keng, H., 1962. Comparative morphological studies in Theaceae. Univ. Calif. publ. Bot. 33:269–384.

Kennard, W. C., 1955. Development of the fruit, seed and embryo of the Paheri Mango. Bot. Gaz. 117:28–32.

Kennedy, P. B., 1900. The structure of the caryopsis of the grasses with reference to their morphology and classification. U.S. Dept. Agr. Agros. Bull. 19:1–44.

Kenoyer, L., 1919. Dimorphic carpellate flowers of *Acalypha indica*. J. Indian bot. Soc. 1:1–5.

Kenyan, F. M. G., 1928. A morphological and cytological study of *Ipomoea trifida*. Bull. Torrey bot. Cl. 55:499–512.

Kerner, A., 1876. Parthenogenesis bei einiger angiospermen Pflanze. S. B. Akad. wiss. Wien. (1) 74:469.

Kerner, A., 1891. Pflanzenleben. 2. Leipzig.

Kerr, E. A., 1954. Seed development in blackberries. Canad. J. Bot. 32:654–672.

Kershaw, E. M., 1900a. The structure and development of the ovule of *Myrica gale*. Ann. Bot. 23:353–362.

Kershaw, E. M., 1900b. Further observations on the structure of the ovule of Myricaceae and allied groups. Ann. Bot. 23:692.

Khan, A. R., 1939. Pollination and fruit formation in Litchi, *Nephelium litchi*. Agric. J. India 1939: 183–187.

Khan, R., 1942. A contribution to the embryology of *Jussieua repens*. J. Indian bot. Soc. 21:267–282.

Khan, R., 1943. The ovule and embryo sac of *Fouquieria*. Proc. Nat. Inst. Sci. India 9:253–256.

Khan, R., 1950. A case of twin ovules in *Isomeris arborea*. Current Sci. 19:326.

Khan, R., 1953. Haustorial behavior of the chalazal end of the embryo sac and reversion of polarity in *Utricularia flexuosa*. Current Sci. 22:179–180.

Khan, R., 1954. A contribution to the embryology of *Utricularia flexuosa*. Phyto-morphology 4:80–117.

Khanna, P., 1956. A contribution to the embryology of *Cyperus rotundus*. Proc. 43rd. Indian Sci. Congr. 3:236–237.

Khanna, P., 1963. Male gametophyte and obturator in *Cyperus rotundus* and *C. triceps*. Current Sci. 32:133–134.

Khanna, P., 1964a. Morphological and embryological studies in Nymphaceae. 1. *Euryale ferox*. Proc. Indian Acad. Sci. B. 59:237–243.

Khanna, P., 1964b. Embryology of *Trichodesma amplexicaule*. Bull. Torrey bot. Cl. 91:105–114.

Khosla, S., 1946. Developmental morphology in some Indian millets. Proc. Indian Acad. Sci. B. 24:207–224.

Khudyak, M. I., 1962. (Morphological-physiological characteristics of the endosperm of Angiosperms during its development). Ukrain bot. Zhur. 19:31–41.

Khushalani, I., 1963a. Floral morphology and embryology of *Melianthus major*. Phyton 10:145–156.

Khushalani, I., 1963b. Floral morphology and embryology of *Acer oblongum*. Phyton 10:275–284.

Kiellander, C. L., 1935. Apomixis bei *Poa serotina*. Bot. Notiser 1935: 87–95.

Kiellander, C. L., 1937. On the embryological basis of apomixis in *Poa palustris*. Svensk bot. Tidskr. 31:425–429.

Kiellander, C. L., 1941. Studies on apospory in *Poa pratensis*. Svensk bot. Tidskr. 35:321–332.

Kiesselbach, T. A., 1926. False polyembryony in maize. Amer. J. Bot. 13:33–34.

Kiesselbach, T. A., 1926. Fasciated kernels, reversed kernels and related abnormalities in maize. Amer. J. Bot. 13:35–39.

Kiesselbach, T. A., 1949. The structure and reproduction of corn. Univ. Nebraska Coll. Agric. Res. Bull. 161:1–96.

Kihara, H. and T. Ono, 1923. (Cytological studies on *Rumex*). Bot. Mag. Tokyo 37:35–36.

Kimura, C., 1952. On the embryo sac of *Populus italica*. Sci. Rpts. Tôhoku Univ. (4) Biol. 16:354–356.

Kimura, C., 1955a. The embryo sac of *Populus sieboldii*. Sci. Rpts. Tôhoku Univ. (4) Biol. 21:122–125.

Kimura, C., 1955b. On the embryo sac of three Japanese species of *Salix*. Sci. Rpts. Tôhoku Univ. (4) Biol. 21:126–130.

Kimura, C., 1963. On the embryo sac formation of some members of the Salicaceae. Sci. Rpts. Tôhoku Univ. (4) Biol. 29:393–398.

Kindler, T., 1914. Gametophyte und Fruchtansatz bei *Ficaria ranunculoides*. Österr. bot. Zeit. 64:73–85.

King, J. R., 1938. Morphological development of the fruit of the olive. Hilgardia 11:437–458.

King, J. R., 1947. Development of ovule and megagametophyte in Pomegranate. Bot. Gaz. 108:394–398.

Kirchner, O., 1904. Parthenogenesis bei Blütenpflanzen. Ber. dtsch. bot. Ges. 22:83–97.

Kirkwood, J. C., 1926. The pollen development in *Lathyrus odoratus*. Ann. Bot. 40:277–313.

Kirkwood, J. E., 1904. The comparative embryology of the Cucurbitaceae. Bull. N.Y. Bot. Gard. 3:313–402.

Kirkwood, J. E., 1907a. The pollen tube in some of the Cucurbitaceae. Bull. Torrey bot. Cl. 33:327–342.

Kirkwood, J. E., 1907b. Some features of pollen formation in the Cucurbitaceae. Bull. Torrey bot. Cl. 34:221–242.

Kirkwood, J. E., 1910. The life history of *Parthenium* (guayule). Amer. Rev. Trop. Agr. 1:193–205.

Kistner, G., 1955. Über plastidenbedingtes Absterben während der Embryoentwicklung einiger Oenotherenbastarde. Z. indukt. Abst. U. Vererbgsl. 86: 521–544.

Klebelsberg, R., 1910. Über die Samenanlage von *Quercus robur* und intraseminale Gefässe. Österr. bot. Zeit. 60:329–335, 378–393.

Klebs, G., 1884. Beiträge zur Morphologie und Biologie der Keimung. Unters. Bot. Inst. Tübingen 1:536–635.

Klercker, J. E. F. de, 1885. Sur l'anatomie et le développement de *Ceratophyllum*. Kgl. Svensk Vet.-Akad. Handl. 9 (10).

Klyuchareva, M. V., 1962. (The participation of many pollen tubes in fertilization.) Trud. Inst. Genet. Akad. Nauk SSSR 29:238–264.

Knapp, D., 1959. Palm culture with special reference to fertilization. Principes J. Palm Soc. 3:13–18.

Knuth, P., 1898. Handbuch der Blütenbiologie. Leipzig.

Kny, L., 1878. Das Scheitelwashsthum von *Hippuris vulgaris* und *Elodea canadensis*. Bot. Zeit. 36:760–762.

Koch, L., 1877a. Zur Entwicklungsgeschichte der Cuscuteen. Verh. Nat. Med. Ver. Heidelberg 1:55–57.

Koch, L., 1877b. Über die Entwicklung des Samens der Orobanchen. Verh. Nat. Med. Ver. Heidelberg 1:199–203.

Koch, L., 1877c. Untersuchungen über die Entwicklung der Crassulaceen. Verh. Nat. Med. Ver. Heidelberg 1:421–422.

Koch, L., 1878. Über die Entwicklung des Samens der Orobanchen. Jahrb. f. wiss. Bot. 11:218–261.

Koch, L., 1879. Untersuchungen über die Entwicklung der Crassulaceen. *In* Carl Winter: Universitäts-Buchhandlung. Heidelberg.

Koch, L., 1882. Die Entwicklung des Samens von *Monotropa hypopitys*. Jahrb. f. wiss. Bot. 13:202–252.

Koch, L., 1887. Die Entwicklungsgeschichte der Orobanchen. Diss. Heidelberg.

Koerniche, M. See Körniche.

Kokieva, E., 1932. (The development of the female gametophyte in *Parthenium argentatum*.) Bot. Zhur. 17:72–99.

Kolbe, F., 1918. Untersuchungen über den Bau der Samenschale an Hilum und Chalaza bei einigen offizinellen Pflanzen. Diss. Berne.

Kolesnikov, S. M. and V. V. Krylova, 1961. (The biology of gametogenesis and embryogenesis and their relationship to organogenesis in plants.) In Plant Morphogenesis. Moskov Univ. 2:382–384.

Komuro, H., 1922. A polyembryonal plant of *Oryza sativa*. Bot. Mag. (Tokyo) 36:23–24.

Konstantinov, A. V., 1958. (Fertilization and early embryogenesis in apple.) Sb. Rabot. Aspir. Molod. Nauch. Sotrud. Vses. Inst. Rasten. 2:84–93.

Konstantinov, A. V., 1960. (The embryology of certain types of apple trees.) Izv. Akad. Nauk SSSR Biol. 2:256–264.

Konstantinov, A. V., 1961. (Specific features of the development of the ovules of apple.) Moskov Univ.: Moskva 2:287–291.

Konstantinov, A. V., 1963. (Contribution to the cytoembryology of wheat-rye amphidiploids.) Trud. Prikl. Bot. Genet. Selek. 35:140–145.

Konycheva, V., 1962. (Biology of flowering and embryology of *Salsola rigida*.) Uzbek. Biol. Zhur. 6:43–48.

Koorders, S. H., 1896. Morphologische und physiologische Embryologie von *Tectona grandis. In* Engler: Bot. Jahrb. 21:458–498.

Kopczynska, K., 1964. Embryo sac development in *Pinguicula vulgaris*. Acta Soc. bot. Polon. 33:141–156.

Kordyum, E. L., 1959. (Comparative embryological investigations of the family Ranunculaceae.) Ukrain. bot. Zhur. 14:40–46.

Kordyum, E. L., 1961a. (The process of pollination and fertilization in some representatives of the crowfoot family.) Ukrain. bot. Zhur. 17:61–67.

Kordyum, E. L., 1961b. (Microsporogenesis and specific characteristics of the development of the tapetum in some species of a genus of the milkweed family, *Vincetoxicum*.) Ukrain. bot. Zhur. 18:6–14.

Kordyum, E. L., 1961c. (On polyembryony in *Vincetoxicum officinale*.) Ukrain. bot. Zhur. 18:54–65.

Kordyum, E. L., 1963. (Peculiarities of the embryology of *Poa bulbosa* var. *vivipara*.) Ukrain. bot. Zhur. 20:43–50.

Kordyum, E. L. and A. P. Boiko, 1962. On the embryology of *Gerbera anandria*. Dokl. Akad. Nauk. Ukrain RSR 8:1109–1112.

Koriba, K., 1927. Entwicklungsmechanische Betrachtungen über die Differenzierung der Geschlechtsorgane bei den Blütenpflanzen. Bot. Mag. (Tokyo). Fujii Commem. Number. 41:110–117.

Körnicke, M., 1896. Untersuchung über die Entstehung und Entwicklung der Sexualorgane von *Triticum*, mit besonderer Berücksichtigung der Kerntheilung. Verhandl. Natur. Hist. Ver. Preussen Rheinl. 53:149–185.

Körnicke, M., 1901a. Über Ortveränderung von Zellkernen. Sitzb. Niederrhein. Ges. Bonn.

Körnicke, M., 1901b. Studien in Embryosack-Mutterzellen. Sitz. Nied. Ges. Nat. Heilk. Bonn 1901: 25–34.

Körnicke, M., 1906. Zentrosomen bei Angiospermen? Zugleich ein Beitrag zur Kenntnis der generativen Elemente im Pollenschlauch. Flora 96:501–522.

Korobova, S. N., 1961. (Microsporogenesis and development of the pollen grain in corn.) Dokl. Akad. Nauk SSSR 136:3–9.

Korobova, S. N., 1962. (The embryology of corn.) Trud. bot. Inst. Akad. Nauk SSSR (7) 5:294–314.

Koschnikoff, 1877. Entwicklungsgeschichte der Araceenblüte. Bjul. Moskov Obsc. Ispyt. Prir. 52.

Koshimizu, T., 1930. Carpobiological studies of *Crinum asiaticum* var. *japonicum*. Mem. Coll. Sci. Kyoto 69:183–227.

Kosmath, L., 1927. Studien über das Antherentapetum. Österr. bot. Zeit. 76:235–241.

Kostoff, D., 1926. Formation of pollen by some varieties of *Capsicum annum*. Ann. Univ. Sofia, Fac. Agric. 4:101–124.

Kostoff, D., 1937. The size of *Nicotiana rustica* x *Nicotiana tobacum* hybrid embryos and hybrids in respect to their parents. Current Sci. 6:326–327.

Kostoff, D., 1939. (Frequency of polyembryony and chlorophyll deficiency in rye.) Dokl. Akad. Nauk. SSSR 24:479–482.

Kostoff, D., 1940. A case of vivipary in rye. Current Sci. 9:279–280.

Kostrioukoff, X., 1930. Cellules mâles dans le *Scirpus lacustris*. Bull. Jard. bot. Kieff 11:10–20.

Kostriukova, K., 1939a. (Spermatogenesis in *Crinum hildebrandtii*. Observations *in vivo*.) Zhur. Inst. bot. Acad. Sci. Ukraine 21/22:157–164.

Kostriukova, K., 1939b. (Observations *in vivo* on the formation of the male sex cells in *Lilium martagon*.) Dokl. Akad. Nauk. SSSR 22:444–447.

Kostriukova, K., 1961. (Fertilization in *Heliopsis helianthoides*.) Zhur. Obshchei Biol. 22:58–65.

Kostriukova, K. and G. Benetskaia, 1939. (Spermatogenesis in *Narcissus poeticus*. Observations *in vivo*.) Bot. Zhur. 24:209–220.

Kostriukova, L. N., 1959. (The male gametophyte of *Vicia sativa*, *V. villosa*, *V. sepium*.) Nauch. Dokl. Vysshei Shkoly. Biol. Nauk. 2:118–120.

Koul, A. K., 1959. Antipodals during the development of caryopsis in *Euchlaena mexicana*. Agra Univ. J. Res. (Sci.) 8:31–33.

Koul, A. K. and B. G. Gahi, 1962. Morphological studies on *Euchlaena mexicana*. Agra Univ. J. Res. (Sci.) 11:195–207.

Kozlov, V. E., 1954. (Morphological and chemical variation in sperms of peas, *Pisum sativum*, during fertilization). Vestn. Leningrad-skoga Univ. 4:27–31.

Kracauer, P., 1930. Die Haploidgeneration von *Canna indica*. Diss. Berlin.

Kraft, E., 1917. Experimentelle und entwicklungsgeschichtliche Untersuchungen an Caryophyllaceen-Blüten. Flora 109:283–356.

Kratzer, J., 1918. Die verwandtschaftlichen Berziehungen der Cucurbitaceen auf Grund ihrer Samenentwicklung mit spezieller Berücksichtigung der Caricaceen, Passifloraceen, Aristolochiaceen und Loasaceen. Flora 110:275–343.

Krauss, L., 1933. Entwicklungsgeschichte der Früchte von *Hordeum, Triticum, Bromus* und *Poa* mit besonderer Berücksichtigung ihrer Samenschalen. Planta 77:733–808.

Krishnamurthy, K. V. and K. A. Rao, 1958. Abnormal pollen tube development in a *Nicotiana* hybrid. Current Sci. 27:397–398.

Krishnamurthy, K. V. and K. A. Rao, 1960. A note on the ovule development in carpelloid stamens of a *Nicotiana* hybrid. Current Sci. 29:23–24.

Krishnaswamy, N. and G. N. R. Ayyangar, 1930. Polyembryony in *Eleusine coracana*. Madras Agric. J. 18:593–595.

Krishnaswamy, N. and G. N. R. Ayyangar, 1937. Cytological studies in *Eleusine coracana*. Beih. bot. Ztbl. 57:297–318.

Kronfeld, M., 1886. Über den Blütenstand der Rohrkolben. S. B. Kais. Akad. wiss. 16:78–109.

Kronfeld, M., 1890. Neue Beiträge zur Biologie der Pflanzen. 10. Fruchtbildung ohne Befruchtung. Biol. Ztbl. 10:65–66.

Krug, C. A., 1934. Beiträge zur Zytologie des Genus *Coffea*. Der Züchter 6:166–168.

Krug, C. A., 1937. Cytological observations in *Coffea*. 3. J. Genetics 34:399–414.

Krug, C. A. and A. Carvalho, 1939. Genetical proof for the existence of Coffee endosperm. Nature 144:515.

Krüger, M., 1932. Vergleichend entwicklungsgeschichtliche Untersuchungen an den Fruchtknoten und Früchten zweier *Solanum*-Chimären und ihrer Elternarten. Planta 17:372–436.

Krupko, S., 1928. Remarques sur le sac embryonnaire de *Gagea lutea*. Obd. Spraw. posiedén Tow. Nauk. Warsaw: 20.3.

Krupko, S., 1944. (On the sterility of *Oxalis cernua* in the Mediterranean). Przyroda 1944: 1–32.

Krupko, S., 1956–1957. (Embryological and cytological studies in some species of Restionaceae. 1. *Hypodiscus aristatus*). 7th. Yearbook of the Polish Soc. Arts & Science Abroad.

Krupko, S., 1962. Embryological and cytological investigations in *Hypodiscus aristatus*. J. Sth. Afr. Bot. 28:21–44.

Krupko, S., 1963. Macrosporogenesis and embryo sac development in *Chondropetalum hookerianum*. Acta Soc. bot. Polon. 32:171–190.

Krupko, S., G. F. Israelstam, and B. Martinovic, 1954. Embryo sac development and chromosome number in *Vanilla roscheri* from Inhaca Island. Sth. Afr. J. Sci. 51:115–117.

Krzyzan, J. et al., 1963. (Cytological and embryological investigations on causes of sterility in four cultivated varieties of cherry.) Poznan. Towar. Przyj. Nauk. Wydz. Mat.-Przyr. Komis. Biol. Prace 18:1–28.

Kshirsagar, B. G., 1960. Contribution to the embryology of *Polycarpaea corymbosa* and *Mollugo stricta* (*M. pentaphylla*). Proc. 47th Indian Sci. Congr. 3:357.

Kubin, E., 1878. Die Entwicklung von *Pistia stratiotes*. Hanstein's Bot. Abh. 3.

Kudryashov, L. V. and Savich, E. I., 1963. (Some data on the embryology of *Alisma plantago-aquatica*.) Byul. Most. Obshch. Ispyt. Prirody. Otd. Biol. 68:50–63.

Kühl, R., 1933. Vergleichend-entwicklungsgeschichtliche Untersuchungen an der Insektivore *Nepenthes*. Beih. bot. Ztbl. 51:311–334.

Kuhn, E., 1908. Über den Wechsel der Zelltypen im Endothecium der Angiospermen. Diss. Zürich.

Kuhn, E., 1928. Zur Zytologie von *Thalictrum*. Jahrb. f. wiss. Bot. 68:382–430. Diss. Hamburg.

Kuhn, E., 1930. Pseudogamie und Androgenesis bei Pflanzen. Züchter 2:124–136.

Kuijt, J., 1955. Dwarf mistletoes. Bot. Rev. 21:137–160.

Kumar, L. S. S., 1942a. Non-heritable polyembryony in *Andropogon sorghum*. Current Sci. 11:241.

Kumar, L. S. S., 1942b. False polyembryony in viviparous *Rhizophora mucronata*. Current Sci. 11:242.

Kumar, L. S. S. and A. Abraham, 1941. Cytological studies in Indian parasitic plants. 1. The cytology of *Striga*. Proc. Indian Acad. Sci. B. 14:509–516.

Kumazawa, M., 1935. The structure and affinities of *Paeonia*. Bot. Mag. (Tokyo) 49:306–315.

Kusano, S., 1908. Further studies on *Aeginetia indica*. Bull. Coll. Agri. Tokyo Imp. Univ. 8:3–20.

Kusano, S., 1915. Experimental studies on the embryonal development in an angiosperm. J. Coll. Agr. Tokyo Imp. Univ. 6:8–120.

Kuwada, Y., 1910a. (On the development of the pollen and the embryo sac, and the formation of the endosperm of *Oryza sativa*.) Bot. Mag. (Tokyo) 23:333–342.

Kuwada, Y., 1910b. A cytological study of *Oryza sativa*. Bot. Mag. (Tokyo) 24:268–280.

Kuwada, Y., 1911. Meiosis in the pollen mother cells of *Zea mays*. Bot. Mag. (Tokyo) 25:163–181.

Kuwada, Y., 1928. On the occurrence of restitution nuclei in the formation of the embryo sac of *Balanophora japonica*. Bot. Mag. (Tokyo) 42:117–129.

Kuyjper, J., 1914. Die Entwicklung des weiblichen Geschlechtsapparats bei *Theobroma cacao*. Rec. Trav. bot. Néerl. 11:37–43.

Lachner-Sandoval, 1892. Beitrag zur Kenntnis der Gattung *Roxburghia*. Bot. Ztbl. 50:65–70, 97–104, 129–135.

LaCour, L. F., 1949. Nuclear differentiation in the pollen grain. Heredity 3:331–337.

Lagerberg, T., 1909. Studien über die Entwicklungsgeschichte und systematische Stellung von *Adoxa moschatellina*. Kgl. Svensk Vet.-Akad. Handl. 44:1–86.

Lakshmanan, K. K., 1961. Embryological studies in the Hydrocharitaceae. 1. *Blyxa octandra*. J. Madras Univ. B. 31:133–142.

Lakshmanan, K. K., 1962. Embryological features of *Pollia sorzogonensis*. Current Sci. 31:308.

Lakshmanan, K. K., 1963a. Embryological studies in the Hydrocharitaceae. 2. *Halophila ovata*. J. Indian bot. Soc. 42:15–18.

Lakshmanan, K. K., 1963b. Embryological studies in the Hydrocharitaceae. 3. *Nechamandra alternifolia*. Rev. Internac. Bot. Exptl. 20:49–58.

Lamm, R., 1937. A contribution to the embryology of potato. Svensk bot. Tidskr. 31:217–220.

Lampe, L., 1931. A microchemical and morphological study of the developing endosperm of maize. Bot. Gaz. 91:337–376.

Lampton, R. K., 1957. Floral morphology in *Asimina triloba*. 1. Development of ovule and embryo sac. J. Torrey bot. Cl. 84:151–156.

Land, W. T. G., 1900. Double fertilization in the Compositae. Bot. Gaz. 30:252–260.

Landes, M., 1946. Seed development in *Acalypha rhomboidea* and some other Euphorbiaceae. Amer. J. Bot. 33:562–568.

Lang, F. X., 1901. Untersuchungen über Morphologie, Anatomie und Samenentwicklung von *Polypompholyx* und *Biblis gigantea*. Flora 88:149–206.

Langdon, L. M., 1934. Embryogeny of *Carya* and *Juglans,* a comparative study. Bot. Gaz. 96:93–117.

Landgon, L. M., 1939. Ontogenetic and anatomical studies of the flower and fruit of the Fagaceae and Juglandaceae. Bot. Gaz. 101:301–327.

Langendorf, J., 1930. Zur Kenntnis der Genetik und Entwicklungsgeschichte von *Oenothera fallax, rubirigida* und *hookeri-albata*. Bot. Arch. 29:474–530.

Langlet, O., 1925. On the embryology of *Adenostyles*. Svensk bot. Tidskr. 19:215–231.

Langlet, O., 1927. Über die Entwicklung des Eiapparates in Embryosack der Angiospermen. Svensk bot. Tidskr. 21:478–485.

Langlet, O., 1928. Einige Beobachtungen über die Zytologie der Berberidazeen. Svensk. bot. Tidskr. 22:169–184.

Lantis, V., 1912. Development of the microsporangia and microspores of *Abutilon theophrasti*. Bot. Gaz. 54:330–335.

LaRue, C. D. and G. S. Avery, 1938. The development of the embryo of *Zizania aquatica* in the seed and in artificial culture. Bull. Torrey bot. Cl. 65:11–21.

Lary de Latour, E., 1908. Sur les particularités cytologiques du développement des cellules-mères du pollen de l'*Agave attenuata*. C. R. Acad. Sci. 146:833–836.

Latter, J., 1925. A preliminary note on the pollen development of *Lathyrus odoratus*. Brit. J. Exp. Biol. 2:199–209.

Latter, J., 1926. The pollen development of *Lathyrus odoratus*. Ann. Bot. 40:277–313.

Laurent, M., 1903a. Sur la formation de l'oeuf et la multiplication d'une antipode dans les Joncées. C. R. Acad. Sci. Paris 137:499–500.

Laurent, M., 1903b. Sur le développement de l'embryon des Joncées. C. R. Acad. Sci. Paris 137:532–533.

Laurent, M., 1904. Recherches sur le développement des Joncées. Ann. Sci. nat. Bot. 19:97–194.

Laurent, V., 1923. Zur Entwicklungsgeschichte von *Corytoloma cyclophyllum*. Svensk bot. Tidskr. 17:164–174.

Lavaille, P., 1911. Observations sur le développement de l'ovaire en fruit chez les Composées. Bull. Soc. bot. France 58.

Lavaille, P., 1912. Recherches sur le développement de l'ovaire en fruit chez les Composées. Ann. Sci. nat. Bot. 9:39–141.

Lavaille, P., 1921. Contribution à l'étude de l'ovaire chez les Composées. Bull. Soc. bot. France 68:414–417.

Lavaille, P., 1922. Sur le rôle digestif de l'épiderme interne du tégument ovulaire des Composées. Bull. Soc. bot. France 69:75–79.

Lavaille, P., 1925a. Sur le sac embryonnaire des Dipsacées. C. R. Acad. Sci. Paris 180:1127–1129.

Lavaille, P., 1925b. Sur les antipodes et la région chalazienne de l'ovule des Dipsacées. C. R. Acad. Sci. Paris 180:1606–1608.

Lavaille, P., 1925c. Sur la nutrition du sac embryonnaire chez *Knautia arvensis*. C. R. Acad. Sci. Paris 180:2055–2056.

Lavaille, P., 1926. Le développement de l'anthère et du pollen chez *Knautia arvensis*. C. R. Acad. Sci. Paris 182:77–79.

Lawalrée, A., 1952. L'embryologie des Lemnaceae. Observations sur *Lemna minor*. Cellule 54:305–326.

Laws, D., 1930. Zytologische Untersuchungen über den Formenkreiss von *Lavandula spica*. Diss. Berlin.

Lawson, A. A., 1898. Some observations on the development of the karyokinetic spindle in the pollen mother cells of *Cobaea scandens*. Proc. Calif. Acad. Sci. 3. (Bot.) 1:169–184.

Leavitt, R. G., 1900. Polyembryony in *Spiranthes cernua*. Rhodora 2:227–228.

Leavitt, R. G., 1901. Notes on the embryology of some New England orchids. Rhodora 3:61–63, 202–205.

Leavitt, R. G. and L. J. Spalding, 1905. Parthenogenesis in *Antennaria*. Rhodora 7:105.

Lebègue, A., 1948a. Embryogénie des Oenotheracées. Développement de l'embryon chez l'*Epilobium montanum*. Bull. Soc. bot. France 95:173–178.

Lebègue, A., 1948b. Embryologie des Crucifères: Polyembryonie chez l'*Arabis lyalli*. Bull. Soc. bot. France 95:250–252.

Lebègue, A., 1948c. Embryogénie des Oenotheracées. Développement de l'embryon chez l'*Epilobium spicatum*. C. R. Acad. Sci. Paris 226:429.

Lebègue, A., 1949. Embryologie des Saxifragacées: Polyembryonie chez le *Bergenia delavayi*. Bull. Soc. bot. France 96:38–39.

Lebègue, A., 1950. Note préliminaire à l'étude embryogénique des Saxifragacées. Genre *Saxifraga*. Bull. Mus. hist. nat. Paris 22:611–614.

Lebègue, A., 1952a. Recherches sur la polyembryonie chez les Rosacées, *Fragaria* et *Alchemilla*. Bull. Soc. bot. France 99:273–275.

Lebègue, A., 1952b. La polyembryonie chez les Angiospermes. Bull. Soc. bot. France 99:329–367.

Lebègue, A., 1952c. Recherches embryogéniques sur quelques Dicotylédones dialypétales. Thèse. Paris.

Lebègue, A., 1953a. Embryogénie des Parnassiacées. Développement de l'embryon chez le *Parnassia palustris*. C. R. Acad. Sci. Paris 236:1693–1695.

Lebègue, A., 1953b. Recherches embryogéniques sur quelques dicotyledones dialypétales. Ann. Sci. nat. Bot. 13:1–160. Thèse. Paris 1952.

Lebègue, A., 1954. Embryogénie des Malvacées. Développement de l'embryon chez les *Lavatera*. C. R. Acad. Sci. Paris 239:1838–1840.

Lebègue, A., 1956a. Embryogénie des Urticacées. Développement de l'embryon chez l'*Urtica dioica*. C. R. Acad. Sci. Paris 242:923–926.

Lebègue, A., 1956b. Embryogénie des Urticacées. Développement de l'embryon chez le *Parietaria officinalis*. C. R. Acad. Sci. Paris 243:817–820.

Lebègue, A., 1956c. Développement de l'embryon chez l'*Urtica urens*. Bull. Soc. bot. France 103:587–590.

Lebon, E., 1929. Sur la formation de l'albumen chez *Impatiens sultani*. C. R. Soc. biol. Paris 101:1168–1170.

Lechmere, A. E., 1910. Two embryo sac mother cells in the ovule of *Fritillaria*. New Phytol. 9:257–259.

Lechner, S., 1914. Anatomische Untersuchungen über die Gattung *Actinidia, Saurauia, Clethra* und *Clematoclethra* mit besonderer Berücksichtigung ihrer Stellung im System. Beih. bot. Ztbl. 32:431–467.

Leclerc du Sablon, M., 1885. Recherches sur la structure et la déhiscence des anthères. Ann. Sci. nat. Biol. (7) 1:97.

Leclerc du Sablon, M., 1908. Structure et développement de l'albumen du caprifiguier. Rev. gén. Bot. 20:14–24.

Leclerc du Sablon, M., 1910. Sur un cas de parthénogénèse du Figuier de Smyrne. Rev. gén. Bot. 22:65–69.

Lecompte, H., 1896. Sur la formation du pollen chez Annonacées. Bull. Mus. hist. nat. Paris 2:152–153.

Ledingham, G. F., 1940. Cytological and developmental studies of hybrids between *Medicago sativa* and a diploid form of *M. falcata*. Genetics 25:1–15.

Lee, J. H. and D. C. Cooper, 1958. Seed development following hybridization between diploid *Solanum* species from Mexico, Central and South America. Amer. J. Bot. 45:104–110.

Lee, R. E., 1961. Pollen dimorphism in *Tripodandra grandiflora*. Baileya 9:53–56.

Leemann, A., 1927. Contribution à l'étude de l'*Asarum europaeum* avec une étude particulière sur le développement des cellules sécrétices. Bull. Soc. bot. gén. Paris 19:92–173.

Leffingwell, A. M., 1930. Morphological study of bulb and flowers of *Camassia quamash*. Res. St. State Coll. Wash. 2:80–89.

Léger, V., 1913. Recherches sur la structure anatomique du tégument séminal des Apocynacées et des Asclepiadacées. Thesis. Paris.

Lehmann, E., 1924. Die Gattung *Epilobium*. Bibliogr. genet. 1:363–416.

Leidicke, J. W., 1903. Beiträge zur Embryologie von *Tropaeolum majus*. Diss. Breslau.

Leitner, J., 1942. Ein Beitrag zur Kenntnis der Pollenkörner der Labiatae. Österr. bot. Zeit. 91:29–40.

Leliveld, J. A., 1935. Cytological studies in the genus *Ulmus*. 2. The embryo sac and seed development in the common dutch elm. Rec. Trav. bot. Néerl. 32:543–573.

Leliveld, J. A., 1938. Vruchtzetting bij Koffie. Arch. Koffiecultuur Ned. Indie 3:127–164.

Lemesle, R., 1929a. Embryologie des Elatinacées. Développement de l'embryon chez l'*Elatine alsinastrum*. C. R. Acad. Sci. Paris 18:1569.

Lemesle, R., 1929b. Les premiers stades du développement de l'embryon chez le *Damasonium stellatum*. Bull. Soc. bot. France 76:74–78.

Lengel, P. A., 1960. Development of the pollen and the embryo sac in *Capsicum frutescens* var. Japanese Variegated Ornamental. Ohio J. Sci. 60:8–12.

Lenoir, M., 1927. Formation des noyaux antipodes dans le sac embryonnaire de *Fritillaria imperialis*. C. R. Acad. Sci. Paris 184:1132–1134.

Leroy, J. F., 1947. La polyembryonie chez les *Citrus*. Son intérêt dans la culture et amélioration. Rev. int. Bot. appl. Paris 27:483–495.

Levan, A., 1936. Zytologische Studien an *Allium schoenoprasum*. Hereditas 22:353–394.

Levan, A., 1937. Eine erbliche Anomalie der Samenanlage bei *Petunia*. Bot. Notiser 1937:35–55.

Levan, A., 1940. The cytology of *Allium amplectens* and the occurrence in nature of its asynapsis. Hereditas 26:353–394.

Levan, A., 1941. Syncyte formation in the pollen mother cells of haploid *Phleum pratense*. Hereditas 27:243–252.

Levine, M., 1915. Somatic and reduction divisions in certain species of *Drosera*. Mem. N.Y. bot. Gdn. 6:125–147.

Lewis, C. E., 1904. Studies on some anomalous dicotyledonous plants. Bot. Gaz. 37:127–138.

Lewis, J. F., 1905. Notes on the development of *Phytolacca decandra*. Johns Hopkins Univ. Circ. 178:34–42.

Lewitzky, G., 1925. (On the phenomenon of abortion in the reproductive organs of *Asparagus officinalis*.) Bull. appl. Bot. Pl. Breed. 14:113–141.

Li, P. C., 1963. A cytochemical study on the stages of development of the microspores and microgametes of some Angiospermae. Acta bot. Sinica 11:283–292.

Lidfors, B., 1897. Zur Physiologie des pflanzlichen Zellkerns. Acta. r. soc. physiogr. Lund.

Liehr, E., 1927. Entwicklungsgeschichtliche und experimentelle Untersuchungen über den rudimentären Fruchtknoten einiger Umbelliferen. Mitt. Inst. allg. Bot. Hamburg 6:361–418.

Leitz, J., 1929. Beiträge zur Zytologie der Gattung *Mentha* Heilund Gewürzpfl. Mitt. dtsch. Hortus-Ges. 12:73–86, 113–131.

Liljefors, A., 1934. Über normale und apospore Embryoentwicklung in der Gattung *Sorbus* nebst einigen Bemerkungen über die Chromosomenzahlen. Svensk bot. Tidskr. 28:290–299.

Liljefors, A., 1953. Studies on propagation, embryology and pollination in *Sorbus*. Acta Hort. Berg. 16:277–329.

Lima-de-Faria, A., 1947. Disturbances in microspore cytology of *Arthoxanthum*. Hereditas 33:539–551.

Limpricht, W., 1902. Beiträge zur Kenntnis der Taccaceen. Diss. Breslau.

Lindau, J., 1891. Zur Entwicklungsgeschichte einiger Samen. Ber. dtsch. bot. Ges. 9:274–279.

Lindau, J., 1928. Linsbauner Handbuch der Pflanzenanatomie. 2. Berlin.

Lindenbein, W., 1932. Karyologische Studien in *Daucus carota*. Ber. dtsch. bot. Ges. 50:399–406.

Linskens, H. F., 1958. Physiologische Untersuchungen zur Reifeteilung. 2. Mitteilung. Über die Änderung des Nukleinsäureugehaltes während der Pollenmeiose und Pollenentwicklung von *Lilium henryi*. Acta bot. Néerl. 7:61–68.

List, A., 1963. Some features of embryo and endosperm development in *Gleditschia triacanthos*. Amer. J. Bot. 50:622.

List, A. and F. C. Steward, 1965. The nucellus, embryo sac, endosperm and embryo of *Aesculus* and their interdependence during growth. Ann. Bot. 29:1–15.

Ljungdahl, H., 1922. Zur Zytologie der Gattung *Papaver*. Svensk bot. Tidskr. 16:103–114.

Lloyd, F. E., 1889. The comparative embryology of the Rubiaceae. Bull. Torrey bot. Cl. 28:1–25.

Lloyd, F. E., 1902. The comparative embryology of the Rubiaceae. Mem. Torrey bot. Cl. 8:1–112.

Lloyd, F. E., 1904. The pollen tube in the Cucurbitaceae and Rubiaceae. Torreya 4:86–91.

Lloyd, F. E., 1905. The pollen tube in *Houstonia:* a preliminary note. Torreya 5:83–85.

Lloyd, F. E., 1910. Development and nutrition of the embryo, seed and carpel in the date, *Phoenix dactylifera*. 21st. Annual Rep. Missouri bot. Gdns. 21:103–164.

Locke, J. F., 1936. Microsporogenesis and cytokinesis in *Asimina triloba*. Bot. Gaz. 98:159–168.

Lodha, B. C., 1963. Embryology of *Orygia decumbens*. Phytomorphology 13:54–59.

Lombard-Dumas, 1904. Variations sexuelles de l'*Aucuba japonica*. Bull. Soc. bot. France 51.

Lonay, H., 1901. Contribution à l'anatomie de Rénonculacées: Structure et péricarpe. Arch. inst. bot. Univ. Liège 3.

Lonay, H., 1922a. Génèse et anatomie des péricarpes et des spermodermes chez les Polygonacées. 1. *Polygonum aviculare.* Mém. Soc. R. Sci. Liège (3) 12:1–88.

Lonay, H., 1922b. Contribution à l'étude des rélations entre la structure des differentes parties de l'ovule et la nutrition générale de celui-ci avant et après la fécondation. Bull. Cl. Sci. Acad. Roy. Belg. (5) 8:24–45.

Lonay, H., 1923. L'ovule du *Polygonum aviculare.* Bull. Soc. Roy. Bot. Belg. 55:175–177.

Long, E. M., 1943. Developmental anatomy of the fruit of deglet moordate. Bot. Gaz. 104:426–436.

Longley, A. E., 1924a. Cytological studies in the genus *Rubus.* Amer. J. Bot. 11:249–282.

Longley, A. E., 1924b. Cytological studies in the genus *Crataegus.* Amer. J. Bot. 11:295–317.

Longley, A. E., 1925. Polycarpy, polyspory and polyploidy in *Citrus* and *Citrus* relatives. Genetics 15:347–351.

Longo, B., 1898. Un nuovo carattere di affinità tra le Calycanthaceae e le Rosaceae desunto dall 'embriologia. C. R. Accad. Lincei, Roma 7:51–52.

Longo, B., 1900. Osservazioni sulle Calycanthaceae. Ann. R. Ist. Bot. Roma 9:1–16.

Longo, B., 1901. La mesogamia nella commune zucca, *Cucurbita pepo.* C. R. Accad. Lincei, Roma (5) 10:168–172.

Longo, B., 1903a. Ricerche sulle Cucurbitaceae e il significo del percorso intercellulare (endotropico) del tubetto pollinico. Mem. R. Accad. naz. Lincei, Roma 4:523–549.

Longo, B., 1903b. La nutrizione dell 'embrione della *Cucurbita* mezzo del tubetto pollinico. Mem. R. Accad. naz. Lincei, Roma (5) 5.

Longo, B., 1904. La nutrizione dell 'embrione delle *Cucurbita* operate per mezzo del tubetto pollinico. Ann. di Bot. (Roma) 1:71–74.

Longo, B., 1905a. Osservazione e ricerche sulla nutrizione dell 'embrione vegetale. Ann. di Bot. (Roma) 2:373–396.

Longo, B., 1905b. Acrogamia aporogamia del *Ficus domestica* (*F. carica*). Ann. di Bot. (Roma) 3:14–17.

Longo, B., 1907. Nuovo ricerche sulla nutrizione dell' embrione vegetale. C. R. Accad. Lincei, Roma (5) 16.

Longo, B., 1908. La poliembrionia nello *Xanthoxylum bungei* senza fecondazione. Bull. Soc. bot. Ital. 1908:113–115.

Longo, B., 1909a. Osservazioni e ricerche sul *Ficus carica.* Ann. di Bot. (Roma) 7:235–256.

Longo, B., 1909b. La parthenocarpia nel *Diospyros virginiana.* C. R. Accad. Lincei, Roma (5) 18:632–635.

Longo, B., 1910a. Ricerche su le *Impatiens.* Ann. di Bot. (Roma) 8:65–77.

Longo, B., 1910b. La parthenocarpia nello *Schinus molle.* C. R. Accad. Lincei, Roma (5) 19:612–615.

Longo, B., 1911a. Sur la pretesa esistenza del micropilo nel *Ficus carica.* Ann. di Bot. (Roma) 9:197–198.

Longo, B., 1911b. Sul *Ficus carica.* Ann. di Bot. (Roma) 9:414–432.

Longo, B., 1914. Ricerche sopra una varietà di *Crataegus azarolus* ad ovuli in gran parte sterili. N. G. bot. Ital. 21:5–14.

Longo, B., 1917. Ricerche su la poliembrionia. Ann. di Bot. (Roma) 14:151.

Longo, B., 1920. Su la parthenocarpia. Riv. di Biol. 2:597.

Longo, B., 1927. Nuovo ricerche sulla nutrizione dell' embrione vegetale. C. R. Accad. Lincei. Roma 16:591–594.

Loschnigg, F., 1926. Bausteine zu einer Monographie von *Ficaria*. In H. Winkler, Beitr. Biol. Pflanz. 14:347–358.

Lötscher, K., 1905. Über den Bau und die Funktion der Antipoden in der Angiospermen-Samenanlage. Flora 94:213–262. Diss. Freiburg.

Lotsy, J. P., 1899. *Balanophora globosa*—eine wenigstens örlichverwittwete Pflanze. Ann. Jard. bot. Buitenz. (2) 1:174–186.

Lotsy, J. P., 1901. *Rhopalocnemis phalloides*. A morphological-systematical study. Ann. Jard. bot. Buitenz. (2) 2:73–101.

Lotsy, P., 1926. Has Winge proved that *Erophila* is not apogamous? Genetica 8:335–344.

Lowe, J. and O. E. Nelson, 1946. Miniature seed: a study in the development of a defective caryopsis in maize. Genetics 31:525–533.

Lubbock, J., 1891. On the fruit and seed of the Juglandaceae. J. Linn. Soc. Lond. (Bot.) 28:247–254.

Lubimenko, W. and A. Maige, 1907. Recherches cytologiques sur le développement des cellules-mères du pollen chez les Nympheacées. Rev. gén. Bot. 19:401–425, 433–458, 474–505.

Lublinerówna, K., 1925a. Recherches sur le développement de l'ovule et de la graine dans le genre *Podophyllum*. Bull. Intern. Acad. Sci. Polon. B. 1925:379–402.

Lublinerówna, K., 1925b. Über die Plastiden in der Eizelle von *Podophyllum peltatum*. Acta Soc. bot. Polon. 2:225–227.

Lublinerówna, K., 1925c. Recherches sur le développement des téguments ovulaires et séminaux dans le genre *Podophyllum*. Acta Soc. bot. Polon. 3:277–282.

Luerssen, C., 1869. Zur Controverse über die Einzelligkeit oder Mehrzelligkeit des Pollens der Onagraceen, Cucurbitaceen und Corylaceen. Jahrb. f. wiss. Bot. 7:34–60.

Lundberg, F., 1931. Bemerkungen über die Embryosackentwicklung bei *Codiaeum*. Bot. Notiser 1931:346–349.

Lundegårdh, H., 1909. Über Reduktionsteilung in den Pollenmutterzellen einiger dicotylen Pflanzen. Svensk bot. Tidskr. 3:78–124.

Lundqvist, G., 1915. Die Embryosackentwicklung von *Pedicularis sceptrum-carolinum*. Zeit. Bot. 7:545–559.

Luxemburg, A., 1927. Recherches cytologiques sur les grains de pollen chez les Malvacées. Bul. Internat. Acad. Polon. B. 1927:363–396.

Ly Thi Ba, 1960. Embryogénie des Rubiacées. Développement de l'embryon chez le *Galium aparine*. C. R. Acad. Sci. Paris 251:1812–1814.

Ly Thi Ba, 1961a. Embryogénie des Rubiacées. Développement de l'embryon chez le *Spermacoce tenuior*. C. R. Acad. Sci. Paris 252:927–929.

Ly Thi Ba, 1961b. Embryogénie des Renonculacées. Développement de l'embryon chez l'*Isopyrum fumarioides*. C. R. Acad. Sci. Paris 253:1603–1605.

Ly Thi Ba, 1961c. Embryogénie des Renonculacées. Développement du proembryon chez le *Trollius europaeus*. C. R. Acad. Sci. Paris 253:2753–2755.

Lynch, R. I., 1880. On the seed structure and germination of *Pachira aquatica* J. Linn. Soc. London (Bot.) 17:147–148.

Lyon, F. M., 1898. A contribution to the life history of *Euphorbia corollata*. Bot. Gaz. 25:418–426.

Lyon, H. L., 1901. Preliminary note on the embryology of *Nelumbo*. Science 13:470.

Lyon, H. L., 1901. Observations on the embryogeny of *Nelumbo*. Minn. bot. Stud. 2:643–655.

Lyon, H. L., 1905. The embryo of the angiosperms. Amer. Nat. 39:13–34.

Maas, J. G. T. A., 1919. De bloembiologie van *Hevea brasiliensis*? Archiv. rubber-culture Ned. Indie Rubberserie 22:288–312.

MacKenney, R. E., 1898. Observations on the development of some embryo sacs. Contrib. bot. Lab. Univ. Pennsylv. 2:80–86.

MacLeod, A. M. and H. McCorquodale, 1958. Comparative studies of embryo and endosperm in the Gramineae. J. Inst. Brew. 64:162–170.

MacMillan, C., 1892. The embryo sac of the Metaspermae. Bot. Gaz. 17:161–162.

MacPhee, H. C., 1924. Meiotic cytokinesis of *Cannabis*. Bot. Gaz. 78:335–341.

Macpherson, G. E., 1921. Comparison of development in dodder and morning glory. Bot. Gaz. 71:392–398.

Madge, M., 1929. Spermatogenesis and fertilization in the cleistogamous flowers of *Viola odorata* var. *praecox*. Ann. Bot. 43:545–577.

Madge, M., 1934. Nuclear migrations in *Hedychium*. Proc. Linn. Soc. Lond. (Bot.) 146:108–109.

Madge, M., 1936. Division of the generative cell in *Hedychium gardnerianum*. Cellule 45:171–176.

Madhulata, 1956. Contribution to the life history of *Begonia picta*. Proc. 43rd. Indian Sci. Congr. 3:232.

Magnus, P., 1869. Zur Morphologie der Gattung *Naias*. Bot. Zeit. 27:769–773.

Magnus, P., 1870. Beiträge zur Kenntnis der Gattung *Naias*. Berlin.

Magnus, W., 1913. Die atypische Embryosackentwicklung der Podostemaceen. Flora 105:275–336.

Magtang, M. V., 1936. Floral biology and morphology of the egg plant. Philippine Agr. 25:30–53.

Mahabale, T. S. and M. S. Chennaveeraiah, 1957. Studies on *Hyphaene indica*. 1. Morphology. Phytomorphology 7:184–194.

Mahabale, T. S. and M. S. Chennaveeraiah, 1961. Cytoembryology of *Dipcadi montanum*. Proc. Natl. Inst. Sci. India. B. 27:153–171.

Mahabale, T. S. and I. N. Solanky, 1953a. Studies in the Chenopodiaceae. 1. Embryology of *Suaeda fruticosa*. J. Univ. Bombay 21:81–92.

Mahabale, T. S. and I. N. Solanky, 1953b. Studies in Chenopodiaceae. 3. Embryology of *Kochia scoparia*. J. Univ. Bombay 22:18–25.

Mahabale, T. S. and I. N. Solanky, 1954a. Studies in Chenopodiaceae. 4. Embryology of *Chenopodium ambrosioides*. J. Univ. Bombay 22:31–42.

Mahabale, T. S. and I. N. Solanky, 1954b. Studies in Chenopodiaceae. 2. Embryology of *Arthrocnemum indicum*. Proc. Indian Acad. Sci. B. 39:212–222.

Mahabale, T. S. and I. N. Solanky, 1954c. Studies in Chenopodiaceae. 5. Embryology of *Chenopodium murale*. J. Univ. Bombay 23:25–37.

Maheshwari, J. K., 1954. Floral morphology and embryology of *Lippia nodiflora*. Phytomorphology 4:217–230.

Maheshwari, P., 1929. Contributions to the morphology of *Boerhaavia diffusa*. 1. J. Indian bot. Soc. 8:219–234.

Maheshwari, P., 1930. Contributions to the morphology of *Boerhaavia diffusa*. 2. J. Indian bot. Soc. 9:42–61.

Maheshwari, P., 1931. Contributions to the morphology of *Albizzia lebbek*. J. Indian bot. Soc. 10:241–264.

Maheshwari, P., 1932. Life history of *Urginea indica*. Proc. 19th. Indian Sci. Congr. 3:310–311.

Maheshwari, P., 1933a. The development of the endosperm in *Asphodelus tenuifolia*. Current Sci. 2:13.

Maheshwari, P., 1933b. A note on the life history of *Hydrilla verticillata*. Current Sci. 2:13.

Maheshwari, P., 1934a. The development of the male gametophyte in *Hydrilla verticillata*. Proc. 21st. Indian Sci. Congr. 3:303.

Maheshwari, P., 1934b. The Indian Mango. Current Sci. 3:97–98.

Maheshwari, P., 1934c. Contributions to the morphology of some Indian Liliaceae. 1. The gametophytes of *Ophiopogon wallichianus*. Proc. Indian Acad. Sci. B. 1:197–204.

Maheshwari, P., 1935. Progress of work done in India on the embryology of Angiosperms. Current Sci. 3:599–605.

Maheshwari, P., 1936. A review of Newmann's paper on "Die Entwicklung des Pollens, der Samenanlage und des Embryosackes von *Pereskia amapola* var. *argentina*." J. Indian bot. Soc. 15:333–334.

Maheshwari, P., 1937. A critical review of the types of embryo sacs in Angiosperms. New Phytol. 36:359–417.

Maheshwari, P., 1941a. Recent work on the types of embryo sacs in Angiosperms. J. Indian bot. Soc. 20:229–261.

Maheshwari, P., 1941b. A note on Dr. Kajale's paper on the Amarantaceae. Current Sci. 10:182.

Maheshwari, P., 1942. The development of the embryo sac of *Euphorbia heterophylla*: a reinvestigation. Proc. Indian Acad. Sci. B. 15:158–166.

Maheshwari, P., 1943a. The mode of endosperm formation in *Vallisneria, Ottelia* and *Limnocharis*. Proc. Nat. Acad. Sci. India 13:260–263.

Maheshwari, P., 1943b. The seed structure of *Ipomoea*, a criticism. Sci. and Cult. 9:557.

Maheshwari, P., 1944a. The origin of the haustoria in the ovule of *Lobelia*. Current Sci. 13:186–187.

Maheshwari, P., 1944b. The origin of endosperm haustoria in *Lobelia*. J. Indian bot. Soc. 23:79–81.

Maheshwari, P., 1945a. Embryology of angiosperms as a field of research. Nature 156:354–355.

Maheshwari, P., 1945b. The place of angiosperm embryology in research and teaching. J. Indian bot. Soc. 24:25–41.

Maheshwari, P., 1945c. On the presence of an obturator in the ovule of *Phyllanthus niruri*. Current Sci. 12:132.

Maheshwari, P., 1946a. The Adoxa type of embryo sac: a critical review. Lloydia 9:73–113.

Maheshwari, P., 1946b. The Fritillaria type of embryo sac: a critical review. J. Indian bot. Soc. (M. O. P. Iyengar Commem. Vol.):101–119.

Maheshwari, P., 1947. Tetranucleate embryo sacs in Angiosperms. Lloydia 10:1–18.

Maheshwari, P., 1948. The angiosperm embryo sac. Bot. Rev. 14:1–56.

Maheshwari, P., 1949. The male gametophyte of angiosperms. Bot. Rev. 15:1–75.

Maheshwari, P., 1950a. Contacts between embryology, physiology and genetics. Presidential address. Proc. 37th. Indian Sci. Congr. 2:135–149.

Maheshwari, P., 1950b. Embryology of angiosperms, its aims and objects. Proc. 7th. Internat. Bot. Congr.: 376.

Maheshwari, P., 1950c. Embryology in relation to taxonomy. Proc. Brit. Assoc. Adv. Sci.: 88.

Maheshwari, P., 1950d. An Introduction to the Embryology of Angiosperms. New York, London.

Maheshwari, P., 1951. Importancia de la embriologia de las Angiospermas en la investigacion y la enseñanza. Bol. Soc. Argent. Bot. 4:1–20.

Maheshwari, P., 1952. Polyembryony in angiosperms. Palaeobotanist 1:319–329.

Maheshwari, P., 1954a. Embryology of angiosperms, a fruitful field for research. Presidential address, Embryology Sect., 8th. Internat. bot. Congr.: 233–243.

Maheshwari, P., 1954b. Embryology and systematic botany. Proc. 8th. Internat. bot. Congr.: 254–255.

Maheshwari, P., 1954c. Embryology of plants. In Encyclopaedia Americana: 186–190.

Maheshwari, P., 1956. Fertilization. In Dictionary of Gardening. The Royal hort. Soc., London: 817.

Maheshwari, P., 1956. The embryology of angiosperms: A retrospect and prospect. Current Sci. 25:106–110.

Maheshwari, P., 1958. Embryology and taxonomy. Mem. Indian bot. Soc. 1:1–9.

Maheshwari, P., 1959. Some examples of the value of embryology to taxonomy. Congr. Internatl. Bot. 9th. 2:246.

Maheshwari, P., 1960. Evolution of the ovule. 7th. Seward Mem. Lecture, Sahni Inst. Palaeobotany, Lucknow: 3–13.

Maheshwari, P., 1962. Contacts between Embryology, Physiology and Genetics. In Proc. Summer School Bot. Darjeeling: 171–192 (eds. P. Maheshwari et al.) New Delhi.

Maheshwari, P. (ed.) 1963a. Recent Advances in the Embryology of Angiosperms. Delhi.

Maheshwari, P., 1963b. History and present status of plant embryology. In Maheshwari, P. (ed.): Recent Advances in the Embryology of Angiosperms. Delhi: 266–296.

Maheshwari, P., 1963c. Embryology in relation to taxonomy. In Vistas in Botany, 4. Recent Researches in Plant Taxonomy (ed., W. B. Turrill): 55–97.

Maheshwari, P., 1964. Embryology in relation to taxonomy. Int. Ser. Monogr. Pure Appl. Biol. 7:55–97.

Maheshwari, P. and R. N. Chopra, 1954. Polyembryony in Opuntia dillenii. Current Sci. 23:130–131.

Maheshwari, P. and R. N. Chopra, 1955. The structure and development of the ovule and seed of Opuntia dillenii. Phytomorphology 5:112–122.

Maheshwari, P. and R. N. Chopra, 1955. Embryological studies in mango, Mangifera indica. Proc. 42nd. Indian Sci. Congr. 3:233.

Maheshwari, P. and O. R. Chowdhry, 1937. A note on the development of the embryo sac in Phyllanthus niruri. Current Sci. 5:535–536.

Maheshwari, P. and H. Gangulee, 1942. The development of the embryo sac in Heckeria umbellata. J. Indian bot. Soc. 21:245–248.

Maheshwari, P. and M. Ghosh 1955. The systematic position of *Exocarpus.* Proc. 42nd. Indian Sci. Congr. 3:234.

Maheshwari, P. and B. L. Gupta, 1934. The development of the female gametophyte of *Ludwigia parviflora* and *Jussieua repens.* Current Sci. 3:107–108.

Maheshwari, P. and A. Hague, 1948. The embryo sac of *Chrysanthemum parthenium.* New Phytol. 48:255–258.

Maheshwari, P. and B. M. Johri, 1940. A note on the embryo sac of *Acalypha indica.* Current Sci. 9:322–323.

Maheshwari, P. and B. M. Johri, 1941. The embryo sac of *Acalypha indica* Beih. bot. Ztbl. 61A:125–136.

Maheshwari, P. and B. M. Johri, 1950a. Development of embryo sac, embryo and endosperm in *Helixanthera ligustrina.* Nature 165:978–979.

Maheshwari, P. and B. M. Johri, 1950b. The occurrence of persistent pollen tubes in *Hydrilla, Ottelia* and *Boerhaavia,* together with a discussion of the possible significance of this phenomenon in the life history of angiosperms. J. Indian bot. Soc. 29: 47–51.

Maheshwari, P. and B. M. Johri, 1956. The morphology and embryology of *Floerkea proserpinacoides,* with a discussion on the systematic position of the family Limnanthaceae. Bot. Mag. (Tokyo), Ogura Comm. Vol. 69:410–423.

Maheshwari, P., B. M. Johri, and S. N. Dixit, 1957. The floral morphology and embryology of the Loranthoideae. J. Madras Univ. B. 27:121–136.

Maheshwari, P., B. M. Johri, and I. K. Vasil, 1962. Proceedings of the Summer School of Botany, 1960. Darjeeling. New Delhi.

Maheshwari, P. and R. Khan, 1953. Development of the embryo sac, endosperm and embryo in *Isomeris arborea:* a reinvestigation. Phytomorphology 3:446–459.

Maheshwari, P. and J. K. Maheshwari, 1955. Floral dimorphism in *Commelina forskalaei* and *C. benghalensis.* Phytomorphology 5:413–422.

Maheshwari, P. and S. Narayanaswami, 1950. Parthenogenetic development of the egg in *Spiranthes australis.* Current Sci. 19:249–250.

Maheshwari, P. and S. Narayanaswami, 1951. Parthenogenetic development of the egg in *Spiranthes australis.* Proc. Linn. Soc. London (Bot.) 53:474–486.

Maheshwari, P. and H. S. Navalakha, 1941. A note on the embryology of *Scoparia dulcis* and *Angelonia grandiflora.* Current Sci. 10:297–298.

Maheshwari, P. and V. Negi, 1955. The embryology of *Dipteracanthus patulus.* Phytomorphology 5:456–472.

Maheshwari, P. and N. S. Rangaswamy, 1960. Embryology of Cotton. *In* Cotton in India—Monograph No. 1: 118–136. Bombay.

Maheshwari, P. and S. K. Roy, 1951. The embryo sac of *Salix.* Phytomorphology 1:70–72.

Maheshwari, P. and S. K. Roy, 1952. The embryo sac and embryo of *Tridax procumbens.* Phytomorphology 2:245–252.

Maheshwari, P. and R. C. Sachar, 1954a. A reinvestigation of the embryology of *Isomeris arborea.* Current Sci. 23:61–63.

Maheshwari, P. and R. C. Sachar, 1954b. The endosperm nodules of *Capsella bursa-pastoris.* Sci. and Cult. 19:413–414.

Maheshwari, P. and R. C. Sachar, 1955. So-called endosperm embryos in *Isomeris arborea.* Nature 176:470–472.

Maheshwari, P. and R. C. Sachar, 1963. Polyembryony. *In* P. Maheshwari, (ed.): Recent Advances in the Embryology of Angiosperms, Delhi: 265–296.

Maheshwari, P., R. C. Sachar, and R. N. Chopra, 1955. Embryological studies in mango, *Mangifera indica*. Proc. 42nd. Indian Sci. Congr. 3:233.

Maheshwari, P. and B. Singh 1934. A preliminary note on the morphology of the aerial and underground flowers of *Commelina benghalensis*. Current Sci. 3:158–160.

Maheshwari, P. and B. Singh, 1943. Studies in the family Alismaceae, 5. The embryology of *Machaerocarpus californicus*. Proc. Nat. Inst. Sci. India 9:311–322.

Maheshwari, P. and B. Singh, 1952. Embryology of *Macrosolen cochinchinensis*. Bot. Gaz. 114:20–32.

Maheshwari, P. and U. B. Singh, 1930. The development of the female gametophyte of *Asphodelus tenuifolius*. J. Indian bot. Soc. 9:31–39.

Maheshwari, P. and A. R. Srinivasan, 1944. Contribution to the embryology of *Rudbeckia bicolor*. New Phytol. 44:135–142.

Maheshwari, S. C., 1954. The embryology of *Wolffia*. Phytomorphology 4:355–365.

Maheshwari, S. C., 1955. The occurrence of bisporic embryo sacs in angiosperms—a critical review. Phytomorphology 5:67–99.

Maheshwari, S. C., 1956a. Endosperm and seed of *Wolffia*. Nature 178:925–926.

Maheshwari, S. C., 1956b. The endosperm and embryo of *Lemna* and systematic position of the Lemnaceae. Phytomorphology 6:51–55.

Maheshwari, S. C. 1958. *Spirodela polyrrhiza:* the link between the aroids and the duckweeds. Nature 181; 1745–1746.

Maheshwari, S. C., 1959. Systematic position of the family Lemnaceae. Congr. Internatl. Bot. 9th. 2:246–247.

Maheshwari, S. C. and B. Baldev, 1958. A contribution to the morphology and embryology of *Commelina forskalaei*. Phytomorphology 8:277–298.

Maheshwari, S. C. and R. N. Kapil, 1963a. Morphological and embryological studies on the Lemnaceae. 1. The floral structure and gametophytes of *Lemna paucicostata*. Amer. J. Bot. 50:677–686.

Maheshwari, S. C. and R. N. Kapil, 1963b. Morphological and embryological studies on the Lemnaceae. 2. The endosperm and embryo of *Lemna paucicostata*. Amer. J. Bot. 50:907–914.

Maheshwari, S. C. and R. N. Kapil, 1964. Morphological and embryological studies on the Lemnaceae. 3. The seed and seedling of *Lemna paucicostata*. J. Indian bot. Soc. 43:270–277.

Maheshwari, S. C. and P. P. Khanna, 1956. The embryology of *Arisaema wallichianum*, and the systematic position of the Araceae. Phytomorphology 6:379–388.

Maheshwari, S. C. and N. Maheshwari, 1963. The female gametophyte, endosperm and embryo of *Spirodela polyrrhiza*. Beitr. z. Biol. Pflanzen. dtsch. 39:179–188.

Maheswari Devi, H., 1957. Embryological studies in the Compositae. *Gerbera jamesonii*. Proc. Indian Acad. Sci. B. 46:68–74.

Maheswari Devi, H., 1962. Embryological studies in Gentianaceae: Gentianoideae and Menyanthoideae. Proc. Indian Acad. Sci. B. 56:195–216.

Maheswari Devi, H., 1963. Embryological studies in Compositae. 4. Heliantheae. Proc. Indian Acad. Sci. B. 58:274–290.

Maheswari Devi, H., 1964. Embryological studies in Asclepiadaceae. Proc. Indian Acad. Sci. B. 60:52–65.

Mahlberg, P. G., 1959. Origin and development of the lactifer in the embryo of *Nerium oleander*. Congr. Internatl. Bot. 9th. 2:247.

Mahlberg, P. G., 1960. Embryogeny and histogenesis in *Nerium oleander*. 1. Organization of primary meristematic tissues. Phytomorphology 10:118–131.

Mahlberg, P. G., 1961. Embryogeny and histogenesis in *Nerium oleander*. 2. Origin and development of the non-articulated laticifer. Amer. J. Bot. 48:90–99.

Mahony, K. L., 1935. Morphological and cytological studies on *Fagopyrum esculentum*. 1. Amer. J. Bot. 22:460–475.

Mahony, K. L., 1936. Morphological and cytological studies on *Fagopyrum esculentum*. 2. Amer. J. Bot. 23:129–133.

Malecka, J., 1961. (Studies in the mode of reproduction of the diploid endemic species, *Taraxacum pieninicum*). Acta Biol. Cracov. Bot. 4:25–42.

Maleeva, Z. P., 1960. (Viability of embryo sac and pollen in alfalfa sown at different dates.) Tr. Prikladnoi Bot. Genet. i Selektsii 33:265–272.

Malte, M. O., 1910. Embryologiska och cytologiska undersökningar öfver *Mercurialis annua*. Diss. Lund.

Maneval, W. E., 1914. The development of *Magnolia* and *Liriodendron,* including a discussion of the primitiveness of the Magnoliaceae. Bot. Gaz. 57:1–31.

Mangenot, G., 1952. L'évolution de l'ovule, du pistil et du fruit. Ann. Biol. 28:149–162.

Mani, A. P., 1960. Development of ovule and embryo sac in *Croton bonplandianum*. Sci. and Cult. 25:439–440.

Mani, V. K. S., 1947. Vivipary in *Pyrus malus*. Current Sci. 16:321.

Mann, G., 1891. Criticism of the views with regard to the embryo sac of angiosperms. Trans. and Proc. Bot. Soc. Edinb. 19:136–148.

Mann, G., 1892. The embryo sac of *Myosurus minimus*. Trans. and Proc. bot. Soc. Edinb. 29:351.

Mann, L. K. and J. Robinson, 1950. Fertilization, seed development and fruit growth as related to fruit set in the Cantaloupe, *Cucumis melo*. Amer. J. Bot. 37:685–697.

Manshard, E., 1936. Embryologische Untersuchungen an *Styrax obassia*. Planta 25:364–383.

Manum, S., 1955. Some remarks on the pollen grains of *Chrysanthemum globosa* and *C. carinatum*. Blyttia 13:90–95.

Marano, I., 1954a. Lo sviluppo del fiore in *Bupleurum dianthifolium* con particolare riguardo ad un corpo citoplasmatico fibrillare nella megasporogenesi. N. G. bot. Ital. 61:201–213.

Marano, I., 1954b. Lo sviluppo del gamitofito femminile in *Bupleurum spinosum*. N. G. bot. Ital. 61:720–721.

Markowski, A., 1912. Beiträge zur Kenntnis der Gattung *Pedilanthus*. Diss. Halle.

Marsden-Jones, E. M., 1935. *Ranunculus ficaria:* life history and pollination. J. Linn. Soc. Lond. (Bot.) 1:31–55.

Martin, A. C., 1946. The comparative internal morphology of seeds. Amer. Midl. Nat. 36:573–660.

Martin, G. W., 1892. Development of the flower and embryo sac in *Aster* and *Solidago*. Bot. Gaz. 17:353–358, 406–411.

Martin, J. N., 1913. The physiology of pollen in *Trifolium pratense*. Bot. Gaz. 56:112–126.

Martin, J. N., 1914. Comparative morphology of some Leguminosae. Bot. Gaz. 58:154–167.

Martin, R. W. and F. H. Smith, 1955. Megagametophyte development in *Chrysanthemum leucanthemum*. Bot. Gaz. 116:243–249.

Martini, E., 1939. Ricerche embriologiche sulle Martyniaceae. N. G. bot. Ital. 46:197–226.

Martinoli, G., 1939. Contributo all'embriologia delle Asteraceae. 1–3. N. G. bot. Ital. 46:259–298.

Martinoli, G., 1940a. Contributo all'embriologia delle Asteraceae. 4–5. N. G. bot. Ital. 47:287–322.

Martinoli, G., 1940b. La priorita della denominazione "tipo *Euphorbia dulcis*" (1927), sulla denominazione "tipo *Fritillaria*" (1937) N. G. bot. Ital. 47:464–468.

Martinoli, G., 1942. Contributo alla embriologia delle Asteraceae. 6. N. G. bot. Ital. 49:311–336.

Martinoli, G., 1943. Contributo all'embriologia delle Asteraceae. 7–8. N. G. bot. Ital. 50:1–23.

Martinoli, G., 1948. Embriologia della *Peperomia maculosa*. N. G. bot. Ital. 55:235–250.

Martinoli, G. and B. Angiolini di Moisè, 1963. Ricerche embriologiche su *Senecio vulgaris* var. *thyrrenus*. N. G. bot. Ital. 70:482–492.

Martins, T., 1909. La macrosporogénèse dans le *Funkia ovata*. Broteria 8:66–75.

Mar'yakhina, I. Y., T. P. Mikulovich, and S. V. Baleva, 1961. (The cytoembryological nature of the stages of organogenesis in *Polygonum* in relation to heterostyly.) *In* (Plant Morphogenesis) Moscow 1:301–304.

Maryanovich, O., 1939. (On the cytology and embryology of the hybrid Fi *Nicotiana rustica*, var. *Unterwalness* x *N. quadrivalvis*.) Zhur. Inst. bot. Acad. Sci. RSS Ukraine 21–22:187–195.

Masand, P., 1963a. Embryology of *Nelsonia campestris*. Phytomorphology 13:82–91.

Masand, P., 1963b. Embryology of *Zygophyllum fabago*. Phytomorphology 13:293–302.

Mascré, M., 1919a. Sur le rôle de l'assise nourricière du pollen. C. R. Acad. Sci. Paris 168:1120–1122.

Mascré, M., 1919b. Nouvelles remarques sur le rôle de l'assise nourricière du pollen. C. R. Acad. Sci. Paris 168:1214–1216.

Mascré, M., 1921. Recherches sur le développement de l'anthère chez les Solanacées. Contribution à l'étude de l'assise nourricière du pollen. Thesis. Paris.

Mascré, M., 1922. L'étamine des Borraginacées. C. R. Acad. Sci. Paris 175:987–989.

Mascré, M., 1925a. Sur le périplasmodium staminal des Commelinacées. C. R. Acad. Sci. Paris 181:1165–1166.

Mascré, M., 1925b. Sur l'évolution de l'étamine des Commelinacées. Bull. Soc. bot. France 72:1060–1066.

Mascré, M., 1928. Sur le tapis staminal et les grains de pollen de l'*Arum maculatum*. C. R. Acad. Sci. Paris 186:1642.

Mascré, M. and R. Thomas, 1930. Le tapis staminal chez les angiosperms. Bull. Soc. bot. France 77:654–664.

Mason, C. T., 1949. Development of the embryo sac in the genus *Limnanthes*. Amer. J. Bot. 36:799.

Mason, H. L., 1938. The flowering of *Wolffiella lingulata*. Madroño 4:241–251.

Massart, J., 1894. La récapitulation et l'innovation en embryologie végétale. Bull. Soc. Roy. bot. Belg. 33:150–247.

Massart, J., 1902. Sur la pollination sans fécondation. Bull. Jard. bot. Brux. 1:89–95.

Masters, N. T., 1869. Vegetable Teratology. London.

Mathé, O., 1928. Développement autonome de l'albumen de Ricin. Etude cytologique. Bull. Soc. hist. nat. Auvergne 1928:41–62.

Mathewson, C. A., 1906. The behavior of the pollen tube in *Houstonia coerulea*. Bull. Torrey bot. Cl. 33:487–493.

Mathur, K. L., 1934. A note on the presence of parietal cells in the nucellus of *Convolvulus arvensis*. Current Sci. 3:160–161.

Mathur, K. L., 1940. A note on the development of the embryo sac of *Vogelia indica*. Current Sci. 9:180–182.

Mathur, K. L. and R. Khan, 1941. The development of the embryo sac in *Vogelia indica*. Proc. Indian Acad. Sci. B. 13:360–368.

Mathur, N., 1956. The embryology of *Limnanthes*. Phytomorphology 6:41–51.

Matsuda, M., 1928. On the origin of big pollen grains with abnormal number of chromosomes. Cellule 38:215–242.

Matthews, J. R. and E. M. Knox, 1926. The comparative morphology of the stamen in the Ericaceae. Trans. and Proc. bot. Soc. Edinb. 29:243–281.

Matthews, J. R. and G. Taylor, 1926. The structure and development of the stamen in *Erica hirtiflora*. Trans. and Proc. bot. Soc. Edinb. 29:235–242.

Matthiessen, A., 1962. A contribution to the embryology of *Paeonia*. Acta Hort. Berg. 20:57–61.

Matthysen, J. D., 1912. Cytologische und anatomische Untersuchungen an *Beta vulgaris*. Zeit. Ver. dtsch. Zuckerind. 49:137–151.

Maugini, E., 1953. Ricerche cito-embriologiche su *Piper medium* var. *ceanothifolium*. Caryologia 5:282–287.

Maugini, E., 1962. Morfologia florale, embriologia ed embriogenesi in *Leontopodium alpinum* var. *typicum*. N. G. bot. Ital. 69:1–18.

Mauritzon, J., 1930. Beitrag zur Embryologie der Crassulaceen. Bot. Notiser 1930:233–250.

Mauritzon, J., 1933a. Studien über die Embryologie der Familien Crassulaceae und Saxifragaceae. Diss. Lund.

Mauritzon, J., 1933b. Über die systematische Stellung der Familien Hydrostachyaceae und Podostemonaceae. Bot. Notiser 1933:172–180.

Mauritzon, J., 1933c. Über die Embryologie der Turneraceae und Frankeniaceae. Bot. Notiser 1933:543–555.

Mauritzon, J., 1934a. Zur Embryologie einiger Lythraceen. Acta Hort. Göteb. 9:1–21.

Mauritzon, J., 1934b. Ein Beitrag zur Embryologie der Phytolaccaceen und Cactaceen. Bot. Notiser 1934:111–135.

Mauritzon, J., 1934c. Etwas über die Embryologie der Zygophyllaceen sowie einige Fragmente über die der Humiriaceen. Bot. Notiser 1934: 409–422.

Mauritzon, J., 1934d. Zur Embryologie einiger Gruinales. Svensk bot. Tidsk. 28:84–102.

Mauritzon, J., 1934e. Zur Embryology der Elaeocarpaceae. Arkiv. f. Bot. 26A:1–8.

Mauritzon, J., 1934f. Die Embryologie einiger Capparidaceen sowie von *Tovaria pendula*. Arkiv. f. Bot. 26A:1–14.

Mauritzon, J., 1934g. Die Endosperm- und Embryoentwicklung einiger Acanthaceen. Lunds Univ. Årsskr. (2) 30:1–41.

Mauritzon, J., 1935a. Embryologische Angaben über Theophrastaceen. Archiv. f. Bot. 28 B(1): 1–4.

Mauritzon, J., 1935b. Über die Embryologie der Familie Rutaceae. Svensk. bot. Tidskr. 29:319–347.

Mauritzon, J., 1935c. Kritik von J. Wiger's Abhandlung "Embryological studies 11:317–327.

Mauritzon, J., 1935d. Etwas über die Embryologie der Bignoniaceen. Bot. Notiser 1935:60–77.

Mauritzon, J., 1935e. Kritik von J. Wiger's Abhandlung "Embryological studies on the families Buxaceae, Meliaceae, Simarubaceae and Burseraceae." Bot. Notiser 1935:490–502.

Mauritzon, J., 1936a. Die Endospermentwicklung von *Sesamum indicum* und *orientale*. Arkiv. f. Bot. 28B:1–6.

Mauritzon, J., 1936b. Zur Embryologie einiger Parietales-Familien. Svensk bot. Tidskr. 30:79–113.

Mauritzon, J., 1936c. Embryologische Angaben über Stackhousiaceae, Hippocrateaceae und Icacinaceae. Svensk bot. Tidskr. 30:541–550.

Mauritzon, J., 1936d. Zur Embryologie und systematischen Abgrenzung der Reihen Terebinthales und Celastrales. Bot. Notiser 1936:161–212.

Mauritzon, J., 1936e. Samenbau und Embryologie einiger Scitamineen. Lunds Univ. Årsskr. (2) 30:1–31.

Mauritzon, J., 1936f. Zur Embryologie der Berberidaceen. Acta Hort. Göteb. 11:1–18.

Mauritzon, J., 1939a. Über die Embryologie von Marcgravia. Bot. Notiser 1939:249–255.

Mauritzon, J., 1939b. Die Bedeutung der embryologischen Forschung für das naturliche System der Pflanzen. Lunds Univ. Årsskr. (2) 35:1–70.

Mauritzon, J., 1939c. Contribution to the embryology of the orders Rosales and Myrtales. Lunds Univ. Årsskr. (2) 35:1–121.

Mayne, W. W., 1937. Annual report of the coffee scientific officer, 1936–1937. The Mysore Coffee Exper. Sta. Bull. 16.

McAllister, F., 1909. The development of the embryo sac of *Smilacina stellata*. Bot. Gaz. 48:200–215.

McAllister, F., 1913. On the cytology and embryology of *Smilacina racemosa*. Trans. Wisc. Acad. Sci., Arts and Letters 17:599–660.

McAllister, F., 1914. The development of the embryo sac in the Convallariaceae. Bot. Gaz. 58:136–153.

McCann, C., 1942. Observations on Indian duckweeds, Lemnaceae. J. Bombay nat. hist. Soc. 43:148–162.

McCann, L. P., 1942. Development of the pistellate flower and structure of the fruit of tung, *Aleurites fordii*. J. Agr. Res. 65:361–378.

McCann, L. P., 1945. Embryology of the Tung tree. J. Agr. Res. 71:215–229.

McCarthy, E. M., 1928. The structure and development of *Astelia nervosa* var. *sylvestris*. Trans. and Proc. New Zeal. Inst. 59:343–360.

McCollum, R. L., 1939. The development of embryo sac and seed of *Commelina angustifolia*. Bull. Torrey bot. Cl. 66:539–548.

McCoy, R. W., 1949. On the embryology of *Swertia carolinensis*. Bull. Torrey bot. Cl. 76:430–439.

McDonald, C. C., 1927. A study of seed development in three species of *Erigeron* with special reference to apogamy. Bull. Torrey bot. Cl. 54:479–497.

McGahan, M. W., 1961. Studies on the seed of Banana. 1. Anatomy of the seed and embryo of *Musa balbisiana*. Amer. J. Bot. 48:230–238.

McKay, J. W., 1947. Embryology of pecan. J. Agr. Res. 74:263–283.

McKenney, R. E. B., 1898. Observations on the development of some embryo sacs. Bot. Contrib. Univ. Pennsylv. 2:80–86.

Meada, Y., 1932. Cytological studies in *Colocasia*. Proc. Crop Sci. Soc. (Japan) 4.

Meier, K. I., 1960. (The embryology of *Nuphar luteum*.) Byull. Moskov Obshch. Ispyt. Prirody Otd. Biol. 65:48–59.

Meier, K. I., 1962. (The embryology of *Coronaria flos-cuculi*.) Bot. Zhur. 47:847–852.

Melikyan, A. P., 1964. (Histogenesis of the seed coat in *Brasenia shreberi* and *Nymphaea capensis*.) Vest. Leningr. Univ. No. 9. Ser. Biol. 2:121–125.

Mellink, J. F. A., 1880. Over de ontwickkeling von den keimsack bij Angiospermen. Ak. Proefschr. Leiden.

Mendes, A. J. T., 1941. Cytological observations in *Coffea*. 6. Embryo and endosperm development in *Coffea arabica*. Amer. J. Bot. 28:784–789.

Mendes, L. O. T., 1947. Poliembrionia em *Hevea brasiliensis*. Rev. Agr. 22:161–164.

Mendiola, N. B., 1926. A manual of plant breeding for the tropics. Manila.

Mereminski, H., 1936. Über Embryosackentwicklung bei *Begonia incana*. Ein Beitrag zur Embryologie der Gattung *Begonia*. Bull. Internat. Acad. Polon. B. 1:53–92.

Merl, E. M., 1915. Beiträge zur Kenntnis der Utricularien und Genliseen. Flora 108:127–200.

Merrell, W. D., 1900. A contribution to the life history of *Silphium*. Bot. Gaz. 29:99–133.

Merry, J., 1937. Formation of periderm in the endosperm of *Crinum asiaticum*. Papers Mich. Acad. Sci, Arts & Letters 22:159–164.

Merry, J., 1941. Studies on the embryo of *Hordeum sativum*. 1. The development of the embryo. Bull. Torrey bot. Cl. 68:585–598.

Merwe, R. B. van der, 1957. (An embryological study on *Themeda triandra*.) J. Sth. Afr. Bot. 23:139–149.

Merz, M., 1897. Untersuchungen über die Samenentwicklung der Utricularieen. Flora 84:69–87.

Messeri, A., 1928. Embriologia di *Grevillea macrostachya*. N. G. bot. Ital. 34:1037–1042.

Messeri, A., 1931. Ricerche embriologiche e cariologiche sopra i genri *Allium* e *Nothoscordum*. N. G. bot. Ital. 38:408–441.

Messeri, A., 1950. Alcuni dati sulla embriologia ed embriogenesi di *Olea europaea*. N. G. bot. Ital. 57:149–169.

Mestre, J. C., 1957a. The presence of two ovules in the ovary of some Cynarées. Observations on *Centaurea collina* and *Carduus defloratus*. Bull. Soc. bot. France 104:37–40.

Mestre, J. C., 1957b. Composées-Cynarées. Développement de l'embryon chez le *Carduus nutans*. C. R. Acad. Sci. Paris 245:355–358.

Mestre, J. C., 1958. Embryogénie des Composées-Cynarées. Développement de l'embryon chez le *Cnicus benedictus.* C. R. Acad. Sci. Paris 247:333–336.

Mestre, J. C., 1964a. Recherches d'embryogénie comparée: Les rapports phylogénétiques des Composées. Thèse. Paris.

Mestre, J. C., 1964b. Embryogénie des Amentacées. Développement de l'embryon chez l'*Alnus glutinosa.* C. R. Acad. Sci. Paris 258:5949–5951.

Metcalfe, C. R., 1936. An interpretation of the morphology of the single cotyledon of *Ranunculus ficaria,* based on embryology and seedling anatomy. Ann. Bot. 50:103–120.

Meunier, A., 1897. Le développement séminal dans le genre *Veronica.* Cellule 12:297–333.

Meyen, F. G. F., 1841. Observations sur la fécondation des végétaux. Ann. Sci. nat. Bot. (2) 15.

Meyer, C. F., 1958. Cell patterns in early embryogeny of the McIntosh apple. Amer. J. Bot. 45:341–349.

Meyer, C. F., 1959. The development of the cotyledons and hypocotyl during the late embryogeny of the McIntosh apple. Congr. Internatl. Bot. 9th. 2:261.

Meyer, J., M. Abgrall, and M. Hortin, 1962. De l'existence chez certaines Salpiglossidées d'un tissu chalazien issu de l'albumen et d'aspect haustorial. C. R. Acad. Sci. Paris 254:2629–2631.

Meyer, K., 1909. Untersuchungen über *Thismia clandestina.* Bull. Soc. Imp. Nat. Mosc. 23:1–18.

Meyer, K., 1925. Über die Entwicklung des Pollens bei *Leontodon autumnalis.* Ber. dtsch. bot. Ges. 43:108–114.

Meyer, S., 1938. Studies in the family Apocynaceae. J. Dept. Sci. Cal. Univ. 1:131–158.

Mez, C., 1887. Beiträge zur Kenntnis der Umbelliferen-Embryos. Verh. Bot. Ver. Prov. Brandenburg 29:30–36.

Mezzetti-Bambacioni, V., 1940. Le modificazioni dell'apice nucellare di *Tulipa gesneriana* in seguito all'impollinazioni. N. G. bot. Ital. 47:421–423.

Mezzetti-Bambacioni, V., 1943. Sulla constituzione del gametofito femminile adulto e sull'origine in *Tulipa gesneriana.* Ann. di Bot. (Roma) 22:153–172.

Michaelis, P., 1925. Zur Cytologie und Embryoentwicklung von *Epilobium.* Ber. dtsch. bot. Ges. 43:61–67.

Michell, M. R., 1915. The embryo sac and embryo of *Striga lutea.* Bot. Gaz. 59:124–135.

Michell, M. R., 1916. The embryo sac of *Richardia africana.* Bot. Gaz. 61:325–336.

Miers, J., 1866. On *Myostoma,* a new genus of the Burmanniaceae. Trans. Linn. Soc. Lond. (Bot.) 25:461–476.

Miers, J. 1881. On a new genus of plants of the family Burmanniaceae. Trans. Linn. Soc. London (Bot.) 20:373–382.

Mildenberger, G., 1963. (Studies on the taxonomy of the genus *Malus.* 2. Embryological investigations.) Arch. f. Gartbau 11:493–503.

Miller, E. C., 1920. Development of the pistillate spikelet and fertilization in *Zea mays.* J. Agr. Res. 18:255–267.

Miller, H. A., and H. J. Kline, 1959. The development of the androecium, the gynoecium and the embryo of *Chenopodium ambrosioides.* Congr. Internatl. 9th. 2:263–264.

400 BIBLIOGRAPHY

Miller, H. A. and R. H. Wetmore, 1945. Studies in the developmental anatomy of *Phlox drummondii*. 1. The embryo. Amer. J. Bot. 32:588–599.

Miller, W. L., 1929. Staminate flower of *Echinocystis lobata*. Bot. Gaz. 88:262–284.

Millsaps, V., 1936. The structure and development of the seeds of *Paulownia tomentosa*. J. Elisha Mitchell Sci. Soc. 52:56–75.

Millsaps, V., 1940. The structure and development of the seed of *Cynoglossum amabile*. J. Elisha Mitchell Sci. Soc. 56:140–164.

Mirande, K., 1905. Recherches sur le développement des Cassythacées. Ann. Sci. nat. Bot. (9) 2:181–287.

Mirbel, C. F. B., 1815. Elements de physiologie végétale et de botanique. Paris.

Mirbel, C. F. B., 1829. Nouvelles recherches sur la structure et les développements de l'ovule végétale. Ann. Sci. nat. 17:302–318.

Mirbel, C. F. B., 1830a. Nouvelles recherches sur la structure et les développements de l'ovule vegetale. Mém. Acad. Roy. Sci. Inst. France 9.

Mirbel, C. F. B., 1830b. Additions aux nouvelles recherches sur la structure et les développements de l'ovule. Mém. Acad. Roy. Sci. Inst. France 9.

Mirbel, C. F. B., 1835. Complément des observations sur le *Marchantia polymorpha*. Mém. Acad. Roy. Sci. Inst. France 13:39–74.

Misra, K. C., 1937. The antipodals of Verbenaceae. Current Sci. 6:98–99.

Misra, K. C., 1939. A contribution to the embryology of the Verbenaceae. Proc. Indian Acad. Sci. B. 9:49–56.

Misra, K. C., 1948. Polyembryony in *Dichanthium annulatum*. Current Sci. 17:91.

Misra, R. C., 1962. Contribution to the embryology of *Arabidopsis thalianum*. Agra Univ. J. Res. (Sci.) 11:191–199.

Misra, R. C., 1964. Ovule in *Plantago*. Current Sci. 33: 438–439.

Misra, S., 1957. Floral morphology of the family Compositae. 1. The flower and gametophytes of *Flaveria repandra*. J. Indian bot. Soc. 36:503–512.

Misra, S., 1964. Floral morphology of the family Compositae. 2. Development of the seed and fruit in *Flaveria repandra*. Bot. Mag. (Tokyo) 77:290–296.

Misra, S., 1965. Floral morphology of the family Compositae. 3. Embryology of *Siegesbeckia orientalis*. Aust. J. Bot. 13:1–10.

Mitra, J. N., 1945. On the development of the female gametophyte in *Hydrolea zeylanica*. Current Sci. 14:206.

Mitra, J. N., 1947a. A contribution to the life history of *Hydrolea zeylanica*. J. Indian bot. Soc. 26:51–61.

Mitra, J. N., 1947b. A contribution to the embryology of some Compositae. J. Indian bot. Soc. 26:105–123.

Mitra, J. N. and R. M. Dutta, 1949. A note on the development of embryo sac and endosperm in *Alangium chinensis*. Bull. bot. Soc. Bengal 3:11–15.

Mladentseva, M. S., 1960. (An embryological study of hop, *Humulus* sp.) Dokl. Moskov. Sel'skokhoz. Akad. im K. A. Timiryazeva 59:171–177.

Mladentseva, M. S., 1963. (Some data on a study of parthenogenesis of hop.) Dokl. Moskov. Sel'skokhoz. Akad. im K. A. Timiryazeva 93:195–201.

Mlodzianowski, F., 1964. The structure and the later stages of development in the embryo sac of *Thamnochortus fruticosus*. Bull. Soc. Amis Sci. et Lett., Poznan. D. 4:3–11.

Mlyniec, W., 1961. The mechanism of pollination and generative reproduction in *Vicia villosa*. Genet. Polon. 2:81–82.

Modilewski, J., 1908a. Zur Embryobildung von *Gunnera chilensis*. Ber. dtsch. bot. Ges. 26:550–556.

Modilewski, J., 1908b. Zur Samenbildung einiger Urticifloren. Flora 98:423–470.

Modilewski, J., 1909a. Zur Embryobildung von *Euphorbia procera*. Ber. dtsch. bot. Ges. 27:21–26.

Modilewski, J., 1909b. Zur Embryobildung einiger Onagraceen. Ber. dtsch. bot. Ges. 27:287–292.

Modilewski, J., 1910. Weitere Beiträge zur Embryobildung einiger Euphorbiaceen. Ber. dtsch. bot. Ges. 28:413–418.

Modilewski, J., 1911. Über die anomale Embryosackbildung bei *Euphorbia palustris* und anderen Euphorbiaceen. Ber. dtsch. bot. Ges. 29:430–436.

Modilewski, J., 1918. (Cytological and embryological studies on *Neottia nidus-avis*.) Verh. Kièw Ges. Nat. 26:1–55.

Modilewski, J., 1925. Zur Kenntnis der Polyembryonie von *Allium odorum*. Bull. Jard. bot. Kieff 2:9–19.

Modilewski, J., 1928a. Weitere Beiträge zur Embryologie und Cytologie von *Allium*-Arten. Bull. Jard. bot. Kieff 7–8:57–61.

Modilewski, J., 1928b. Die embryologische Entwicklung von *Thesium intermedium*. Bull. Jard. bot. Kieff 7–8:65–70.

Modilewski, J., 1929. Der weibliche Gametophyt der Angiospermen. Ukrain. Bot. Rev. 5:5–40.

Modilewski, J., 1930. Neue Beiträge zur Polyembryonie von *Allium odorum*. Ber. dtsch. bot. Ges. 48:285–294.

Modilewski, J., 1931. Die Embryobildung bei *Allium odorum*. Bull. Jard. bot. Kieff 12–13:27–48.

Modilewski, J., 1936. (Cytological investigation of the genus *Nicotiana*. 1. Cytology and embryology of the amphidiploid *Nicotiana ditagla*.) Zhur. Inst. bot. Akad. Sci. Ukraine 7:7–29.

Modilewski, J., 1937a. (Cytogenetical investigation of the genus *Nicotiana*. 3. Cytology and embryology of the hybrid *N. rustica*, Var. *Azerbaidzhan*, x *N. glauca*.) Zhur. Inst. bot. Akad. Sci. Ukraine 11:59–71.

Modilewski, J., 1937b. (Cytogenetical investigation of the genus *Nicotiana*. 4. On the embryology and cytology of the species of section Petunioides and the classification of the genus *Nicotiana*.) Zhur. Inst. bot. Akad. Sci. Ukraine 13–14:63–79.

Modilewski, J. S., 1957. (On the process of fecundation in Angiosperms or how not to defend "somatic fecundation.") Ukrain. bot. Zhurn. 14:86–98.

Modilewski, J. S. and R. A. Beilis, 1937. (The embryology and cytology of wheat. 1. Embryogenesis of wheat, from the archesporium to the embryo.) Zhurn. Inst. bot. Akad. Sci. RSS Ukraine 21–22:127–141.

Modilewski, J. S. and R. A. Beilis, 1938. (The embryology and cytology of wheat. 2. The stages of the maturing of the embryo and caryopsis, of their germination and of earing.) Zhurn. Inst. bot. Akad. Sci. RSS Ukraine 26–27:13–39.

Modilewski, J. and L. Dzubenko, 1937. (Cytological investigation of the genus *Nicotiana*. 5. A cytological and embryological study of the hybrids *N. rustica* x *N. paniculata*; *N. paniculata* x *N. glauca* and *N. rustica* x *N. glauca*.) Zhur. Inst. bot. Akad. Sci. Ukraine 13–14:109–125.

Modilewski, J. and L. Dzubenko, 1940. (Cytogenetical investigations of the genus *Nicotiana*. 8.) Zhur. Inst. bot. Acad. Sci. Ukraine 31:3–12.

402 BIBLIOGRAPHY

Moffett, A. A., 1932. Studies on the formation of multinuclear giant pollen grains in *Kniphofia*. J. Genet. 25:315–337.

Moggi, G., 1950. Embryologia ed embriogenesi in *Cytisus laburnam*. N. G. bot. Ital. 57:186–209.

Mohan Ram, H. Y., 1956. Endosperm and embryo development in some Acanthaceae. Proc. 43rd. Indian Sci. Congr. 3:235–236.

Mohan Ram, H. Y., 1959a. Embryological characters in the classification of the Acanthaceae. Congr. Internatl. Bot. 9th. 2:267.

Mohan Ram, H. Y., 1959b. Endosperm in *Eranthemum nervosum*. Current Sci. 28:169–170.

Mohan Ram, H. Y., 1960a. The development of the seed of *Andrographis serpyllifolia*. Amer. J. Bot. 47:215–219.

Mohan Ram, H. Y., 1960b. Post-fertilization studies in the ovule of *Ruellia tuberosa*. Lloydia 23:21–27.

Mohan Ram, H. Y., 1961. Seed development in *Adhatoda vasica*. Canad. J. Bot. 30:207–214.

Mohan Ram, H. Y., 1962. Post-fertilization development of the ovule in *Barleria cristata*. J. Indian bot. Soc. 41:288–296.

Mohan Ram, H. Y. and I. Kamini, 1964. Embryology and fruit development in *Withania somnifera*. Phytomorphology 14:574–587.

Mohan Ram, H. Y. and P. Masand, 1962. Endosperm and seed development in *Andragraphis echioides*. Current Sci. 31:7–8.

Mohan Ram, H. Y. and P. Masand, 1963. Embryology of *Nelsonia campestris*. Phytomorphology 13:82–91.

Mohan Ram, H. Y. and R. Nath, 1964. The morphology and embryology of *Cannabis sativa*. Phytomorphology 14:414–429.

Mohan Ram, H. Y. and A. Satsangi, 1963. Induction of cell divisions in mature endosperm of *Ricinus communis* during germination. Current Sci. 32:28–29.

Mohan Ram, H. Y. and P. P. Sehgal, 1958. Life history of *Justicia simplex*. Phytomorphology 8:124–136.

Mohan Ram, H. Y. and M. Wadhi, 1964. Endosperm in Acanthaceae. Phytomorphology 14:388–413.

Mohan Ram, H. Y. and M. Wadhi, 1965. Embryology and the delimitation of the Acanthaceae. Phytomorphology 15:201–205.

Mohl, H. von, 1855. Der vorgebliche entcheidende Sieg der Schleiden'schen Befruchtungslehre. Bot. Zeit. 13:385–388.

Mohrbutter, C., 1936. Embryologische Studien an Loganiaceen. Planta 26:64–80.

Moissl, E., 1941. Vergleichende embryologische Studien über die Familie der Caprifoliaceae. Österr. bot. Zeit. 90:153–212.

Mol, W. E. de, 1923. Duplication of generative nuclei by means of physiological stimuli and its significance. Genetica 5:225–272.

Molliard, M., 1895. Sur le sort des cellules antipodes chez le *Knautia arvensis*. Bull. Soc. bot. France 42:9–10.

Molliard, M., 1896. Sur la formation du pollen dans les ovules du *Petunia hybrida*. Rev. gén. Bot. 8:46.

Money, L. L., I. W. Bailey, and B. G. L. Swamy, 1950. Morphology and relationships of the Monimiaceae. J. Arnold Arboret. 31:372–404.

Monnier, G. le, 1887. Sur la valeur morphologique de l'albumen chez les angiospermes. Jour. de Bot. 1:140–142.

Montanelli, R., 1907. Sulla divisione delle cellule madri del polline nelle Cucurbitaceae. Bull. soc. bot. Ital.:116–119.

Montemartini, L., 1899. Contributo allo studio del'anatomia del frutto e del seme delle Opunzie. Atti Ist. Bot. Univ. Pavia (2) 5:59–68.

Montemartini, L., 1905. Studio anatomico sulla *Datisca cannabina*. Ann. di Bot. (Roma) 3:101–112.

Montéverdé, M., 1880. Recherches embryologiques sur l'*Orchis maculata*. Bull. Acad. St. Petersb. 26:326–335.

Montgomery, F. H. and S.-J. Yang, 1960. Cytological studies on the genus *Erigeron*. Canad. J. Bot. 38:381–386.

Moore, R. J., 1948. Cytotaxonomic studies in the Loganiaceae. 2. Embryology of *Polypremum procumbens*. Amer. J. Bot. 35:403–410.

Moore, R. J. and D. R. Lindsay, 1953. Fertility and polyploidy of *Euphorbia cyparissias* in Canada. Canad. J. Bot. 31:152–163.

Moore, W. and M. E. Behney, 1908. The condition of certain winter buds. Bot. Gaz. 45:54.

Moquin-Tandon, A., 1841. Eléments de Tératologie végétale ou Histoire abrégée des anomalies de l'organisation dans les végétaux. Paris.

Morley, T., 1953. The genus *Mouriria*. Univ. Calif. Publ. Bot. 26:223–313.

Morong, T., 1888. Studies in the Typhaceae. Bull. Torrey bot. Cl. 15:1–8.

Morrison, J. W., 1955. Fertilization and post-fertilization development in wheat. Canad. J. Bot. 33:168–176.

Morse, W. C., 1907. Contribution to the life history of *Cornus florida*. Ohio Nat. 8:197–204.

Morstatt, H. 1902. Beiträge zur Kenntnis der Resedaceen. Diss. Heidelberg.

Moskov, I. V., 1964. (The development of the embryo in some *Paeonia* varieties.) Bot. Zhur. 49:887–894.

Mottier, D. M., 1892. On the development of the embryo sac of *Arisaema triphyllum*. Bot. Gaz. 17:258–260.

Mottier, D. M., 1893a. On embryo sac and embryo of *Senecio aureus*. Bot. Gaz. 18:245–253.

Mottier, D. M., 1893b. Development of the embryo sac in *Acer rubrum*. Bot. Gaz. 18:375–377.

Mottier, D. M., 1895. Contributions to the embryology of the Ranunculaceae. Bot. Gaz. 20:241–248, 296–304.

Mottier, D. M., 1897. Beiträge zur Kenntnis der Kernteilung in den Pollenmutterzellen einiger Dikotylen und Monokotylen. Jahrb. f. wiss. Bot. 30:169–204.

Mottier, D. M., 1898a. Über das Verhalten der Kerne bei der Entwicklung des Embryosackes und die Vorgänge bei der Befruchtung. Jahrb. f. wiss. Bot. 31:125–158.

Mottier, D. M., 1898b. Endosperm haustoria in *Lilium candidum*. Proc. Indiana Acad. Sci. 8:168–169.

Mottier, D. M., 1903. The behavior of the chromosomes in the spore mother cells of higher plants and the homology of the pollen- and the embryo sac-mother cells. Bot. Gaz. 35:250–282.

Mottier, D. M., 1904. Fecundation in plants. Carnegie Inst., Washington.

Mottier, D. M., 1905. The embryology of some anomalous dicotyledons. Ann. Bot. 19:447–463.

Mottier, D. M., 1914. Mitosis in the pollen mother cells in *Acer negundo* and *Staphylea trifolia*. Ann. Bot. 28:115–133.

Movsesyan, S. N., 1963. (Behaviour of the male gamete of *Rudbeckia sullivanti.*) Isv. Akad. Nauk. Arm. SSR Biol. Nauk. 16:43–47.

Movsesyan, S. N., 1964. (Fertilization in *Rudbeckia maxima.*) Isv. Akad. Nauk. Arm. SSR Biol. Nauk. 17:77–83.

Mowery, M., 1929. Development of the pollen grain and the embryo sac of *Agropyron repens.* Bull. Torrey bot. Cl. 56:319–324.

Mücke, M., 1908. Über den Bau und die Entwicklung der Früchte und über die Herkunft von *Acorus calamus.* Bot. Zeit. 66:1–23.

Mühlethaler, K., 1933. Herkunft der Pollenklebstoffe und Funktion der Antherenhaare von *Cucurbita pepo.* Beih. bot. Ztbl. 50.

Mukherjee, P. K., 1957. Studies in the embryology of *Euphorbia hypericifolia.* Bull. bot. Soc. Univ. Saugar 9:7–18.

Mukherjee, P. K., 1958. The female gametophyte of *Acalphya malabarica,* with a brief discussion on the Penaea type of embryo sac. J. Indian bot. Soc. 37:504–508.

Mukherjee, P. K., 1961a. Embryology of two Euphorbiaceae. Proc. Indian Acad. Sci. B. 53:217–229.

Mukherjee, P. K., 1961b. Embryology of *Polygala.* Bull. bot. Soc. Coll. Sci. Nagpur 2:58–70.

Mukherjee, P. K., 1961c. Study of mature embryo, seed coat and fruit wall in *Euphorbia cristata.* J. biol. Sci. Bombay 4:1–5.

Mukherjee, P. K., 1962. Gametophytes of three Euphorbiaceae. Bull. bot. Soc. Coll. Sci. Nagpur 3:10–14.

Mukherjee, P. K., 1964. Further contribution to the embryology of the genus *Acalypha.* Proc. Nat. Acad. Sci. India B. 34:129–141.

Mukherjee, P. K. and M. D. Padhye, 1964. Contribution to the embryology of the genus *Phyllanthus.* Proc. Nat. Acad. Sci. India B. 34:117–128.

Mukherjee, P. K. and P. Venugopalan, 1957. Male and female gametophytes of *Ionidium suffruticosum.* J. Indian bot. Soc. 36:513–518.

Mukherjee, S. K., 1952. Abnormal microsporocytes in *Caesalpina pulcherrima.* Current Sci. 21:290.

Mukkada, A. J., 1962. Some observations on the embryology of *Dicraea stylosa.* *In* Plant Embryology: A Symposium. CSIR New Delhi:139–145.

Mukkada, A. J., 1963. The embryology of *Indotristicha ramosissima.* Proc. 50th. Indian Sci. Congr. 3:387.

Mukkada, A. J., 1964. An addition to the bisporic embryo sacs—the Dicraea type. New Phytol. 63:289–292.

Mulay, B. N., N. C. Nair, and M. S. R. K. Sastry, 1953. Contribution to the embryology of Vitaceae. 1. Male and female gametophytes of *Vitis pedata.* Proc. Rajasthan Acad. Sci. 4:17–28.

Müller, D., 1857. Über die Befruchtung der unkompletten Blüten einiger *Viola-*Arten. Bot. Zeit.

Müller, K., 1847. Beiträge zur Entwicklungsgeschichte des Pflanzenembryo. Bot. Zeit. 5:737–742, 753–761, 769–778.

Müller-Stoll, W. R. and G. Lerch, 1957. Über Nachweis, Entstehung und Eigenschaften der Kallosebildungen in Pollenschläuchen. Flora 144:297–334.

Müntzing, A., 1928. Pseudogamie in der Gattung *Potentilla.* Hereditas 11:267–283.

Müntzing, A., 1933. Apomictic and sexual seed formation in *Poa*. Hereditas 17:131–154.

Müntzing, A., 1940. Further studies on apomixis and sexuality in *Poa*. Hereditas 26:115–190.

Müntzing, A., 1947. Some observations on pollination and fruit setting in Ecuaderian *Cacao*. Hereditas 33.

Müntzing, A. and G. Müntzing, 1941. Some new results concerning apomixis, sexuality and polymorphism in *Potentilla*. Bot. Notiser 1941:237–278.

Müntzing, A. and G. Müntzing, 1945. The mode of reproduction of hybrids between sexual and apomictic *Potentilla argentea*. Bot. Notiser 1945:49–71.

Murbeck, S., 1897. Om vegetativ embryobilding hos flertalet Alchemillor och den förklaring öfver formfeständigheten inom slägtet, som densamma innebär. Bot. Notiser 1897:273–277.

Murbeck, S., 1901a. Über das Verhalten des Pollenschlauches bei *Alchemilla arvensis* und das Wesen der Chalazogamie. Lunds Univ. Årssk. (2). 36:1–18.

Murbeck, S., 1901b. Parthenogenetische Embryobildung in der Gattung *Alchemilla*. Lunds Univ. Årssk. (2) 36:1–41.

Murbeck, S., 1902a. Über Anomalien im Baue des Nucellus und des Embryosackes bei parthenogenetischen Arten der Gattung *Alchemilla*. Lunds Univ. Årssk. 38:1–10.

Murbeck, S., 1902b. Über die Embryologie von *Ruppia rostellata*. Kgl. Svensk Vet.-Akad. Handl. 36:1–21.

Murbeck, S., 1904. Parthenogenese bei den Gattungen *Taraxacum* und *Hieracium*. Bot. Notiser 1904:285–296.

Murbeck, S., 1916. Über die Organisation, Biologie und verwandtschaftliche Beziehungen der Neuradoideen. Lunds Univ. Årssk. (12) 2. (6).

Murgai, P., 1959. The development of the embryo in *Paeonia*: a reinvestigation. Phytomorphology 9:275–277.

Murgai, P., 1962. Embryology of *Paeonia*, together with a discussion on its systematic position. *In* Plant Embryology: A Symposium. CSIR. New Delhi:215–223.

Murphy, J. B., 1946. Megasporogenesis and development of the embryo sac of *Allium cernuum*. Bot. Gaz. 108:129–136.

Murthy, K. L., 1934. Gametogenesis and embryogeny of some Commelinaceae. Current Sci. 3:258–259.

Murthy, K. L., 1938. Gametogenesis and embryogeny in some Commelinaceae. J. Indian bot. Soc. 17:101–116.

Murthy, S. K. N., 1933a. Studies on the life history of *Limnophyton obtusifolium*. Current Sci. 2:53–54.

Murthy, S. K. N., 1933b. Cytological and morphological studies in *Limnophyton obtusifolium*. J. Mysore Univ. 7:1–32.

Murthy, S. K. N., 1935a. The life history of *Ottelia alismoides*. Proc. Indian Acad. Sci. B. 2:59–66.

Murthy, S. K. N., 1935b. A reply to the post-script of the paper on "Studies in the family Alismaceae. 1. *Limnophyton obtusifolium*" by B. M. Johri. J. Indian bot. Soc. 14:351.

Murthy, S. N., 1940. Studies in the Labiatae. 1. Embryology of *Ocimum sanctum, O. canum* and *O. basilicum*. J. Mysore Univ. B. 1:97–104.

Murthy, S. N., 1941a. The development of endosperm in *Leucas aspera*. Current Sci. 10:257–259.

Murthy, S. N., 1941b. Morphological studies on the Sapotaceae. 1. Embryology of *Bassia latifolia* and related genera. J. Mysore Univ. B. 2:67–80.

Murthy, S. N., 1942. Endosperm formation in *Anisomeles* sp. Current Sci. 11:284–285.

Murthy, S. N., 1946. Studies in the Labiateae. 2 Contribution to the morphology of *Ocimum adscendens*. J. Univ. Bombay 14:37–46.

Murthy, S. N., 1947. Studies in the Labiateae. 4. Contribution to the morphology of *Orthosiphon stramineus*. J. Indian bot. Soc. 26:87–94.

Murty, Y. S., 1959a. Studies in the order Piperales. 3. A contribution to the study of floral morphology of some species of *Peperomia*. J. Indian bot. Soc. 38:120–139.

Murty, Y. S., 1959b. Studies in the order Piperales. 5. A contribution to the study of floral morphology of some species of *Piper*. Proc. Indian Acad. Sci. B. 49:52–65.

Murty, Y. S., 1960. Studies in the order Piperales. 8. A contribution to the morphology of *Houttuynia cordata*. Phytomorphology 10:329–341.

Mutafjan, E. M., 1964. (Megasporogenesis and formation of the embryo sac in *Capsicum*.) Izv. Akad. Nauk. Arm. SSR, Biol. Nauk. 17:95–99.

Muzik, T. J., 1954. Development of fruit, seed, embryo and seedling of *Hevea braziliensis*. Amer. J. Bot. 41:39–43.

Myers, O., 1964. Megasporogenesis, megagametophyte development and endosperm development in *Hypericum virginicum*. Amer. J. Bot. 51:664 (Abstract.)

Nagaraj, M., 1952. Floral morphology of *Populus deltoides* and *P. tremuloides*. Bot. Gaz. 114:222–243.

Nagaraj, M., 1955. Floral morphology of *Terminalia belerica*. Current Sci. 24:89–90.

Nägeli, K., 1842. Zur Entwicklungsgeschichte des Pollens bei den Phanerogamen. Zürich.

Nagl, W., 1962. Über Endopolyploidie, Restitutionskernbildung und Kernstrukturen im Suspensor von Angiospermen und einer Gymnosperme. Österr. bot. Zeit. 109:431–494.

Nair, N. C., 1956. Early endosperm development in Meliaceae. Sci. and Cult. 22:34–35.

Nair, N. C., 1958. Studies on Meliaceae. 3. Floral morphology and embryology of *Sandoricum indicum*. Rev. Internac. Bot. Exptl. 10:145–151.

Nair, N. C., 1959a. Studies on Meliaceae. 1. Floral morphology and embryology of *Naregamia alata*. J. Indian bot. Soc. 38:353–366.

Nair, N. C., 1959b. Studies on Meliaceae. 2. Floral morphology and embryology of *Melia azedarach*. J. Indian bot. Soc. 38:367–378.

Nair, N. C. and V. Abraham, 1963. A contribution to the morphology and embryology of *Micrococca mercurialis*. J. Indian bot. Soc. 42:583–593.

Nair, N. C. and P. N. Bahl, 1956. Vascular anatomy of the flower of *Myristica malabarica*. Phytomorphology 6:127–134.

Nair, N. C. and I. Gupta, 1961. A contribution to the morphology and embryology of *Fagonia cretica*. J. Indian bot. Soc. 40:635–640.

Nair, N. C. and R. K. Jain, 1956. Floral morphology and embryology of *Balanites roxburghii*. Lloydia 19:269–279.

Nair, N. C. and T. C. Joseph, 1957. Floral morphology and embryology of *Samadera indica*. Bot. Gaz. 119:104–115.

Nair, N. C. and T. Joseph, 1960. Morphology and embryology of *Cardiospermum halicacabum*. J. Indian bot. Soc. 39:176–194.

Nair, N. C. and R. K. Joshi, 1958. Floral morphology of some members of the Simaroubaceae. Bot. Gaz. 120:88–99.

Nair, N. C. and S. Kahate, 1961. Floral morphology and embryology of *Parkinsonia aculeata*. Rev. Internac. Bot. Exptl. 17:77–90.

Nair, N. C. and K. Kanta, 1961. Studies in Meliaceae. 4. Floral morphology and embryology of *Azadirachta indica:* a reinvestigation. J. Indian bot. Soc. 40:382–396.

Nair, N. C. and M. Maitreyi, 1962. Morphology and embryology of *Sebastiana chamaelea*. Bot. Gaz. 124:58–68.

Nair, N. C. and V. J. Nair, 1963. Floral morphology of *Boerhaavia verticillata*. Current Sci. 32:322–324.

Nair, N. C. and P. N. N. Nambisan, 1957. Contribution to the floral morphology and embryology of *Leea sambucina*. Bot. Notiser 1957: 160–172.

Nair, N. C. and K. R. Narayanan, 1961. Studies on the Aristolochiaceae. 2. Contribution to the embryology of *Bragantia wallichii*. Lloydia 24:199–203.

Nair, N. C. and V. Parasuraman, 1954. Gametophytes of *Vitis pallida*. Current Sci. 23:163–164.

Nair, N. C. and V. Parasuraman, 1962. Embryological studies of *Vitis pallida*. Rev. Internac. Bot. Exptl. 18:157–164.

Nair, N. C. and N. P. Sukumaran, 1960. Floral morphology and embryology of *Brucea amarissima*. Bot. Gaz. 121:175–185.

Nair, N. C. and P. L. Suri, 1957. A contribution to the embryology of *Vitis latifolia*. Sci. and Cult. 22:387.

Naithani, S. P., 1933. A contribution to the morphology of *Digera arvensis*. Bull. Acad. Sci. U. P., India 3:119–128.

Naithani, S. P., 1937. Chromosome studies in *Hyacinthus orientalis*. 3. Reversal of sexual state in the anthers of *H. orientalis* var. Yellow Hammer. Ann. Bot. 1:369–377.

Nakajima, Y., 1928. Über das Vorkommen kleiner embryonaler Körperchen in der Frucht von *Crinum latifolium*. Sci. Rpts. Tôhoku Imp. Univ. Sendai (4) 3:431–442.

Namakawa, 1919. Über das Öffnen der Antheren bei einigen Solanaceen. Bot. Mag. (Tokyo) 33:62.

Nambiar, M. C. and M. S. Swaminathan, 1960. Chromosome morphology, microsporogenesis and pollen fertility in some varieties of coconut. Indian J. Genet. and Pl. Breeding 20:200–211.

Nanetti, A., 1912. Sulle probabili cause della parthenocarpia del *Solanum muricatum*. N. G. bot. Ital. 19:91–111.

Narang, N., 1953. The life history of *Stackhousia linariaefolia*, with a discussion on its systematic position. Phytomorphology 3:485–493.

Narasimha, P., 1962. A note on the embryology of *Micrococca mercurialis*. Current Sci. 31:426–427.

Narasimhachar, S. G., 1936. Megasporogenesis and embryo sac formation in two species of Meliaceae. Current Sci. 5:298–299.

Narasimhachar, S. G., 1938. Megasporogenesis and female gametophyte of *Malpigia punicifolia*. Current Sci. 6:507–508.

Narasimhachar, S. G., 1948. A contribution to the embryology of *Acacia farnesiana*. Proc. Indian Acad. Sci. B. 28:144–149.

408   BIBLIOGRAPHY

Narasimhachar, S. G., 1949. A contribution to the embryology of *Drosera bur-manni*. Proc. Indian Acad. Sci. B. 29:98–104.

Narasimhachar, S. G., 1951a. An embryological study of *Mimosa pudica*. Proc. Indian Acad. Sci. B. 33:192–198.

Narasimhachar, S. G., 1951b. A contribution to the embryology of *Drosera indica*. Proc. Indian Acad. Sci. B. 33:290–295.

Narayan, K. N., 1955. Cytogenetic studies of apomixis in *Pennisetum: Pennisetum clandestinum*. Proc. Indian Acad. Sci. B. 41:196–208.

Narayan, K. N., 1962. Apomixis in some species of *Pennisetum* and in *Panicum antidotale*. *In* Plant Embryology: A Symposium. CSIR, New Delhi: 55–61.

Narayana, H. S., 1962a. Post-fertilization study on *Moringa oleifolia*—a reinvestigation. Phytomorphology 12:65–69.

Narayana, H. S., 1962b. Studies in the Capparidaceae. 1. The embryology of *Capparis decidua*. Phytomorphology 12:167–177.

Narayana, H. S., 1962c. Seed structure in the Aizoaceae. *In* Proc. Summer School of Botany. Darjeerling. 1960. (ed., P. Maheshwari et al.): 220–230.

Narayana, H. S., 1965. Studies in the Capparidaceae. 2. Floral morphology and embryology of *Cadaba indica* and *Crataeva nurvala*. Phytomorphology 15:158–175.

Narayana, H. S. and P. K. Arora, 1963a. Floral anatomy of *Monsonia senegalensis*. Current Sci. 32:185.

Narayana, H. S. and P. K. Arora, 1963b. The embryology of *Monsonia senegalensis*. Amer. Midl. Nat. 70:309–318.

Narayana, H. S. and K. Jain, 1962. A contribution to the embryology of *Limeum indicum*. Lloydia 25:100–108.

Narayana, H. S. and B. C. Lodha, 1961. Contribution to the development of male and female gametophytes of *Glinus lotoides*. Proc. 48th. Indian Sci. Congr. 3:274.

Narayana, H. S. and B. C. Lodha, 1963. Embryology of *Orygia decumbens*. Phytomorphology 13:54–59.

Narayan, H. S. and C. G. P. Rao, 1962. Floral anatomy of *Seetzenia orientalis*. Current Sci. 31:209–211.

Narayana, H. S. and C. G. P. Rao, 1963. Floral morphology and embryology of *Seetzenia orientalis*. Phytomorphology 13:197–205.

Narayana, L. L., 1957a. Embryology of two Simaroubaceae. Current Science 26:323–324.

Narayana, L. L., 1957b. Study of the gametophytes in *Garuga pinnata*. Sci. and Cult. 23:248–249.

Narayana, L. L., 1958. Floral anatomy and embryology of *Cipadessa baccifera*. J. Indian bot. Soc. 37:147–151.

Narayana, L. L., 1959. Microsporogenesis and female gametophyte in *Boswellia serrata*. Current Sci. 28:77–78.

Narayana, L. L., 1960a. Embryology of Staphyleaceae. Current Sci. 29:403–404.

Narayana, L. L., 1960b. Studies in Erythroxylaceae. 1. Proc. Indian Acad. Sci. B. 51:270–275.

Narayana, L. L., 1960c. Studies in Burseraceae. 1. J. Indian bot. Soc. 39:204–209.

Narayana, L. L., 1960d. Studies in Burseraceae. 2. J. Indian bot. Soc. 39:402–409.

Narayana, L. L., 1962. Development of embryo in *Biophytum intermedium* and *Oxalis pubescens*. J. Indian bot. Soc. 41:156–159.

Narayana, L. L., 1963a. A note on the embryology of a few Rutaceae. Current Sci. 32:516–517.

Narayana, L. L., 1963b. Contributions to the embryology of Balsaminaceae. J. Indian bot. Soc. 42:102–109.

Narayana, L. L., 1964a. Embryology of a few species of *Erythroxylum*. Current Sci. 33:441–442.

Narayana, L. L., 1964b. A contribution to the floral anatomy and embryology of Linaceae. J. Indian bot. Soc. 43:343–357.

Narayana, L. L. and M. Sayeeduddin, 1959. A study of the gametophytes in *Impatiens leschenaultia*. J. Indian bot. Soc. 38:391–397.

Narayana, R., 1954a. Female gametophyte, endosperm and embryo of *Lysiana exocarpi*. Current Sci. 23:23–24.

Narayana, R., 1954b. Contribution to the embryology of *Dendrophthoe*. Phytomorphology 4:173–179.

Narayana, R., 1955. Floral morphology and embryology of *Nuytsia floribunda*. Proc. 42nd. Indian Sci. Congr. 239–240.

Narayana, R., 1956. Morphological and embryological studies in the Loranthaceae-Loranthoideae. 3. *Dendrophthoe neelgherrensis*. J. Mysore Univ. B. 16:185–205.

Narayana, R., 1958a. Morphological and embryological studies in the family Loranthaceae. 2. *Lysiana exocarpi*. Phytomorphology 8:146–168.

Narayana, R., 1958b. Morphological and embryological studies in the family Loranthaceae. 3. *Nuytsia floribunda*. Phytomorphology 8:306–323.

Narayanan, C. R., 1956. Studies in the Acanthaceae. Microsporogenesis in *Justicia betonica*, *Barleria prionitis* and *Ruellia tuberosa*. J. Madras Univ. B. 26:189–207.

Narayanaswami, S., 1940. Megasporogenesis and the origin of triploids in *Saccharum*. Indian J. Agr. Sci. 10:534–551.

Narayanaswami, S., 1952. Microsporogenesis and male gametophyte in *Eleusine coracana*. Current Sci. 21:19–21.

Narayanaswami, S., 1953. The structure and development of the caryopsis in some Indian millets. 1. *Pennisetum typhoideum*. Phytomorphology 3:98–112.

Narayanaswami, S., 1954. The structure and development of the caryopsis in some Indian millets. 2. *Paspalum scrobiculum*. Bull. Torrey bot. Cl. 81:288–299.

Narayanaswami, S., 1955a. The structure and development of the caryopsis in some Indian millets. 3. *Panicum miliare* and *P. miliaceum*. Lloydia 18:61–73.

Narayanaswami, S., 1955b. The structure and development of the caryopsis in some Indian millets. 4. *Echinochloa frumentacea*. Phytomorphology 5:161–171.

Narayanaswami, S., 1955c. The structure and development of the caryopsis in some Indian millets. 5. *Eleusine coracana*. Michigan Acad. Sci., Arts & Letters 40:33–46.

Narayanaswami, S., 1956. The structure and development of the caryopsis in some Indian millets. 6. *Setaria italica*. Bot. Gaz. 118:112–122.

Narayanaswami, S. and S. K. Roy, 1960a. Embryology of the genus *Psidium*. J. Indian bot. Soc. 39:35–45.

Narayanaswami, S. and S. K. Roy, 1960b. Embryo sac development and polyembryony in *Syzygium cumini*. Bot. Notiser 1960: 273–284.

Narayanaswami, S. and S. Sawhney, 1959. Microsporogenesis and embryo sac development in *Casearia tomentosa*. Rev. Internac. Bot. Exptl. 13:133–144.

Nast, C. G., 1935. Morphological development of the fruit of *Juglans regia*. Hilgardia 9:345–381.

Nast, C. G., 1941. The embryogeny and seedling morphology of *Juglans regia*. Lilloa 6:163–205.

Nast, C. G. and I. W. Bailey, 1945. Morphology and relationships of *Trochodendron* and *Tetracentron*. 2. Inflorescence, flower and fruit. J. Arnold Arb. 26:267–276.

Nast, C. G., and I. W. Bailey, 1946. Morphology of *Euptelea* and comparison with *Trochodendron*. J. Arnold Arb. 27:186–192.

Nawaschin, S., 1892. Zur Embryobildung der Birke. Bull. Acad. Imp. Sci. St. Pétersb. (3) 13:345–348.

Nawaschin, S., 1894a. Über die gemeine Birke, *Betula alba*, und die morphologische Deutung der Chalazogamie. Mém. Acad. Imp. Sci. St. Pétersb. (7) 52 (12).

Nawaschin, S., 1894b. Kurzer Bericht meiner fortgesetzten Studien über die Embryologie der Betulinen. Ber. dtsch. bot. Ges. 12:163–169.

Nawaschin, S., 1895a. Ein neues Beispiel der Chalazogamie. Bot. Ztbl. 63:353–357.

Nawaschin, S., 1895b. Neue Ergebnisse über die Embryologie der Hazel, *Corylus avellana*. Bot. Ztbl. 63:104–106.

Nawaschin, S., 1897. Über die Befruchtung bei *Juglans regia* und *J. nigra*. Trav. Soc. Imp. nat. St. Pétersb. 28.

Nawaschin, S., 1898a. Über das Verhalten des Pollenschlauches bei der Ulme. Bull. Acad. Imp. Sci. Pétersb. 8:345–357.

Nawaschin, S. G., 1898b. Resultate einer Revision der Befruchtungsvorgänge bei *Lilium martagon* und *Fritillaria tenella*. Bull. Acad. Imp. Sci. St. Pétersb. (5) 9:377–382.

Nawaschin, S., 1899a. Neue Beobachtungen über Befruchtung bei *Fritillaria tenella* und *Lilium martagon*. Bot. Ztbl. 77:62.

Nawaschin, S., 1899b. Zur Entwicklungsgeschichte der Chalazogamen: *Corylus avellana*. Bull. Acad. Imp. Sci. St. Pétersb. (5) 10:375–391.

Nawaschin, S., 1899c. Die Entwicklung der Samenknospe und über den Weg des Pollenschlauches bei *Alnus viridis*. Bot. Ztbl. 77.

Nawaschin, S., 1900a. Sur la fécondation chez les Composées et les Orchidées. Bull. Acad. Imp. Sci. St. Pétersb. (5) 13:335–340.

Nawaschin, S., 1900b. Über die Befruchtungsvorgänge bei einigen Dicotyledoneen. Ber. dtsch. bot. Ges. 18:224–230.

Nawaschin, S., 1900c. Doppelte Befruchtung bei den Orchideen. Ber dtsch. bot. Ges. 18:224–230.

Nawaschin, S., 1909. Über das selbständige Bewegungsvermögen der Spermakerne bei einigen Angiospermen. Österr. bot. Zeit. 59:457–467.

Nawaschin, S. G., 1910. Näheres über die Bildung der Spermakerne bei *Lilium martagon*. Ann. Jard. bot. Buitenz. 3:871–904.

Nawaschin, S. G. and W. W. Finn, 1912. Zur Entwicklungsgeschichte der Chalazogamen *Juglans nigra* und *Juglans regia*. Mém. Soc. Nat. Kieff. 22:1–85.

Nawaschin, S. and W. W. Finn, 1913. Zur Entwicklungsgeschichte der Chalazogamen *Juglans regia* und *Juglans nigra*. Mém. Acad. Imp. Sci. St. Pétersb. (8) 31:1–59.

Navashina, M. A., Z. V. Bolkhovskikh, and L. M. Makushenko, 1959. (A morphological-physiological investigation of pollen tubes.) 1st. Conf. on Cytology. Leningrad: 101–103.

Navashina, M. S. and H. Gerassimova-Navashina, 1959. Fertilization and events leading up to fertilization, and their bearing on the origin of Angiosperms. Congr. Internatl. Bot. 9th. 2:279.

Negodi, G., 1930. Sporofilli e gametofiti in *Urtica caudata*. Ann. di Bot. Roma 18:325–328.

Negodi, G., 1936a. Costiluzione dei gametofiti e cariologia di *Bellis integrifolia*. Atti Soc. Nat. Mat. Modena (6) 15.

Negodi, G., 1936b. Cariologia e costituzione dei gametofiti di *Bellium bellidioides*. Bull. Soc. Adriatica Sci. Nat. 25.

Němec, B., 1898. Über den Pollen der petaloiden Antheren von *Hyacinthus orientalis*. Rozpraxy České Akad. Prag. (2) 7. (17).

Němec, B., 1910a. Über das Schicksal der syndiploiden Kerne und Zellen. Ber. dtsch. bot. Ges. 38.

Němec, B., 1910b. Das Problem der Befruchtungsvorgänge und andere cytologische Fragen. Berlin.

Němec, B., 1912. Über die Befruchtung bei *Gagea*. Bull. Internat. Acad. Sci. Bohême 17:1–17.

Němec, B., 1931. Fecundation in *Gagea lutea*. Preslia 10:104–110.

Netolitsky, F., 1926. Anatomie der Angiospermen-Samen. Berlin.

Neuffer, M. G., 1964. Tetrasporic embryo sac formation in trisomic sectors of maize. Science 144:874–876.

Neumann, M., 1935. Die Entwicklung des Pollens, der Samenanlage und des Embryosackes von *Pereskia amapola* var. *argentina*. Österr. bot. Zeit. 84:1–30.

Neumann, O., 1939. Über die Bildung der Wurzelhaube bei *Juglans, Mimosa* und *Lupinus*. Planta 30:1–20.

Nevins, B. J., 1927. The development of the megagametophyte of *Furcraea andina*. Amer. J. Bot. 14:370–378.

Newman, I. V., 1928. The life history of *Doryanthes excelsa*. 1. Some ecological and vegetative features and spore production. Proc. Linn. Soc. N.S.W. 53:499–538.

Newman, I. V., 1929. The life history of *Doryanthes excelsa*. 2. The gametophytes, seed production, chromosome number and general conclusions. Proc. Linn. Soc. N.S.W. 54:411–435.

Newman, I. V., 1933. Studies in the Australian Acacias. 2. The life history of *Acacia baileyana*. 1. Some ecological and vegatative features, sporo production and chromosome number. Proc. Linn. Soc. N.S.W. 45:145–171.

Newman, I. V., 1934a. Studies in the Australian Acacias. 3. Supplementary observations on the habit, carpel, spore production and chromosomes of *Acacia baileyana*. Proc. Linn. Soc. N.S.W. 59:237–251.

Newman, I. V., 1934b. Studies in Australian Acacias. 4. The life history of *Acacia baileyana*. 2. Gametophytes, fertilization, seed production and germination and general conclusion. Proc. Linn. Soc. N.S.W. 59:277–313.

Newman, I. V., 1934c. Polyspermy and the endosperm. Nature 133:650.

Newton, W. C. F., 1926. Chromosome studies in *Tulipa* and some related genera. J. Linn. Soc. Lond. (Bot.) 47:339–354.

Nichols, M. L., 1908. The development of the pollen of *Sarracenia*. Bot. Gaz. 45:31–37.

Nicolas, G., 1915. L'*Urtica pilulifera* n'est pas une espèce parthénogénétique. Bull. Soc. hist. nat. Afr. Nord. 7:78–79.

412 BIBLIOGRAPHY

Nicolayeva, Z. V., 1962. (Microsporogenesis in *Fraxinus* spp.). Bot. Zhur. 47:1333–1338.

Nicoloff, T., 1904–1905. Sur le type floral et le développement des fruits de Juglandacées. Jour. de Bot. 18:134–152, 380–385. 19:63–68, 69–84.

Nicoloff, T., 1911. L'ovule et le sac embryonnaire de Platanacées. C. R. Acad. Sci. Paris 153:287–290.

Nicolosi-Roncati, F., 1903. La formazione del endosperma nell'*Anona cherimolia*. Bull. Soc. bot. Ital. 10.

Nicolosi-Roncati, F., 1905a. Sviluppo dell'ovulo e del seme nella *Anona cherimolia*. Atti Accad. Sci. Nat. Catania (4) 18.

Nicolosi-Roncati, F., 1905b. La formazioni dell'endosperme nell'*Anona*. Atti Accad. Sci. Nat. Catania (4) 18.

Nielsen, E. L., 1945. Cytology and breeding behavior of selected plants of *Poa pratensis*. Bot. Gaz. 106:357–382.

Nielsen, E. L., 1946. The origin of multiple macrogametophytes in *Poa pratensis*. Bot. Gaz. 108:41–50.

Nielsen, E. L., 1947a. Developmental sequence of embryo and endosperm in apomictic and sexual forms of *Poa pratensis*. Bot. Gaz. 108:531–534.

Nielsen, E. L., 1947b. Macrosporogenesis and fertilization in *Bromus inermis*. Amer. J. Bot. 34:431–433.

Nietsch, H., 1941. Zur systematischen Stellung von *Cyanastrum*. Österr. bot. Zeit. 90:31–52.

Niimoto, D. H. and Y. Sagawa, 1961. Ovule development in *Dendrobium*. Amer. Orchid Soc. Bull.: 813–819.

Niimoto, D. H. and Y. Sagawa, 1962. Ovule development in *Phalaenopsis*. Caryologia 15:89–97.

Nikolov, K., 1963. (Cytological and embryological investigations on *Medicago sativa*.) Akad. Selsk. Nauk. Bulg. Inst. Rasten. Izv. 16:57–70.

Nilsson, H., 1941. Die Homologie des angiospermen Embryosackes. Bot. Notiser 1941: 50–58.

Nirula, R. L., 1945a. Embryological and cytological studies in the family Asclepiadaceae. 2. An outline of meiosis in *Daemia extensa*, with special reference to the rôle of nucleolus. Proc. Indian Acad. Sci. B. 21:174–177.

Nirula, R. L., 1945b. Embryological and cytological studies in the family Asclepiadaceae. 4. On the development of embryo sac and endosperm in *Daemia extensa*. Proc. Indian Acad. Sci. B. 21:181–185.

Nirula, R. L. and R. H. Richharia, 1945. Embryological and cytological studies in the family Asclepiadaceae. 3. The development and arrangement of microspores in *Hemidesmus indicus*. Proc. Indian Acad. Sci. B. 21:178–180.

Nishimura, M., 1922a. On the germination and the polyembryony of *Poa pratensis*. Bot. Mag. (Tokyo) 36:47–54.

Nishimura, M., 1922b. Comparative morphology and development of *Poa pratensis*, *Phleum pratense* and *Setaria italica*. Jap. J. Bot. 1:55–85.

Nissen, O., 1937. Spalteåpringenes størrelse hos tvillingplanter med ulike kromosomtall. Bot. Notiser 1937:28–34.

Nitzschke, J., 1914. Beiträge sur Phylogenie der Monokotylen, gegründet auf der Embryosackentwicklung apokarper Nymphaeaceen und Helobien. Beitr. Biol. Pfl. 12:223–267.

Noack, K., 1939. Über Hypericum-Kreuzungen. 6. Fortpflanzungs-Verhältnisse und Bastarde von *Hypericum perforatum*. Ztschr. f. Inductive Abstam. u. Vererbo. 76:569–601.

Noguchi, T., 1940. On cytological studies in *Reineckea carnea*. Bot. Mag. (Tokyo) 54:483–493.

Noguchi, Y., 1928. Cytological studies on a case of pseudogamy in the genus *Brassica*. Proc. Imp. Acad. Japan 4:617–619.

Noguchi, Y., 1929. Zur Kenntnis der Befruchtung und Kornbildung bei der Reispflanzen. Jap. J. Bot. 4:385–403.

Nohara, S., 1934. Gametogenesis and embryogeny of *Sesamum indicum*. J. Coll. Agr. Tokyo Imp. Univ. 13:9–25.

Noll, F., 1883. Entwicklungsgeschichte der *Veronica*-Blüte. Diss. Marburg.

Noll, W., 1935. Embryonalentwicklung von *Biophytum dendroides*. Planta 24:609–648.

Nordheim, K., 1930. Entwicklungsgeschichtlich-zytologische und microchemische Untersuchungen an *Conium maculatum*. Diss. Berlin.

Nörner, C., 1881. Beiträge zur Embryoentwicklung der Gramineen. Flora 16:241–251, 257–266, 273–284.

Norris, H. W., 1892. Development of the ovule in *Grindelia squarrosa*. Amer. Nat. 26:703–704.

Nothnagel, M., 1918. Fecundation and formation of the primary endosperm nucleus in certain Liliaceae. Bot. Gaz. 66:143–161.

Nygren, A., 1946. The genesis of some Scandinavian species of *Calamagrostis*. Hereditas 32:131–262.

Nygren, A., 1949. Apomictic and sexual reproduction in *Calamagrostis purpurea*. Hereditas 35:285–300.

Nygren, A., 1950a. A preliminary note on cytological and embryological studies in atctic Poae. Hereditas 36:231–232.

Nygren, A., 1950b. Cytological and embryological studies in arctic Poae. Symb. bot. Upsaliensis 10:1–64.

Nygren, A., 1950c. A cytological and embryological study of *Antennaria porsildii*. Hereditas 36:483–486.

Nygren, A., 1954. Apomixis in Angiosperms 2. Bot. Rev. 20:577–649.

Oehler, E., 1927. Entwicklungsgeschichtlich-zytologische Untersuchungen an einigen saprophytischen Gentianaceen. Planta 3:641–733.

Oehlkers, F., 1923. Entwicklungsgeschichte von *Monophyllaea horsfieldii*. Beih. bot. Ztbl. 39:128–151.

Oes, A., 1914. Beiträge zur Entwicklungsgeschichte der Annonaceen. Verh. naturf. Ges. Basel 25:168–178.

Ogura, H., 1964. On the embryo sac of two species of *Tricyrtis*. Sci. Rpts. Tôhoku Univ. (4) Biol. 30:219–222.

Ohga, I., 1937. On the fertilization of *Nelumbo nucifera*. Cytologia. Fujii Jubl. Vol.: 1033–1035.

Ohga, I. and Y. Sinotô, 1924. Cytological studies on *Sciaphila japonica*. Bot. Mag. Tokyo 38:202–207.

Ohga, I. and Y. Sinotô, 1932. (Cytological studies on *Sciaphila japonica*. 2. On pollen and embryo sac development.) Bot. Mag. (Tokyo) 46:311–315.

Ohlendorf, O., 1907. Beiträge zur Anatomie und Biologie der Früchte und Samen einheimischer Wasser- und Sumpfpflanzen. Diss. Erlangen.

Oikawa, K., 1937. A note on the development of the embryo sac in *Cardiocrinum cordatum*. Sci. Rpts. Tôhoku Imp. Univ. (4) Biol. 11:303–305.

Oikawa, K., 1940. The embryo sac of *Erythronium japonicum*. Bot. Mag. (Tokyo) 54:366–369.

Oikawa, K., 1950. Embryo sac development of *Clintonia udensis*. Bull. Liberal Arts Dept., Mie Univ., Tsu, Japan 4:37–43.

Oikawa, K., 1956. (Development of embryo sac in *Chionographis japonica*.) Bull. Liberal Arts Dept., Mie Univ., Tsu, Japan 15:39–42.

Oikawa, K., 1959. Development of the embryo sac and endosperm of *Amana latifolia*. Bull. Liberal Arts Dept., Mie Univ., Tsu, Japan 21:85–92.

Oikawa, K., 1961a. The embryo sac of *Chionographis japonica*. Sci. Rpts. Tôhoku Univ. (4) Biol. 27:155–158.

Oikawa, K., 1961b. The embryo sac development in *Amana elulis*. Sci. Rpts. Tôhoku Univ. (4) Biol. 27:175–181.

Okabe, S., 1930. (Parthenogenesis in *Houttuynia cordata*.) Jap. J. Genet. 6:14–19.

Okabe, S., 1932. (Parthenogenesis in *Ixeris dentata*.) Bot. Mag. Tokyo 46:518–523.

Okabe, S., 1963. Cytological studies of the apomixis in angiosperms. 1. Apomixis in the genus *Boehmeria*. Sci. Rpts. Tôhoku Univ. (4) Biol. 29:207–215.

Oksijuk, P., 1927. (Development of the sugar beet, *Beta vulgaris*.) Bul. Jard. bot. Kieff 5–6:145–164.

Oksijuk, P., 1928. Zur Blütenbiologie der Zuckerrübe. Ber. dtsch. bot. Ges. 46:403–408.

Oksijuk, P., 1929. (Anomalien in der Embryosackentwicklung bei *Reseda alba*.) Akad. Nauk. Ukraine 15:37–50.

Oksijuk, P., 1935. (Zur Cytologie und Embryologie der Resedaceen.) Zhur. Inst. bot. Akad. Sci. RSS Ukraine 4:15–18.

Oksijuk, P., 1937. (Vergleichende zytologisch-embryologische Untersuchung der Familie Resedaceae. 1. *Reseda* und *Astrocarpus*.) Zhur. Inst. bot. Akad. Sci. RSS Ukraine 12:3–46.

Oksijuk, P., 1938. (A comparative cytologico-embryological study of the family Resedaceae.) Zhur. Inst. bot. Acad. Sci. Ukraine 18–19:51–56.

Oksijuk, P. F., 1957. (Once again on the so-called somatic fecundation in plants.) Ukrain. bot. Zhur. 14:99–104.

Oldén, E. J., 1953. Sexual and apomictic seed formation in *Malus sieboldii*. Bot. Notiser 1953:105–128.

Oliver, F. W., 1888. On the structure, development and affinities of *Trapella*, a new genus of Pedaliaceae. Ann. Bot. 2:75–115.

Oliver, F. W., 1891. On *Sarcodes sanguinea*. Ann. Bot. 4:303–326.

O'Mara, J., 1933. Division of the generative nucleus in the pollen tube of *Lilium*. Bot. Gaz. 94:567–578.

O'Neal, C. E., 1920. Microsporogenesis in *Datura stramonium*. Bull. Torrey bot. Cl. 47:231–241.

O'Neal, C. E., 1923. A study of the embryo sac development and accompanying phenomena in *Oenothera rubrinervis*. Bull. Torrey bot. Cl. 50:133–146.

Ono, T., 1926. Embryologische Studien an *Heloniopsis brevicarpa*. Sci. Rpts. Tôhoku Imp. Univ. (4) Biol. 2:93–104.

Ono, T., 1928a. Embryologische Studien an einigen Pontederiaceen. Sci. Rpts. Tôhoku Imp. Univ. (4) Biol. 3:407–415.

Ono, T., 1928b. (Endosperm formation in the Liliaceae.) Bot. Mag. (Tokyo) 42:445–448.

Ono, T., 1928c. Further investigations on the cytology of *Rumex*. Bot. Mag. (Tokyo) 42:524–533.

Ono, T., 1929. Embryologie der Liliaceae, mit besonderer Rücksicht auf die Endospermbildung. 1. Melanthioideae und Aletroideae. Sci. Rpts. Tôhoku Univ. (4) Biol. 4:381–393.

Ono, T., 1935. Chromosomen und Sexualität von *Rumex acetosa*. Sci. Repts. Tôhoku Imp. Univ. (4) Biol. 10:41–210.

Oppermann, M., 1904. A contribution to the life history of *Aster*. Bot. Gaz. 37:353–362.

Orlova, I. N., 1963. (Abnormalities in the embryonic development as the cause of partial sterility of the apple tree, *Malus*.) Bot. Zhur. 48:87–93.

Orr, M. Y., 1921a. The occurrence of tracheids in the nucellus of *Steriphoma eleomides*. Notes Roy. bot. Gdn. Edinb. 60:241–242.

Orr, M. Y., 1921b. The occurrence of a tracheal tissue enveloping the embryo in certain Capparidaceae. Notes Roy. bot. Gdn. Edinb. 60:249–257.

Orr, M. Y., 1921c. The structure of the ovular integuments and development of the testa in *Cleome* and *Isomeris*. Notes Roy. bot. Gdn. Edinb. 60:243.

Orr, M. Y., 1921d. Observations on the structure of the seed in the Capparidaceae and Resedaceae. Notes Roy. bot. Gdn. Edinb. 60:259.

Orr, M. Y., 1923. Polyembryony in *Sarcococca ruscifolia*. Notes Roy. bot. Gdn. Edinb. 14:21–23.

Osawa, J., 1912. Cytological and experimental studies in *Citrus*. J. Coll. Agr. Imp. Univ. Tokyo 4:83–116.

Osawa, J., 1913a. On the development of the pollen grain and embryo sac of *Daphne*, with special reference to the sterility of *Daphne odora*. J. Coll. Agr. Imp. Univ. Tokyo 4:237–264.

Osawa, J., 1913b. Studies on the cytology of some species of *Taraxacum*. Arch. f. Zellf. 10:450–469.

Osterwalder, A., 1898. Beiträge zur Embryologie von *Aconitum napellus*. Flora 85:254–292.

Osterwalder, A., 1910. Blütenbiologie, Embryologie und Entwicklung der Frucht unserer Kernobstbäume. Landwirt. Jahrb. 39.

Ota, T., 1957. Division of the generative cell in the pollen tube. Cytologia 22:15–27.

Ottley, A. M., 1918. A contribution to the life history of *Impatiens sultani*. Bot. Gaz. 66:289–317.

Overbeek, J. van, M. E. Conklin, and A. F. Blakeslee, 1941. Chemical stimulation of ovule development and its possible relation to parthenogenesis. Amer. J. Bot. 28:647–656.

Overton, E., 1891. Beitrag zur Kenntnis der Entwicklung und Vereinigung der Geschlechtsprouducte bei *Lilium martagon*. Fest. f. Nägeli und Kölliker. Zürich.

Overton, J. B., 1902. Parthenogenesis in *Thalictrum purpurascens*. Bot. Gaz. 33:363–375.

Overton, J. B., 1904. Über Parthenogenesis bei *Thalictrum purpurascens* var. *mitteil*. Ber. dtsch. bot. Ges. 22.

Pace, L., 1907. Fertilization in *Cypripedium*. Bot. Gaz. 44:353–374.

Pace, L., 1909. The gametophytes of *Calopogon*. Bot. Gaz. 48:126–137.

Pace, L., 1912. *Parnassia* and some allied genera. Bot. Gaz. 54:306–329.

Pace, L., 1913. Apogamy in Atamosco. Bot. Gaz. 56:376–394.

Pace, L., 1914. Two species of *Gyrostachis*. Baylor Univ. Bull. 17:1–16.

Padhye, M. D., 1959. Microsporogenesis and male gametophyte of *Cyperus compressus*. J. Biol. Sci. 2:116–117.

Padhye, M. D., 1960. A contribution to the life history of *Kyllinga triceps*. Bull. bot. Soc. Coll. Sci. Nagpur 1:1–15.

Padhye, M. D., 1962a. Fertilization and seed development in *Nechamandra alternifolia*. Bull. bot. Soc. Coll. Sci. Nagpur 3:92–100.

Padhye, M. D., 1962b. Solanad type of embryo development in *Gomphrena celosioides*, a member of the Amarantaceae. J. Indian bot. Soc. 41:52–63.

Padhye, M. D., 1963. Two types of embryo development in *Passiflora foetida*. Current Sci. 32:373–374.

Padhye, M. D. and B. G. Deshpande, 1960. The male and female gametophytes of *Passiflora foetida*. Proc. Indian Acad. Sci. B. 52:124–130.

Padhye, M. D. and S. K. Moharir, 1958. Studies in embryology of *Cyperus tagetum*. Proc. Indian Acad. Sci. B. 48:89–95.

Padhye, M. D. and H. Rao, 1960. Contribution to the embryology of *Lagarosiphon roxburghii*. Proc. 47th. Indian Sci. Congr. 3.

Padhye, M. D. and H. Rao, 1963. Contribution to the embryology of *Nechamandra alternifolia*. Bull. bot. Soc. Coll. Sci. Nagpur 4:39–44.

Padmanabhan, D., 1959. The development of endosperm in *Lantana camara*. Proc. Indian Acad. Sci. B. 49:420–427.

Padmanabhan, D., 1960a. The embryology of *Avicennia officinalis*. 1. Floral morphology and gametophytes. Proc. Indian Acad. Sci. B. 52:131–145.

Padmanabhan, D., 1960b. A contribution to the embryology of *Michelia champaca*. J. Madras Univ. B. 30:155–165.

Padmanabhan, D., 1961a. A contribution to the embryology of *Epithema carnosum*. J. Madras Univ. B. 31:37–46.

Padmanabhan, D., 1961b. Embryogenesis in *Dorstenia indica*. J. Madras Univ. B. 31:47–51.

Padmanabhan, D., 1961c. A contribution to the embryology of *Gomphandra polymorpha*. Proc. Natl. Inst. Sci. India B. 27:389–398.

Padmanabhan, D., 1962a. Taxonomic notes on the genus *Avicennia*. Current Sci. 31:434–435.

Padmanabhan, D., 1962b. The embryology of *Avicennia officinalis*. 3. The embryo. J. Madras Univ. B. 32:13–19.

Padmanabhan, D., 1962c. A reinvestigation of the endosperm and endothelium in *Tridax procumbens*. Phytomorphology 12:356–361.

Padmanabhan, D., 1964. The embryology of *Avicennia officinalis*. 2. Endosperm. Phytomorphology 14:442–451.

Paetow, W., 1931. Embryologische Untersuchungen an Taccaceen, Meliaceen und Dilleniaceen. Planta 14:441–470.

Pagni, P., 1958. Ricerche cito-embriologiche su *Oenothera acaulis*. Caryologia 11:181–202.

Paizieva, S. A., 1962. (The anatomy and morphology of the embryo and seedling in *Cousinia umbrosa*, *C. pseudoarctium* and *Arctium leiospermum*.) Vest. Leningrad Univ. 21:148–153.

Pal, B. P., 1963. Embryology and plant breeding. J. Indian bot. Soc., Maheshwari Commem. Vol. 42 A: 27–34.

Pal, B. P. and T. N. Rao, 1941. Ovule mortality in gram, *Cicer arietinum*. Proc. Indian Acad. Sci. B. 13:50–61.

Pal, N., 1951a. On the embryology of *Terminalia catapa*. Sci. and Cult. 17:178–179.

Pal, N., 1951b. Studies in the embryology of some Verbenaceae. J. Indian bot. Soc. 30:59–74.

Pal, N., 1951c. Studies in the embryology of the Verbenaceae. J. Indian bot. Soc. 31:297–315.

Pal, N., 1952. A contribution to the life histories of *Stellaria media* and *Polycarpon loeflingiae*. Proc. Nat. Inst. Sci. India B. 18:363–378.

Pal, N., 1959. Floral organogeny and development of male and female gametophytes in two species of Scrophulariaceae. J. Asiatic Soc. 1:245–249.

Pal, N., 1960. Development of the seed of *Mittettia ovalifolia*. Bot. Gaz. 122:130–137.

Palamarchuk, I. A., 1959. (On the part played by the endosperm and the suspensor in the development of seeds of *Lupinus polyphyllus*.) Byul. Gl. Bot. Sada Akad. Nauk SSSR 33:78–94.

Palamarchuk, I. A., 1962. (The development and structure of endosperm in siliceous corn, Maize.) *In* (The Morphology of Corn) Moscow: 121–139.

Palamarchuk, I. A. and E. D. Gogoleva, 1962. (Macrosporogenesis and development of the female gametophyte in the siliceous variety of corn, Maize.) *In* (The Morphology of Corn) Moscow: 110–120.

Paliwal, R. L., 1950a. Life history of *Coriandrum sativum*. Prox. 37th. Indian Sci. Congr. 3:47.

Paliwal, R. L., 1950b. Life history of *Cucumis melo* var. *pubescens*. Proc. 37th. Indian Sci. Congr. 3:47.

Paliwal, R. L., 1951. Polarity of male cells in pollen grains of some Umbelliferae. Current Sci. 20:17.

Paliwal, R. L., 1956. Morphological and embryological studies in some Santalaceae. Agra Univ. J. Res. (Sci.) 5:193–284.

Palm, B., 1914a. Zur Embryologie der Gattungen *Aster* und *Solidago*. Acta Hort. Berg. 5:1–18.

Palm, B., 1914b. Über die Embryosackentwicklung einiger Kompositen. Svensk bot. Tidskr. 8:447–453.

Palm, B., 1915. Studien über Konstruktionstypen und Entwicklungswege des Embryosackes der Angiospermen. Diss. Stockholm.

Palm, B., 1920. Preliminary notes on pollen development in tropical monocotyledons. Svensk bot. Tidskr. 14:261–266.

Palm, B., 1922a. Das Endosperm von *Hypericum*. Svensk bot. Tidskr. 16:60–68.

Palm, B., 1922b. The embryo sac of *Vittadinia*. Ann. Jard. bot. Buitenz. 32:89–98.

Palm, 1925. Embryological notes on tropical Compositae. 1. *Vernonia chinensis* and *V. cineraria*. Ann. Jard. bot. Buitenz. 34:188–192.

Palm, B., 1934. Ein neur Embryosacktypus bei *Rudbeckia hirta*. Bot. Notiser 1934:423–427.

Palm, B. and A. A. L. Rutgers, 1917. The embryology of *Aucuba japonica*. Rec. Trav. bot. Néerl. 14:119–126.

Palm, B. T., 1931. Antipodals in *Zinnia, Z. grandiflora*. Trans. Illinois State Acad. Sci. 24:143–147.

Palm, P., 1922. Zaadvorming en zaadsteriliteit in Deli-Tabak. Bull. Deli Proefstation Medan-Sumatra 16.

Palser, B. F., 1951a. Early endosperm development and embryogeny in *Cassiope hypnoides*. Trans. Illinois Acad. Sci. 44:51–57.

418 BIBLIOGRAPHY

Palser, B. F., 1951b. Studies of floral morphology in the Ericales. 1. Organography and vascular anatomy in the Andromedeae. Bot. Gaz. 112:447–485.

Palser, B. F., 1952. Studies of floral morphology in the Ericales. 2. Megasporogenesis and megasporophyte development in the Andromedeae. Bot. Gaz. 114:33–52.

Palser, B. F., 1954. Organography and vascular anatomy in several species of Arbuteae. Phytomorphology 4:335–354.

Palser, B. F., 1958. Studies of floral morphology in the Ericales. 4. Observations on three members of the Gaultherieae. Trans. Illinois Acad. Sci. 51:24–34.

Palser, B. F., 1959. Some aspects of embryology in the Ericales. Proc. 9th. Internat. bot. Congr. 2:292–293.

Palser, B. F., 1961. Some aspects of embryology in the Ericales. In Recent Advances in Botany. Toronto 1:685–689.

Palser, B. F., 1963. Studies of floral morphology in the Ericales. 6. The Diapensiaceae. Bot. Gaz. 124:200–219.

Panchaksharappa, M. G., 1959. Embryological studies in Costus speciosus. Proc. 46th. Indian Sci. Congr. 3:282.

Panchaksharappa, M. G., 1962a. Embryological studies in some members of the Zingiberaceae. In Plant Embryology: A Symposium. CSIR, New Delhi: 224–228.

Panchaksharappa, M. G., 1962b. Embryological studies in the family Zingiberaceae. 1. Costus speciosus. Phytomorphology 12:418–430.

Panda, B. S. and R. M. Datta, 1961. Studies on the callose plug formation in the pollen tubes of Corchorus siliquosus, a wild jute of America. Sci. and Cult. 27:490–492.

Pandey, K. K., 1955. Seed development in diploid, tetraploid and diploid-tetraploid crosses of Trifolium pratense. J. Indian Genetics and Pl. Breeding 15:25–35.

Pankow, H., 1958. Über den Pollenkitt bei Galanthus nivalis. Flora 146:240–253.

Pannocchia, F., 1938. Embriologia e cariologia del genere Vinca. N. G. bot. Ital. 45:157–187.

Pantulu, J. V., 1941. Some unusual megaspore tetrads in the Leguminosae. Current Sci. 10:175–176.

Pantulu, J. V., 1942. A contribution to the life history of Desmodium gangeticum. J. Indian bot. Soc. 21:137–144.

Pantulu, J. V., 1945. Studies in the Caesalpiniaceae. 1. A contribution to the embryology of the genus Cassia. J. Indian bot. Soc. 24:10–24.

Pantulu, J. V., 1951. Studies in the Caesalpiniaceae. 2. Development of the endosperm and embryo in Cassia occidentalis. J. Indian bot. Soc. 30:95–99.

Parameswaran, N., 1959. A contribution to the embryology of Theriophonum minutum. Proc. Indian Acad. Sci. B. 50:15–25.

Parameswaran, N., 1961. Ruminate endosperm in the Canellaceae. Current Sci. 30:344–345.

Parameswaran, N., 1962. Floral morphology and embryology in some taxa of the Canellaceae. Proc. Indian Acad. Sci. B. 55:167–182.

Pardi, P., 1933a. Embriologia della Periploca graeca. N. G. bot. Ital. 40:141–172.

Pardi, P., 1933b. Contributo all'embriologia delle Asclepiadaceae. N. G. bot. Ital. 40:560–569.

Parkin, J., 1953. The Durian theory—a criticism. Phytomorphology 3:80–88.

Parks, M., 1935. Embryo sac development and cleistogamy in *Commelinantia pringlei*. Bull. Torrey bot. Cl. 62:91–104.

Paroli, V., 1939. Contributo allo studio embriologico delle Tamaricacee. Ann. di Bot. (Roma) 22:1–18.

Passmore, S. F., 1930. Microsporogenesis in Cucurbitaceae. Bot. Gaz. 90:213–223.

Pastrana, M. D., 1932. Sporogenesis and sex determination in *Begonia schmidtiana*. Amer. J. Bot. 19:365–384.

Pastrana, M. D. and J. K. Santos, 1931. A contribution to the life history of *Dendrobium anosmum*. Nat. and appl. Sci. Bull. Philippines Univ. 1:133–144.

Patankar, T. B. V., 1956. Further contributions to the embryology of *Drosera burmanni*. Proc. Indian Acad. Sci. B. 43:161–171.

Patel, J. S. and G. V. Narayana, 1935. A rare instance of polyembryony in *Arachis hypogaea*. Current Sci. 4:32–33.

Patel, N. K., 1960. Some preliminary observations on the floral structures of the Oleaceae. Current Sci. 29:59.

Patermann, H., 1935. Beiträge zur Zytologie der Verbenaceen. Diss. Berlin.

Paterson, B. R., 1961. Studies of floral morphology in the Epacridaceae. Bot. Gaz. 122:259–279.

Paul, A. K., 1937. Development of ovule and embryo sac of *Tamarindus indica*. J. Indian bot. Soc. 16:151–157.

Paul, A. K. and R. M. Datta, 1950a. The chromosome number and the development of the embryo sac in *Crotalaria intermedia*. Sci. and Cult. 15:280–281.

Paul, A. K. and R. M. Datta, 1950b. Development of the female gametophyte of *Oryza coarctata*. Sci. and Cult. 15:487–488.

Paul, A. K. and R. M. Datta, 1953. On the morphology and development of the female gametophyte in *Oryza coarctata*. Philipp. J. Sci. 82:15–18.

Pavari, F., 1957. Ricerche embriologiche e cariologiche su *Cestrum elegans*. Caryologia 9:436–452.

Pax, F., 1882. Beitrag zur Kenntniss des Ovulums von *Primula elatior* und *officinalis*. Diss. Breslau.

Payer, J. B., 1857. Traité d'organogénie comparée de la fleur. Paris.

Payne, N. A., 1935. The flower and seed of *Mollugo verticillata*. Bull. Univ. Kansas 36:5–25.

Pearson, H. M., 1932. Parthenocarpy and seed abortion in *Vitis vinifera*. Proc. Amer. Soc. hort. Sci. 29:169–175.

Pearson, O. H., 1933. Study of the life history of *Brassica oleracea*. Bot. Gaz. 94:534–550.

Péchoutre, F., 1901. Développement de l'ovule et de la graine du *Geum urbanum*. Jour. de Bot. 15:213–217.

Péchoutre, F., 1902. Contribution à l'étude du développement de l'ovule et de la graine des Rosacées. Ann. Sci. nat. Bot. (8) 16:1–158.

Pellegrini, O., 1954. Ricerche embriologiche sulla famiglia delle Caesalpiniaceae. Delphinoa 7:138–160.

Pellegrini, O., 1955. Particulare formazione austoriale di natura endospermica e comportamento delle antipode in *Laurus nobilis*. Delphinoa 8:155–161.

Peltrisot, C. N., 1904. Développement et structure de la graine chez les Ericacées. Jour. de Bot. 18:234–242, 309–367, 386–402. Thèse. Paris.

Penland, C. W. T., 1923. Cytological behaviour in *Rosa*. Bot. Gaz. 76:403–410.

Percival, J., 1921. The Wheat Plant. London.

Periasamy, K., 1954. On the floral biology of some members of Annonaceae. J. Univ. Madras B. 24:7–12.

Periasamy, K., 1961. Studies on seeds with ruminate endosperm. 1. Morphology of ruminating tissue in *Myristica fragrans.* J. Univ. Madras. B. 31:53–58.

Periasamy, K., 1962a. Studies on seeds with ruminate endosperm. 2. Development of rumination in the Vitaceae. Proc. Indian Acad. Sci. B. 56:13–26.

Periasamy, K., 1962b. The ruminate endosperm: development and types of rumination. *In* Plant Embryology: a Symposium. CSIR, New Delhi: 62–74.

Periasamy, K., 1963. Studies on seeds with ruminate endosperm. 3. Development of rumination in certain members of the Apocynaceae. Proc. Indian Acad. Sci. B. 58:325–332.

Periasamy, K., 1964a. Studies on seeds with ruminate endosperm. 4. Development of rumination in *Coccoloba uvifera.* J. Indian bot. Soc. 43:543–547.

Periasamy, K., 1964b. Studies on seeds with ruminate endosperm. 5. Seed development and rumination in two genera of the Rubiaceae. Proc. Indian Acad. Sci. B. 60:351–360.

Periasamy, K., 1965. An instance of abnormal megasporogenesis in *Peperomia.* Current Sci. 34:57–58.

Periasamy, K. and N. Parameswaran, 1962. Extraovular outgrowths in the Rubiaceae. Current Sci. 31:300–301.

Periasamy, K. and B. G. L. Swamy, 1956. The conduplicate carpel of *Cananga odorata.* J. Arnold Arb. 37:366–372.

Periasamy, K. and B. G. L. Swamy, 1959. Studies in the Annonaceae. 1. Microsporogenesis in *Cananga odorata* and *Miliusa wightiana.* Phytomorphology 9:251–263.

Periasamy, K. and B. G. L. Swamy, 1961. Studies in the Annonaceae. 2. The development of ovule and seed in *Cananga odorata* and *Miliusa wightiana.* Proc. Indian bot. Soc. 40:206–216.

Periasamy, K. and B. G. L. Swamy, 1964. Is the microsporangium of angiosperms wall-less? Current Sci. 33:735–738.

Perkins, J. R., 1898. Beiträge zur Kenntnis der Monimiaceae. 1. Bot. Jahrb. 25:547–577.

Perotti, R., 1913. Centribuzione all'embriologia delle Dianthaceae. Ann. di. Bot. (Roma) 11:371–399.

Perrot, E. and P. Guérin, 1903. Les *Didierea* de Madagascar. Jour. de bot. Paris 17:233–251.

Persidsky, D., 1914. (Einige Fälle anomaler Bildung des Embryosackes bei *Delphinium elatum.*) Mém. Soc. Nat. Kieff. 23:97–112.

Persidsky, D., 1926. (Embryology of *Orobanche cumana* and *O. ramosa.*) Bull. Jard. bot. Kieff 4:6–10.

Persidsky, D., 1934. (On the development of the endosperm and haustorium in *Linaria genistaefolia.*) Bull. Jard. bot. Kieff 17:11–18.

Persidsky, D., 1935. (On the development of endosperm in Solanaceae.) Zhur. Inst. bot. Akad. Sci. RSS Ukraine 4:35–45.

Persidsky, D., 1940. (Embryological and cytological investigations of barley, *Hordeum distichum.*) Bot. Zhur. 1:145–153.

Persidsky, D. and J. Modilewski, 1935. (Cytological and embryological studies of the chief varieties of *Nicotiana rustica.*) Zhur. Inst. bot. Akad. Sci. RSS Ukraine 3:33–49.

Peter, J., 1920. Zur Entwicklungsgeschichte einiger Calycanthaceen. Beitr. Biol. Pflanz. 14:59–84. Diss. Halle-Wittenberg.

Peters, C. A., 1897–1898. Reproductive organs and embryology of *Drosera*. Proc. Amer. Assoc. Adv. Sci. 46:275.

Peters, K., 1908. Vergleichende Untersuchungen über die Ausbildung der sexuellen Reproduktionsorgane bei *Convolvulus* und *Cuscuta*. Diss. Zürich.

Petersen, H. E., 1911. Om Mangelen af de for Umbellifererne ejendommelige övre aborterede Aeg hos *Hydrocotyle*. Biol. Arb. till. Eug. Warming. Köbenhavn.

Petersen, H. E., 1912. The structure and biology of arctic flowering plants. 2. Diapensiaceae. *Diapensia lapponica*. Medd. om Grønland 36:141–154.

Petit, A., 1928. Le sac embryonnaire et la formation de l'albumen chez le *Fumaria officinalis*. C. R. Soc. biol. Lille 99:1961–1963.

Petit-Thouars, A. A. du, 1808. Observations sur la germination de l'*Allium fragrans* et de quelques autres plantes dont les graines renferment plusieurs embryons distincts. Nouv. Bull. Sci. Soc. Phil. Paris 1:198.

Petit-Thouars, A. A. du, 1810. Sur un graine de Mais contenant deux embryons. Bull. Soc. philom. Paris 1:126.

Petrov, D. F., 1939. (On the occurrence of facultative pseudogamy in a triploid variety of raspberries "Immer tragende," *R. idaeus*.) Dokl. Akad. Nauk. SSSR 22:352–353.

Petrova, L. R. and S. N. Drozdov, 1963. (Effect of late night frosts on the formation of reproductive organs of spring wheat.) Bot. Zhur. 48:1097–1107.

Pfeffer, W., 1872. Blüthenentwicklung der Primulaceen und Ampelideen. Jahrb. f. wiss. Bot. 8:194–215.

Pfeiffer, N. E., 1914. Morphology of *Thismia americana*. Bot. Gaz. 57:122–135.

Pfeiffer, N. E., 1918. The sporangia of *Thismia americana*. Bot. Gaz. 66:354–363.

Pfeiffer, W. M., 1912. The morphology of *Leitneria floridana*. Bot. Gaz. 53:189–203.

Pfitzer, E., 1880. Beobachtungen über Bau und Entwicklung der Orchideen. 5. Zur Embryoentwicklung und Keimung der Orchideen. Verh. nat.-med. ver. Heidelb. 2:23–30.

Pfitzer, P., 1962. Apomixis und Embryosackentwicklung in der Gattung *Aglaonema*. Portug. Acta Biol. A. 6:279–393.

Phatak, V. G. and K. B. Ambegaokar, 1955. Embryological studies in the Acanthaceae. 1. The female gametophyte. J. Univ. Baroda 4:87–97.

Phatak, V. G. and K. B. Ambegaokar, 1956. Embryological studies in the Acanthaceae. 2. Endosperm and embryo development in *Barleria prionitis*. J. Univ. Baroda 5:73–87.

Phatak, V. G. and K. B. Ambegaokar, 1957. Embryological studies in the Acanthaceae. 3. Endosperm and embryo development in *Acanthus ilicifolius*. J. Univ. Baroda 6:1–10.

Phatak, V. G. and K. B. Ambegaokar, 1961a. Embryological studies in the Acanthaceae. 4. Development of embryo sac and seed formation in *Haplanthus tentaculatus*. J. Indian bot. Soc. 40:525–534.

Phatak, V. G. and K. B. Ambegaokar, 1961b. Embryological studies in the Acanthaceae. 6. Development of embryo sac and endosperm in *Hemigraphis latebrosa* var. *heyneana* and *Seriococalyx scaber*. J. Univ. Poona (Sci.) 22:139–145.

Phatak, V. G. and K. B. Ambegaokar, 1963. Embryological studies in Acanthaceae. 5. Development of embryo sac and endosperm in *Blepharis maderaspatensis*. Proc. Indian Acad. Sci. B. 57:88–95.

Phillipis, A. V. de, 1936. Ricerche embryologiche sur *Ruscus aculeatus*. N. G. bot. Ital. 53:707–734.

Phouphas, C., 1951. Nouvelles observations embryogéniques sur les *Impatiens*. Bull. Soc. bot. France 98:238–241.

Pickett, F. L., 1913. The development of the embryo sac of *Arisaema triphyllum*. Bull. Torrey bot. Cl. 40:229–235.

Pickett, F. L., 1915. A contribution to our knowledge of *Arisaema triphyllum*. Mem. Torrey bot. Cl. 16:1–55.

Pickett, F. L., 1916. The wandering tapetal nuclei of *Arisaema*. Amer. J. Bot. 3:461–469.

Piech, K., 1924a. Zur Entwicklung der Pollenkörner bei *Scirpus lacustris*. Bull. Acad. Polon. B: 113–123.

Piech, K., 1924b. Über die Teilung des primären Pollenkerns und die Entstehung der Spermazellen bei *Scirpus palustris*. Bull. Acad. Polon. B: 605–621.

Piech, K., 1928a. Zytologische Studien an der Gattung *Scirpus*. Bull. Acad. Polon. B: 1–43.

Piech, K., 1928b. Über die Entstehung der generativen Zelle bei *Scirpus uniglumis* durch "freie Zellbildung." Planta 6:96–117.

Pienaar, R. de V., 1952. The origin and development of the embryo sac and young embryo of *Loranthus rubromarginatus*. Trans. Roy. Soc. Sth. Afr. 33:223–237.

Pierpaoli, I., 1917. Ricerche anatomiche, istologiche ed embriologiche sulla *Putoria calabrica*. Ann. di Bot. (Roma) 14:83–100.

Pigott, E. M., 1915. Notes on *Nothopanax arboreum*, with some reference to the development of the gametophytes. Trans. and Proc. New Zeal. Inst. 47:599–612.

Pigott, E. M., 1927. Observations on *Corynocarpus laevigata*, the Karaka. Trans. and Proc. New Zeal. Inst. 58:57–71.

Pijl, L. van der, 1931. Über Polyembryonie, insbesonders von *Eugenia*. Handl. Z. Ned.-Ind. Nat.-Wet. Congr. 319–320.

Pijl, L. van der, 1934. Über die Polyembryonie bei *Eugenia*. Rec. Trav. bot. Néerl. 31:113–187.

Pijl, L. van der, 1955. Sarcotesta, aril, pulpa and the evolution of the angiosperm fruit. 1. 2. Proc. Kon. Ned. Acad. Wet Amsterdam C. 58:154–161, 307–312.

Pijl, L. van der, 1957. On the arilloids of *Nephelium*, *Euphorbia*, *Litchi* and *Aesculus*, and the seeds of Sapindaceae in general. Acta bot. Néerl. 6:618–641.

Pijl, L. van der, 1960. Comment on the paper by A. R. Kadry: the seed of *Cardiospermum halicacabum*—a criticism. Acta bot. Néerl. 9:332.

Pinto-Lopes, J., 1948. On the differentiation of the nuclei in pollen grains of angiosperms. Portg. Acta Biol. A. 2:237–247.

Pisek, A., 1922. Chromosomenverhältnisse, Reduktionsteilung und Revision der Keimentwicklung der Mistel, *Viscum album*. Ber. dtsch. bot. Ges. 40:406–409.

Pisek, A., 1923. Chromosomenverhältnisse, Reduktionsteilung und Revision der Keimentwicklung der Mistel, *Viscum album*. Jahrb. f. wiss. Bot. 62:1–19.

Pisek, A., 1924. Antherenentwicklung und meiotische Teilung bei der Wacholdermistel, *Arceuthobium oxycedri;* Antherenbau und Chromosomenzahlen von *Loranthus europaeus*. S. B. Akad. wiss. Wien (1) 133:1–15.

BIBLIOGRAPHY 423

Pobedimova, E. G., 1929. Der Polymorphismus von *Stellaria media*. Bull. Jard. bot. URSS. 28:5-6.

Poddubnaja-Arnoldi, V. A., 1927. Spermatogenesis bei einigen Compositen. Planta 4:284-298.

Poddubnaja-Arnoldi, V. A., 1931. Ein Versuch der Anwendung der embryologischen Methode bei der Lösung einiger systematischer Fragen. 1. Vergleichende embryologiche -zytologische Untersuchungen über die Gruppe Cynareae, Fam. Compositae. Beih. bot. Ztbl. 48 A:141-237.

Poddubnaja-Arnoldi, V. A., 1933a. Geschlechtliche und ungeschlechtliche Fortpflanzung bei einigen *Chondrilla*-Arten. Planta 19:46-86.

Poddubnaja-Arnoldi, V. A., 1933b. Künstliche Kultur und zytologische Untersuchung des Pollenschlauches von *Senecio platanifolius*. Planta 19:299-304.

Poddubnaja-Arnoldi, V. A., 1933c. Spermazellen in der Dipsacaceae. Planta 21:381-386.

Poddubnaja-Arnoldi, V. A., 1936. Beobachtungen über die Keimung des Pollens einiger Pflanzen auf künstlichem Nährboden. Planta 25:502-529.

Poddubnaja-Arnoldi, V. A., 1939a. (Development of pollen and embryo sac in interspecific hybrids of *Taraxacum*.) Dokl. Akad. Nauk SSSR 24:374-377.

Poddubnaja-Arnoldi, V. A., 1939b. (Embryogenesis in remote hybridization in the genus *Taraxacum*.) Dokl. Akad. Nauk SSSR 24:382-385.

Poddubnaja-Arnoldi, V. A., 1959. Study of fertilization and embryogenesis in certain angiosperms, using living material. Amer. Nat. 93:161-169.

Poddubnaja-Arnoldi, V. A., 1961. (The significance of embryology in genetics and selection.) Bjul. Glavnogo Bot. Sada. Acad. Nauk. SSSR 44:32-38.

Poddubnaja-Arnoldi, V. A., 1964a. (General Embryology of the Angiosperms.) Moscow.

Poddubnaja-Arnoldi, V. A., 1964b. (Research on fertilization and embryogenesis in some Angiospermae.) *In* (Problems of Recent Embryology.) Moskov. Univ.: 25-32.

Poddubnaja-Arnoldi, V. A. and V. Dianova, 1934. Eine zytoembryologische Untersuchung Arten der Gattung *Taraxacum*. Planta 23:19-46.

Poddubnaja-Arnoldi, V. A. and Z. M. Pashchenko, 1962. (The development and structure of the male gametophyte in *Zea mays*.) *In* (Morphology of Corn): 162-170.

Poddubnaja-Arnoldi, V. A., N. Steschina, and A. Sosnovetz, 1935. Der Charakter und die ursachen der Sterilät bei *Scorzonera tau-saghys*. Beih. bot. Ztbl. 53:309-339.

Poddubnaja-Arnoldi, V. A., N. V. Zinger, T. P. Petrovskaya, and N. N. Polunina, 1959. Histochemical study of pollen and pollen tubes in the Angiosperms. Congr. Internatl. Bot. 9th. 2:302-303.

Poerck, R. A. de, 1950. Contribution à l'étude der Palmier à huile African, *Elaeis guinensis*. Ole'agineux 5:623-628.

Pohl, F., 1922. Zur Kenntnis unserer Beerenfrüchte. Beih. bot. Ztbl. 39:206-221.

Poindexter, C. C., 1903. The development of the spikelet and grain of corn. Ohio Nat. 4:3-9.

Pointeau, A., 1809. Mémoire sur l'embryon des Graminées, des Cyperacées et du *Nelumbo*. Ann. Mus. hist. nat. Paris 13:381-400.

Poljakova, T. F., 1958. (Development of the male gametophyte in *Trifolium pratense*. 1. Changes in the vegetative nucleus and formation of the generative cell.) Vest. Leningrad. Univ. 3:63-76.

424 BIBLIOGRAPHY

Poljakova, T. F., 1961. (The rôle of the vegetative nucleus in the development of the male gametophyte.) Tsitologija (Moscow) 3:254–265.

Poljakova, T. F. and S. E. Podstavek, 1961. (On the behavior of the tube nucleus in plants with the binuclear and trinuclear type of pollen grains.) Dokl. Akad. Nauk SSSR 133:526–528.

Polunina, N. N., 1957. (On the flowering and embryology of *Feijoa*.) Byul. Gl. Bot. Sada Akad. Nauk SSSR 29:60–71.

Polunina, N. N., 1958. (Concerning the biology of flowering and embryology of *Callistemon lanceolatus*.) Bot. Zhur. 43:1169–1178.

Poole, A. L., 1952. The development of *Nothofagus* seed. Trans. Roy. Soc. N. Z. 80:207–212.

Pope, M. N., 1937. The time factor in pollen tube growth and fertilization in barley. J. Agr. Res. 54:525–529.

Pope, M. N., 1943a. The temperature factor in fertilization and growth of the barley ovule. J. Agr. Res. 66:389–402.

Pope, M. N., 1943b. Cleavage polyembryony in barley. J. Hered. 35:5.

Pope, M. N., 1946. The course of the pollen tube in cultivated barley. J. Amer. Soc. Agron. 38:432–440.

Popham, R. A., 1938. A contribution to the life history of *Galinsoga ciliaris*. Bot. Gaz. 99:543–555.

Popoff, A., 1935. Über die Fortpflanzungsverhältnisse der Gattung *Potentilla*. Planta 24:510–522.

Porsch, O., 1904. Der Spaltöffnungsapparat von *Casuarina* und seine phyletische Bedeutung. Österr. bot. Zeit. 1.

Porsch, O., 1907. Versuch einer Phylogenie des Embryosackes und der doppelten Befruchtung der Angiospermen. Vorh. K. K. zool.-bot. Ges. Wien: 120–134.

Porsch, O., 1907. Versuch einer phylogenetischen Erklärung des Embryosackes und der doppelten Befruchtung der Angiospermen. Diss. Wien.

Porter, T. R., 1936. Development of the megagametophyte and embryo of *Allium mutabile*. Bot. Gaz. 98:317–327.

Portheim, L. R. von, 1901. Beiträge zur Entwicklungsgeschichte der Achaena und des Embryos der Kompositen. 1. *Senecio vulgaris*. Sitzb. dtsch. Nat.-Med. Ver. Böhmen "Lotos" 21.

Poulsen, V. A., 1886. Bidrag till Triuridaceernes naturhistorie. Vidensk. Medd. nat. Foren. Kjöbenhavn 1884–86:161–179.

Poulsen, V. A., 1905. *Sciaphila nana*. Vidensk. Medd. nat. Foren. Kjöbenhavn 1884–1886.

Povilaitis, B. and J. W. Boyes, 1956a. A cytological study of autotetraploid red clover. Amer. J. Bot. 43:169–174.

Povilaitis, B. and J. W. Boyes, 1956b. A study of fertility in diploid Dollard red clover. Canad. J. Plant Sci. 36:59–71.

Povilaitis, B. and J. W. Boyes, 1959. Embryo sac production in relation to seed yields of diploid Dollard red clover. Canad. J. Plant Sci. 39:364–374.

Povilaitis, B. and J. W. Boyes, 1960. Ovule development in diploid red clover. Canad. J. Bot. 38:507–532.

Powers, I., 1945. Fertilization without reduction in guayule, *Parthenium argentatum*; and a hypothesis as to the evolution of apomixis and polyploidy. Genetics 30:323–346.

Powers, L. and R. C. Rollins, 1945. Reproduction and pollination studies on guayule, *Parthenium argentatum* and *P. incanum*. Amer. Soc. Agron. J. 37:96–112.

Prakash, R. and B. Chatterjee, 1953. Cytological study of *Solanum macranthum*. Current Sci. 22:84–85.

Prakash, S., 1960a. The endosperm of *Arachis hypogaea*. Phytomorphology 10:60–64.

Prakash, S., 1960b. Morphological and embryological studies in the family Loranthaceae. 6. *Peraxilla tetrapetala*. Phytomorphology 10:224–234.

Prakash, S., 1961. Morphological and embryological studies in the family Loranthaceae. 7. *Atkinsonia ligustrina*. Phytomorphology 11:325–335.

Prakash, S., 1963. Morphological and embryological studies in the family Loranthaceae. 10. *Barathranthus axanthus*. Phytomorphology 13:97–103.

Pratt, C. and I. Einset, 1955. Development of the embryo sac in some American blackberries. Amer. J. Bot. 42:637–645.

Preda, A., 1897. Recherches sur le sac embryonnaire de quelques Narcissées. Bull. herb. Boissier (5) 1:948–952.

Price, S., 1959. Critique on apomixis in sugarcane. Econ. Bot. 13:67–74.

Pritchard, A. N., 1962. The cytology and reproduction of *Paspalum yaguaronense*. Aust. J. Agr. Res. 13:206–211.

Pritchard, H. N., 1964. A cytochemical study of embryo sac development in *Stellaria media*. Amer. J. Bot. 51:371–378.

Prohaska, K., 1883. Der Embryosack und die Endospermbildung in der Gattung *Daphne*. Bot. Zeit. 41:865–868.

Prosina, M. N., 1930a. Embryologische Untersuchungen an *Eremurus spectabilis* var. *regeli*. Planta 9:748–759.

Prosina, M. N., 1930b. Über die *Cypripedium*-typus abweichende Embryosackentwicklung von *Cypripedium guttatum*. Planta 12:532–544.

Prosina, M. N., 1953. (Embryologische Untersuchung des Spitzahorns, *Acer platanoides*.) Bjul. Moskov Obsc. Ipyt. Prir. Biol. 58:66–75.

Puri, V., 1934. A note on the embryo sac and embryo of *Moringa oleifolia*. Proc. Indian Acad. Sci. B. 1:279–282.

Puri, V., 1939a. Studies in the order Parietales. 1. A contribution to the morphology of *Tamarix chinensis*. Beih. bot. Ztbl. 59A: 335–349.

Puri, V., 1939b. Studies in the order Parietales. 2. A contribution to the morphology of *Garcinia livingstonii*. Proc. Indian Acad. Sci. B. 9:74–86.

Puri, V., 1941. Life history of *Moringa oleifolia*. J. Indian bot. Soc. 20:263–284.

Puri, V. and B. Singh, 1935. Studies in the family Amarantaceae. 1. The life history of *Digera arvensis*. Proc. Indian Acad. Sci. B. 1:893–908.

Purkinje, J. E., 1830. De cellulis antherarum fibrosis nec non de granorum pollinarium formis. Vratislaviae.

Py, G., 1929. Recherches cytologiques sur l'assise nourricière des grains de pollen d'*Helleborus foetidus, Euphorbia sauliana* et *E. peplus* C. R. Acad. Sci. Paris. 189:1298.

Py, G., 1932. Recherches cytologiques sur l'assise nourricière des microspores et les microspores des plantes vasculaires. Rev. gén. Bot. 44:316–413, 450–462, 484–500.

Quibell, C. H., 1941. Floral anatomy and morphology of *Anemopsis californica*. Bot. Gaz. 102:749–758.

Quintanilha, A., A. Cabral, and L. Quintanilha, 1947. Abnormal female gametophytes in relation with polyembryonic seeds in upland cotton. Sth. Afr. J. Sci. 43:158–166.

Quisumbing, E. and J. B. Juliano, 1927. Development of ovule and embryo sac of *Cocos nucifera.* Bot. Gaz. 84:279–293.

Raciborski, M., 1893. Über die Chromatophilie der Embryosackkerne. Anz. Akad. Wiss. Krakau: 247–258.

Raciborski, M., 1894. Die Morphologie der Calombeen und Nymphaeaceae. Flora 78:244–279.

Radermacher, A., 1925. Die Gametophyten von *Nipa fruticans* und *Actinophloeus macarthuri,* sowie ein Versuch die systematik der Angiospermen durch die haploide Generation zu ergänzen. Ann. Jard. bot. Buitenz. 35:1–54. Thesis. Utrecht.

Radionenko, A. J., 1963. (Some observations on the embryology of apricot, *Armeniaca vulgaris.*) Ukrain. Bot. Zhur. 20:15–23.

Radlkofer, L., 1856. Die Befruchtung der Phanerogamen. Ein Beitrag zur Entscheidung des darüber bestehenden Streites. Leipzig.

Raghavan, T. S., 1937. Studies in the Capparidaceae. 1. The life history of *Cleome chelidonii.* J. Linn. Soc. London (Bot.) 51:43–72.

Raghavan, T. S., 1938. Morphological and cytological studies in the Capparidaceae. 2. Floral morphology and cytology of *Gynandropsis pentaphylla.* Ann. Bot. 2:75–95.

Raghavan, T. S. *et al.,* 1939. Division of the generative cell in *Impatiens balsamina.* Cytologia 9:389–392.

Raghavan, T. S. and K. V. Krishnamurty, 1947. Cytological studies in *Sesamum.* 1. Cytology of parents *S. orientale* and *S. prostratum,* and the sterile amphidiploid. Proc. Indian Acad. Sci. B. 26:236–275.

Raghavan, T. S. and K. Rangaswamy, 1941. Studies in the Rubiaceae. 1. Development of female gametophyte and embryo formation in *Dentella repens* and *Oldenlandia alata,* and some cytotaxonomical considerations. J. Indian bot. Soc. 20:341–356.

Raghavan, T. S. and V. K. Srinivasan, 1940a. Studies in the Indian Aizoaceae. Ann. Bot. 4:651–661.

Raghavan, T. S. and V. K. Srinivasan, 1940b. A contribution to the life history of *Bergia capensis.* J. Indian bot. Soc. 19:283–291.

Raghavan, T. S. and V. K. Srinivasan, 1941a. Studies in the Rubiaceae. 2. *Spermococe hispidula, Guettarda speciosa* and some cytomorphological considerations. Proc. Indian Acad. Sci. B. 14:412–426.

Raghavan, T. S. and V. K. Srinivasan, 1941b. Morphological and cytological studies in the Scrophulariaceae. 3. A contribution to the life history of *Ilysanthes parviflora.* Proc. Indian Acad. Sci. B. 13:24–32.

Raghavan, T. S. and V. K. Srinivasan, 1941c. Morphological and cytological studies in the Scrophulariaceae. 4. The development of the embryo sac and endosperm in *Scoparia dulcis.* Proc. Indian Acad. Sci. B. 13:229–234.

Raghavan, T. S. and V. K. Srinivasan, 1941d. Cyto-morphological features of *Portulaca tuberosa.* Proc. Indian Acad. Sci. B. 14:472–488.

Raghavan, T. S. and V. K. Srinivasan, 1942. A contribution to the life history of *Vahlia viscosa* and *V. oldenlandioides.* Proc. Indian Acad. Sci. B. 15:83–105.

Raghavan, T. S. and K. R. Venkatasubban, 1940. Studies in the Bignoniaceae. 1. Chromosome number and epidermal hydathodes in *Spathodea campanulata.* J. Indian bot. Soc. 19:293.

Raghavan, T. S. and K. R. Venkatasubban, 1941a. Contribution to the cytology of *Tridax procumbens*. Proc. Indian Acad. Sci. B. 13:85–108.

Raghavan, T. S. and K. R. Venkatasubban, 1941b. Studies in the Capparidaceae. 7. The floral morphology of *Crataeva religiosa*. Proc. Indian Acad. Sci. B. 13:235–243.

Raghavan, T. S. and K. R. Venkatasubban, 1941c. Contribution to the morphology and cytology of *Alpinia calcarata*, with special reference to the theory of Zingiberous flowering. Proc. Indian Acad. Sci. B. 13:325–344.

Rai, S., 1939. Development of the female gametophyte in *Capparis aphylla*. Proc. 26th. Indian Sci. Congr. 2:123–124.

Raineri, L., 1952. Lo sviluppo dei fiori femminili di *Schinus molle*. N. G. bot. Ital. 59:46–63.

Raj, B., 1964. Female gametophyte of *Buckleya lanceolata*. Current Sci. 33:348–349.

Raju, M. V. S., 1952a. Embryology of Sabiaceae. Current Sci. 21:107–108.

Raju, M. V. S., 1952b. Embryology of Passifloraceae. Current Sci. 21:288–289.

Raju, M. V. S., 1953. Embryology of *Anagallis pumila*. Proc. Indian Acad. Sci. B. 36:34–42.

Raju, M. V. S., 1956a. Embryology of the Passifloraceae. 1. Gametogenesis and seed development of *Passiflora calcarata*. J. Indian bot. Soc. 35:126–138.

Raju, M. V. S., 1956b. Development of embryo sac and seed coat in *Turnera ulmifolia* var. *angustifolia*. Bot. Notiser 1936:308–312.

Raju, M. V. S., 1957. Some aspects of the embryology of *Dianella nemorosa*. J. Indian bot. Soc. 36:223–226.

Raju, M. V. S., 1958. Seed development and fruit dehiscence in *Ionidium suffruticosum*. Phytomorphology 8:218–224.

Raju, M. V. S., 1961. Morphology and anatomy of the Saururaceae. 1. Floral anatomy and embryology. Ann. Miss. bot. Gdn. 48:107–124.

Raju, M. V. S. and A. N. Rao, 1953. The development of the male and female gametophytes in *Mallotus albus*. J. Mysore Univ. 13:5–8.

Ram, M., 1956. Floral morphology and embryology of *Trapa bispinosa*, with a discussion on the systematic position of the genus. Phytomorphology 6:312–323.

Ram, M., 1957. Morphological and embryological studies in the family Santalaceae. 1. *Comandra umbellata*. Phytomorphology 7:24–35.

Ram, M., 1959a. Occurrence of embryo sac-like structures in the microsporangia of *Leptomeria billardieri*. Nature 184:912–915.

Ram, M., 1959b. Morphological and embryological studies in the family Santalaceae. 2. *Exocarpus*, with a discussion on its systematic position. Phytomorphology 8:4–19.

Ram, M., 1959c. Morphological and embryological studies in the family Santalaceae. 3. *Leptomeria*. Phytomorphology 9:20–33.

Ram, M., 1960. Occurrence of endosperm haustorium in *Cannabis sativa*. Ann. Bot. 24:79–82.

Ramam, S. S., 1954. Gametogenesis and fertilization of *Stephegyne parviflora*. Agra Univ. J. Res. (Sci.) 3:343–348.

Ramamurti, B. A., 1958. Life history of *Heliotropium curassavicum*. J. Vikram Univ. 2:134–137.

Ramiah, K., N. Parthasarathy, and S. Ramanusam, 1935. Polyembryony in rice, *Oryza sativa*. Indian J. Agric. Sci. 5:119–124.

Randall, T. E. and C. M. Rich, 1945. A cytogenetic study of polyembryony in *Asparagus officinalis*. Amer. J. Bot. 32:560–569.

Randolph, L. F., 1936. Developmental morphology of the caryopsis in maize. J. Agr. Res. 53:881–916.

Randolph, L. F. and H. E. Fischer, 1939. The occurrence of parthenogenetic diploids in tetraploid maize. Proc. Nat. Acad. Sci. (Wash.) 25:161–164.

Rangasamy, K., 1934. Contribution to the life history of *Vallisneria spiralis*. J. Indian bot. Soc. 13:129–148.

Rangasamy, K., 1935. On the cytology of *Pennisetum typhoideum*. J. Indian bot. Soc. 14:125–131.

Rangasamy, K., 1941a. Cyto-morphological studies in *Asteracantha longifolia* (*Hygrophila spinosa*). Proc. Indian Acad. Sci. B. 14:149–165.

Rangasamy, K., 1941b. A morphological study of the flower of *Blyxa echinosperma*. J. Indian bot. Soc. 20:123–133.

Rangaswamy, N. S., 1963. Control of fertilization and embryo development. *In* P. Maheshwari (ed.), Recent Advances in the Embryology of Angiosperms. Delhi: 327–353.

Ranquini, J. H., 1928. Células de tapete de núcleos tabicados o virtualmente multiples. Bull. inst. Catalana hist. nat. (2) 8:71–76.

Rao, A. N., 1951. A note on the embryology of *Dioscorea oppositifolia*. Current Sci. 20:162–163.

Rao, A. N., 1953a. Embryology of *Dioscorea oppositifolia*. Phytomorphology 3:121–126.

Rao, A. N., 1953b. Embryology of *Shorea talura*, Phytomorphology 3:476–484.

Rao, A. N., 1953c. Inverted polarity in the embryo sac of *Saurauia nepaulensis*. Current Sci. 22:282.

Rao, A. N., 1954. A case of polyembryony in *Trichopus zelanicus*. Sci. and Cult. 20:143–144.

Rao, A. N., 1955a. Gametogenesis in *Dillenia pentagyna*. Current Sci. 24:62.

Rao, A. N., 1955b. A contribution to the embryology of *Vateria indica*. Proc. Nat. Inst. Sci. India 21:247–255.

Rao, A. N., 1955c. Embryology of *Trichopus zeylanicus*. J. Indian bot. Soc. 34:213–221.

Rao, A. N., 1956a. Development of gametophytes in *Hopea wightiana*. J. Mysore Univ. 15:7–15.

Rao, A. N., 1956b. A contribution to the embryology of *Agrostistachys meeboldii*. Sci. and Cult. 21:470–472.

Rao, A. N., 1956c. Life history of *Shorea robusta*. Current Sci. 25:128–129.

Rao, A. N., 1957a. The development of flowers within the ovary of *Raphanus sativus*. Proc. Iowa Acad. Sci. 64:127–131.

Rao, A. N., 1957b. A contribution to the embryology of Dilleniaceae. Proc. Iowa Acad. Sci. 64:172–176.

Rao, A. N., 1957c. The embryology of *Hypericum patulum* and *H. mysorense*. Phytomorphology 7:36–45.

Rao, A. N., 1959. Flower development and gametogenesis in *Oenothera laciniata*. Proc. Iowa Acad. Sci. 66:91–97.

Rao, A. N., 1961. Fibrous thickenings in the anther epidermis of *Wormia burbidgei*. Current Sci. 30:426.

Rao, A. N., 1962. Floral anatomy and gametogenesis in *Hopea racophloea*. J. Indian bot. Soc. 41:557–562.

Rao, A. N., 1964a. Notes on the embryology of *Hevea brasiliensis*. Current Sci. 33:739-740.

Rao, A. N., 1964b. Occurrence of polyembryony in *Vanda* during *in vivo* and *in vitro* conditions. Experimentia 20:388.

Rao, A. N., 1964c. An embryological study of *Salomonia cantoniensis*. New Phytol. 63:281-288.

Rao, A. N., 1964d. Stamens and carpels within the ovary of *Durio zibethinus*. Singapore bot. Gard. Bull. 20:287-294.

Rao, A. N. and S. Shamanna, 1963. Rudimentary aril in *Sanguinaria canadensis*. Canad. J. Bot. 41:1529-1530.

Rao, D. and L. L. Narayana, 1965. Embryology of Linaceae. Current Sci. 34:92-93.

Rao, K. V. R., 1940. Gametogenesis and embryogeny in five species of the Convolvulaceae. J. Indian bot. Soc. 19:53-69.

Rao, L. N., 1942. Studies in the Santalaceae. Ann. Bot. 6:151-175.

Rao, P. N., 1962. A note on the embryology of *Micrococca mercurialis*. Current Sci. 31:426-427.

Rao, P. R. M., 1963. Suspensor polyembryony in *Garrya veatchii*. Current Sci. 32:468-469.

Rao, P. S. P., 1963. Some embryological observations of *Guiera senegalensis*. Current Sci. 32:30-31.

Rao, V. S., 1936a. Studies on Capparidaceae. 1. The embryo sac of *Maerua arenaria*. J. Indian bot. Soc. 15:71-75.

Rao, V. S., 1936b. A contribution to the morphology of *Antigonon leptopus*. J. Indian bot. Soc. 15:105-114.

Rao, V. S., 1936c. Studies on Capparidaceae. 2. The embryology of *Gynandropsis pentaphylla*. J. Indian bot. Soc. 15:335-344.

Rao, V. S., 1938a. Studies on Capparidaceae. 3. Genus *Capparis*. J. Indian bot. Soc. 17:69-80.

Rao, V. S., 1938b. The correlation between embryo type and endosperm type. Ann. Bot. 2:535-536.

Rao, V. S., 1940. The occurrence of pollen grains in the ovary wall of *Dianthus*. Current Sci. 9:77.

Rao, V. S., 1944. Development of the embryo sac in the Convolvulaceae. J. Indian bot. Soc. 23:164-169.

Rao, V. S., 1953. The floral anatomy of some Bicarpellatae. 1. Acanthaceae. J. Univ. Bombay 21:7-34.

Rao, V. S., 1959. Nuclear endosperm or non-cellular endosperm? Ann. Bot. 23:364.

Rao, V. S. and A. Ganguli, 1963. Studies in the floral anatomy of the Apocynaceae. J. Indian bot. Soc. 42:419-435.

Raspail, F. V., 1824. Sur la formation de l'embryon des Graminées. Ann. Sci. nat. 4:271-319.

Rassner, E., 1932. Primitive und ungeleitete Merkmale im Blütenbau einiger Ranunculaceen. Planta 15.

Rau, M. A., 1940a. Studies in the Apocynaceae. J. Indian bot. Soc. 19:33-44.

Rau, M. A., 1940b. An embryological study of *Suriana maritima*. Proc. Indian Acad. Sci. B. 11:100-106.

Rau, M. A., 1942. Development of the embryo sac and embryo in *Streblus asper*. J. Mysore Univ. B. 2:109-114.

Rau, M. A., 1950a. Endosperm in *Cassia tora*. Nature 165:157.

Rau, M. A., 1950b. Integumentary vascular tissue in *Cassia tora*. Current Sci. 19:186–187.

Rau, M. A., 1950c. Development of the embryo in *Trigonella foenum-graecum*. J. Indian bot. Soc. 29:210–213.

Rau, M. A., 1950d. The suspensor haustorium of some species of *Crotalaria*. Ann. Bot. 14:557–562.

Rau, M. A., 1951a. The mechanism of nutrition in the developing seed of *Vigna catjang*. New Phytol. 50:121–123.

Rau, M. A., 1951b. The endosperm in *Rothia trifoliata*. Ann. Bot. 15:175–177.

Rau, M. A., 1951c. Development of embryo in *Aeschynomene indica*. New Phytol. 50:124–126.

Rau, M. A., 1951d. The endosperm in *Crotalaria*. Current Sci. 20:73–74.

Rau, M. A., 1951e. Development of the embryo in certain members of the Papilionaceae. Phytomorphology 1:80–86.

Rau, M. A., 1951f. The endosperm in some of the Papilionaceae. Phytomorphology 1:153–158.

Rau, M. A., 1951g. The endosperm in some species of *Cassia*. Svensk bot. Tidskr. 45:516–522.

Rau, M. A., 1953. Some observations on the endosperm in Papilionaceae. Phytomorphology 3:209–222.

Rau, M. A., 1954a. The endosperm in the Leguminosae. 8th. Internat. Bot. Congr. (Paris): 249–250.

Rau, M. A., 1954b. The development of the embryo of *Cyamopsis, Desmodium* and *Lespedeza*, with a discussion on the position of the Papilionaceae in the system of embryogenic classification. Phytomorphology 4:418–430.

Rau, M. A., 1955. Embryological studies in the Leguminosae. J. Mysore Univ. B. 14:63–75.

Rau, M. A., 1962. Review of recent work on the embryogeny of some families of disputed systematic position. *In* Plant Embryology: a Symposium. CSIR, New Delhi: 75–80.

Rau, N. S., 1930. On reduction division in the pollen mother cells of *Cyanotis cristata*. J. Indian bot. Soc. 9:79–113.

Rauch, K. V., 1936. Cytologische-embryologische Untersuchungen an *Scurrula atropurpurea* und *Dendrophthoe pentandra*. Ber. schweiz. bot. Ges. 45:5–61.

Ravasini, R., 1912a. Sul *Ficus carica*—riposta al Prof. B. Longo. Arch. Farm. e Sci. Affini 1:14–31.

Ravasini, R., 1912b. Ancora sul *Ficus carica*. Archiv. Farm. e Sci. Affini 1:85–116.

Razi, B. A., 1949. Embryological studies of two members of the Podostemaceae. Bot. Gaz. 111:211–218.

Razi, B. A., 1955. Some aspects of the embryology of *Zeylanidium olivaceum* and *Lawia zeylanica*. Bull. bot. Soc. Bengal 9:36–41.

Razi, B. A. and K. Subramanyam, 1953. Embryology of the Dipsacaceae. 1. Glands. The male and female gametophytes. Proc. Indian Acad. Sci. B. 36:249–257.

Razmologov, V. P., 1958. (Embryologic investigations of the orchid, *Phalaenopsis schilleriana*). Byul. Gl. Bot. Sada Akad. Nauk 32:67–72.

Reece, P. C., 1939. The floral anatomy of the avocado. Amer. J. Bot. 26:429–433.

Reed, C. F., 1955. The comparative morphology of the Olacaceae, Opiliaceae and Octoknemaceae. Mem. Soc. Broteriana 10:29–79.

Reed, E. L., 1924. Anatomy, embryology and ecology of *Arachis hypogaea*. Bot. Gaz. 78:289–310.

Reed, H. S., 1903. The development of the macrosporangium of *Yucca filamentosa*. Bot. Gaz. 35:209–214.

Reeder, J. R., 1953. The embryo of *Streptochaeta* and its bearing on the homology of the coleoptile. Amer. J. Bot. 40:77–80.

Reeder, J. R., 1956. The embryo of *Jouvea pilosa* as further evidence for the foliar nature of the coleoptile. Bull. Torrey bot. Cl. 83:1–4.

Reeder, J. R., 1957. The embryo in grass systematics. Amer. J. Bot. 44:756–768.

Reeder, J. R., 1959. The grass embryo in systematics. Congr. Internatl. Bot. 9th. 2:321–322.

Reeder, J. R., 1962. The bambusoid embryo: a reappraisal. Amer. J. Bot. 49:639–641.

Rees-Leonard, O. L., 1935. Macrosporogenesis and development of the macrogametophyte of *Solanum tuberosum*. Bot. Gaz. 96:734–750.

Reese, G., 1958. Cyto-systematische Notizen zur Gattung *Nitraria*. Flora 146:478–488.

Reeve, R. M., 1948. Late embryogeny and histogenesis in *Pisum*. Amer. J. Bot. 35:591–602.

Reeves, J. H., 1957. Megasporogenesis and megagametogenesis in *Polygala polygama*. Virginia Coop. Wildlife Res. Unit Release 57:1–3; Virginia J. Sci. 8:303.

Reeves, R. G., 1928. Partition wall formation in the pollen mother cells of *Zea mays*. Amer. J. Bot. 15:114–122.

Reeves, R. G., 1930a. Nuclear and cytoplasmic division in the microsporocytes of alfalfa. Amer. J. Bot. 17:29–40.

Reeves, R. G., 1930b. Development of the ovule and embryo sac of alfalfa. Amer. J. Bot. 17:239–246.

Reeves, R. G. and C. C. Valle, 1934. Anatomy and microchemistry of the cotton seed. Bot. Gaz. 93:259–277.

Regen, L., 1941. The development of the embryo sac in *Agave virginica*. Bull. Torrey bot. Cl. 68:229–236.

Reiche, V. K., 1921. Zur Kenntnis von *Sechium edule*. Flora 14:232–248.

Reichenbach, H. G., 1852. De pollinis Orchidearum genesi ac structura et de Orchideis in artem ac systema regigendis. Leipzig.

Reinwardt, 1824. Osservatio de Mangiferae semine polyembryoneo. Act. Acad. Nat. Curios. 12:343.

Reiser, R., 1911. Beiträge zur Kenntnis der Gattung *Epirrhizanthes*. Bull. intern. Acad. Cracovie B:351–358.

Reisseck, S., 1843. Monocotyledonischer Embryo. Bot. Zeit. 1:611–614.

Renner, O., 1914. Befruchtung und Embryobildung bei *Oenothera lamarckiana* und einigen verwandten Arten. Flora 107:115–150.

Renner, O., 1916. Zur Terminologie des pflanzlichen Generationwechsels. Biol. Ztbl. 36:337–374. Zeit. f. Bot. 13:609–621.

Renner, O., 1921. Heterogamie im weiblichen Geschlecht und Embryosackentwicklung bei den Oenotheren. Zeit. f. Bot. 13:609–621.

Renzoni-Cela, G., 1963. Ricerche cito-embriologiche e distribuzione geografica di *Cirsium casabonae*. N. G. bot. Ital. 70:493–504.

Reusch, J. D., 1961. The relationship between reproductive factors and seed set in *Paspalum dilatatum*. Sth. Afr. J. Agr. Sci. 4:513–530.

432 BIBLIOGRAPHY

Reuther, E., 1876. Beiträge zur Entwicklungsgeschichte der Blüthe. Bot. Zeit. 34:385-395, 401-447.

Riatt, A. H., 1916. Development of the ovule of *Impatiens pallida*. Plant World 19:195-203.

Richard, L.-C., 1808. Demonstrations botaniques ou Analyse du fruit considéré en générale. Paris.

Richard, L.-C., 1811. Analyse botanique des embryons endorhizes ou monocotylédonés, et particulièrement de celui des Graminées. Ann. Mus. hist. nat. Paris 17:223-251, 442-487.

Richharia, R. H., 1934. The number of microsporangia in each stamen in Asclepiadaceae. Current Sci. 2:340-342.

Richter-Landmann, W., 1959. Der Befruchtungsvorgang bei *Impatiens glandulifera* unter Berücksichtigung der plasmatischen Organelle von Spermazelle, Eizelle und Zygote. Planta 53:162-177.

Rick, C. M., 1946. The development of sterile ovules in *Lycopersicum esculentum*. Amer. J. Bot. 33:250-256.

Riddle, L. C., 1898. The embryology of *Alyssum macrocarpum*. Bot. Gaz. 26:314-324.

Riddle, L. C., 1905a. Notes on the morphology of *Philotria*. Ohio Nat. 5:304-305.

Riddle, L. C., 1905b. Development of the embryo sac and embryo of *Staphylea trifoliata*. Ohio Nat. 5:320-325.

Riddle, L. C., 1905c. Development of the embryo sac and embryo of *Batrachium longirostris*. Ohio Nat. 5:353-363.

Rietsema, J., B. Blondel, S. Satina, and A. F. Blakeslee, 1955. Studies on ovule and embryo growth in *Datura*. 1. A growth analysis. Amer. J. Bot. 42:449-455.

Riley, H. P., 1942. Development of the embryo sac of *Iris fulva* and *I. hexagona* var. *giganticoerula*. Trans. Amer. Micros. Soc. 61:328-335.

Risch, C., 1956. Die Pollenkörner der Labiaten. Willdenowia 1:617-641.

Risse, K., 1926. Chromosomenzahlen und Periplasmodiumbildung in der Familie der Dipsacaceae. Ber. dtsch. bot. Ges. 44:296-297.

Risse, K., 1929. Beiträge zur Zytologie der Dipsacaceae. Bot. Arch. Mez. 23:266-288.

Ritzerow, H., 1908. Über Bau und Befruchtung kleistogamer Blüten. Flora 98:163-212.

Robbins, W. W. and H. A. Borthwick, 1925. Development of the seed of *Asparagus officinalis*. Bot. Gaz. 80:426-438.

Robyns, W., 1938. Sur un cas de Polyembryonie dans le *Juglans nigra*. Ann. Soc. Sci. Brux. 58:120-129.

Robyns, W., 1941. Sur un nouveau cas de polyembryonie dans le *Juglans nigra*. Bull. Soc. Roy. bot. Belg. 74:167-172.

Robyns, W. and A. Louis, 1942. Beschouwingen over Polyembryonie en Polyspermie bij de Bedektzadigen. Verh. Kon. vlaam. Acad. Wetenschp. Belg. 4:5-112.

Rocén, T., 1924a. Portulacaceernas embryologi. Vortragsreferat. Svensk bot. Tidskr. 18:527-528.

Rocén, T., 1924b. Nyctaginiaceernas embryologi. Vortragsreferat. Svensk bot. Tidskr. 18:159-160.

Rocén, T., 1926. Några drag ur caryophyllaceernas embryologi. Vortragsreferat. Svensk bot. Tidskr. 20:97-98.

Rocén, T., 1927. Zur Embryologie der Centrospermen. Diss. Uppsala.

Rocén, T., 1928. Beitrag zur Embryologie der Crassulaceen. Svensk bot. Tidskr. 22:368–376.

Rodkiewicz, B., 1961. (Phases of embryo sac development and pollen grain development in *Lilium candidum*.) Acta Soc. bot. Polon. 30:749–754.

Rodolico, A., 1930. Embriologia del *Buphthalmum salicifolium*. N. G. bot. Ital. 37:392–408.

Rodolico, A., 1933. Appunti sulla cariologia e sull'embriologia delle Inuleae. N. G. bot. Ital. 40.

Rodrigo, P., 1926. A case of polyembryony in rice. Philipp. Agric. 14:629–630.

Roeper, J., 1824. Enumeratio Euphorbiarum qui in Germania et Panonia giguntur. Göttingen.

Roever, W. E., 1935. Nuclear behavior in the tapetum of *Hosta caerulea*, with special reference to the divisions. Bull. Torrey bot. Cl. 62:345–358.

Rohrbach, P., 1866. Über den Blütenbau und die Befruchtung von *Epipogium gmelini*. Göttingen.

Rohrbach, P., 1869. Die Samenknospe der Typhaceen. Bot. Zeit. 27:479–480.

Romanov, I. D., 1936. Die Embryosackentwicklung in der Gattung *Gagea*. Planta 25:438–458.

Romanov, I. D., 1938. Eine neue Form des Embryosackes von Adoxa-Typus bei *Tulipa tetraphylla* und *T. ostrovskiana*. Dokl. Akad. Nauk SSSR 19:113–115.

Romanov, I. D., 1939. Zwei neue Embryosackformen in der Gattung *Tulipa*. Dokl. Akad. Nauk SSSR 22:140–142.

Romanov, I. D., 1944. (Embryo sac evolution in flowering plants.) Diss. Tashkent.

Romanov, I. D., 1957. (Embryo sac in the genus *Tulipa*.) Dokl. Akad. Nauk SSSR (Bot.) 115:1025–1027.

Romanov, I. D., 1959. The embryo sac and pollen morphology in *Tulipa*. Congr. Internatl. Bot. 9th. 2:331–332.

Rombach, S., 1911. Die Entwicklung der Samenknospe bei den Crassulaceen. Rec. Trav. bot. Néerl. 8:182–200.

Romell, L. G., 1919. Notes on the embryology of *Salsola kali*. Svensk bot. Tidsk. 13:212–214.

Roper, R. B., 1952. The embryo sac of *Butomus umbellatus*. Phytomorphology 2:61–74.

Rosanoff, S., 1865. Zur Kenntniss des Baues und der Entwicklungsgeschichte des Pollens der Mimoseae. Jahrb. f. wiss. Bot. 4:441–450.

Rosanoff, S., 1866. Morphologisch-embryologische Studien. Jahrb. f. wiss. Bot. 5:72–82.

Roscoe, M. V., 1927a. Cytological studies in the genus *Wistaria*. Bot. Gaz. 84:171–186.

Roscoe, M. V., 1927b. Cytological studies in the genus *Typha*. Bot. Gaz. 84:392–406.

Rosell, M. E., 1936. Morphology of the flower, fruit and seed of *Raphanus sativus*. Philipp. Agric. 25:521–540.

Rosén, W., 1932. Zur Embryologie der Campanulaceen und Lobeliaceen. Acta Hort. Göteb. 7:31–42.

Rosén, W., 1935. Beitrag zur Embryologie der Stylidiaceen. Bot. Notiser 1935: 273–278.

Rosén, W., 1937. Beiträge zur Kenntnis der Embryologie der Goodeniaceen. Acta Hort. Göteb. 12:1–10.

Rosén, W., 1940a. Seed development of *Litorella uniflora*. Acta Hort. Göteb. 14:177–184.

Rosén, W., 1940b. Notes on the embryology of *Globularia vulgaris*. Bot. Notiser 1940:253–261.

Rosén, W., 1944. The embryo sac of *Rudbeckia*. Acta Hort. Göteb. 15:267–273.

Rosén, W., 1946. Further notes on the embryology of the Goodeniaceae. Acta Hort. Göteb. 16:235–249.

Rosén, W., 1947. The female gametophyte in *Nolana* and endosperm development in Tubiflorae. Bot. Notiser 1945:372–382.

Rosén, W., 1949. Endosperm development in Campanulaceae and closely related families. Bot. Notiser 1949:137–147.

Rosenberg, O., 1899. Physiologisch-cytologische Untersuchungen über *Drosera rotundifolia*. Diss. Bonn.

Rosenberg, O., 1901a. Über die Pollenbildung von *Zostera*. Medd. Stockholms Högsk. Bot. Inst.: 1–21.

Rosenberg, O., 1901b. Über die Embryologie von *Zostera marina*. Kgl. Svensk. Vet.-Akad. Handl. 27:1–26.

Rosenberg, O., 1906. Über die Embryobildung in der Gattung *Hieracium*. Ber. dtsch. bot. Ges. 24:157–161.

Rosenberg, O., 1907. Experimental and cytological studies in the *Hieracia*. 2. Cytological studies on the apogamy in *Hieracium*. Bot. Tidssk. 25:143–170.

Rosenberg, O., 1909a. Cytologische und morphologische Studien an *Drosera longifolia* x *rotundifolia*. Kgl. Svensk. Vet.-Akad. Handl. 43:1–64.

Rosenberg, O., 1909b. Zur Kenntnis von den Tetradenteilungen der Compositen. Svensk bot. Tidskr. 3:64–77.

Rosenberg, O., 1912. Über dei Apogamie bei *Chondrilla juncea*. Svensk bot. Tidsk. 6:914–919.

Rosenberg, O., 1917. Die Reduktionsteilung und ihre Degeneration in *Hieracium*. Svensk bot. Tidsk. 11:145–206.

Rosenberg, O., 1930. Apogamie und Parthenogenesis bei Pflanzen. *In* Baur, E. and M. Hartman, Berlin: Handbuch der Vererbungswissenschaft 12:1–66.

Rosenberg, O., 1946. The influence of low temperature on the development of the embryo sac mother cell in *Lilium longiflorum*. Hereditas 32:65–92.

Rosendahl, C. O., 1906. Preliminary note on the embryogeny of *Symplocarpus foetidus*. Science 23:590.

Rosendahl, C. O., 1909. Embryo sac development and embryology of *Symplocarpus foetidus*. Minn. bot. Stud. 4:1–9.

Rosonoff, S., 1865. Zur Kenntnis des Baues und der Entwicklungsgeschichte des Pollens der Mimosaceae. Jahrb. f. wiss. Bot. 4:441–450.

Rössler, W., 1911. Ein neuer Fall des Durchganges eines Pollenschläuches durch das Integument. Ber. dtsch. bot. Ges. 29:370–375.

Rössler, W., 1917. Pollenschläuche und Embryosackhaustorien von *Plantago major*. Ber. dtsch. bot. Ges. 35:460–463.

Rostowzew, S., 1905. Zur Biologie und Morphologie der Wasserlinsen. Ann. Inst. agron. Moscow 11:1–222.

Roth, F., 1906. Die Fortpflanzungsverhältnisse bei der Gattung *Rumex*. Diss. Bonn.

Roth, I., 1955. Zur morphologischen Deutung des Grasembryos und verwandter Embryotypen. Flora 42:564–600.

Roth, I., 1957. Histogenese und Entwicklungsgeschichte des *Triticum*. Flora 44:163–212.

Roth, I., 1959. Histogenesis and morphological interpretation of the grass embryo. Congr. Internatl. Bot. 9th. 2:334.

Rousi, A., 1956. Cytotaxonomy and reproduction in the apomictic *Ranunculus auricomus*. Ann. Bot. Soc. Zool. Bot. Fennica, Vanamo 29:1–64.

Rowlee, W. W., 1896. The stigma and pollen of *Arisaema*. Bull. Torrey bot. Cl. 23:369–370.

Rowlee, W. W. and M. W. Doherty, 1898. The histology of the embryo of Indian corn. Bull. Torrey bot. Cl. 25:211–315.

Rowlee, W. W. and G. T. Hastings, 1898. The seed and seedlings of some Amentiferae. Bot. Gaz. 26:349–353.

Rowley, J. R., 1963. Ubisch body development in *Poa annua*. Grana palyn. 4:25–36.

Roy, B., 1933. Studies in the development of the female gametophyte in some leguminous crops of India. Indian J. Agric. Sci. 3:1098–1107.

Roy, S. K., 1953. Embryology of *Eugenia jambos*. Current Sci. 22:249–250.

Roy, S. K., 1955. Embryology of *Eugenia bracteata*. Current Sci. 24:348–349.

Roy, S. K., 1960. Embryology of *Eugenia malaccensis*. Current Sci. 29:189–190.

Roy, S. K., 1961. Embryology of *Eugenia fruticosa*. Proc. Natl. Acad. Sci. India B. 31:80–87.

Roy, S. K., 1962. A contribution to the embryology of *Myrtus communis*. Proc. Natl. Acad. Sci. India B. 32:305–311.

Roy, S. K. and R. Sahai, 1962. The embryo sac and embryo of *Syzygium caryophyllifolium*. J. Indian bot. Soc. 41:45–51.

Rubashevskaia, M. K., 1931. Observations on the wild carrot in cultivation and under natural conditions. Bull. Appl. Bot. Gen. and Pl. Breeding 26:194–252.

Rübel, E., 1908. Überwinterungsstadien von *Loiseleuria procumbens*. Ber. dtsch. bot. Ges. 26A:803–808.

Rudenko, F. E., 1961. (Spermatogenesis and fertilization in a *Mahonia* exotic, *Mahonia aquifolium*.) Bjul. Moskov Obsch. Ispyt. Prir. Biol. 66:133–137.

Rudenko, F. E., 1962. (Data on the embryogenesis of certain high-mountain plants of the Carpathians.) Nauch. Dokl. Vyssh. Shkoly. Biol. Nauk. 1:119–122.

Rudenko, K. Y., 1961a. (Fertilization in some alpine plants of the Carpathians.) Ukrain. bot. Zhur. 17:34–41.

Rudenko, K. Y., 1961b. (Apomixis in certain high-mountain plants of the Ukrainian Carpathians.) Ukrain. bot. Zhur. 18:24–31.

Rudenko, T., 1929. Bildung der Spermazellen bei *Scrophularia nodosa* und *Scrophularia alata* bei der Teilung der generativen Zelle im Pollenschläuch. Bull. Jard. bot. Kieff 9:18–30.

Rudenko, T., 1930. Male cells of Scrophulariaceae. Spermatogenesis and fertilization in *Lathyraea squamaria*. Bull. Jard. bot. Kieff 11:41–55.

Rudloff, C. F., 1930. Entwicklungsphysiologische Studien in der Gattung *Fragaria*. 1. Gartenbauwissenschaft 3:79–100.

Rudloff, C. F., 1930. Entwicklungsphysiologische Studien in der Gattung *Fragaria*. ungünstiger Witterungsverhältnisse auf die Reduktionsteilung und die Embryosackentwicklung bei verschiedenen Önotheren. Planta 18:104.

Ruehle, K., 1924. Beiträge zur Kenntnis der Gattung *Prunus*. Bot. Arch. 8:224–249.

Ruhland, W. and K. Wetzel, 1924. Der Nachweis von Chloroplasten in den generativen Zellen von Pollenschläuchen. Ber. dtsch. bot. Ges. 42:3–14.

Rupert, J., 1902. Beiträge zur Kenntnis des anatomischen Baues des Gynoeceums bei *Lamium* und *Rosmarinus*. Lotus 22.

Russell, A., 1919. A comparative study of *Floerkea proserpinacoides* and allies. Contrib. Bot. Lab. Univ. Pennsylv. 4:401–418.

Rutgers, F. L., 1922. Embryo sac and embryo of *Moringa oleifera*. Ann. Jard. bot. Buitenz. 32.

Rutgers, F. L., 1923a. The female gametophyte of angiosperms. Ann. Jard bot. Buitenz. 33:1–5.

Rutgers, F. L., 1923b. Embryo sac and embryo of *Moringa oleifera*. The female gametophyte of angiosperms. Ann. Jard. bot. Buitenz. 33:1–66.

Ruth, C. M., 1943. Contributions to the morphology and anatomy of the Russian dandelion, *T. kok-saghyz*. U.S. Dept. Agric. Tech. Bull. 843:1–24.

Rutishauser, A., 1935a. Entwicklungsgeschichtliche und zytologische Untersuchungen an *Korthalsella dacrydii*. Ber. schweiz. bot. Ges. 44:389–436.

Rutishauser, A., 1935b. Blütenmorphologische und embryologische Untersuchungen an dem Viscoideen *Korthalsella opuntia* und *Ginalloa linearis*. Ber. schweiz. bot. Ges. 47:5–28.

Rutishauser, A., 1937. Entwicklungsgeschichtliche Untersuchungen an *Thesium rostratum*. Nat. Ges. Schaffh. 13:25–47.

Rutishauser, A., 1939. Zur Embryologie pseudogamer Potentillen. Nat. Ges. Schaffh. 15:203–215.

Rutishauser, A., 1943a. Über die Entwicklungsgeschichte pseudogamer Potentillen. Arch. Julius Klaus.-Stift. 18:687–691.

Rutishauser, A., 1943b. Untersuchungen über die Fortpflanzung und Bastardbildung apomiktischer Potentillen. Ber. schweiz. bot. Ges. 53:1–83.

Rutishauser, A., 1945a. Über die Fortpflanzung einiger Bastarde von pseudogamen Potentillen. Arch. Julius Klaus.-Stift. 20:300–314.

Rutishauser, A., 1945b. Zur Embryologie amphimiktischer Potentillen. Ber. schweiz. bot. Ges. 55:19–32.

Rutishauser, A., 1946. Über kreuzungsversuche mit pseudogamen Potentillen. Arch. Julius Klaus-Stift. 21:469–472.

Rutishauser, A., 1948. Pseudogamie und Polymorphie in der Gattung *Potentilla*. Arch. Julius Klaus-Stift. 23:267–423.

Rutishauser, A., 1949. Pseudogamie und Sexualität einiger Potentillen. Ber. schweiz. bot. Ges. 59:409–420.

Rutishauser, A., 1953–1954. Die Entwicklungserregung des Endosperms bei pseudogamen *Ranunculus*-Arten. Nat. Ges. Schaffh. 25:1–45.

Rutishauser, A., 1954. Entwicklungserregung der Eizelle bei pseudogamen Arten der Gattung *Ranunculus*. Ber. schweiz. Acad. med. wiss. 10:491–512.

Rutishauser, A., 1956. Cytogenetik des Endosperms. Ber. schweiz. bot. Ges. 66:318–336.

Rutishauser, A., 1959. Pseudogamous reproduction and evolution. Congr. Internatl. Bot. 9th. 2:337.

Ruttle, M. L., 1931. Cytological and embryological studies on the genus *Mentha*. Die Gartenbauwissenschaft 4:428–468.

Ruttle, M. L., 1932. Chromosome number, embryology and inheritance in the genus *Lycopus*. Die Gartenbauwissenschaft 7:154–177.

Ruys, J. D., 1925. Contribution à l'histoire du développement des Mélastomatacées. Enumération des plantes Phanérogames Angiospermes examinées au point de vue de la Karyologie. Ann. Jard. bot. Buitenz. 34:1–123. Diss. Leiden.

Rybchenko, O. I., 1959. (The development of ovules in parthenocarpic tomato fruits.) Ukrain. Bot. Zhur. 16:44–56.

Rybchenko, O. I., 1963. (Cytoembryological research on the development of the male gametophyte in the Solanaceae.) Ukrain. Bot. Zhur. 20:3–14.

Rybchenko, O. I., 1964. (Specific features of cytoembryological processes in the potato, *Solanum tuberosum*.) Ukrain. Bot. Zhur. 21:37–46.

Rychlewski, J., 1958. Cyto-embryological investigations on *Sesleria tatrae*. Acta Biol. Cracov. Bot. 1:103–113.

Rychlewski, J., 1961. Cyto-embryological studies in the apomictic species *Nardus stricta*. Acta Biol. Cracov. Bot. 4:1–23.

Saakyar, T. A., 1962. (The embryological study of the fertilization process of the cotton plant with various methods of pollination.) Izv. Akad. Nauk. Armyansk. SSR. Biol. Nauk 15:59–66.

Sabet, Y. S., 1931. Development of the embryo sac in *Calotropis procera*, with special reference to endosperm formation. Ann. Bot. 45:513–518.

Sachar, R. C., 1953. A reinvestigation of the morphology of *Argemone mexicana*. Current Sci. 22:381–383.

Sachar, R. C., 1955. The embryology of *Argemone mexicana:* a reinvestigation. Phytomorphology 5:200–218.

Sachar, R. C., 1956a. The embryology of *Argemone mexicana:* a criticism. Phytomorphology 6:148–151.

Sachar, R. C., 1956b. The embryology of *Isomeris:* a reinvestigation. Phytomorphology 6:346–363.

Sachar, R. C. and U. Arora, 1963. Some embryological aspects of *Amomum dealbatum* and *Hedychium acuminatum*. Bot. Gaz. 124:353–360.

Sachar, R. C. and R. N. Chopra, 1957. A study of the endosperm and embryo in *Mangifera*. Indian J. Agr. Sci. 27:219–228.

Sachar, R. C. and H. Y. Mohan Ram, 1958. The embryology of *Eschscholtzia californica*. Phytomorphology 8:114–124.

Sachar, R. C. and P. Murgai, 1958. Embryology of *Aerva tomentosa*. Current Sci. 27:105–107.

Sachs, J., 1874. Lehrbuch der Botanik. Leipzig.

Safeeulla, K. M., 1950. Development of the female gametophyte and endosperm in *Glossostigma spathulatum*. Proc. 37th. Indian Sci. Congr. 3:47.

Safeeulla, K. M. and H. C. Govindu, 1949. The development of the female gametophyte and endosperm in *Moniera hamiltoniana*. Proc. 36th. Indian Sci. Congr. 3:129–130.

Safeeulla, K. M. and H. C. Govindu, 1950. The development of the female gametophyte and endosperm in *Bacopa hamiltoniana*. Lloydia 13:179–182.

Safijowska, L. D., 1935a. Spermatogenesis bei Campanulaceae. Bull. Sci. Univ. Kyiw 1:265–278.

Safijowska, L. D., 1935b. Do etmbriologii *Adenophora liliiflora*. J. Inst. Bot. Acad. Sci. Ukraine: 85–98.

Safijowska, L. D., 1939. On the embryology of the family Caryophyllaceae. Inst. Sci. Biol. Res. Univ. Kiev 1:119–134.

Safijowska, L. D., 1955. On the form and structure of male gametes in angiosperms. Proc. Shevch. Sci. Soc. 3:39–47.

Safijowska, L. D., 1960. Male gametophyte in *Enkianthus*. Bot. Gaz. 121:185–190.

Safwat, F. M., 1962. The floral morphology of *Sesamone* and the evolution of the pollinating apparatus in Asclepiadaceae. Ann. Missouri bot. Gdn. 49:95–129.

Sagawa, J. and D. H. Nimoto, 1961. Ovule development in *Dendrobium phalaenopsis*. A. S. B. Bull. 8:33.

Sahni, B., 1934. Exembryonate seeds. Current Sci. 3:109–110.

Sahni, B. and B. M. Johri, 1936. Pollen grains in the stylar canal and in the ovary of an angiosperm. Current Sci. 4:587–589.

Said, C., 1960. (Anatomical research on the androecium of *Commelina chamissonis*.) Bull. Soc. nat. hist. Afr. Nord 51:159–174.

Saksena, H. B., 1954. Floral morphology and embryology of *Fumaria parviflora*. Phytomorphology 4:409–417.

Salisbury, E. J., 1931. On the morphology and ecology of *Ranunculus parviflorus*. Ann. Bot. 45:539–578.

Samal, K. K., 1936. The development of the embryo sac and embryo in *Crotalaria juncea*. J. Indian bot. Soc. 15:19–31.

Sampathkumaran, M. A. and C. V. K. Iyengar, 1929. Development of the embryo sac and haustorium in *Ilysanthes parviflora*. Proc. 16th. Indian Sci. Congr. 3:250.

Samuels, J. A., 1912. Etudes sur le développement du sac embryonnaire et sur la fécondation chez le *Gunnera macrophylla*. Arch. f. Zellf. 8:52–120. Thèse. Paris.

Samuelsson, G., 1913. Studien über die Entwicklungsgeschichte einiger Bicornestypen. Ein Beitrag zur Kenntnis der systematischen Stellung der Diapensiaceen und Empetraceen. Svensk bot. Tidskr. 7:97–188.

Samuelsson, G., 1914. Über die Pollenentwicklung von *Anona* und *Aristolochia* und ihre systematische Bedeutung. Svensk bot. Tidskr. 8:181–189.

Sanchez, S. T., 1938. Embryo sac development in *Euphorbia heterophylla*. Bull. Univ. Philipp. Nat. Appl. Sci. 6:59–75.

Sandeen, F., 1868. Bidrag till kännedomen om Gräsembryots byggnad och utveckling. Lunds Univ. Årsskr. 5:1–20.

Sandt, W., 1921. Beiträge zur Kenntnis Begoniaceen. Flora 114:329–384.

Sâné, Y. K., 1939. A contribution to the embryology of the Aponogetonaceae. J. Indian bot. Soc. 18:79–92.

Sansome, E. R., S. Satina, and A. F. Blakeslee, 1942. Disintegration of ovules in tetraploid-diploid and in incompatible species crosses of *Datura*. Bull. Torrey bot. Cl. 69:405–420.

Santos, J. K., 1928. A cytological study of *Cocos nucifera*. Philipp. J. Sci. 37:417–437.

Santos, J. K., 1933. Morphology of the flower and mature grain of Philippine rice. Philipp. J. Sci. 52:475–503.

Santos, J. K., 1937. Macrosporogenesis of *Lilium philippinense*. Cytologia. Fujii Jubl. Vol. 41:822–835.

Sanz, C., 1945. Pollen tube growth in intergeneric pollinations on *Datura stramonium*. Proc. Natl. Acad. Sci. (Wash.) 31:361–367.

Sarfatti, G., 1958. Ricerche sull'endosperma e l'austorio endospermatico di *Prunus communis*. N. G. bot. Ital. 65:371–375.

Sarfatti, G., 1960. Studies on the membrane of the almond endosperm haustorium. Ann. Bot. 24:451–457.

Sarfatti, G., 1961. Accrescimento del pericarpo, seme, endosperma ed embrione in *Prunus amygdalus*. N. G. bot. Ital. 68:118–135.

Sarfatti, G., 1962. Prime ricerche al microscopio elettronico sull'endosperma del mandorlo, *Prunus amygdalus*. Caryologia 15:1–20.

Sargant, E., 1896a. Direct nuclear division in the embryo sac of *Lilium martagon*. Ann. Bot. 10:107–108.

Sargant, E., 1896b. The formation of sexual nuclei in *Lilium martagon*. 1. Oogenesis. Ann. Bot. 10:445–477.

Sargant, E., 1897. The formation of the sexual nuclei in *Lilium martagon*. 2. Spermatogenesis. Ann. Bot. 11:187–224.

Sargant, E., 1900. Recent work on the results of fertilization in angiosperms. Ann. Bot. 14:689–712.

Sargant, E. and A. Arber, 1915. The comparative morphology of the embryo and seedling in the Gramineae. Ann. Bot. 29:161–222.

Sass, J. E., 1946. The development of endosperm and antipodal tissue in Argentine waxy maize. Amer. J. Bot. 33:791–795.

Sass, J. E. and G. F. Sprague, 1950. The embryology of germless maize. Iowa State Coll. J. Sci. 24:209–218.

Sastri, R. L. N., 1952. Studies in Lauraceae. 1. Floral anatomy of *Cinnamomum iners* and *Cassytha filiformis*. J. Indian bot. Soc. 31:240–246.

Sastri, R. L. N., 1954a. Deveopment of the embryo of *Cocculus villosus*. Current Sci. 23:187–188.

Sastri, R. L. N., 1954b. Embryological studies in Menispermaceae. 1. *Tiliacora racemosa*. Proc. Nat. Inst. Sci. India 20:494–505.

Sastri, R. L. N., 1955a. Development of the embryo of *Polyalthia longifolia*. Current Sci. 24:51.

Sastri, R. L. N., 1955b. Structure and development of nutmeg seed. Current Sci. 24:172–173.

Sastri, R. L. N., 1955c. Embryology of *Ceratophyllum demersum*. Proc. 42nd. Indian Sci. Congr. 3:226.

Sastri, R. L. N., 1956a. The gametophytes of *Mahonia leschenaultii* (*Berberis leschenaultii*.) Proc. 43rd. Indian Sci. Congr. 3:224–225.

Sastri, R. L. N., 1956b. Embryo sac haustoria in *Cassytha filiformis*. Current Sci. 25:401–402.

Sastri, R. L. N., 1957a. The embryology of *Cassytha filiformis*. Proc. 44th. Indian Sci. Congr. 3:240–241.

Sastri, R. L. N., 1957b. The vascularization of the ovules in *Saccopetalum tomentosum*. Current Sci. 26:183.

Sastri, R. L. N., 1957c. On the division of pollen mother cells in some Annonaceae. Sci. and Cult. 22:633–634.

Sastri, R. L. N., 1958a. Floral morphology and embryology of some Dilleniaceae. Bot. Notiser 1958:495–511.

Sastri, R. L. N., 1958b. Studies in Lauraceae. 2. Embryology of *Cinnamomum* and *Litsea*. J. Indian bot. Soc. 37:266–278.

Sastri, R. L. N., 1959. Vascularization of the carpel of *Myristica fragrans*. Bot. Gaz. 121:92–95.

Sastri, R. L. N., 1962. Studies in the Lauraceae. 3. Embryology of *Cassytha*. Bot. Gaz. 123:197–206.

Sastri, R. L. N., 1963. Studies in the Lauraceae. 4. Comparative embryology and phylogeny. Ann. Bot. 27:425–433.

Sastri, R. L. N., 1964. Embryological studies in the Menispermaceae. 2. Embryo and seed development. Bull. Torrey bot. Cl. 91:79–85.

Sateishi, S., 1927. (On the development of the embryo sac and fertilisation of *Acalpyha australis*.) Bot. Mag. Tokyo 41:477–485.

Satina, S. and A. F. Blakeslee, 1935a. Cytological effects of a gene in *Datura* which causes dyad formation in sporogenesis. Bot. Gaz. 96:521–532.

Satina, S. and A. F. Blakeslee, 1935b. Fertilization in the incompatible cross *Datura stramonium* x *D. metel*. Bull. Torrey bot. Cl. 62:301–312.

Satina, S. and A. F. Blakeslee, 1941. Contribution of the three germ layers to the formation of ovules in *Datura stramonium*. Amer. J. Bot. 28:5.

Satina, S., J. Rappaport, and A. F. Blakeslee, 1950. Ovular tumors connected with incompatible crosses in *Datura*. Amer. J. Bot. 37:576–586.

Sato, D., 1938. Karyotype alteration and phylogeny. 4. Karyotypes in Amaryllidaceae with special reference to the SAT chromosome. Cytologia 9:203–242.

Sato, H., 1956a. Morphological and physiological studies on occurrence of abortive seeds in leguminous forage crops. 2. Formation of one-seeded pod in red clover. Proc. Crop Sci. Soc. Japan 24:224–226.

Sato, H., 1956b. Morphological and physiological studies on occurrence of abortive seeds in Leguminous forage crops. 3. Formation of one-seeded pod in sweet clover. Proc. Crop. Sci. Soc. Japan 25:109–110.

Sato, H., 1957. Morphological and physiological studies on occurrence of abortive seeds in leguminous forage crops. 4. Occurrence of abortive seeds and their position in pod of common vetch, *Vicia sativa*. Proc. Crop Sci. Soc. Japan 26:68–70.

Sato, H., 1958. Morphological and physiological studies on occurrence of abortive seeds in Leguminous forage crops. 5. Formation of one-seeded pod in kidney vetch. Proc. Crop Sci. Soc. Japan 27:115–117.

Sauer, L. W., 1909. Nuclear divisions in the pollen mother cells of *Convallaria majalis*. Ohio Nat. 9:497–505.

Savchenko, M. I., 1956. (On divergences in the development of the ovule in some angiospermous plants.) Bot. Zhur. 44:786–804.

Savchenko, M. I., 1960. (Anomalies in the structure of angiosperm ovules.) Dokl. Akad. Nauk SSSR 130:1154–1157.

Savelli, R., 1928. Poliembrionia in *Cannabis sativa*. Arch. Botan. 4:128–137.

Sawyer, M. L., 1917. Pollen tube and spermatogenesis in *Iris*. Bot. Gaz. 64:159–164.

Sax, H. J., 1954. Polyploidy and apomixis in *Cotoneaster*. J. Arnold Arbor. 35:334–365.

Sax, K., 1916. Fertilization in *Fritillaria pudica*. Bull. Torrey bot. Cl. 43:505–522.

Sax, K., 1921. Sterility in wheat hybrids. 1. Sterility relationship and endosperm development. Genetics 6:399–416.

Sax, K., 1922. Sterility in wheat hybrids. 3. Endosperm development and F2 sterility. Genetics 7:553–558.

Sax, K., 1935. The effect of temperature on nuclear differentiation in microspore development. J. Arnold Arbor. 16:301–310.

Sax, K. and H. W. Edmonds, 1933. Development of the male gametophyte in *Tradescantia*. Bot. Gaz. 95:156–163.

Sax, K. and L. Husted, 1936. Polarity and differentiation in microspore development. Amer. J. Bot. 23:606–608.

Sax, K. and J. G. O'Mara, 1941. Mechanism of mitosis in pollen tubes. Bot. Gaz. 102:629–636.

Saxena, N. P., 1963. Twin embryo sacs in *Saxifraga diversifolia*. Sci. and Cult. 29:614–615.

Saxena, N. P., 1964a. Studies in the family Saxifragaceae. 1. A contribution to the morphology and embryology of *Saxifraga diversifolia*. Proc. Indian Acad. Sci. B. 60:38–51.

Saxena, N. P., 1964b. Studies in the family Saxifragaceae. 2. Development of ovule and megagametophyte in *Parnassia nubicola*. Proc. Indian Acad. Sci. B. 60:196–202.

Saxton, W. T., 1907. On the development of the ovule and embryo sac in *Cassia tomentosa*. Trans. Sth. Afr. Phil. Soc. 18:1–5.

Saxton, W. T., 1910. The ovule of the Bruniaceae. Trans. Roy. Soc. Sth. Afr. 2:27–31.

Scarascia, G. T., 1953. Sviluppo del tappeto dell'antera in *Nicotiana tabacum* var. *bright*. Caryologia 5.

Schachner, J., 1924. Beiträge zur Kenntnis der Blüten- und Samenentwicklung der Scitamineen. Flora 117:16–40.

Schacht, H., 1850. Entwicklungsgeschichte des Pflanzenembryos. Diss. Amsterdam.

Schacht, H., 1851. Entwicklungsgeschichte des Pflanzenembryos. Ann. Sci. nat. Bot. (3) 15:80–109.

Schacht, H., 1853. Entwicklungsgeschichte der Blüthe und Frucht von *Manglesia cuneata*. Bot. Zeit. 2:465–471.

Schacht, H., 1855a. Über die Entstehung des Pflanzenkeims. Flora, 13:161–170.

Schacht, H., 1855b. Über die Befruchtung der *Pedicularis silvatica*. Flora 38:449–461, 465–476.

Schacht, H., 1855c. Sur l'origine de l'embryon végétal. Ann. Sci. nat. Bot. 3:188–208.

Schacht, H., 1855d. Über die Entstehung des Keimes von *Tropaeolum majus*. Bot. Zeit. 13:641–650.

Schacht, H., 1858. Über Pflanzenbefruchtung. Jahrb. f. wiss. Bot. 1:193–232.

Schacht, H., 1859. Madeira und Teneriffe mit ihrer Vegetation. Berlin.

Schacht, H., 1860. Über den Bau einiger Pollenkörner. Jahrb. f. wiss. Bot. 2:107–168.

Schacht, H., 1863. Über die Zellstoffäden in der vorderen Aussackung des Embryosackes von *Pedicularis silvatica*. Jahrb. f. wiss. Bot. 3:339–351.

Schacht, H., 1865. Die Blüthe und Befruchtung von *Santalum album*. Pringsheim's Jahrb. 4:1–22.

Schacht, H., 1866. Die Blüthe und die Befruchtung von *Santalum album*. Jahrb. f. wiss. Bot. 4:1–19.

Schaeppi, H., 1942. Morphologische und entwicklungsgeschichtliche Untersuchungen an den Blüten von *Thesium*. Nat. Ges. Winterthur. 23:41–61.

Schaeppi, H. and F. Steindl, 1937. Blütenmorphologische und embryologische Untersuchungen an *Osyris alba*. Ber. schweiz. bot. Ges. 47:369–392.

Schaeppi, H. and F. Steindl, 1942. Blütenmorphologische und embryologische Untersuchungen an Loranthoideen. Vjschr. naturf. Ges. Zürich 87:301–372.

Schaeppi, H. and F. Steindl, 1945. Blütenmorphologische und embryologische Untersuchungen an einigen Viscoideen. Vjschr. naturf. Ges. Zürich 90:1–46.

Schaffner, J. H., 1896. The embryo sac of *Alisma plantago*. Bot. Gaz. 21:123–132.

Schaffner, J. H., 1897a. Contribution to the life history of *Sagittaria variabilis*. Bot. Gaz. 23:252–273.

Schaffner, J. H., 1897b. The embryo sac and associated structures. Bot. Gaz. 23:412–422.

Schaffner, J. H., 1897c. Contribution to the life history of *Lilium philadelphicum*. 3. Division of the macrospore nucleus. Bot. Gaz. 23:430–452.

Schaffner, J. H., 1897d. The development of the stamens and carpels of *Typha latifolia*. Bot. Gaz. 24:93–102.

Schaffner, J. H., 1901. A contribution to the life history and cytology of *Erythronium*. Bot. Gaz. 31:369–387.

Schaffner, J. H., 1904a. The jacket layer in *Sassafras*. Ohio Nat. 4:191–193.

Schaffner, J. H., 1904. Some morphological peculiarities of the Nymphaceae and Helobiae. Ohio Nat. 4:83–92.

Schaffner, J. H., 1908. On the origin of polar conjugation in angiosperms. Ohio Nat. 8:255–258.

Schaffner, M., 1906. The embryology of the Shepherd's Purse. Ohio Nat. 7:1–8.

Schagen, R., 1956. Embryologische Untersuchungen am Freigenblattkürbis (*Cucurbita ficifolia*) nach Bestäubung mit Pollen des Gartenkürbis (*C. pepo.*) Flora 143:91–126.

Schanderl, H., 1949. Die Entwicklungsgeschichte des Embryos bei den Rosaceengattungen *Prunus, Pyrus* und *Malus*. Der Züchter 19:206–210.

Schanderl, H., 1964. Investigations on floral biology and embryo formation in *Juglans regia*. Biol. Ztbl. 83:71–103.

Schertz, F. M., 1919. Early development of floral organs and embryonic structures of *Scrophularia marylandica*. Bot. Gaz. 68:441–450.

Schilbersky, K., 1890. (On polyembryony.) Potfüz. z. Tennesz., Budapest: 77.

Schiller, J., 1907. Untersuchungen über die Embryogenie der Gattung *Gnaphalium*. Österr. bot. Zeit. 57.

Schindler, A. K., 1913. Einige Bemerkungen über *Lespedeza,* und ihre nächsten Verwandten. Bot. Zahrb. 49:570–658.

Schips, M., 1913. Zur Öffnungsmeckanik der Antheren. Diss. Freiburg.

Schkorbatow, L., 1912. Parthenogenetische und Apogame Entwicklung bei den Blüthenpflanzen. Entwicklungsgeschichtliche Studien an *Taraxacum officinale*. Trav. Soc. Nat. Univ. Imp. Kharkow 45:15–25.

Schleiden, M. J., 1837. Einige Blicke auf die Entwicklungsgeschichte des vegetablischen Organismus bei den Phanerogamen. Arch. Bwl. Naturg. (3) 1:289–320.

Schleiden, M. J., 1839a. Über Bildung des Eichens und Entstehung des Embryos bei den Phanerogamen. Verh. Kais. Leop.-Carol. Ak. Naturf. 11:29–58.

Schleiden, M. J., 1839b. Sur la formation de l'ovule et l'origine de l'embryon dans les Phanérogames. Ann. Sci. nat. Bot. (2) 11:129–141.

Schleiden, M. J. and T. Vogel, 1838. Über das Albumen insbesondere des Leguminosen. Verh. Kais. Leop.-Carol. dtsch. Akad. 19:51–96.

Schlimbach, H., 1924. Beiträge zur Kenntnis der Samenanlagen und Samen der Amaryllidaceen mit Berücksichtigung des Wassergehaltes der Samen. Flora 117:41–54.

Schloms, M., 1958. Zur Frage der unterschiedlichen Embryonalentwicklung nach reziproker Artkreuzung. Eine Untersuchung bei Riesenkürbis (*Cucurbita maxima*) und Gartenkürbis (*C. pepo*). Flora 146:586–615.

Schlotterbeck, J. O., 1896. Beiträge zur Entwicklungsgeschichte pharmakognostisch wichtiger Samen. Diss. Bern.

Schlotterbeck, J. O., 1898. The development of the seed of *Melampyrum pratense* and of *Croton tiglium*. Proc. Amer. Assoc. Adv. Sci. 46:275–278.

Schmid, B., 1901. Beiträge zur Embryobildung einiger Dicotylen. Bot. Zeit. 60:207–230.

Schmid, E., 1906. Beiträge zur Entwicklungsgeschichte der Scrophulariaceen. Beih. bot. Ztbl. 20:175–299. Diss. Zürich.

Schmid, W., 1925. Morphologische, anatomische und entwicklungsgeschichtliche Untersuchungen an *Mesembrianthemum pseudotruncatellum*. Vjschr. naturf. Ges. Zürich 70:1–96.

Schmidt, H., 1907. Über die Entwicklung der Blüten und Blütenstände von *Euphorbia* und *Diplocyathium*. Beih. bot. Ztbl. 22:20–69.

Schnarf, K., 1914. Beiträge zur Kenntnis der Samenentwicklung einiger europäischer *Hypericum*-Arten. S. B. Acad. wiss. Wien (1) 123.

Schnarf, K., 1917a. Zur Entwicklungsgeschichte von *Plantago media*. S. B. Acad. wiss. Wien (1). 126:927–950.

Schnarf, K., 1917b. Beiträge zur Kenntnis der Samenentwicklung der Labiaten. Denkschr. Acad. wiss. Wien. 94:211–275.

Schnarf, K., 1919. Beobachtungen über die Endospermentwicklung von *Hieracium aurantiacum*. S. B. Acad. wiss. Wien (1) 128:1–17.

Schnarf, K., 1921a. Kleine Beiträge zur Entwicklungsgeschichte der Angiospermen. 1. *Gilia millefoliata*. Österr. bot. Zeit. 70:153–158.

Schnarf, K., 1921b. Kleine Beiträge zur Kenntnis der Entwicklungsgeschichte der Angiospermen. 2. *Klugia zeylanica*. Österr. bot. Zeit. 70:255–261.

Schnarf, K., 1922a. Kleine Beiträge zur Kenntnis der Entwicklungsgeschichte der Angiospermen. 3. Samenentwicklung einiger *Viola*-Bastard. Österr. bot. Zeit. 71:190–199.

Schnarf, K., 1922b. Beiträge zur Kenntnis des Blüten baues von *Alangium*. S. B. Acad. wiss. Wien. 131:199–208.

Schnarf, K., 1923. Kleine Beiträge zur Entwicklungsgeschichte der Angiospermen. 4. Über Verhalten des Antherentapetums einiger Pflanzen. Österr. bot. Zeit. Jahrb. 1923:242–245.

Schnarf, K., 1924. Bemerkungen zur Stellung der Gattung *Saurauia* im System. S. B. Acad. wiss. Wien (1) 133:17–28.

Schnarf, K., 1925. Kleine Beiträge zur Kenntnis der Entwicklungsgeschichte der Angiospermen. 5. Über zwei Kritische Fälle der Endospermentwicklung (*Verbena* und *Triglochin*). Österr. bot. Zeit. 74:40–50.

Schnarf, K., 1926. Kleine Beiträge zur Kenntnis der Entwicklungsgeschichte der Angiospermen. 6. Über die Samenentwicklung einiger Gramineen. Österr. bot. Zeit. 75:105–113.

Schnarf, K., 1928a. Über die Endospermentwicklung bei *Ornithogalum*. Österr. bot. Zeit. 77:173–177.

Schnarf, K., 1928b. Über das Embryosackhaustorium bei *Anthericum*. Österr. bot. Zeit. 77:287–291.

Schnarf, K., 1929a. Die Embryologie der Liliaceae und ihre systematische Bedeutung. S. B. Acad. wiss. Wien. (1) 138:69–92.

Schnarf, K., 1929b. Embryologie der Angiospermen. Berlin.

Schnarf, K., 1930. Zur Kenntnis der Samenanlage von *Roridula*. Österr. bot. Zeit. 79:180–183.

Schnarf, K., 1931a. Vergleichende Embryologie der Angiospermen. Berlin.

Schnarf, K., 1931b. Ein Beitrage zur Kenntnis der Samenentwicklung der Gattung *Cochlospermum*. Österr. bot. Zeit. 80:45–50.

Schnarf, K., 1933. Die Bedeutung des embryologischen Forschung für das natürliche System der Pflanzen. Biol. Gen. 10:271–288.

Schnarf, K., 1936. Contemporary understanding of embryo sac development among angiosperms. Bot. Rev. 2:565–585.

Schnarf, K., 1937a. Ziele und Wege der vergleichenden Embryologie der Blütenpflanzen. Verh. zool. bot. Ges. Wien. 86–87:140–147.

Schnarf, K., 1937b. Studien über den Bau der Pollenkörner der Angiospermen. Planta 27:450–465.

Schnarf, K., 1939. Variation im Bau des Pollenkörner des Angiospermen. Tab. Biol. Periodicae., Hague, 17:72–89.

Schnarf, K., 1941. Vergleichende Zytologie des Geschlechtsapparates des Kormophyten. *In* Monographien zur vergleichenden Zytologie. Berlin.

Schnarf, K., 1944. Ein Beitrag zur Kenntnis der Verbreitung des Aloïns und ihrer systematischen Bedeutung. Österr. bot. Zeit. 93:113–122.

Schnarf, K., 1948. Der Umfang der Lilioideae im natürlichen System. Österr. bot. Zeit. 95:257–269.

Schnarf, K. and R. Wunderlich, 1939. Zur vergleichenden Embryologie der Liliaceae-Asphodeloideae. Flora 33:297–327.

Schnegg, H., 1902. Beiträge zur Kenntnis der Gattung *Gunnera*. Flora 90:161–208.

Schneider, G. W., 1953. Megagametogenesis and embryology in a diploid and an aneuploid apple. Amer. J. Bot. 40:196–203.

Schneider, H., 1914. Morphologische und entwicklungsgeschichtlichte Untersuchungen an *Thelygonum cynocrambe*. Flora 106:1–41.

Schneider, J. M., 1908. Der Öffnungsmechanismus der *Tulipa*-Anthere, Altstätten.

Schneider, M., 1932. Untersuchungen über die Embryobildung und Entwicklung der Cyperaceen. Beih. bot. Ztbl. 49:649–674.

Schniewind-Thies, J., 1901. Die Reduktion der Chromosonmenzahl und die folgenden Kernteilungen in den Embryosackmutterzellen der Angiospermen. Thesis. Jena.

Schoch, M., 1920. Entwicklungsgeschichtlich-cytologische Untersuchungen über die Pollenbildung und Bestäubung bei einigen *Burmannia*-Arten. Arb. Inst. allg. Bot. Pflanzenphys. Univ. Zürich 24. Diss. Zürich.

Schoch-Bodmer, H., 1945. Über das Spitzenwachstum der Pollenschläuche. Ber. schweiz. bot. Ges. 55:154–168.

Schoenebeck, B., 1924. Die Antipodenvermehrung der Typhaceen. Ber. dtsch. bot. Ges. 42:296–299.

Schöffel, K., 1932. Untersuchungen über den Blütenbau der Ranunculaceen. Planta 17:342–344.

Schönland, S., 1883. Über die Entwicklung der Blüte und Frucht bei den Platanen. Engler's bot. Jahrb. 4:308–327.

Schorbatow, L., 1911–1912. Parthenogenese und apogame Entwicklung bei den Blütenpflanzen. Entwicklungsgeschichtliche Studien an *Taraxacum officinale*. Trav. Soc. nat. Univ. imp. Kharkhow 45:15–55.

Schrenk, H., 1894. Teratological notes. Bull. Torrey bot. Cl. 21:226–227.

Schroeder, C. A., 1952. Floral development, sporogenesis and embryology in the avocado, *Persea americana*. Bot. Gaz. 113:270–278.

Schroeder, C. A., 1955. Pollen production in avocado. Yearb. Calif. Avoc. Soc. 39:184–186.

Schulle, H., 1933. Zur Entwicklungsgeschichte von *Thesium montanum*. Flora 27:140–184.

Schulz-Gaebel, H. H., 1930. Entwicklungsgeschichtlich-zytologische Studien an der Umbelliferenunterfamilie der Apioideae. Beitr. Biol. Pfl. begr. von Cohn 18:345–398.

Schumann, K., 1898. Gesamtbeschreibung der Kakteen. Neudamm.

Schürhoff, P. N., 1915. Amitosen von Riesenkernen im Endosperm von *Ranunculus acer*. Jahrb. f. wiss. Bot. 55:499–519.

Schürhoff, P. N., 1916. Über dreikernige Pollenkörner bei angiospermen Pflanzen. Mikrokosmos 10:141–143.

Schürhoff, P. N., 1919a. Über die Teilung des generativen Kerns vor der Keimung des Pollenkorns. Arch. f. Zellfors. 15.

Schürhoff, P. N., 1919b. Zur Phylogenie des angiospermen Embryosackes. Ber. dtsch. bot. Ges. 37:161–169.

Schürhoff, P. N., 1920a. Der Embryosack von *Tussilago farfara*. Ber. dtsch. bot. Ges. 38:217–219.

Schürhoff, P. N., 1920b. Die Antipodenvermehrung der Sparganiaceae. Ber. dtsch. bot. Ges. 38:346–349.

Schürhoff, P. N., 1921a. Die Entwicklungsgeschichte von *Ilex aquifolium*. Ber. dtsch. bot. Ges. 39:377–379.

Schürhoff, P. N., 1921b. Über die Tielung des generativen Kernes vor der Keimung des Pollenkorns. Arch. f. Zellf. 15:145–159.

Schürhoff, P. N., 1922a. Die Teilung des vegetativen Pollenkerns bei *Eichhornia crassipes*. Ber. dtsch. bot. Ges. 40:60–63.

Schürhoff, P. N., 1922b. Die Befruchtung von *Viscum album*. Ber. dtsch. bot. Ges. 40:314–316.

Schürhoff, P. N., 1922c. Zur Polyembryonie von *Allium odorum*. Ber. dtsch. bot. Ges. 40:374–381.

Schürhoff, P. N., 1923. Zur Apogamie von *Calycanthus*. Flora 116:73–84.

Schürhoff, P. N., 1924a. Die Haploidgeneration der Blütenpflanzen (siphonogamen Embryophyten). Bot. Jahrb. 59:198–293.

Schürhoff, P. N., 1924b. Zytologische Untersuchungen in der Reihe der Geraniales. Jahrb. f. wiss. Bot. 63:707–759.

Schürhoff, P. N., 1924c. Die geschlechtsbegrenzte Vererbung der Kleistogamie bei *Plantago* sect. *Novorbis*. Ber. dtsch. bot. Ges. 42:311–321.

Schürhoff, P. N., 1925a. Zur Zytologie von *Saxifraga*. Jahrb. f. wiss. Bot. 64:443–499.

Schürhoff, P. N., 1925b. Zur Zytologie von *Melandrium*-Zwittern. Ber. dtsch. bot. Ges. 43:450–454.

Schürhoff, P. N., 1926a. Zur Pleiophylie der Sympetalen auf Grund ihrer Haplontenentwicklung. Rep. spec. nov. reg. Veget. Beih. 41:3–14.

Schürhoff, P. N., 1926b. Die Zytologie der Blütenpflanzen. Stuttgart.

Schürhoff, P. N., 1926c. (Synergid haustoria in the Calendulaceae and Arctotidae and systematic relationships in the Compositae). Ber. dtsch. bot. Ges. 44:665–673.

Schürhoff, P. N., 1927. Zytologische Untersuchungen über *Mentha*. Beitr. Biol. Pfl. begr. Cohn 15:129–146.

Schürhoff, P. N., 1928. Über die Entwicklung des Eiapparates des Angiospermen. Ber. dtsch. bot. Ges. 46:560–572.

Schürhoff, P. N., 1929. Über die systematische Stellung der Pittosporaceae. Beitr. z. Biol. Pfl. 17:72–86.

Schürhoff, P. N., 1931. Die Haploidgeneration der Balsamineen und ihre Verwertung für die Systematik. Engler's bot. Jahrb. 64:324.

Schürhoff, P. N. and J. Jüssen, 1925. Nuzellarpolyembryonie bei *Spathiphyllum patinii*. Ber. dtsch. bot. Ges. 43:454–456.

Schürhoff, P. N. and H. Müller, 1937. Zytologische Untersuchungen über die Haploid generation der Apocynaceen. Cytologia. Fujii Jubl. Vol.

Schwarze, C., 1914. Vergleichende entwicklungsgeschichtliche und histologische Untersuchungen reduzierter Staubblätter. Diss. Tübingen.

Schwarzenbach, F., 1922. Untersuchungen über die Sterilität von *Cardamine bulbifera* unter der Annahme des hybriden Ursprungs dieser Art. Flora 115:393–514.

Schweiger, J., 1905. Beiträge zur Kenntnis der Samenentwicklung der Euphorbiaceen. Flora 94:339–379.

Schweiger, J., 1909. Vergleichende Untersuchungen über *Sarracenia* und *Cephalotus follicularis* betreffs ihrer Verwandtschaft. Beih. bot. Ztbl. 25:490–539.

Schwencke, E. H., 1931. Zytologische Untersuchungen einiger Verbenaceen. Diss. Berlin.

Schwere, S., 1896. Zur Entwicklungsgeschichte der Frucht von *Taraxacum officinale*. Ein Beitrag zur Embryologie der Compositen. Flora 82:32–66.

Sciple, R. S. and G. W. Johnston, 1963. Cytology of microsporogenesis in *Lathyrus hirsutus*. Cytologia 28:343–350.

Scott, F. M., 1953. The physical consistency of the endosperm of *Echinocystis macrocarpa*. Phytomorphology 3:66–76.

Scott, J., 1864. Observations on the functions and structure of the reproductive organs in the Primulaceae. Proc. Linn. Soc. Lond. 8:78–126.

Scrobischewski, W., 1884. Über die Bedeutung des Fadenapparates bei *Viscum album*. Bot. Ztbl. 18:156–157.

Sears, P. B., 1917. Amiotic parthenogenesis in *Taraxacum vulgare* and *T. laevigatum*. Ohio J. Sci. 27:97–100.

Sears, P. B., 1922. Variation in cytology and gross morphology of *Taraxacum*. Bot. Gaz. 73:308–325.

Seaton, S., 1908. The development of the embryo sac of *Nymphaea advena*. Bull. Torrey bot. Cl. 35:283–289.

Seefeldner, G., 1912. Die Polyembryonie bei *Cynanchum vincetoxicum*. S. B. Acad. wiss. Wien. (1) 121:274–296.

Seelieb, W., 1924. Beiträge zur Entwicklungsgeschichte von *Tofieldia calyculata*. Bot. Notiser 1924: 172–178. Diss. Zürich.

Selling, O., 1947. Studies in Hawaiian Pollen Statistics. 2. The pollen of the Hawaiian Phanerogams. Spec. Publ. Bishop Mus. 38.

Semianinova, M., 1925. Etude embryologique de l'*Ophrys myodes*. Zeit. Russ. bot. Ges. 9:10–14.

Sen, N. K. and R. Krishnan, 1961. Binucleate pollen mother cells in *Clitoria ternata*. Current Sci. 30:306–307.

Sen, P. K., 1938. Annual Report of the Horticultural Research Station of the United Provinces and Bihar. India.

Sen, P. K. and P. C. Mallik, 1940. The embryo of the Indian mangos, *Mangifera indica*. Indian J. Agric. Sci. 10:750–760.

Serguéeff, M., 1907. Contribution à la morphologie et la biologie des Aponogetonacées. Thèse. Genève.

Servettaz, C., 1909. Monographie des Eléagnacées. Beih. Bot. Ztbl. 25.

Seshagiriah, K. N., 1932a. Development of the female gametophyte and embryo in *Spiranthes australis*. Current Sci. 1:102.

Seshagiriah, K. N., 1932b. Pollen sterility in *Zeuxine sulcata*. Current Sci. 3:205–206.

Seshagiriah, K. N., 1934. Seeds and seedlings of *Tinospora cordifolia*. Current Sci. 3:264.

Seshagiriah, K. N., 1941. Morphological studies in Orchidaceae. 1. *Zeuxine sulcata*. J. Indian bot. Soc. 20:357–365.

Sethi, M. L., 1930. Microsporogenesis in *Cassia didymobotrya*. J. Indian bot. Soc. 9:126–139.

Shadowsky, A., 1912. Beiträge zur Embryologie der Gattung *Epirrhizanthes*. Biol. Zeit. Moskau 2:28–52.

Shadowsky, A. E., 1924. Embryological researches on *Plantago major*, f. *phyllostachya*. Bjul. Moskov Obsc. Ispyt. Prir. Biol. 33:234–259.

Shadowsky, A. E., 1925a. Über die Entwicklung des Embryosackes bei *Pancratium maritinum*. Ber. dtsch. bot. Ges. 43:361–365.

Shadowsky, A. E., 1925b. (Types of development of the pollen and their phylogenetic significance.) Bull. appl. Bot. Pl. Breeding, Leningrad 14:133–142.

Shadowsky, A. E., 1925c. (Types of embryo sac development in angiosperms.) J. Soc. bot. Russ. 10:353–372.

Shadowsky, A. E., 1926. Der antipodiale Apparat bei Gramineen. Flora 120:344–370.

Shadowsky, A. E., 1931. Einige Angaben über die Embryologie von *Pistia stratioites*. Ber. dtsch. bot. Ges. 49:350–356.

Shah, C. K., 1962. Pollen development in some members of the Cyperaceae. *In* Plant Embryology: a Symposium. CSIR, New Delhi: 81–93.

Shah, C. K., 1963. The life history of *Juncus bufonius*. J. Indian bot. Soc. 42:238–251.

Shah, C. K., 1964. Embryo development in *Eleocharis palustris*. Nat. Canad. 35:41–49.

Shah, C. K., 1965. Embryogeny in some Cyperaceae. Phytomorphology 15:1–9.

Shah, G. L., 1953. On the megaspore arrangement in *Peucedanum grande*. Current Sci. 22:311–312.

Shamanna, S., 1954. A contribution to the embryology of *Olax wightiana*. Proc. Indian Acad. Sci. B. 39:249–256.

Shamanna, S., 1955. A contribution to the embryology of *Opilia amentacea*. Current Sci. 24:165–167.

Shamanna, S., 1961. A contribution to the embryology of *Strombosia ceylanica*. Proc. Indian Acad. Sci. B. 54:12–16.

Shams-ul-Islam-Khan, 1951. Pollen sterility in *Solanum tuberosum*. Cytologia 16.

Sharma, G., 1956. Studies in the family Euphorbiaceae. 1. The gametophytes of *Chrozophora rottleri*. J. Indian bot. Soc. 35:189–193.

448   BIBLIOGRAPHY

Sharma, K. D., 1955. Cyto-embryological studies in some Indian Euphorbiaceae. Sci. and Cult. 21:270–271.

Sharma, V. K., 1962. Embryology of *Lagotis glauca*. Current Sci. 31:342–344.

Sharma, Y. M. L., 1938. A note on gametogenesis in a few members of Sterculiaceae. Current Sci. 8:284–285.

Sharma, Y. M. L., 1939. Gametogenesis and embryogeny of *Tamarix ericoides*. Ann. Bot. 3:861–870.

Sharma, Y. M. L., 1940. Evidence for the Fritillaria type of embryo sac in *Tamarix ericoides*. Current Sci. 9:26.

Sharman, B. C., 1942. A twin seedling in *Zea mays*. Twinning in the Gramineae. New Phytol. 41:125–129.

Sharp, L. W., 1911. The embryo sac of *Physostegia*. Bot. Gas. 52:218–225.

Sharp, L. W., 1912. The orchid embryo sac. Bot. Gaz. 54:372–385.

Shattuck, C. H., 1905. A morphological study of *Ulmus americana*. Bot. Gaz. 40:209–223.

Shaw, C. H., 1904. Note on the sexual generation and development of the seed coats in certain Papaveraceae. Bull. Torrey bot. Cl. 31:429–433.

Shepherd, K., 1954. Seed fertility of the Gros Michel banana in Jamaica. J. hort. Sci. 29:1–11.

Shepherd, K., 1960. Seed fertility of edible bananas. J. hort. Sci. 35:6–20.

Sheth, A. A., L. Yu, and J. Edwardson, 1956. Sterility in Pangola grass, *Digitaria decumbens*. Agron. Jour. 48:505–507.

Shiam, R., 1963. Morphological studies of *Cyperus esculentus*. Agra Univ. J. Res. (Sci.) 12:181–184.

Shibata, K., 1902a. Die Doppelbefruchtung bei *Monotropa uniflora*. Flora 90:61–66.

Shibata, K., 1902b. Experimentelle Studien über die Entwicklung des Endosperms bei *Monotropa*. Biol. Ztbl. 22:705–714.

Shibata, K. and K. Miyake, 1908. Über Parthenogenesis bei *Houttuynia cordata*. Bot. Mag. Tokyo 22:141–144.

Shilova, N. V., 1962. (The structure of the embryo and the germ in the subfamily Andromedoideae.) Bot. Zhur. 47:344–353.

Shimotomai, N., 1937. Chromosomenzahlen bei einigen Arten von *Chrysanthemum*. Zeit. ind. Abst. U. Veretb.-lehre 74.

Shivaramiah, G., 1964a. A contribution to the embryology of *Utricularia exoleta*. Current Sci. 33:501–503.

Shivaramiah, G., 1964b. A contribution to the embryology of *Utricularia wallichiana*. Current Sci. 33:657–658.

Shivaramiah, G. and R. C. Dutt, 1964. A contribution to the embryology of *Rondeletia amoena*. Current Sci. 33:280–281.

Shivaramiah, G. and P. S. Ganapathy, 1961. A contribution to the embryology of *Knoxia corymbosa*. Current Sci. 30:190–191.

Shkurenko, S. Y., 1961. (The cytochemical and cytoembryological characteristics of the sexual process in wheat-rye hybrids of the first generation.) Vestnik Sel'skokhoz Nauki 7:31–41.

Shmarhon', Y. M., 1964. (Embryological processes in the apple, *Malus domestica*.) Ukrain. bot. Zhur. 21:12–19.

Shoemaker, D. N., 1902. Notes on the development of *Hamamelis virginiana*. Johns Hopkins Univ. Circ. 21:86–87.

Shoemaker, D. N., 1905. On the development of *Hamamelis virginiana*. Bot. Gaz. 39:245–266.

Shoemaker, J. S., 1926. Pollen development in the apple, with special reference to chromosome behavior. Bot. Gaz. 81:148–172.

Shoemaker, J. S., 1928. Cherry pollination studies. Ohio Agric. Exp. Sta. Bull.

Shoji, T. and T. Nakamura, 1928. On the dioecism of garden asparagus, *Asparagus officinalis*. Jap. J. Bot. 4:125–151.

Showalter, A. M., 1921. An orthotropous ovule in *Hyacinthus orientalis*. Torreya 21:62–63.

Showalter, A. M., 1935. A study of the chromosomes and degenerating microspore tissue in *Mirabilis*. Amer. J. Bot. 22:594–608.

Shreve, F., 1905. The development of *Sarracenia purpurea*. Johns Hopkins Univ. Circ. 178:31–34.

Shreve, F., 1906. The development and anatomy of *Sarracenia purpurea*. Bot. Gaz. 42:107–126.

Shuhart, D. V., 1927. The morphological differentiation of the pistillate flowers of the pecan. J. Agric. Res. 35:687–696.

Shuhart, D. V., 1932. Morphology and anatomy of the fruit of *Hicoria pecan*. Bot. Gaz. 93:1–20.

Shukla, R. D., 1954. Gametophytes in *Balsamodendron mukul*. Current Sci. 23:333.

Shukla, R. D., 1960. A contribution to the family Zygophyllaceae. 1. Development of male and female gametophytes of *Fagonia cretica*. Bull. bot. Soc. Univ. Saugor 12:1–7.

Shukla, R. D., 1962. A contribution to the family Zygophyllaceae. Development of male and female gametophytes of *Fagonia cretica*. Proc. 49th. Indian Sci. Congr. 3:278.

Shukla, T. C., 1954. Behaviour of tapetal cells during microsporogenesis of *Lens esculenta*. Current Sci. 23:365.

Sienicka, A., 1929. Über den Blütenbau und die Pollenbildungsvorgänge bei *Hemerocallis fulva*. fl. *pleno*. Acta Soc. bot. Polon. 6:296–334.

Silow, R. A., 1931. A preliminary report on pollen tube growth in red clover, *Trifolium pratense*. Welsh Pl. Breeding Sta. Bull. 12.

Silow, R. A. and G. S. Stephens, 1944. Twinning in cotton. Jour. Hered. 35:76–78.

Silva, B. L. T. de, 1945. A contribution to the life history of *Gloriosa superba*. Ceyl. J. Sci. A 12:155–159.

Simmonds, N. W., 1961. Megasporogenesis and female fertility in three edible triploid bananas. J. Genet. 57:269–278.

Simonet, M., 1932. Recherches cytologiques et génétiques chez les *Iris*. Bull. biol. France et Belg. 66:255–444.

Simonet, M., 1934. Nouvelles recherches cytologiques et génétiques chez *Iris*. Ann. Sci. nat. Bot. (10) 16:231–383.

Simoni, D., 1937. Osservazioni sulla fertillità e ricerche citologiche-embryologiche in *Tulipa gesneriana*. Lav. Inst. bot. gen. Univ. Zurigo (2) 22:1–72; Boll. della Soc. Ticinese Sci. nat. 32. Diss. Zürich.

Simonyan, E. G., 1963. (The development and structure of the male gametophyte of *Triticum timopheevi* and its hybrids.) Izv. Min. Proiz. Zagot. Sel'sk. Prod. Arm. SSSR 6:53–60.

Singh, B., 1934. The seeds of *Tinospora cordifolia*. Current Sci. 3:265.

Singh, B., 1936. The life history of *Ranunculus sceleratus*. Proc. Indian Acad. Sci. B. 4:75–91.

Singh, B., 1950. The embryology of *Dendrophthoe falcata*. Proc. 37th. Indian Sci. Congr. 3.

Singh, B., 1952a. A contribution to the floral morphology and embryology of *Dendrophthoe falcata.* J. Linn. Soc. Lond. (Bot.) 53:449–473.

Singh, B., 1952b. Studies on the structure and development of seeds of Cucurbitaceae. 1. Seeds of *Echinocystis wrightii.* Phytomorphology 2:201–209.

Singh, B., 1953. Studies on the structure and development of seeds of Cucurbitaceae. Phytomorphology 3:224–239.

Singh, B., 1959. Studies in the family Malpighiaceae. 1. The morphology of *Thryallis glauca.* Hort. Adv. 3:1–19.

Singh, B., 1961a. Studies in the family Malpighiaceae. 2. Morphology of *Malpighia glabra.* Hort. Adv. 5:83–95.

Singh, B., 1961b. Studies in the family Malpighiaceae. 3. Development and structure of the seed and fruit of *Malpighia glabra.* Hort. Adv. 5:145–155.

Singh, B., 1962. Studies in angiospermic parasites. 1. *Dendrophthoe falcata,* its life history, list of hosts and control measures. Bull. Nat. bot. Gdn. Lucknow 69:1–75.

Singh, B., 1964. Development and structure of angiosperm seed. 1. Bull. Nat. bot. Gdn. Lucknow 89:1–115.

Singh, B. and T. N. Shivapuri, 1935. The gametophytes of *Neptunia oleracea.* Proc. Indian Acad. Sci. B. 1:423–434.

Singh, D., 1954. Floral morphology and embryology of *Hedera nepalensis.* Agra J. Res. (Sci.) 3:289–299.

Singh, D., 1955a. Cytoplasmic nodules in the endosperm of some Cucurbitaceae. Nature 176:607–608.

Singh, D., 1955b. Embryological studies in *Cucumis melo* var. *pubescens.* J. Indian bot. Soc. 34:72–78.

Singh, D., 1956a. A contribution to the embryology of some members of the Cucurbitaceae. Proc. 43rd. Indian Sci. Congr. 3:222–223.

Singh, D., 1956b. Life history of *Viola tricolor.* Proc. 43rd. Indian Sci. Congr. 3:223.

Singh, D., 1957. Endosperm and its chalazal haustorium in Cucurbitaceae. Agra Univ. J. Res. (Sci.) 6:75–89.

Singh, D., 1961a. Studies on endosperm and development of seeds in Cucurbitaceae and some related families. Agra Univ. J. Res. (Sci.) 10:117–123.

Singh, D., 1961b. Development of embryo in the Cucurbitaceae. J. Indian bot. Soc. 40:620–623.

Singh, D., 1962a. Structure and development of ovule and seed in *Viola tricolor* and *Ionidium suffruticosum.* Proc. 49th. Indian Sci. Congr. 3:264.

Singh, D., 1962b. The structure and development of ovule and seed of *Passiflora foetida.* Agra Univ. J. Res. (Sci.) 11:99–110.

Singh, D., 1963a. Studies on the persistent pollen tubes of the Cucurbitaceae. J. Indian bot. Soc. 42:208–213.

Singh, D., 1963b. Structure and development of ovule and seed of *Viola tricolor* and *Ionidium suffruticosum.* J. Indian bot. Soc. 42:448–462.

Singh, D., 1964a. A further contribution to the endosperm of the Cucurbitaceae. Proc. Indian Acad. Sci. B. 60:399–413.

Singh, D., 1964b. Cytoplasmic nodules in the endosperm of angiosperms. Bull. Torrey bot. Cl. 91:86–94.

Singh, D. and J. S. Gupta, 1956. Cytoplasmic nodules in endosperm of *Coriandrum sativum.* Sci. and Cult. 22:343–344.

Singh, D. and S. Gupta, 1963. Some interesting features in the male gametophyte of *Viola odorata*. Current Sci. 32:183–184.

Singh, D. and D. S. Negi, 1962. A contribution to the morphology and embryology of *Dicentra scandens*. Agra. Univ. J. Res. (Sci.) 11:143–155.

Singh, Dh. and R. Shyam, 1958. Sterility in gram, *Cicer arietinum*. Current Sci. 27:491–492.

Singh, Dh. and R. Shyam, 1959. Ovule sterility in gram, *Cicer arietinum*. Current Sci. 28:294–295.

Singh, R. P., 1954. Structure and development of seeds in the Euphorbiaceae. *Ricinus communis*. Phytomorphology 4:118–123.

Singh, R. P., 1956. Development of endosperm and embryo in *Phyllanthus niruri*. Agra Univ. J. Res. (Sci.) 5:163–167.

Singh, R. P., 1959. On the structure and development of seeds in *Euphorbia geniculata*. J. Indian bot. Soc. 38:103–108.

Singh, R. P., 1962. Forms of ovules in Euphorbiaceae. *In* Plant Embryology: a Symposium. CSIR, New Delhi: 124–128.

Singh, S. N., 1958. A note on partial parthenocarpy in the genus *Luffa*. Current Sci. 27:54–55.

Singh, S. P., 1954. Morphological studies on *Morus* spp. Agra Univ. J. Res. (Sci.) 3:323–341.

Singh, S. P., 1960a. Morphological studies in some members of the family Pedaliaceae. Agra Univ. J. Res. (Sci.) 9:217–220.

Singh, S. P., 1960b. Morphological studies in some members of the family Pedaliaceae. 1. *Sesamum indicum*. Phytomorphology 10:65–82.

Singh, S. P., 1963. Morphological studies in some members of the family Pedaliaceae. Agra Univ. J. Res. (Sci.) 12:143–166.

Singh, S. P. and H. H. Hadley, 1961. Pollen abortion in cytoplasmic male sterile *Sorghum*. Crop Sci. 1:430–432.

Singh, U. P., 1959. Embryony in loquat, *Eriobotrya japonica*. Current Sci. 28:162–163.

Singh, U. R., 1962. Studies in the fruit-drop of mango. 4. Embryo development, its degeneration and studies of fruit-pedicel and abscission zone. Hort. Adv. 5:218–227.

Sizova, M. A., 1958a. (Studies on fertilization processes in flax plants.) Tr. Priklad. Bot. Genet. Selektsii 31:61–81.

Sizova, M. A., 1958b. (The fertilization process in flax, *Linum usitatissimum*.) Tr. Priklad. Bot. Genet. Selektsii 33:155–172.

Sizova, M. A., 1961. (Embryological studies during crossing of flax.) Vest. Sel'skok. Nauk 5:39–43.

Sizova, M. A., 1963. (The process of fertilization in the tetraploid forms of fiber flax, *Linum usitatissimum*, pr. *elongata*.) Bot. Zhur. 48:537–544.

Skalińska, M., 1952. Cytoecological studies in *Poa alpina* var. *vivipara*. Bull. Internat. Acad. Polon. B. 253:283.

Skalińska, M., 1959. Embryological studies in *Poa granitica*, an apomictic species of the Carpathian Range. Acta Biol. Cracov. Bot. 2:91–112.

Skawińska, R., 1962. (Apomixis in *Hieracium alpinum*.) Acta Biol. Cracov. Bot. 5:89–96.

Skottsberg, C., 1913. Morphologische und embryologische Studien über des Myzodendraceae. Kgl. Svensk. Vet.-Akad. Handl. 51:1–34.

Skvarla, J. J. and D. A. Larson, 1963. Nature of cohesion within pollen tetrads of *Typha latifolia*. Science 140:173–175.

Smart, C., 1952. The life history of *Tupeia*. Trans. Roy. Soc. N. Z. 79:459–466.

Smith, A., 1896. Abortive flower buds of *Trillium*. Bot. Gaz. 22:402–403.

Smith, A. C., 1904. The structure and parasitism of *Aphyllon uniflorum*. Contrib. Bot. Lab. Univ. Pennsyl. 2:111–121.

Smith, B. E., 1934. A taxonomic and morphological study of the genus *Cuscuta*, dodders, in North Carolina. J. Elisha Mitchell Sci. Soc. 50:283–302.

Smith, B. W., 1946. Macrosporogenesis and embryogeny in *Arachis hypogaea* as related to seed failure. Amer. J. Bot. 33:826.

Smith, B. W., 1948. Hybridity and apomixis in the perennial grass, *Paspalum dilatatum*. Genetics 33:628–629.

Smith, B. W., 1950. *Arachis hypogaea*, aerial flower and subterranean fruit. Amer. J. Bot. 37:802–815.

Smith, B. W., 1954. *Arachis hypogaea*. Reproductive efficiency. Amer. J. Bot. 41:607–616.

Smith, B. W., 1956a. *Arachis hypogaea*. Normal megasporogenesis and syngamy with occasional single fertilization. Amer. J. Bot. 43:81–89.

Smith, B. W., 1956b. *Arachis hypogaea*. Embryogeny and the effect of peg-elongation upon embryo and endosperm growth. Amer. J. Bot. 43:233–240.

Smith, C. M., 1929. Development of *Dionaea muscipula* 1. Flower and seed. Bot. Gaz. 89:507–530.

Smith, F. H., 1933. Nuclear divisions in the tapetal cells of *Galtonia candicans*. Amer. J. Bot. 20:341–347.

Smith, F. H., 1942. Development of the gametophytes and fertilization in *Camassia*. Amer. J. Bot. 29:657–663.

Smith, F. H., 1943. Megagametophyte of *Clintonia*. Bot. Gaz. 105:263–267.

Smith, F. H., 1955. Megagametophyte development in five species of *Erythronium*. Amer. J. Bot. 42:213–222.

Smith, F. H. and Q. D. Clarkson, 1956. Cytological studies of interspecific hybridization in *Iris* subsect. Californicae. Amer. J. Bot. 43:582–588.

Smith, O., 1935. Pollination and life history studies of the tomato, *Lycopersicum esculentum*. Cornell Univ. Agr. Exp. Sta. Mem. 184:3–16.

Smith, P. M., 1916. The development of the embryo and seedling in *Dioscorea villosa*. Bull. Torrey bot. Cl. 43:545–558.

Smith, R. W., 1898. A contribution to the life history of the Pontederiaceae. Bot. Gaz. 25:324–337.

Smith, R. W., 1908. Endosperm of Pontederiaceae. Bot. Gaz. 45:338–339.

Smith, R. W., 1910. The floral development and embryogeny of *Eriocaulon septangulare*. Bot. Gaz. 49:281–289.

Smith, R. W., 1911. The tetranucleate embryo sac of *Clintonia*. Bot. Gaz. 52:209–217.

Smith-White, S., 1955a. Chromosome numbers and pollen types in the Epacridaceae. Aust. J. Bot. 3:48–67.

Smith-White, S., 1955b. The life history and genetic system of *Leucopogon juniperinus*. Heredity 9:79–91.

Smith-White, S., 1959. Pollen development patterns in the Epacridaceae. A problem in cytoplasm-nucleus interaction. Proc. Linn. Soc. N.S.W., 84:8–35.

Snoad, B., 1954. Abortive meiosis in plasmodial pollen mother cells of *Helianthemum*. Ann. Bot. 18:1–6.

Snyder, L. A., 1957. Apomixis in *Paspalum secans*. Amer. J. Bot. 44:318–324.

Snyder, L. A., A. R. Hernandez, and H. E. Warmke, 1955. The mechanism of apomixis in *Pennisetum ciliare*. Bot. Gaz. 116:209–221.

Söderberg, E., 1919. Über die Pollenentwicklung bei *Chamaedorea corallina*. Svensk bot. Tidsk. 13:204–211.

Söderberg, E., 1929. Bemerkungen zur Nomenklatur der parthenogenetischen *Erigeron*-Arten. Svensk bot. Tidsk. 23:261–262.

Sokolśkaja, B. P., 1938. On polyembryony in seeds of *Citrus*. Soviet. Subtrop. 44:66–67.

Solms-Laubach, H. G., 1870. Die Familie der Lennoaceen. Abh. naturf. Ges. Halle 11:119–178.

Solms-Laubach, H. G., 1874. Über den Bau der Samen in den Familien der Rafflesiaceae und Hydnoraceae. Bot. Zeit. 32:337–342, 353–358, 369–374, 385–389.

Solms-Laubach, H. G., 1878. Über monokotyle Embryonen mit scheitelbürtigem Vegetationspunkt. Bot. Zeit. 36:65–74, 81–93.

Solms-Laubach, H. G., 1898. Die Entwicklung des Ovulums und des Samens bei *Rafflesia* und *Brugmansia*. Ann. Jard. bot. Buitenz. Suppl. 2:11–22.

Solntseva, M. P., 1961. (Some data on the fertilization process in *Fragaria ananasa*.) Bot. Zhur. 46:371–377.

Solntseva, M. P. and M. S. Yakovlev, 1964. (Conditions determining the development of monocotyledony during early embryogenesis in feather grass, *Stipa* spp.) Bot. Zhur. 49:625–633.

Soltwedel, F., 1882. Freie Zellbildung im Embryosack der Angiospermen mit besonderer Berücksichtigung der hierbei stattfinden Vorgänge der Kernteilung. Jen. Zeit. f. Nat. 15:341–380.

Somego, M. and K. Kawandbe, 1961. (Breeding of *Eucalyptus*. 1. On the meiosis of *Eucalyptus*). J. Japanese Forest. Soc. 43:139–141.

Sommer, B.-S., 1929. Über Entwicklungshemmungen bei Samenlagen. Flora 124:63–94.

Souèges, R., 1907. Développement et structure du tégument seminal chez les Solanacées. Ann. Sci. nat. Bot. (9) 6:1–24. Thèse. Paris.

Souèges, R., 1910a. Un cas de développement anormal de l'embryon chez l'*Anemone pulsatilla*. Bull. Soc. bot. France 57:47–48.

Souèges, R., 1910b. Sur la présence de protoplasme supérieur (ergastoplasme) dans les antipodes des Renonculacées. Bull. Soc. bot. France 57:102–108.

Souèges, R., 1910c. Recherches sul l'embryogénie des Renonculacées-Clématidées. 1. L'embryon. Bull. Soc. bot. France 57:242–250, 266–275.

Souèges, R., 1910d. Recherches sur l'embryologie des Renonculacées-Clématidées. 2. Les parties de la graine et du fruit autres que l'embryon. Bull. Soc. bot. France 57:509–517, 569–576.

Souèges, R., 1911a. Recherches sur l'embryogénie des Renonculacées-Anémonées. Genre *Anemone*. Bull. Soc. bot. France 58:128–135, 144–151, 188–195.

Souèges, R., 1911b. Recherches sur l'embryogénie des Renonculacées-Anémonées. *Myosurus minimus*. Bull. Soc. bot. France 58:542–549, 629–636, 718–725.

Souèges, R., 1911c. Sur le développement de l'embryon chez le *Myosurus minimus*. C. R. Acad. Sci. Paris 153:686–688.

Souèges, R., 1912a. Recherches sur l'embryogénie des Renonculacées-Anémonées, *Myosurus minimus*. Bull. Soc. bot. France 59:23–31, 51–56.

Souèges, R., 1912b. Recherches sur l'embryogénie des Renonculacées-Anémonées. Genre *Adonis*. Bull. Soc. bot. France 59:474–482, 545–550, 602–609.

Souèges, R., 1912c. Développement de l'ovule et du sac embryonnaire chez les *Adonis*. Anatom. Anzeiger 41:209–240.

Souèges, R., 1913a. Recherches sur l'embryogénie des Renonculacées-Renonculées. *Ficaria ranunculoides*. 1. Le carpelle, l'ovule et le sac embryonnaire. Bull. Soc. bot. France 60:150–157.

Souèges, R., 1913b. Recherches sur l'embryongénie des Renonculacées-Renonculées. *Ficaria ranunculoides*. 2. L'embryon. Bull. Soc. bot. France 60:237–243, 283–289.

Souèges, R., 1913c. Recherches sur l'embryogénie des Renonculacées-Renonculées. Genre *Ranunculus*. Bull. Soc. bot. France 60:506–514, 542–549, 615–621.

Souèges, R., 1914a. Recherches sur l'embryogénie des Renonculacées. Conclusions générales. Bull. Soc. bot. France 61:27–32.

Souèges, R., 1914b. Nouvelles recherches sur l'embryogénie des Crucifères. C. R. Acad. Sci. Paris 158:1356–1359.

Souèges, R., 1914c. Nouvelles recherches sur le développement de l'embryon chez les Crucifères. Ann. Sci. nat. Bot. (9) 19:311–339.

Souèges, R., 1916. Les principales divisions de l'oeuf et l'origine de l'hypophyse chez le *Capsella bursa-pastoris*. C. R. Acad. Sci. Paris 163:158–160.

Souèges, R., 1917a. Embryogénie des Alismacées. 1. Développement du proembryon chez le *Sagittaria sagittaefolia*. C. R. Acad. Sci. Paris. 165:715–717.

Souèges, R., 1917b. Embryogénie des Alismacées. 2. Différenciation du cône végétatif de la tige chez le *Sagittaria sagittaefolia*. C. R. Acad. Sci. Paris 165:1014–1017.

Souèges, R., 1918a. Embryogénie des Alismacées. Différenciation de l'extrémité radiculaire chez le *Sagittarid sdgittaefolia*. C. R. Acad. Sci. Paris 166:49–51.

Souèges, R., 1918b. Embryogénie des Liliacées. Développement de l'embryon chez l'*Anthericum ramosum*. C. R. Acad. Sci. Paris 167:34–37.

Souèges, R., 1919a. Embryogénie des Polygonacées. Développement de l'embryon chez le *Polygonum persicaria*. C. R. Acad. Sci. Paris 168:791–793.

Souèges, R., 1919b. Embryogénie des Polygonacées. Développement de l'embryon chez les *Rumex* et les *Rheum*. C. R. Acad. Sci. Paris 169:919.

Souèges, R., 1919c. Recherches sur l'embryogénie des Polygonacées, *Polygonum persicaria*. Bull. Soc. bot. France 56:168–199.

Souèges, R., 1919d. Les premières divisions de l'oeuf et les différenciations du suspenseur chez le *Capsella bursa-pastoris*. Ann. Sci. nat. Bot. (10) 1:1–28.

Souèges, R., 1920a. Recherches sur l'embryogénie des Polygonacées. *Rumex*. Bull. Soc. bot. France 57:1–11.

Souèges, R., 1920b. Recherches sur l'embryogénie des Polygonacées. *Rheum emodi*. Bull. Soc. bot. France 67:77–85.

Souèges, R., 1920c. Développement de l'embryon chez le *Chenopodium bonus-henricus*. Bull. Soc. bot. France 67:233–257.

Souèges, R., 1920d. Embryogénie des Chenopodiacées. Développement de l'embryon chez le *Chenopodium bonus-henricus*. C. R. Acad. Sci. Paris 170:467–469.

Souèges, R., 1920e. Embryogénie des Oenothéracées. Développement de l'embryon chez l'*Oenothera biennis*. C. R. Acad. Sci. Paris 170:946–948.

Souèges, R., 1920f. Embryogénie des Solancées. Développement de l'embryon chez les *Nicotiana*. C. R. Acad. Sci. Paris 170:1125–1127.

Souèges, R., 1920g. Embryogénie des Solanacées. Développement de l'embryon chez les *Hyoscyamus* et *Atropa*. C. R. Acad. Sci. Paris 170:1279–1281.

Souèges, R., 1920h. Embryogénie des Composées. Les premiers stades du développement de l'embryon chez le *Senecio vulgaris*. C. R. Acad. Sci. Paris 171:254–256.

Souèges, R., 1920i. Embryogénie des Composées. Les derniers stades du développement de l'embryon chez le *Senecio vulgaris*. C. R. Acad. Sci. Paris 171:356–357.

Souèges, R., 1920j. Embryogénie des Urticacées. Développement de l'embryon chez l'*Urtica pilulifera*. C. R. Acad. Sci. Paris 171:1009–1011.

Souèges, R., 1921a. Embryogénie des Scrofulariacées. Développement de l'embryon chez le *Veronica arvensis*. C. R. Acad. Sci. Paris 172:703–705.

Souèges, R., 1921b. Embryogénie des Labiées. Développement de l'embryon chez le *Mentha viridis*. C. R. Acad. Sci. Paris 172:1057–1058.

Souèges, R., 1921c. Embryogénie des Labiées. Développement de l'embryon chez le *Glechoma hederacea* et le *Lamium purpureum*. C. R. Acad. Sci. Paris 173:48–50.

Souèges, R., 1921d. Embryogénie des Boragacées. Les premiers termes du développement de l'embryon chez le *Myosotis hispida*. C. R. Acad. Sci. Paris 173:726–728.

Souèges, R., 1921e. Embryogénie des Boragacées. Les derniers stades du développement de l'embryon chez le *Myosotis hispida*. C. R. Acad. Sci. Paris 173:848–850.

Souèges, R., 1921f. Développement de l'embryon chez l'*Urtica pilulifera*. Bull. Soc. bot. France 68:172–188, 280–294.

Souèges, R., 1921g. Recherches sur l'embryogénie des Labiées. Bull. Soc. bot. France 68:441–464.

Souèges, R., 1922a. Embryogénie des Rosacées. Les premiers stades du développement du l'embryon chez le *Geum urbanum*. C. R. Acad. Sci. Paris 174:1070–1072.

Souèges, R., 1922b. Embryogénie des Rosacées. Les derniers stades du développement de l'embryon chez le *Geum urbanum*. C. R. Acad. Sci. Paris 174:1197–1199.

Souèges, R., 1922c. Recherches embryogéniques sur l'*Hippurus vulgaris*. C. R. Acad. Sci. Paris 175:529–532.

Souèges, R., 1922d. Embryogénie des Caryophyllacées. Les premiers stades du développement de l'embryon chez le *Sagina procumbens*. Les derniers stades du développement chez le *Sagina procumbens*. C. R. Acad. Sci. Paris 175:709–711, 894–896.

Souèges, R., 1922e. Embryogénie des Malvacées. Développement de l'embryon chez le *Malva rotundifolia*. C. R. Acad. Sci. Paris 175:1435–1436.

Souèges, R., 1922f. Recherches sur l'embryogénie des Solanacées. (Nicotianées; Hyoscyamées; Daturées; Atropées.) Bull. Soc. bot. France 69:163–178, 136–241, 352–365, 555–585.

Souèges, R., 1923a. Embryogénie des Valerianacées. Développement de l'embryon chez le *Valerianella olitoria*. C. R. Acad. Sci. Paris 176:1081–1083.

Souèges, R., 1923b. Embryogénie des Geraniacées. Développement de l'embryon chez l'*Erodium cicutarium*. C. R. Acad. Sci. Paris 176:1565–1567.

Souèges, R., 1923c. Embryogénie des Geraniacées. Développement de l'embryon chez le *Geranium molle*. C. R. Acad. Sci. Paris 177:556–559.

Souèges, R., 1923d. Embryogénie des Joncacées. Développement de l'embryon chez le *Luzula forsteri*. C. R. Acad. Sci. Paris 177:705–708.

Souèges, R., 1923e. Embryogénie des Plantaginacées. Développement de l'embryon chez le *Plantago lanceolata*. C. R. Acad. Sci. Paris 177:964–967.

Souèges, R., 1923f. Embryogénie des Salicacées. Développement de l'embryon chez le *Salix triandra*. C. R. Acad. Sci. Paris 177:1234–1237.

Souèges, R., 1923g. Développement de l'embryon chez le *Myosotis hispida*. Bull. Soc. bot. France 70:385–401.

Souèges, R., 1923h. Développement de l'embryon chez le *Geum urbanum*. Bull. Soc. bot. France 70:645–660.

Souèges, R., 1924a. Embryogénie des Polygonacées. Le développement de l'embryon chez le *Polygonum aviculare*. C. R. Acad. Sci. Paris 178:409–412.

Souèges, R., 1924b. Embryogénie des Graminées. Développement de l'embryon chez le *Poa annua*. C. R. Acad. Sci. Paris 178:860–862.

Souèges, R., 1924c. Embryogénie des Linacées. Développement de l'embryon chez le *Linum catharticum*. C. R. Acad. Sci. Paris 178:1307–1310.

Souèges, R., 1924d. Embryogénie des Rubiacées. Développement de l'embryon chez le *Sherardia arvensis*. C. R. Acad. Sci. Paris 178:1919–1921.

Souèges, R., 1924e. Embryogénie des Typhacées. Développement de l'embryon chez le *Sparganium simplex*. C. R. Acad. Sci. Paris 179:198–200.

Souèges, R., 1924f. Embryogénie des Euphorbiacées. Développement de l'embryon chez l'*Euphorbia exigua*. C. R. Acad. Sci. Paris 179:989–991.

Souèges, R., 1924g. Développement de l'embryon chez le *Sagina procumbens*. Bull. Soc. bot. France 71:590–614.

Souèges, R., 1924h. Développement de l'embryon chez le *Linum catharticum*. Bull. Soc. bot. France 71:925–938.

Souèges, R., 1925a. Embryogénie des Hypericacées. Développement de l'embryon chez l'*Hypericum perforatum*. C. R. Acad. Sci. Paris 180:949–951.

Souèges, R., 1925b. Embryogénie des Lythracées. Développement de l'embryon chez le *Lythrum salicaria*. C. R. Acad. Sci. Paris 180:1417–1418.

Souèges, R., 1925c. Embryogénie des Rutacées Développement de l'embryon chez le *Ruta graveolens*. C. R. Acad. Sci. Paris 180:1957–1959.

Souèges, R., 1925d. Embryogénie des Crassulacées. Développement de l'embryon chez le *Sedum acre*. C. R. Acad. Sci. Paris 181:521–522.

Souèges, R., 1925e. Développement de l'embryon chez le *Sherardia arvensis*. Bull. Soc. bot. France 72:546–564.

Souèges, R., 1925f. Développement de l'embryon chez l'*Euphorbia exigua*. Bull. Soc. bot. France 72:1018–1031.

Souèges, R., 1926a. Embryogénie des Ombellifères. Développement chez le *Carum carvi*. C. R. Acad. Sci. Paris 182:339–341.

Souèges, R., 1926b. Embryogénie des Liliacées. Développement de l'embryon chez l'*Allium ursinum*. C. R. Acad. Sci. Paris 182:1344–1346.

Souèges, R., 1926c. Embryogénie des Liliacées. Développement de l'embryon chez le *Muscari comosum*. C. R. Acad. Sci. Paris 183:233–235.

Souèges, R., 1926d. Embryogénie des Papavéracées. Développement du proembryon chez le *Papaver rhoeas*. C. R. Acad. Sci. Paris 183:902–904.

Souèges, R., 1926e. Embryogénie des Papavéracées. Les derniers stades du développement de l'embryon chez le *Papaver rhoeas*. C. R. Acad. Sci. Paris 183:1119–1120.

Souèges, R., 1926f. Développement de l'embryon chez le *Ruta graveolens*. Bull. Soc. bot. France 73:245–260.

Souèges, R., 1926g. Un mode d'avortement du sac embryonnaire chez le *Papaver rhoeas*. Bull. Soc. bot. France 73:636–640.

Souèges, R., 1926h. Polyembryonie chez le *Plantago lanceolata*. Bull. Soc. bot. France 73:955–957.

Souèges, R., 1927a. Embryogénie des Légumineuses. Développement du proembryon chez le *Trifolium minus*. C. R. Acad. Sci. Paris 184:1018–1019.

Souèges, R., 1927b. Embryogénie des Légumineuses. Les derniers stades du développement de l'embryon chez le *Trifolium minus*. C. R. Acad. Sci. Paris 184:1196–1198.

Souèges, R., 1927c. Embryogénie des premiers stades du développement de l'embryon chez le *Medicago lupulina*. C. R. Acad. Sci. Paris 185:1062–1064.

Souèges, R., 1927d. Embryogénie des Légumineuses. Les derniers stades du développement de l'embryon chez le *Medicago lupulina*. C. R. Acad. Sci. Paris 185:1206–1208.

Souèges, R., 1927e. Développement de l'embryon chez le *Sedum acre*. Bull. Soc. bot. France 74:234–251.

Souèges, R., 1928. Développement de l'embryon chez le *Papaver rhoeas*. Bull. Soc. bot. France 75:452–469.

Souèges, R., 1929a. Recherches sur l'embryogénie des Légumineuses, *Medicago lupulina*. Bull. Soc. bot. France 76:93–112.

Souèges, R., 1929b. Recherches sur l'embryogénie des Légumineuses, *Trifolium minus*. Bull. Soc. bot. France 76:338–346.

Souèges, R., 1929c. Recherches sur l'embryogénie des Légumineuses, *Lotus corniculatus*. Bull. Soc. bot. France 76:527–540.

Souèges, R., 1930. Recherches sur l'embryogénie des Ombellifères, *Carum carvi*, *Pimpinella saxifraga*. Bull. Soc. bot. France 77:494–511.

Souèges, R., 1931a. Recherches sur l'embryogénie des Liliacées. *Anthericum ranosum* et *Allium ursinum*. Bull. Soc. bot. France 78:662–681.

Souèges, R., 1931b. L'embryon chez le *Sagittaria sagittifolia*. Le cône végétatif de la tige et l'extrémite radiculaire chez le monocotyledones. Ann. Sci. nat. Bot. (10) 13:353–402.

Souèges, R., 1932a. Recherches sur l'embryogénie des Liliacées, *Muscaria comosum*. Bull. Soc. bot. France 79:11–23.

Souèges, R., 1932b. Les méthodes de travail en embryologie végétale. Bull. Soc. Fr. Micr. 1:88–104.

Souèges, R., 1933. Recherches sur l'embryogénie des Joncacées. *Luzula fosteri* et *Juncus effusus*. Bull. Soc. bot. France 80:51–69.

Souèges, R., 1934a. L'hypophyse et l'epiphyse: les problèmes d'histogenèse qui leur sont liés. 1. L'hypophyse: son rôle variable dans la construction de l'extrémité radiculaire. Bull. Soc. bot. France 81:1–27.

Souèges, R., 1934b. L'hypophyse et l'epiphyse: les problèmes d'histogenèse qui leur sont liés. 2. L'épiphyse: importance générale de cette notion chez les Dicotyledones. Bull. Soc. bot. France 81:28–61.

Souèges, R., 1934c. Embryologie végétale: la physiologie embryonnaire. Rev. gén. Sci. pur. et app. Paris 45:141–171.

Souèges, R., 1934d. Embryologie végétale. Résumé historique. 1re époque: des origines à Hanstein (1870). Paris.

Souèges, R., 1934e. Embryologie végétale. Résumé historique. 2e époque: de Hanstein (1870) à nos jours. Paris.

Souèges, R., 1934–1951. Exposés d'embryologie et de morphologie végétales. 10 vols. Paris.

Souèges, R., 1935a. Embryogénie des Oenothéracées. Les principaux termes du développement de l'embryon chez le *Ludwigia palustris*. C. R. Acad. Sci. Paris 200:1626–1628.

Souèges, R., 1935b. Embryogénie des Rosacées. Développement de l'embryon chez le *Potentilla reptans*. C. R. Acad. Sci. Paris 200:1972–1974.

Souèges, R., 1935c. Embryogénie des Verbénacées. Développement de l'embryon chez le *Verbena officinalis*. C. R. Acad. Sci. Paris 201:234–236.

Souèges, R., 1953d. Embryogénie des Verbénacées. Les premiers termes du développement de l'albumen chez le *Verbena officinalis*. C. R. Acad. Sci. Paris 201:529–531.

Souèges, R., 1935e. Embryogénie des Résédacées. Développement de l'embryon chez le *Reseda luteola*. C. R. Acad. Sci. Paris 201:910–911.

Souèges, R., 1935f. Recherches embryologiques sur les Verbascées. Les types secondaires du développement embryonnaire. Bull. Soc. bot. France 82:328–334.

Souèges, R., 1935g. Polyembryony chez le *Potentilla reptans*. Bull. Soc. bot. France 82:381–384.

Souèges, R., 1935h. Observations embryologiques sur quelques *Fragaria* de culture. Bull. Soc. bot. France 82:458–461.

Souèges, R., 1935i. La segmentation. 1. Les fondements. 2. Les phénomènes internes. Paris.

Souèges, R., 1935j. La cellule embryonnaire. Paris.

Souèges, R., 1936a. Embryogénie des Saxifragacées. Développement de l'embryon chez le *Saxifraga granulata*. C. R. Acad. Sci. Paris 202:240–242.

Souèges, R., 1936b. Embryogénie des Hypericacées. Développement de l'embryon chez l'*Androsaemum officinale*. C. R. Acad. Sci. Paris 202:679–681.

Souèges, R., 1936c. Embryogénie des Droseracées. Développement de l'embryon chez le *Drosera rotundifolia*. C. R. Acad. Sci. Paris 202:1457–1459.

Souèges, R., 1936d. Embryogénie des Campanulacées. Développement de l'embryon chez le *Campanula patula*. C. R. Acad. Sci. Paris 202:2009–2011.

Souèges, R., 1936e. Embryogénie des Papavéracées. Développement de l'embryon chez le *Chelidonium majus*. C. R. Acad. Sci. Paris 203:678–680.

Souèges, R., 1936f. Modifications au tableau récapitulatif des lois du développement chez *Sedum acre*. Le type embryonomique de cette espèce chez les autre Crassulacées. Bull. Soc. bot. France 83:13–18.

Souèges, R., 1936g. Les relations embryogéniques des Crassulacées, Saxifragacées et Hypericacées. Bull. Soc. bot. France 83:317–329.

Souèges, R., 1936h. Développement de l'embryon chez le *Schizanthus* et les *Petunias*. Bull. Soc. bot. France 83:570–577.

Souèges, R., 1936i. La segmentation. 3. Les phénomènes externes. 4. Les blastomères. Paris.

Souèges, R., 1936j. La différenciation. 2nd. fasc. 3. La différenciation organique. Paris.

Souèges, R., 1937a. Embryogénie des Primulacées. Développement de l'embryon chez le *Samolus valerandi*. C. R. Acad. Sci. Paris 204:145–147.

Souèges, R., 1937b. Embryogénie des Dipsacacées. Développement de l'embryon chez le *Scabiosa succisa*. C. R. Acad. Sci. Paris 204:292–294.

Souèges, R., 1937c. Embryogénie des Amarantacées. Développement de l'embryon chez l'*Amarantus retroflexus*. C. R. Acad. Sci. Paris 204:892–894.

Souèges, R., 1937d. Embryogénie des Plombagacées. Développement de l'embryon chez l'*Armeria plantaginea*. C. R. Acad. Sci. Paris 204:1583–1585.

Souèges, R., 1937e. Embryogénie des Violacées. Développement de l'embryon chez le *Viola tricolor*. C. R. Acad. Sci. Paris 205:169–171.

Souèges, R., 1937f. Embryogénie des Convolvulacées. Développement de l'embryon chez le *Convolvulus arvensis*. C. R. Acad. Sci. Paris 205:813–815.

Souèges, R., 1937g. L'embryon chez les *Amarantus*. Relations embryologiques entre les Solanacées et les Centrospermales. Bull. Soc. bot. France 84:242–255.

Souèges, R., 1937h. Développement de l'embryon chez le *Radiola linoides*. Bull. Soc. bot. France 84:297–306.

Souèges, R., 1937i. Développement de l'embryon chez l'*Helianthemum guttatum*. Bull. Soc. bot. France 84:400–407.

Souèges, R., 1937j. Embryogénie des Papavéracées. Développement de l'embryon chez le *Chelidonium majus*. Ann. Sci. nat. Bot. (10) 19:445–466.

Souèges, R., 1937k. Les lois du développement. Paris.

Souèges, R., 1937l. Titres et travaux scientifiques (1934–1937). Saint-Dizier.

Souèges, R., 1938a. Embryogénie des Campanulacées Développement de l'embryon chez le *Jasione montana*. C. R. Acad. Sci. Paris 206:278–280.

Souèges, R., 1938b. Embryogénie des Portulacacées. Développement de l'embryon chez le *Portulaca oleracea*. C. R. Acad. Sci. Paris 206:768–770.

Souèges, R., 1938c. Embryogénie des Illécébracées. Développement de l'embryon chez le *Scleranthus perennis*. C. R. Acad. Sci. Paris 206:1404–1406.

Souèges, R., 1938d. Embryogénie des Nyctaginacées. Développement de l'embryon chez l'*Oxybaphus viscosus*. C. R. Acad. Sci. Paris 206:1830–1832.

Souèges, R., 1938e. Embryogénie des Boragacées. Développement de l'embryon chez le *Lycopsis arvensis*. C. R. Acad. Sci. Paris 207:640–642.

Souèges, R., 1938f. Embryogénie des Boragacées. Développement de l'embryon chez l'*Echium vulgare*. C. R. Acad. Sci. Paris 207:871–872.

Souèges, R., 1938g. Embryogénie des Illécébracées. Développement de l'embryon chez le *Herniaria glabra*. Bull. Soc. bot. France 85:353–363.

Souèges, R., 1938h. Embryogénie et classification. 1. L'espèce et les classifications actuelles. Paris.

Souèges, R., 1939a. Embryogénie des Cucurbitacées. Développement de l'embryon chez le *Bryonia dioica*. C. R. Acad. Sci. Paris 208:227–229.

Souèges, R., 1939b. Embryogénie des Begoniacées. Développement de l'embryon chez le *Begonia semperflorens*. C. R. Acad. Sci. Paris 208:535–536.

Souèges, R., 1939c. Embryogénie des Polémoniacées. Développement de l'embryon chez le *Polemonium coeruleum*. C. R. Acad. Sci. Paris 208:1338–1340.

Souèges, R., 1939d. Embryogénie des Rhamnacées. Développement de l'embryon chez le *Ceanothus azureus*. C. R. Acad. Sci. Paris 208:1673–1675.

Souèges, R., 1939e. Embryogénie des Ericacées. Développement de l'embryon chez le *Pyrola rotundifolia*. C. R. Acad. Sci. Paris 209:635–637.

Souèges, R., 1939f. Embryogénie des Oxalidacées. Développement de l'embryon chez l'*Oxalis corniculata*. C. R. Acad. Sci. Paris 209:698–700.

460 BIBLIOGRAPHY

Souèges, R., 1939g. Les lois du développement chez le *Polemonium caeruleum*. Bull. Soc. bot. France 86:289–297.

Souèges, R., 1939h. Embryogénie et classification. 2. Essai d'un système embryogénique. Partie générale. Paris.

Souèges, R., 1940a. Embryogénie des Bignoniacées. Développement de l'embryon chez le *Catalpa kaempferi*. C. R. Acad. Sci. Paris 210:116–118.

Souèges, R., 1940b. Embryogénie des Myrtacées. Développement de l'embryon chez le *Myrtus communis*. C. R. Acad. Sci. Paris 210:548–550.

Souèges, R., 1940c. Embryogénie des Loganiacées. Développement de l'embryon chez le *Buddleia variabilis*. C. R. Acad. Sci. Paris 211:139–140.

Souèges, R., 1940d. Embryogénie des Haloragacées. Développement de l'embryon chez le *Myriophyllum alterniflorum*. C. R. Acad. Sci. Paris 211:185–187.

Souèges, R., 1940e. Embryogénie des Potamogétonacées. Développement de l'embryon chez le *Potamogeton natans*. C. R. Acad. Sci. Paris 211:232–233.

Souèges, R., 1941a. Embryogénie des Boragacées. Développement de l'embryon chez le *Symphytum officinale*. C. R. Acad. Sci. Paris 212:245–246.

Souèges, R., 1941b. Embryogénie des Valérianacées. Développement de l'embryon chez le *Centranthus*. C. R. Acad. Sci. Paris 212:718–720.

Souèges, R., 1941c. Embryogénie des Tiliacées. Développement de l'embryon chez le *Tilia platyphyllos*. C. R. Acad. Sci. Paris 212:998–1000.

Souèges, R., 1941d. Embryogénie des Rhamnacées. Développement de l'embryon chez le *Rhamnus frangula*. C. R. Acad. Sci. Paris 213:39–41.

Souèges, R., 1941e. Embryogénie des Polygalacées. Développement de l'embryon chez le *Polygala vulgaris*. C. R. Acad. Sci. Paris 213:446–448.

Souèges, R., 1941f. Embryogénie des Fumariacées. L'origine du corps de l'embryon chez le *Fumaria officinalis*. C. R. Acad. Sci. Paris 213:528–530.

Souèges, R., 1941g. Embryogénie des Fumariacées. La différenciation des régions fondamentales du corps chez la *Fumaria officinalis*. C. R. Acad. Sci. Paris 213:699–702.

Souèges, R., 1941h. Variantes dans les deux premiers groupes de la classification embryogénique. Bull. Soc. bot. France 88:602–608.

Souèges, R., 1942a. Embryogénie des Thyméleacées. Développement de l'embryon chez le *Daphne mezereum*. C. R. Acad. Sci. Paris 214:569–571.

Souèges, R., 1942b. Embryogénie des Oléacées. Développement de l'embryon chez le *Ligustrum ovalifolium*. C. R. Acad. Sci. Paris 215:328–330.

Souèges, R., 1942c. Embryogénie des Polémoniacées. Développement de l'embryon chez le *Gilia tricolor*. C. R. Acad. Sci. Paris 215:543–545.

Souèges, R., 1943a. Embryogénie des Fumariacées. L'origine et les premières divisions de la cellule embryonnaire proprement dite chez l'*Hypecoum procumbens*. C. R. Acad. Sci. Paris 216:310–311.

Souèges, R., 1943b. Embryogénie des Fumariacées. Le différenciation des régiones fondamentales du corps chez l'*Hypecoum procumbens*. C. R. Acad. Sci. Paris 216:354–356.

Souèges, R., 1943c. Embryogénie des Scheuchzériacées. Développement de l'embryon chez le *Triglochin maritimum*. C. R. Acad. Sci. Paris 216:746–748.

Souèges, R., 1943d. Embryogénie des Actinidiacées. Développement de l'embryon chez l'*Actinidia chinensis*. C. R. Acad. Sci. Paris 217:430–432.

Souèges, R., 1943e. Embryogénie des Gentianacées. Développement de l'embryon chez le *Menyanthes trifoliata*. C. R. Acad. Sci. Paris 217:488–490.

Souèges, R., 1943f. Embryogénie des Boragacées. Développement de l'embryon chez l'*Heliotropium peruvianum*. C. R. Acad. Sci. Paris 217:551–553.

Souèges, R., 1945a. Embryogénie des Ombellifères. Développement de l'embryon chez l'*Apium inundatum*. C. R. Acad. Sci. Paris 220:128–131.

Souèges, R., 1945b. Embryogénie des Balsaminacées. Développement de l'embryon chez l'*Impatiens balfourii*. C. R. Acad. Sci. Paris 220:837–840.

Souèges, R., 1945c. Embryogénie des Polémoniacées. Développement de l'embryon chez le *Polemonium pauciflorum*. C. R. Acad. Sci. Paris 220:897–900.

Souèges, R., 1945d. Embryogénie des Illécébracées. Développement de l'embryon chez le *Polycarpon tetraphyllum*. C. R. Acad. Sci. Paris 221:41–44.

Souèges, R., 1945e. Embryogénie des Portulacacées. Développement de l'embryon chez le *Claytonia perfoliata*. C. R. Acad. Sci. Paris 221:111–113.

Souèges, R., 1945f. Embryogénie des Caryophyllacées. Développement de l'embryon chez l'*Arenaria serpyllifolia*. C. R. Acad. Sci. Paris 221:320–322.

Souèges, R., 1945g. Embryogénie des Caprifoliacées. Développement de l'embryon chez le *Lonicera biflora*. C. R. Acad. Sci. Paris 221:480–482.

Souèges, R., 1946a. Embryogénie des Fumariacées. Les premiers termes du développement de l'embryon chez le *Corydalis lutea*. C. R. Acad. Sci. Paris 222:161–163.

Souèges, R., 1946b. Embryogénie des Fumariacées. La différenciations des régions fondamentales du corps chez le *Corydalis lutea*. C. R. Acad. Sci. Paris 222:253–255, 699–701.

Souèges, R., 1946c. Embryogénie des Fumariacées. Développement de l'embryon chez le *Corydalis cheilanthifolia*. C. R. Acad. Sci. Paris 222:523–524.

Souèges, R., 1946d. Embryogénie des Papilionacées. Développement de l'embryon chez *Melilotus arvensis*. C. R. Acad. Sci. Paris 222:1361–1363.

Souèges, R., 1946e. Embryogénie des Papilionacées. Développement de l'embryon chez l'*Orobus vernus* (*Lathyrus vernus*). C. R. Acad. Sci. Paris 223:60–62.

Souèges, R., 1946f. Embryogénie des Papilionacées. Développement de l'embryon chez le *Vicia sepium*. C. R. Acad. Sci. Paris 223:389–391.

Souèges, R., 1946g. Embryogénie des Papilionacées. Développement de l'embryon chez l'*Orobus tuberosus* (*Lathyrus macrorrhizus*). C. R. Acad. Sci. Paris 223:493–495.

Souèges, R., 1946h. Embryogénie des Oenothéracées. Développement de l'embryon chez le *Circaea lutetiana*. C. R. Acad. Sci. Paris 223:700–702.

Souèges, R., 1946i. Embryogénie des Papilionacées. Développement de l'embryon chez l'*Ervum hirsutum* (*Vicia hirsuta*). C. R. Acad. Sci. Paris. 223:838–840.

Souèges, R., 1946j. Embryogénie des Fumariacées. L'embryon chez le *Corydalis cheilanthifolia*. Les Fumariacées et la classification embryogénique. Ann. Sci. nat. Bot. (2) 7:2–17.

Souèges, R., 1947a. Embryogénie des Papilionacées. Développement de l'embryon chez le *Genista tinctoria*. C. R. Acad. Sci. Paris 224:79–81.

Souèges, R., 1947b. Le principe de la correspondance des formes. C. R. Acad. Sci. Paris 224:312–314.

Souèges, R., 1947c. Variantes dans la série C de la classifications périodique. C. R. Acad. Sci. Paris 224:978–981.

Souèges, R., 1947d. Embryogénie des Papilionacées. Développement de l'embryon chez le *Coronilla minima*. C. R. Acad. Sci. Paris 224:1254–1256.

Souèges, R., 1947e. Les notions de tétrade première et de tétrade seconde. C. R. Acad. Sci. Paris 224:1599–1602.

Souèges, R., 1947f. Développement de l'embryon chez l'*Ulex europaeus*. C. R. Acad. Sci. Paris 225:341.

Souèges, R., 1947g. Embryogénie des Papilionacées. Développement de l'embryon chez le *Sarothamnus scoparius* (*Cytisus scoparius*). C. R. Acad. Sci. Paris 225:776–778.

Souèges, R., 1947h. Les lois du développement de l'embryon chez le *Coronilla minima*. Bull. Soc. bot. France 94:272–276.

Souèges, R., 1948a. Embryogénie des Papavéracées. Développement de l'embryon chez le *Roemeria violacea* (*R. hybrida*). C. R. Acad. Sci. Paris 226:979–981.

Souèges, R., 1948b. Embryogénie des Papilionacées. Développement de l'embryon chez le *Vicia faba* (*Faba vulgaris*). C. R. Acad. Sci. Paris 226:2101–2103.

Souèges, R., 1948c. Embryogénie des Caprifoliacées. Développement de l'embryon chez le *Symphoricarpos occidentalis*. C. R. Acad. Sci. Paris 227:1066–1068.

Souèges, R., 1948d. Embryogénie et classification. 3. Essai d'un système embryogénique. Partie speciale: Ire période du système. Paris.

Souèges, R., 1949a. Développement de l'embryon chez le *Galega officinalis*. C. R. Acad. Sci. Paris 228:1540.

Souèges, R., 1949b. Embryogénie des Papavéracées. Développement de l'embryon chez l'*Eschscholtzia californica*. C. R. Acad. Sci. Paris 229:485–487.

Souèges, R., 1949c. Embryogénie des Papavéracées. Développement de l'embryon chez l'*Argemone mexicana*. C. R. Acad. Sci. Paris 229:573–576.

Souèges, R., 1949d. Développement de l'embryon chez le *Glycine soja*. C. R. Acad. Sci. Paris 229:1183.

Souèges, R., 1950a. Embryogénie des Boragacées. Développement de l'embryon chez le *Lithospermum arvense*. C. R. Acad. Sci. Paris 230:2142–2145.

Souèges, R., 1950b. Embryogénie des Boragacées. Développement de l'embryon chez le *Cerinthe minor*. C. R. Acad. Sci. Paris 231:200–202.

Souèges, R., 1950c. Développement de l'embryon chez le *Psoralia bituminosa*. C. R. Acad. Sci. Paris 231:429.

Souèges, R., 1950d. Développement de l'embryon chez le *Phaseolus vulgaris*. C. R. Acad. Sci. Paris 231:627.

Souèges, R., 1951a. Embryogénie des Papilionacées. L'embryon et le suspenseur chez l'*Anthyllis vulneraria*. C. R. Acad. Sci. Paris 232:581–584.

Souèges, R., 1951b. Embryogénie des Boragacées. Développement de l'embryon chez l'*Onosma nanum*. C. R. Acad. Sci. Paris 232:2164–2167.

Souèges, R., 1951c. Embryogénie des Rubiacées. Développement de l'embryon chez le *Richardsonia pilosa* (*R. brasiliensis*). C. R. Acad. Sci. Paris 233:5–8.

Souèges, R., 1951d. Embryogénie et classification. 4. Essai d'un systeme embryogénique. Partie spéciale. 2e periode du système. Paris.

Souèges, R., 1952a. Embryogénie des Boragacées. Développement de l'embryon chez le *Lithospermum officinale*. C. R. Acad. Sci. Paris 233:217–219.

Souèges, R., 1952b. Embryogénie des Amaryllidacées. Développement de l'embryon chez le *Pancratium maritimum*. C. R. Acad. Sci. Paris 234:1300.

Souèges, R., 1952c. Embryogénie des Zygophyllacées. Développement de l'embryon chez le *Tribulus terrestris*. C. R. Acad. Sci. Paris 234:1817.

Souèges, R., 1952d. L'albumen et l'embryon chez le *Callitriche vernalis* (*C. verna*). C. R. Acad. Sci. Paris 235:453–456.

Souèges, R., 1952e. Embryogénie des Ombellifères. Développement de l'embryon chez l'*Astrantia major*. C. R. Acad. Sci. Paris 235:674–677.

Souèges, R., 1953a. Embryogénie des Zygophyllacées. Développement de l'embryon chez le *Zygophyllum fabago*. C. R. Acad. Sci. Paris 236:1316.

Souèges, R., 1953b. Embryogénie des Péganacées. Développement de l'embryon chez le *Peganum harmala*. C. R. Acad. Sci. Paris 236:2185.

Souèges, R., 1953c. Embryogénie des Papilionacées. Développement de l'embryon chez l'*Onobrychis sativa*. C. R. Acad. Sci. Paris 237:450–452.

Souèges, R., 1953d. Embryogénie des Papilionacées. Développement de l'embryon chez l'*Ornithopus perpusillus*. C. R. Acad. Sci. Paris 237:1199–1201.

Souèges, R., 1953e. A propos des rapports embryogéniques du *Peganum harmala*. Ann. Sci. nat. Bot. (2) 14:225–251.

Souèges, R., 1954a. L'origine du cône végétatif de la tige et la question de la "terminalité" du cotyledon des monocotylédones. Ann. Sci. nat. Bot. (2) 15:1–20.

Souèges, R., 1954b. Embryogénie et classification. Congr. Internatl. Bot. 8th.

Souèges, R., 1954c. La vie végétale: La cinématique de la vie. Paris.

Souèges, R., 1954d. Embryogénie des Ombellifères. Développement de l'embryon chez le *Silaus pratensis*. C. R. Acad. Sci. Paris 238:1948–1951.

Souèges, R., 1954e. Embryogénie des Ombellifères. Développement de l'embryon chez l'*Anthriscus cerefolium*. C. R. Acad. Sci. Paris 239:141–144.

Souèges, R., 1954f. Embryogénie des Ombellifères. Développement de l'embryon chez le *Torilus anthriscus*. C. R. Acad. Sci. Paris 239:377–379.

Souèges, R., 1954g. Embryogénie des Ombellifères. Développement de l'embryon chez le *Laserpitium siler*. C. R. Acad. Sci. Paris 239:1104–1106.

Souèges, R., 1954h. Embryogénie des Ombellifères. Développement de l'embryon chez le *Peucedanum austriacum*. C. R. Acad. Sci. Paris 239:1327–1330.

Souèges, R., 1955a. Embryogénie des Ombellifères. Développement de l'embryon chez les *Ammi*. C. R. Acad. Sci. Paris 240:1169–1171.

Souèges, R., 1955b. Embryogénie des Ombellifères. Développement de l'embryon chez l'*Eryngium amethystinum*. C. R. Acad. Sci. Paris 240:1596–1598.

Souèges, R., 1955c. Développement de l'embryon chez l'*Hippocrepis comosa*. C. R. Acad. Sci. Paris 240:2100.

Souèges, R., 1955d. Embryogénie des Cneoracées. Développement de l'embryon chez le *Cneorum tricoccum*. C. R. Acad. Sci. Paris 241:1240–1243.

Souèges, R., 1955e. Embryogénie des Ombellifères. Développement de l' embryon chez le *Seseli montanum*. C. R. Acad. Sci. Paris 241:265–268.

Souèges, R., 1956a. Développement de l'embryon chez l'*Hedysarum coronarium*. C. R. Acad. Sci. Paris 242:704.

Souèges, R., 1956b. Essai d'embryogénie comparée dans les limites des Hédysarées. Ann. Sci. nat. Bot. (2) 17:325–352.

Souèges, R., 1957. Embryogénie des Dipsacacées. Développement de l'embryon chez le *Scabiosa columbaria*. C. R. Acad. Sci. Paris 245:465–468.

Souèges, R., 1958a. Embryogénie des Commélinacées. Développement de l'embryon chez le *Commelina communis*. C. R. Acad. Sci. Paris 246:2082–2086.

Souèges, R., 1958b. Embryogénie des Commélinacées. Développement de l'embryon chez le *Rhoeo discolor*. C. R. Acad. Sci. Paris 246:2436–2440.

Souèges, R., 1958c. Embryogénie des Ombellifères. Développement de l'embryon chez l'*Hydrocotyle vulgaris*. C. R. Acad. Sci. Paris 247:1274–1279.

Souèges, R., 1959. Embryogénie des Caprifoliacées. Développement de l'embryon chez le *Sambucus nigra*. C. R. Acad. Sci. Paris 248:1072–1078.

Souèges, R., 1961a. Embryologie Végétale: Proarchétypes, Archétypes et Sous-archétypes en embryogénie. 1. Les Proarchétypes dans a première période du système embryogénique. C. R. Acad. Sci. Paris 252:1536–1541.

Souèges, R., 1961b. Embryologie Végétale: Proarchétypes, Archétypes et Sous-archétypes en embryogénie. 2. Les Proarchétypes dans la deuxième période du système embryogénique. C. R. Acad. Sci. Paris 252:2045–2049.

Souèges, R., 1961c. Embryologie Végétale: Proarchétypes, Archétypes et Sous-archétypes en embryogénie. 3. Les Sous-archétypes. C. R. Acad. Sci. Paris 252:2481–2486.

Souèges, R., 1961d. Embryologie Végétale: Les types embryonomiques par super-position en embryogénie. Examples chez les Dicotylédones. C. R. Acad. Sci. Paris 252:2650–2655.

Souèges, R., 1961e. Embryologie Végétale: Les types embryonomiques irréguliers en embryogénie. Examples chez les Dicotylédones. C. R. Acad. Sci. Paris 252:3167–3172.

Souèges, R., 1961f. Embryologie Végétale: Réponse aux observations critiques de D. A. Johansen relatives à mon essai de classification embryogénique. C. R. Acad. Sci. Paris 252:3359–3364.

Souèges, R., 1961g. Embryologie Végétale: Embryogénie et classification. Notions préliminaires fondamentales. Concepts nouveaux apportés par l'embryogénie. C. R. Acad. Sci. Paris 252:3906–3911.

Souèges, R., 1961h. Embryogénie et classification. L'oeuve synthétique de l'embryogénie. C. R. Acad. Sci. Paris 253:25–30.

Souèges, R., 1961i. Embryologie Végétale: Embryogénie et classification. L'oeuvre analytique de l'embryogénie. C. R. Acad. Sci. Paris 253:351–356.

Souèges, R., 1961j. Embryogénie et classification: Mode d'expression du système embryogénique periodique. Séries divergentes. C. R. Acad. Sci. Paris 253:1149–1154.

Souèges, R., 1962. Embryogénie des Dipsacacées. Développement de l'embryon chez le Dipsacus sylvestris. C. R. Acad. Sci. Paris 256:2268–2273.

Souèges, R., 1963a. Embryogénie des Dipsacacées. Développement de l'embryon chez le Cephalaria tatarica. C. R. Acad. Sci. Paris 256:45–48.

Souèges, R., 1963b. Embryogénie des Dipsacacées. Développement de l'embryon chez le Knautia arvensis. C. R. Acad. Sci. Paris 256:1190–1194.

Souèges, R. and P. Crété, 1952. Les acquisitions les plus récentes de l'embryogénie des Angiospermes (1947–1951). Ann. Biol. 28:9–45.

Spangler, R. C., 1925. Female gametophyte of Trillium sessile. Bot. Gaz. 79:217–221.

Sporne, K. R., 1954. A note on nuclear endosperm as a primitive character among dicotyledons. Phytomorphology 4:275–278.

Sprague, G. F., 1932. The nature and extent of heterofertilization in Maize. Genetics 17:358–368.

Sprague, T. A., 1926. The morphology and taxonomic position of the Adoxaceae. J. Linn. Soc. Lond. (Bot.) 47:471–487.

Sprecher, A., 1919. Etude sur la semence et la germination de Garcinia man-gostana. Rev. gén. Bot. 31:513–531, 609–633.

Srimathi, R. A. and M. Sreenivasaya, 1962. Occurrence of endopolyploidy in the haustorium of Santalum album. Current Sci. 31:69–70.

Srinath, K. V., 1934. Life history of Herpestis monniera. Current Sci. 3:257–258.

Srinath, K. V., 1938–1939. Development of the endosperm in Calceolaria. Proc. Linn. Soc. Lond. (2) (Bot.) 151:136.

Srinath, K. V., 1940. Morphological studies in the genera *Calceolaria* and *Herpestis*. Proc. Linn. Soc. Lond. (2) (Bot.) 2:152–174.

Srinivasachar, D., 1940a. Morphological studies in the family Anacardiacea. J. Mysore Univ. B. 1:83–91.

Srinivasachar, D., 1940b. Embryological studies of some members of Rhamnaceae. Proc. Indian Acad. Sci. B. 11:107–116.

Srinivasachar, D., 1942. A contribution to the embryology of the genus *Polygala*. Proc. Nat. Acad. Sci. India 12:1–6.

Srinivasan, A. R., 1941. Cytomorphological features of *Limnanthemum cristatum* and *Enicostemma littorale*. Proc. Indian Acad. Sci. B. 14:529–542.

Srinivasan, A. R., 1942. Contribution to the morphology of *Pedalium murex* and *Sesamum indicum*. Proc. Indian Acad. Sci. B. 16:155–164.

Srinivasan, A. R., 1946. Morphological and cytological studies in Scrophulariaceae. 5. *Striga euphrasioides*. Proc. Indian Acad. Sci. B. 24:21–33.

Srinivasan, V. K., 1940. Morphological and cytological studies in the Scrophulariaceae. 2. Floral morphology and embryology of *Angelonia grandiflora*. J. Indian bot. Soc. 19:197–222.

Srivastava, G. L., 1939. Contribution to the morphology of *Orobanche aegyptiaca*. Proc. Nat. Acad. Sci. India B. 9:58–68.

Srivastava, R. K., 1952. Contribution to the embryology of Indian Euphorbiaceae. 1. *Euphorbia rothiana*. Ann. Bot. 16:505–511.

Srivastava, R. K. and G. P. Agarwal, 1953. Development of the female gametophyte and endosperm in *Chrozophora rottleri*. Bot. Gaz. 114:348–350.

Srivastava, R. N., 1954. Cleistogamy in Til, *Sesamum orientale*. Current Sci. 23:268.

Staedtler, G., 1923. Über Reduktionserscheinungen im Bau der Antherenwand von Angiospermen-Blüten. Flora 116:85–108.

Stahel, G., 1928. Beiträge zur Kenntnis der Blütenbiologie von Kakao, *Theobroma cacao*. Verh. kon. Akad. v. wet. Amsterdam 25.

Stapf, O., 1904. On the fruit of *Melocanna bambusoides*, an endospermless viviparous genus of Bambuseae. Trans. Linn. Soc. London (2) (Bot.) 6:401.

Stauffer, H. U., 1957. Zur Stellung der Gattung *Okoubaka*. Santales-Studien. 1. Ber. schweiz. bot. Ges. 67:422–427.

Stebbins, G. L., 1932a. Cytology of *Antennaria*. 1. Normal species. Bot. Gaz. 94:134–151.

Stebbins, G. L., 1932b. Cytology of *Antennaria*. 2. Parthenogenetic species. Bot. Gaz. 94:322–344.

Stebbins, G. L., 1938. Cytogenetic studies in *Paeonia*. 2. The cytology of the diploid species and hybrids. Genetics 23:83–110.

Stebbins, G. L., 1941. Apomixis in the Angiosperms. Bot. Rev. 7:507–542.

Stebbins, G. L. and E. B. Babcock, 1939. The effect of polyploidy and apomixis on the evolution of species in *Crepis*. J. Hered. 30:519–530.

Stebbins, G. L. and J. A. Jenkins, 1939. Aposporic development in the North American species of *Crepis*. Genetica 21:191–224.

Steffen, K., 1946. Bemerkungen zur Polarität der Angiospermeneizelle. Z. Natur. 1:331–336.

Steffen, K., 1948. Mehrzelliges Archesp. bei Balsaminaceen. Planta 36:203–213.

Steffen, K., 1951. Zur Kenntnis des Befruchtungsverganges bei *Impatiens glanduligera*. Cytologische Studien am Embryosack der Balsamineen. Planta 39:175–244.

Steffen, K., 1952. Die Embryoentwicklung von *Impatiens glanduligera*. Flora 139:394–461.

Steffen, K., 1953. Zytologische Untersuchungen an Pollenkorn und -schlauch. 1. Phasenkontrast-optische Lebenduntersuchungen an Pollenschläuchen von *Galanthus nivalis*. Flora 140:140–174.

Steffen, K., 1956. Endomitosen im Endosperm von *Pedicularis palustris*. Planta 47:625–652.

Steffen, K., 1963a. Male Gametophyte. In Maheshwari, P. (ed.). Recent Advances in the Embryology of Angiosperms. Delhi: 15–40.

Steffen, K., 1963b. Fertilization. In Maheshwari, P. (ed.). Recent Advances in the Embryology of Angiosperms. Delhi:105–133.

Steffen, K. and W. Landmann, 1958. Entwicklungsgeschichtliche und cytologische Untersuchungen am Balkentapetum von *Gentiana cruciata* und *Impatiens glandulifera*. Planta 50:423–460.

Steinbauer, G. P., 1943. Frequency of polyembryony in *Fraxinus* seeds. Bot. Gaz. 105:85.

Steindl, F., 1935. Pollen- und Embryosackentwicklung bei *Viscum album* und *V. articulatum*. Ber. schweiz. bot. Ges. 44:343–388.

Steindl, F., 1945. Beitrag zur Pollen- und Embryobildung bei *Cynomorium coccineum*. Arch. Julius Klaus.-Stift. 20:342–355.

Steinegger, P., 1933. Zytologische bedingte Ei- und Zygotensterilität bei triploiden Apfelsorten. Ber. schweiz. bot. Ges. 42:285–338.

Stenar, H., 1924a. Om embryologien hos Hypoxidoideae-Hypoxideae. Svensk bot. Tidskr. 18:524.

Stenar, H., 1924b. Om embryologien hos amaryllidaceer. Svensk bot. Tidskr. 18:526–527.

Stenar, H., 1925a. Embryologische und zytologische Studien über *Limnanthes douglasii*. Svensk bot. Tidskr. 19:133–152.

Stenar, H., 1925. Embryologische Studien. 1. Zur Embryologie einiger Columniferen. 2. Die Embryologie der Amaryllidaceen. Diss. Uppsala.

Stenar, H., 1927a. Über die Entwicklung des siebenkernigen Embryosackes bei *Gagea lutea*, nebst einigen Bemerkungen über die Reduktionsteilung bei *Gagea minima*. Svensk bot. Tidskr. 21:344–360.

Stenar, H., 1927b. Zur Entwicklungsgeschichte der Gattung *Anigosanthus*. Bot. Notiser 1927:104–114.

Stenar, H., 1928a. Zur Embryologie der *Veratrum*- und *Anthericum*-Gruppe. Bot. Notiser 1928:357–378.

Stenar, H., 1928b. Zur Embryologie der *Asphodeline*-Gruppe. Ein Beitrag zur systematischen Stellung der Gattungen *Bulbine* und *Paradisia*. Svensk bot. Tidskr. 22:145–159.

Stenar, H., 1931. Die Art der Pollenbildung bei *Narthecium ossifragum*. Bot. Notiser 1931:51–54.

Stenar, H., 1932a. Parthenogensis in der Gattung *Calamagrostis*. Embryobildung bei *Calamagrostis obtusata* und *C. purpurea*. Arkiv. f. wiss. Bot. 25 A:1–8.

Stenar, H., 1932b. Studien über die Entwicklungsgeschichte von *Nothoscordum fragrans* und *N. striatum*. Svensk bot. Tidskr. 26:25–44.

Stenar, H., 1933. Zur Embryologie der *Agapanthus*-Gruppe. Bot. Notiser 1933: 520–530.

Stenar, H., 1934. Embryologiche und zytologische Beobachtungen über *Maianthemum biflorum* und *Smilacina stellata*. Arkiv. f. wiss. Bot. A 26:1–20.

Stenar, H., 1935. Embryologische Beobachtungen über *Scheuchzeria palustris*. Bot. Notiser 1935: 78–86.

Stenar, H., 1937a. Zur Embryosackentwicklung einiger Malpighiazeen. Bot. Notiser 1937: 110–118.

Stenar, H., 1937b. Vorläufige Mitteilung über die Embryologie einiger Liliifloren. Heimbyg. Tidsk. Jämten 1937.

Stenar, H., 1937c. Om *Achroanthes monophyllos,* dess geografiska utbredning och embryologi. Heimbyg. Tidsk. Jämten 1937–38: 177–221.

Stenar, H., 1938a. Das Endosperm bei *Hypericum acutum*. Bot. Notiser 1938: 515–527.

Stenar, H., 1938b. Die systematische Stellung der Gattung *Xiphidium*. Svensk bot. Tidskr. 32:274.

Stenar, H., 1940. Biologiska och embryologiska notiser rörande *Calypso bulbosa*. Heimbyg. Tidsk. Jämten 1948:184–189.

Stenar, H., 1941. Über die Entwicklung des Embryosackes bei *Convallaria majalis*. Bot. Notiser 1941:123–128.

Stenar, H., 1942. Zur Embryologie der *Dracaena*-Gruppe. Heim. Tidsk. Fornvård. 8:183–195.

Stenar, H., 1949. Zur Kenntnis der Embryologie und der Rapidenzellen bei *Bowiea volubilis* und anderen Liliazeen. Acta Hort. Berg. 15:45–63.

Stenar, H., 1950. Studien über das Endosperm bei *Galtonia candicans* und anderen Scilloideen. Acta Hort. Berg. 15:169–184.

Stenar, H., 1951a. Zur Embryologie von *Haemanthus katharinae,* nebst Erörterungen über das helobiale Endosperm in den Amaryllidaceae und Liliaceae. Acta Hort. Berg. 16:57–72.

Stenar, H., 1951b. Zur Embryologie der Gattung *Phaedranassa* nebst einer Übersicht über den Endospermtyp bei den Amaryllidaceae. Bot. Notiser 1951:209–228.

Stenar, H., 1952. Notes on the embryology and anatomy of *Luzuriaga latifolia*. Acta Hort. Berg. 16:219–232.

Stenar, H., 1953. The embryo sac type in *Smilacina, Polygonatum* and *Theropogon*. Phytomorphology 3:326–338.

Stenzel, G., 1890. Blütenbildungen bei Schneeglöckchen und Samenformen bei der Eiche. Bibl. bot. 21.

Stephens, E. L., 1908. A preliminary note on the embryo sac of certain Penaeaceae. Ann. Bot. 22:329–330.

Stephens, E. L., 1909a. The embryo sac and embryo of certain Penaeaceae. Ann. Bot. 23:363–378.

Stephens, E. L., 1909b. The embryo sac and embryo of *Geissoloma marginata*. New Phytol. 8:345–348.

Stephens, E. L., 1909c. Recent progress in the study of the embryo sac in angiosperms. New Phytol. 8:377–387.

Sterling, C., 1955a. Nucellus and endosperm in the seed of lima bean, *Phaseolus lunatus*. Bull. Torrey bot. Cl. 82:39–49.

Sterling, C., 1955b. Embryogeny in the lima bean. Bull. Torrey bot. Cl. 82:325–338.

Stern, K., 1917. Beiträge zur Kenntnis der Nepenthaceen. Flora 109:213–282.

Steude, H., 1935. Beiträge zur Morphologie und Anatomie von *Mourera aspera*. Beih. bot. Ztbl. A. 53:627–650.

468 BIBLIOGRAPHY

Stevens, N. E., 1911. Dioecism in trailing arbutus, with notes on the morphology of the seed. Bull. Torrey bot. Cl. 38:531-543.

Stevens, N. E. 1912a. The morphology of the seed of the buckwheat. Bot. Gaz. 53:59-66.

Stevens, N. E., 1912b. Observations on heterostylous plants. Bot. Gaz. 53:277-308.

Stevens, N. E., 1919. The development of the endosperm in *Vaccinium corymbosum*. Bull. Torrey bot. Cl. 46:465-468.

Stevens, W. C., 1898. The behavior of kinoplasm and nucleolus in the division of the pollen mother cells of *Asclepias cornuti*. Kansas Univ. Quart. A. 7:77-85.

Stevenson, G. B., 1934. The life history of the New Zealand species of the parasitic genus *Korthalsella*. Trans. Proc. Roy. Soc. N. Z. 64:175-190.

Stiffler, E. G., 1925. Development of embryo sac in *Gasteria, Cyrtanthus* and *Veltheimia*. Bot. Gaz. 79:207-216.

Stokes, G. W., 1955. Seed development and failure in horseradish. J. Hered. 46:15-21.

Stolt, K. A. H., 1921. Zur Embryologie der Gentianaceen und Menyanthaceen. Kgl. Svensk. Vet.-Akad. Handl. 61:1-56. Diss. Uppsala.

Stolt, K. A. H., 1927. Über die Embryologie von *Gentiana prostrata* und die Antipodalen der Gentianaceen. Bot. Notiser 1927:225-242.

Stolt, K. A. H., 1928. Die Embryologie von *Myriophyllum alterniflorum*. Svensk bot. Tidskr. 22:305-319.

Stolt, K. A. H., 1936. Beiträge zur Embryologie der Lentibulariaceen. Svensk bot. Tidskr. 30:690-696.

Stomps, T. J., 1911. Kernteilung und Synapsis bei *Spinacea oleracea*. Biol. Ztbl. 31:257-309. Diss. Amsterdam. 1910.

Stomps, T. J., 1930. Über parthenogenetische Oenotheren. Ber. dtsch. bot. Ges. 48:119-126.

Stomps. T. J., 1931. Weiteres über Parthenogenesis bei *Oenothera*. Ber. dtsch. bot. Ges. 49:258-266.

Stork, H. E., 1920. Studies in the genus *Taraxacum*. Bull. Torrey bot. Cl. 47:199-210.

Stoudt, H. N., 1960. Sporogenesis in *Magnolia kobus*. 1. Microsporogenesis. Proc. Pennsylv. Acad. Sci. 34:29-33.

Stout, A. B., 1912. The individuality of the chromosomes and their serial arrangements in *Carex aquatilis*. Arch f. Zellf. 9:114-140.

Stover, E., 1932. Life history of *Nymphoides peltatum*. Bot. Gaz. 93:474-483.

Stover, E. C., 1937. The embryo sac of *Eragrostis ciliensis*. A new type of embryo sac and a summary of grass embryo sac investigations. Ohio J. Sci. 37:172-184.

Stow, I., 1927. A cytological study on pollen sterility in *Solanum tuberosum*. Jap. J. Bot. 3:217-238.

Stow, I., 1930. Experimental studies in the formation of embryo saclike giant pollen grains in the anther of *Hyacinthus orientalis*. Cytologia 1:417-439.

Stow, I., 1934. On the female tendencies of the embryo saclike pollen grain of *Hyacinthus orientalis*. Cytologia 5:88-108.

Stow, I., 1936. A cytological study on the pollen sterility in *Solanum tuberosum*. Proc. Imp. Acad. Japan 2:426-430.

Strasburger, E., 1877. Über Befruchtung und Zellteilung. Jen. Zeit. f. Naturw. 11:435-536.

Strasburger, E., 1878. Über Polyembryonie. Jen. Zeit. f. Naturw. 12:647–670.
Strasburger, E., 1879a. Die Angiospermen und die Gymnospermen. Jena.
Strasburger, E., 1879b. Neue Beobachtungen über Zellbildung und Zellteilung. Bot. Zeit. 37:265–279, 281–288.
Strasburger, E., 1880a. Einige Bermerkungen über vielkernige Zellen und Embryogenie von *Lupinus*. Bot. Zeit. 38:845–854, 858–868.
Strasburger, E., 1880b. Über Zellbildung und Zellteilung. Jen. Zeit. f. Nat. 13.
Strasburger, E., 1882a. Über den Bau und das Wachstum vegetabilischer Zellhäute. Jena.
Strasburger, E., 1882b. Über den Teilungsvorgang der Zellkerne und das Verhältnis der Kernteilung zur Zellteilung. Arch. microsk. Anat. 21:476–590.
Strasburger, E., 1884a. Die Endospermbildung bei *Daphne*. Ber. dtsch. bot. Ges. 2:112–114.
Strasburger, E., 1884b. Neuere Untersuchungen über den Befruchtungsvorgang bei den Phanerogamen als Grundlage für eine Theorie der Zeugung. Jena.
Strasburger, E., 1885. Zu *Santalum* und *Daphne*. Ber. dtsch. bot. Ges. 3:105–113.
Strasburger, E., 1886. Über fremdartige Bestäubung. Jahrb. f. wiss. Bot. 17:50–98.
Strasburger, E., 1889. Über das Wachsthum vegetabilischer Zellhäute. Histolog. Beitr. 2:80.
Strasburger, E., 1900. Einige Bemerkungen zur Frage nach der doppelten Befruchtung bei Angiospermen. Bot. Zeit. 58:293–316.
Strasburger, E., 1901a. Einige Bemerkungen zu der Pollenbildung bei *Asclepias*. Ber. dtsch. bot. Ges. 19:450–461.
Strasburger, E., 1901b. Über Befruchtung. Bot. Zeit. 59:353–358.
Strasburger, E., 1902. Ein Beitrag zur Kenntnis von *Ceratophyllum submersum* und phylogenetische Erörterungen. Jahrb. f. wiss. Bot. 37:477–526.
Strasburger, E., 1904. Anlage des Embryosacks und Prothalliumbildung bei der Eibe nebst anschliessen Erörterungen. Haeckel. Denkschr. nat. Ges. Jena 11.
Strasburger, E., 1905a. Die Samenanlage von *Drimys winteri* und die Endospermbildung bei Angiospermen. Flora 95:215–231.
Strasburger, E., 1905b. Die Apogamie der Eualchemillen und allgemeinne Gesichtspunkte, die sich aus ihr ergeben. Jahrb. f. wiss. Bot. 41:88–164.
Strasburger, E., 1908. Chromosomenzahlen, Plasmastrukturen, Vererbungsträger und Reduktionsteilung. Jahrb. f. wiss. Bot. 45:477–570.
Strasburger, E., 1909a. Zeitpunkt der Bestimmung des Geschlechtes, Apogamie, Parthenogenesis und Reduktionsteilung. Histolog. Beitr. 7:1–124.
Strasburger, E., 1909b. Die Apogamie von *Wikstroemia indica*, und das Verhalten der normal geschlechtlichen Thymelaeaceen. Histolog. Beitr. 7.
Strasburger, E., 1909c. Das weitere Schicksal meiner isolierten Weiblichen *Mercurialis annua*–Pflanzen. Zeit. f. Bot. 1:506–525.
Strasburger, E., 1910a. Sexuelle und apogame Fortpflanzung bei der Urticaceen. Jahrb. f. wiss. Bot. 47:245–288.
Strasburger, E., 1910b. Über geschlectbestimmende Ursachen. Jahrb. f. wiss. Bot. 48:427–520.
Stratton, M. E., 1923. The morphology of the double kernel in *Zea mays* var. *polysperma*. N.Y. (Cornell) Agr. Expt. Sta. Mem. 69.
Stromberg, B., 1956. The embryo sac development of the genus *Freycinetia*. Svensk bot. Tidskr. 50:129–134.

Stuart, C. P. C., 1916. Sur le développement des cellules génératrices de *Camellia theifera*. Ann. Jard. bot. Buitenz. 30:1–22.

Sturm, K., 1910. Monographische Studien über *Adoxa moschatellina*. Jahrb. nat. Ges. Zürich 54:1–72 Diss. Zürich.

Subba Rao, A. M., 1937. A note on the development of the female gametophytes of some Malpighiaceae and polyembryony in *Hiptage madablota*. Current Sci. 6:280–282.

Subba Rao, A. M., 1939. The ovule and embryo sac development of some Malpighiaceae. Current Sci. 8:79–81.

Subba Rao, A. M., 1940a. Cytology and embryogeny in *Artocarpus integrifolia*. J. Mysore Univ. B. 2:63–73.

Subba, Rao, A. M., 1940b. Studies in the Malpighiaceae. 1. Embryo sac development and embryogeny in the genera *Hiptage, Banisteria* and *Stigmatophyllum*. J. Indian bot. Soc. 18:145–156.

Subba Rao, A. M., 1941. Studies in the Malpighiaceae. 2. Structure and development of the ovules and embryo sacs of *Malpighia coccifera* and *Tristellateia australis*. Proc. Nat. Inst. Sci. India 7:393–404.

Subramanyam, K., 1942. Gametogenesis and embryogeny in a few members of the Melastomaceae. J. Indian bot. Soc. 21:69–85.

Subramanyam, K., 1944. A contribution to the life history of *Sonerila wallichii*. Proc. Indian Acad. Sci. B. 19:115–120.

Subramanyam, K., 1946. Further contribution to the embryology of the genus *Osbeckia*. J. Mysore Univ. B. 7:1–11.

Subramanyam, K., 1947. A case of polyembryony in *Wahlenbergia gracilis*. Current Sci. 16:350.

Subramanyam, K., 1948a. An embryological study of *Melastoma malabathricum*. J. Indian bot. Soc. 27:11–19.

Subramanyam, K., 1948b. A contribution to the embryology of *Wahlenbergia gracilis*. Proc. Nat. Inst. Sci. India 14:359–366.

Subramanyam, K., 1949. An embryological study of *Lobelia pyramidalis,* with special reference to the mechanism of nutrition of the embryo in the family Lobeliaceae. New Phytol. 48:365–373.

Subramanyam, K., 1950a. Development of embryo sac and endosperm in *Stylidium tenellum*. Current Sci. 19:294.

Subramanyam, K., 1950b. An embryological study of *Levenhookia dubia*. Proc. nat. Inst. Sci. India B. 16:245–253.

Subramanyam, K., 1950c. A contribution to our knowledge of the systematic position of the Sphenocleaceae. Proc. Indian Acad. Sci. B. 31:60–65.

Subramanyam, K., 1951a. Embryology of *Oxyspora paniculata*. Phytomorphology 1:205–212.

Subramanyam, K., 1951b. Interrelationships of Campanulatae. J. Mysore Univ. B. 12:5–13.

Subramanyam, K., 1951c. Studies on the relationships of the Melastomaceae. J. Mysore Univ. B. 12:1–4.

Subramanyam, K., 1951d. A morphological study of *Stylidium graminifolium*. Lloydia 14:65–81.

Subramanyam, K., 1951e. Flower structure and seed development in *Isotoma fluviatilis*. Proc. Nat. Inst. Sci. India 17:275–285.

Subramanyam, K., 1951f. Origin and nature of haustoria in *Lobelia cardinalis*. Bot. Gaz. 112:319–322.

Subramanyam, K., 1953. The nutritional mechanism of embryo sac and embryo in the families Campanulaceae, Lobeliaceae and Stylidiaceae. J. Mysore Univ. B. 13:1–4.

Subramanyam, K., 1960a. Nutritional mechanism of the seed. 1. Nutritional mechanism of the embryo sac. J. Madras Univ. B. 30:29–44.

Subramanyam, K., 1960b. Nutritional mechanism of the seed. 2. Nutritional mechanism of the embryo. J. Madras Univ. B. 30:45–56.

Subramanyam, K., 1961. Symposium on plant embryology. J. Sci. Ind. Res. A. 20:477–483.

Subramanyam, K., 1962. Embryology in relation to systematic botany, with particular reference to the Crassulaceae. *In* Plant Embryology: A Symposium. CSIR. New Delhi: 94–112.

Subramanyam, K., 1963. Embryology of *Sedum ternatum*. J. Indian bot. Soc. Maheshwari Commen. Vol. 42 A: 259–275.

Subramanyam, K. and H. C. Govindu, 1948. The development of the female gametophyte in *Oenothera odorata*. J. Indian bot. Soc. 27:25–30.

Subramanyam, K. and H. C. Govindu, 1949. The development of the male and female gametophyte in *Lilium neilgherrense*. J. Indian bot. Soc. 28:36–41.

Subramanyam, K. and A. N. Rao, 1952. A contribution to the embryology of *Chlorophytum attenuatum*. Proc. Indian Acad. Sci. B. 36:191–197.

Suda, Y., 1963. Cytological observations on triploid *Salix* x *gracilistyloides* mstr. *sympolyandra* and tetraploid *Salix bakko*. Sci. Rpts. Tôhoku Univ. (4) Biol. 29:35–44.

Suguira, T., 1925. Meiosis in *Tropaeolum majus*. Bot. Mag. (Tokyo) 39:47–54.

Suita, N., 1936. Studies on the male gametophyte in angiosperms. 1. Studies in the degenerating process of the pollen tube nucleus, with special reference to Feulgen's reaction. Bot. and Zool. (Tokyo) 4:2033–2044.

Suita, N., 1937a. Studies on the male gametophyte in angiosperms. 2. Differentiation and behavior of the vegetative and generative elements in the pollen grains of *Crinum*. Cytologia. Fujii Jubl. Vol.: 920–933.

Suita, N., 1937b. Studies on the male gametophyte in angiosperms. 3. On the mature pollen grains in angiosperms. Bot. Mag. (Tokyo) 51:524–530.

Suita, N., 1938. Studies on the male gametophyte in angiosperms. 4. Behavior of the "droplet sheath" in the pollen tube. Cytologia 8:532–541.

Sukačev, V. N., 1940. Polymorphismus und Apomizis bei den Arten der Gattung *Adenophora*. Bot. Zhur. 25:297–303.

Sulbha, K., 1954a. The embryo sac of *Scilla*. Current Sci. 23:98–99.

Sulbha, K., 1954b. The embryology of *Iphigenia indica*. Phytomorphology 4:180–191.

Sulbha, K., 1957. Embryology of *Brassica juncea*. J. Indian bot. Soc. 36:292–301.

Sulbha, K. and M. S. Swaminathan, 1959. Effect of grafting on fruit-set and embryo development in crosses between *Corchorus olitorius* and *C. capsularis*. Current Sci. 28:460–461.

Sulmont, G. and A. Lebegue, 1964. Embryogeny in Papaveraceae: Development of embryo in *Meconopsis cambrica*. C. R. Acad. Sci. Paris 258:3890–3893.

Sundar Rao, Y., 1940a. Male and female gametophytes of *Polemonium caeruleum*, with a discussion of the affinities of the family Polemoniaceae. Proc. Nat. Inst. Sci. India 6:695–704.

Sundar, Rao, Y., 1940b. Structure and development of the embryo sac of *Drimiopsis kirki* and *Allium govanianum*. J. Indian bot. Soc. 19:273–282.

Suneson, S., 1933. Zur Embryologie der Gattung *Viburnum*. Bot. Notiser 1933:181–194.

Surface, F. M., 1905. Contribution to the life history of *Sanguinaria canadensis*. Ohio Nat. 6:379–385.

Surkova, L. I. and K. P. Skipina, 1963. (An embryological study of *Prunus* var. Vengerka Italian.) *In* (A collection of scientific work from the Sochinsk experimental station of subtropical and southern fruit crops.) 17:143–152.

Süssenguth, K., 1921a. Beiträge zur Frage des systematischen Anschlusses der Monocotylen. Beih. bot. Ztbl. 38:1–79. Diss. München. 1919.

Süssenguth, K., 1921b. Bemerkungen zur meiotischen und somatischen Kernteilung bei einigen Monokotylen. Flora 119:313–328.

Süssenguth, K., 1923. Über die Pesudogamie bei *Zygopetalum mackayi*. Ber. dtsch. bot. Ges. 41:16–23.

Süssenguth, K., 1927. Über die Gattung *Lennoa*. Flora 122:264–305.

Sutaria, R. N., 1930. Microsporogenesis in *Raphanus sativus*. J. Indian bot. Soc. 9:253–256.

Svedelius, N., 1902. Zur Kenntnis der saprophytischen Gentianaceen. Svensk. Vet.-Akad. Handl. 28. (3) 4.

Svedelius, N., 1904. On the life history of *Enalus acoroides*. Ann. Roy. bot. Gdns. Peradeniya 2:267–297.

Svedelius, N., 1910. Om den florala organisationen hos Aracé-släktet *Lagenandra*. Svensk. bot. Tidsk. 4:225–252.

Svedelius, N., 1911. Om fröbyggnaden hos släktena *Wormia* och *Dillenia*. Ett bidrag till Dilleniacéernas morfologi. Svensk bot. Tidskr. 5:152–173.

Svedelius, N., 1932. On different types of pollination in *Vallisneria spiralis* and *Vallisneria americana*. Svensk bot. Tidskr. 26:1–12.

Svensson, H. G., 1922. Embryologien hos *Lycopsis arvensis*. Svensk bot. Tidskr. 16:137–138.

Svensson, H. G., 1923a. Om endospermet hos *Lappula*. Svensk bot. Tidskr. 17:387–388.

Svensson, H. G., 1923b. Om *Heliotropium*-gruppens embryologi. Svensk bot. Tidskr. 17:388–389.

Svensson, H. G., 1923c. Embryologien hos borraginacé-släktena *Echium* och *Onosma*. Svensk bot. Tidskr. 17:390.

Svensson, H. G., 1925. Zur Embryologie der Hydrophyllaceen, Boraginaceen und Heliotropiaceen mit besonderer Rücksicht auf die Endospermbildung. Uppsala Univ. Årssk. 2:1–176. Diss. Uppsala.

Svensson, H. G., 1926. Zytologische-embryologische Solanaceenstudien. 1. Über die Samenentwicklung von *Hyoscyamus niger*. Svensk bot. Tidskr. 20:420–434.

Svensson, H. G., 1928. Zur Entwicklungsgeschichte der Blüten und Samen von *Limosella aquatica*. Svensk bot. Tidskr. 22:462–476.

Swaminathan, M. S., 1954. Microsporogenesis in some commercial potato varieties. J. Hered. 45:265–272.

Swamy, B. G. L., 1941a. Contributions to the life history of *Bignonia megapatomica*. J. Indian bot. Soc. 20:299–305.

Swamy, B. G. L., 1941b. The development of the male gametes in *Cymbidium bicolor*. Proc. Indian Acad. Sci. B. 14:454–460.

Swamy, B. G. L., 1942a. Embryological studies in Palmae. A preliminary note on the megasporogenesis in *Areca catechu*. Current Sci. 11:109.

Swamy, B. G. L., 1942b. Morphological studies in three species of *Vanda*. Current Sci. 11:285–286.

Swamy, B. G. L., 1942c. Female gametophyte and embryogeny in *Cymbidium bicolor*. Proc. Indian Acad. Sci. B. 15:194–201.

Swamy, B. G. L., 1943a. Embryology of Orchidaceae. Current Sci. 12:13–17.

Swamy, B. G. L., 1943b. Gametogenesis and embryogeny of *Eulophia epidendraea*. Proc. Natl. Inst. Sci. India 9:59–65.

Swamy, B. G. L., 1944a. A reinvestigation of the embryo sac of *Eragrostis cilianensis*. Current Sci. 13:103–104.

Swamy, B. G. L., 1944b. A reinvestigation of the embryo sac of *Piper betel*. Proc. Natl. Acad. Sci. India 14:109–113.

Swamy, B. G. L., 1944c. A preliminary note on the embryology of *Casuarina equisetifolia*. Proc. Indian Acad. Sci. B. 20:187–191.

Swamy, B. G. L., 1944d. The embryo sac and the embryo of *Satyrium nepalense*. J. Indian bot. Soc. 23:66–70.

Swamy, B. G. L., 1945a. Embryo sac and fertilization in *Cypripedium spectabile*. Bot. Gaz. 107:291–295.

Swamy, B. G. L., 1945b. The embryo sac of *Heckeria subpeltata*. J. Indian bot. Soc. 24:1–3.

Swamy, B. G. L., 1946a. Some notes on the embryo of *Cymbidium bicolor*. Current Sci. 15:139–140.

Swamy, B. G. L., 1946b. Development of endosperm in *Zephyranthes andersonii*. Proc. Nat. Inst. Sci. India 12:187–190.

Swamy, B. G. L., 1946c. Embryology of *Habenaria*. Proc. Natl. Inst. Sci. India 12:413–426.

Swamy, B. G. L., 1946d. Endosperm in *Hypericum mysorense*. Ann. Bot. 9:165–169.

Swamy, B. G. L., 1946e. Inverted polarity of the embryo sac of angiosperms and its relation to the archegonium theory. Ann. Bot. 9:171–183.

Swamy, B. G. L., 1946f. The embryology of *Zeuxine sulcata*. New Phytol. 45:132–136.

Swamy, B. G. L., 1947. On the life history of *Vanilla planifolia*. Bot. Gaz. 108:449–456.

Swamy, B. G. L., 1948a. The embryology of *Epidendrum prismatocarpum*. Bull. Torrey bot. Cl. 75:245–249.

Swamy, B. G. L., 1948b. Agamospermy in *Spiranthes cernua*. Lloydia 11:149–162.

Swamy, B. G. L., 1948c. On the post-fertilization development of *Trillium undulatum*. Cellule 52:7–14.

Swamy, B. G. L., 1948d. A contribution to the life history of *Casuarina*. Proc. Amer. Acad. Arts & Sci. 77:1–32.

Swamy, B. G. L., 1948e. A contribution to the embryology of the Marcgraviaceae. Amer. J. Bot. 35:628–633.

Swamy, B. G. L., 1949a. Embryological studies in the Orchidaceae. 1. Gametophytes. Amer. Midl. Nat. 41:184–201.

Swamy, B. G. L., 1949b. Embryological studies in the Orchidaceae. 2. Embryogeny. Amer. Midl. Nat. 41:202–232.

Swamy, B. G. L., 1949c. Further contributions to the morphology of the Degeneriaceae. J. Arnold Arb. 30:10–38.

474   BIBLIOGRAPHY

Swamy, B. G. L., 1949d. A reinvestigation of the embryo sac of *Maianthemum canadense*. Bull. Torrey bot. Cl. 76:17–23.

Swamy, B. G. L., 1952. Some aspects in the embryology of *Zygogynum bailloni*. Proc. Nat. Inst. Sci. India 18:399–406.

Swamy, B. G. L., 1953a. Some observations on the embryology of *Decaisnea insignis*. Proc. Nat. Inst. Sci. India 19:307–310.

Swamy, B. G. L., 1953b. Morphology and relationships of the Chloranthaceae. J. Arnold Arbor. 34:375–408.

Swamy, B. G. L., 1960. Contributions to the embryology of *Canjera rheedii*. Phytomorphology 10:397–409.

Swamy, B. G. L., 1962. The embryo of Monocotyledons: A working hypothesis from a new approach. *In* Plant Embryology—A Symposium. CSIR., New Delhi: 113–123.

Swamy, B. G. L., 1964a. Observations on the floral morphology and embryology of *Stemona tuberosa*. Phytomorphology 14:458–468.

Swamy, B. G. L., 1964b. Macrogametophytic ontogeny in *Schisandra chinensis*. J. Indian bot. Soc. 43:391–396.

Swamy, B. G. L. and I. W. Bailey, 1949. The morphology and relationships of *Cercidiphyllum*. J. Arnold Arb. 30:187–210.

Swamy, B. G. L. and B. P. Balakrishna, 1946. Female gametophyte of *Acalypha tricolor*. J. Indian bot. Soc. 25:67–69.

Swamy, B. G. L. and P. M. Ganapathy, 1957a. A new type of endosperm haustorium in *Nothapodytes foetida*. Phytomorphology 7:331–336.

Swamy, B. G. L. and P. M. Ganapathy, 1957b. On endosperm in Dicotyledons. Bot. Gaz. 119:47–50.

Swamy, B. G. L. and K. K. Lakshmanan, 1962a. Contributions to the embryology of the Najadaceae. J. Indian bot. Soc. 41:247–267.

Swamy, B. G. L. and K. K. Lakshmanan, 1962b. The origin of epicotylary meristem and cotyledon in *Halophila ovata*. Ann. Bot. 26:243–249.

Swamy, B. G. L. and D. Padmanabhan, 1961a. Notulae embryologicae. 1. The functions of endosperm in *Avicennia officinalis*. Current Sci. 30:424–425.

Swamy, B. G. L. and D. Padmanabhan, 1961b. The quadrant proembryo of *Epithema carnosum*. Proc. Indian Acad. Sci. B. 53:166–172.

Swamy, B. G. L. and D. Padmanabhan, 1961c. Embryogenesis in *Sphenoclea zeylanica*. Proc. Indian Acad. Sci. B. 54:169–187.

Swamy, B. G. L. and D. Padmanabhan, 1962. A renaissance of angiosperm embryogenesis. J. Indian bot. Soc. 41:422–435.

Swamy, B. G. L. and N. Parameswaran, 1960. A contribution to the embryology of *Begonia crenata*. J. Indian bot. Soc. 39:140–148.

Swamy, B. G. L. and N. Parameswaran, 1963. The Helobial endosperm. Biol. Revs. 38:1–50.

Swamy, B. G. L. and K. Periasamy, 1955. Contributions to the embryology of *Acrotrema arnottianum*. Phytomorphology 5:301–314.

Swamy, B. G. L. and J. D. Rao, 1963. The endosperm in *Opilia amentacea*. Phytomorphology 13:423–428.

Swingle, L. D., 1908. Embryology of *Myosurus minimus*. Amer. Nat. 42:582–591.

Sybenga, J., 1960. (The genetics and cytology of coffee. A review of the literature.) Turrialba 10:83–140.

Sykes, M. G., 1909. Note on the nuclei of some unisexual plants. Ann. Bot. 23:341.

Täckholm, G., 1914. Zur Kenntnis der Embryosackentwicklung von *Lopezia coronata*. Svensk bot. Tidskr. 8:223–234.

Täckholm, G., 1915. Beobachtungen über die Samenentwicklung einiger Onagraceen. Svensk bot. Tidskr. 9:294–361.

Täckholm, G., 1916. Zur Antipodenentwicklung der Compositengattungen *Cosmidium* und *Cosmos*. Svensk bot. Tidskr. 10:423–437.

Täckholm, G., 1923. Zytologische Studien über die Gattung *Rosa*. Acta Hort. Berg. 7:97–381.

Täckholm, G. and E. Söderberg, 1917. Über die Pollenentwicklung bei *Cinnamomum* nebst Erörterungen über die phylogenetische Bedeutung des Pollentyps. Arkiv. f. Bot. 15:1–14.

Täckholm, G. and E. Söderberg, 1918. Neue Beispiele der simultanen und successiven Wandbildung in den Pollenmutterzellen. Svensk bot. Tidskr. 12:189–201.

Tahara, M., 1915a. (Cytological studies on *Chrysanthemum*.) Bot. Mag. (Tokyo) 29:92–104.

Tahara, M., 1915b. (Parthenogenesis in *Erigeron annuus*.) Bot. Mag. (Tokyo) 29:245–254.

Tahara, M., 1921. Cytologische Untersuchungen an einigen Kompositen. J. Coll. Sci. Imp. Univ. Tokyo 43:1–53.

Tamari, K., 1901. (Concerning the fruits of *Diospyros kali*.) Bull. Soc. Agric. Japan: 233–234.

Tanaka, N., 1939a. Chromosome studies in Cyperaceae. 5. Pollen development of *Carex grallatoria* var. *heteroclita*. Jap. J. Genet. 15:153–157.

Tanaka, N., 1939b. Chromosome studies in Cyperaceae. 7. Chromosome number and pollen development of *Fimbristylis*. Bot. Mag. Tokyo 53:480–487.

Tanaka, N., 1940. Chromosome studies in Cyperaceae. 6. Pollen development and additional evidence for the compound chromosome in *Scirpus lacustris*. Cytologia 10:348–362.

Tanaka, N., 1941. Chromosome studies in Cyperaceae. 12. Pollen development in five genera, with special reference to *Rhyncospora*. Bot. Mag. Tokyo 55:55–65.

Tanaka, N., 1950. Gametogenesis and fertilization in the genus *Carex*. Coord. Comm. Res. Genetics 1:133–137.

Tandon, S. L. and P. N. Bali, 1955. Morphological and cytological studies of the diploid and the naturally occurring triploid in *Lantana camara*. Indian J. Hort. 12:1–5.

Tandon, S. L. and B. M. Kapoor, 1962a. Nuclear variation in the endosperm of *Zephyranthes ajax* and its causes. Sci. and Cult. 28:189–190.

Tandon, S. L. and B. M. Kapoor, 1962b. Contributions to the cytology of endosperm in some angiosperms. 1. *Zephyranthes ajax*. Caryologia 15:21–41.

Tanfani, E., 1888. Nota preliminare sul frutto e sul seme delle Apiaceae. N. G. bot. Ital. 20:307–313.

Tang, S. H., 1962. (Sporogenesis and gametophyte development in *Eucommia ulmoides*.) Acta bot. Sinica 10:29–34.

Tannert, P., 1905. Entwicklung und Bau der Blüte und Frucht von *Avena sativa*. Diss. Zürich.

Tarasevich, Y. I., 1963. (Comparative embryological investigation of diploid and tetraploid forms of the radish plant.) Vest. Akad. Nauk Belorussk. SSSR., Biyal. Nauk 1:42–46.

Tassi, F., 1898a. Dello sviluppo dell'ovulo e del sacco embrionale nella *Tibouchina holosericea*. Boll. Lab. Ord. bot. Siena 1:162–165.

Tassi, F., 1898b. Le Proteaceae in specie dello *Stenocarpus sinuatus*. Studio anatomo-morphologico comparativo. Boll. Lab. et Orto bot. Siena 1.

Tassi, F., 1900. Sulla structura dell'ovulo dell'*Hydromystria stolonifera*. Boll. Orto. bot. Siena 3:81–88.

Tatachar, T., 1940. The development of the embryo sac and formation of haustoria in *Lantana indica* and *Stachytarpheta indica*. J. Indian bot. Soc. 19:45–52.

Tateishi, S., 1927. On the development of the embryo sac and fertilization of *Acalypha australis*. Bot. Mag. Tokyo 41:477–485.

Tateishi, S., 1929. Embryologische Studien an der Gattung *Chrysanthemum*. Jap. J. Bot. 4:317–326.

Taylor, A. R. A., 1957. Studies of the development of *Zostera marina*. 1. The embryo and seed. Canad. J. Bot. 35:477–499.

Taylor, W. R., 1920. A morphological and cytological study of reproduction in the genus *Acer*. Contrib. bot. Lab. Univ. Pennsylv. 5:111–138.

Taylor, W. R., 1921. The embryogeny of *Cyrtanthus parviflorus*. Amer. J. Bot. 8:502–506.

Tchernoyarow, M., 1915. Les nouvelles données dans l'embryologie du *Myosurus minimus*. Mém. Soc. Nat. Kiew 24:95–170.

Tchernoyarow, M., 1926. Befruchtungserscheinungen bei *Myosurus minimus*. Österr. bot. Zeit. 75:197–206.

Telesca, M. R., 1962. (A contribution to the embryology of *Phyteuma limonifolium*.) N. G. bot. Ital. 69:372–378.

Terada, S., 1928. Embryological studies in *Oryza sativa*. J. Coll. Agr., Hokkaido. Imp. Univ. Sapporo, Japan 19:245–260.

Teriokhin, E. S., 1962a. (The development of the endosperm and the character of the zygote growth in the European species of *Pyrola*). Bot. Zhur. 47:254–258.

Teriokhin, E. S., 1962b. (The development of embryos in certain Pyroleae-Monotropoideae.) Bot. Zhur. 47:1811–1816.

Teriokhin, E. S., 1963. (The development of the ovule and the female gametophyte in Pyroleae and Monotropeae.) Bot. Zhur. 48:406–414.

Thathachar, T., 1942a. Studies in Oxalidaceae, *Biophytum sensitivum, Averrhoa carambola* and *A. bilimbi*. J. Indian bot. Soc. 21:21–30.

Thathachar, T., 1942b. Studies in Gesneriaceae. Gametogenesis and embryogeny in *Didymocarpus tomentosa*. J. Indian bot. Soc. 21:185–193.

Thathachar, T., 1943. Studies in Gesneriaceae. Development of seed of *Rhynchoglossum obliquum*. J. Indian bot. Soc. 22:51–57.

Thathachar, T., 1952. Morphological studies in the Euphorbiaceae. 1. *Acalypha lanceolata*. Phytomorphology 2:197–201.

Thathachar, T., 1953a. Morphological studies in the Euphorbiaceae. 2. *Mallotus philippensis*. Proc. Nat. Inst. Sci. India 19:469–474.

Thathachar, T., 1953b. Morphological studies in the Euphorbiaceae. J. Univ. Mysore B. 13:43–68.

Thirumalachar, M. J. and B. A. Khan, 1941. Megasporogenesis and endosperm formation in *Eriodendron anfractuosum*. Proc. Indian Acad. Sci. B. 14:461–465.

Thoday, D. and E. T., Johnson, 1930. On *Arceuthobium pusillum*. 2. Flowers and fruit. Ann. Bot. 44:813–824.

Thomas, E. M., 1900a. On the presence of vermiform nuclei in a dicotyledon. Ann. Bot. 14:318–319.

Thomas, E. M., 1900b. Double fertilization in a dicotyledon: *Caltha palustris* Ann. Bot. 14:527–537.

Thomas, P. T., 1940. Reproductive versatility in *Rubus*. 2. The chromosomes and development. J. Genetics 40:119–128.

Thomas, R., 1931. Recherches cytologiques sur le tapis staminal et sur les eléménts polliniques chez les angiospermes. Thèse. Paris.

Thompson, P. A., 1963. The development of embryo, endosperm and nucellus tissues in relation to receptacle growth in the strawberry. Ann. Bot. 27:589–605.

Thompson, R. C., 1933. A morphological study of flower and seed development in Cabbage. J. Agr. Res. 27:215–237.

Tiagi, B., 1950. The embryology of *Cistanche tubulosa*. Proc. 37th. Indian Sci. Cong. 3:48–49.

Tiagi, B., 1951a. A contribution to the morphology and embryology of *Cuscuta hyalina* and *C. planiflora*. Phytomorphology 1:9–21.

Tiagi, B., 1951b. Studies in the family Orobanchaceae. 3. A contribution to the embryology of *Orobanche cernua* and *O. aegyptiaca*. Phytomorphology 1:158–169.

Tiagi, B., 1952a. Studies in the family Orobanchaceae. 1. A contribution to the embryology of *Cistanche tubulosa*. Lloydia 15:129–148.

Tiagi, B., 1952b. Studies in the family Orobanchaceae. 2. A contribution to the embryology of *Aeginetia indica*. Bull. Torrey bot. Cl. 79:63–78.

Tiagi, B., 1956. A contribution to the embryology of *Striga orobanchoides* and *S. euphrasioides*. Bull. Torrey bot. Cl. 83:154–170.

Tiagi, B., 1963. Studies in the family Orobanchaceae. 4. Embryology of *Boschniackia himalaica* and *B. tuberosa,* with remarks on the evolution of the family. Bot. Notiser 1963:81–93.

Tiagi, B. and S. Taimni, 1960. Embryo sac development in *Vernonia cinerascens,* and seed development in *V. cinerea*. Current Sci. 29:406.

Tiagi, B. and S. Taimni, 1963. Floral morphology and embryology of *Vernonia cinerascens* and *V. cinerea*. Agra Univ. J. Res. (Sci.) 12:123–137.

Tiagi, Y. D., 1954a. Morphology of the ovule and fruit of *Opuntia dillenii*. Proc. 41st. Indian Sci. Congr. 3:143.

Tiagi, Y. D., 1954b. Studies in the floral morphology of *Opuntia dillenii*. 1. Development of the ovule and gametophytes. Bot. Notiser: 343–356.

Tiagi, Y. D., 1956. Polyembryony in *Mammillaria tenuis*. Bull. bot. Soc. Univ. Saugar B. 8:25–27.

Tiagi, Y. D., 1957. Studies in floral morphology. 3. A contribution to the floral morphology of *Mammillaria tenuis*. J. Univ. Saugar B. 6:7–31.

Tiagi, Y. D., 1963. Vascular anatomy of the flower of certain species of the Calycanthaceae. Proc. Indian Acad. Sci. B. 58:224–234.

Tieghem, P. van, 1869. Anatomie de la fleur femelle et du fruit du noyer. Bull. Soc. bot. France 16:412–419.

Tieghem, P. van, 1884. Sur la structure et les affinités des Pittosporées. Bull. Soc. bot. France 31.

Tieghem, P. van, 1895a. Observations sur la structure et la dehiscence des anthères des Loranthacées etc. Bull. Soc. bot. France 42:363–368.

Tieghem, P. van, 1895b. Sur la structure et les affinités des *Tupeia, Ginalloa, Phoradendron* et *Dendrophthora,* de la famille des Loranthacées. Bull. Soc. bot. France 42:643–652.

Tieghem, P. van, 1896a. Sur l'organization florale des Balanophoracées. Bull. Soc. bot. France 43:295–310.

Tieghem, P. van, 1896b. Sur les Phanérogames à ovule sans nucelle, formant le groupe des Innucellées des Santalinées. Bull. Soc. bot. France 43:543–577.

Tieghem, P. van, 1897a. Morphologie de l'embryon et de la plantule chez les Graminées et les Cypéracées. Ann. Sci. Nat. Bot. (8) 3:259–309.

Tieghem, P. van, 1897b. Sur la structure de l'ovule et de la graine chez les Hydnoracées. Jour. de Bot. 11:233–235.

Tieghem, P. van, 1898. Structure de quelques ovules et parti qu'on en peu tirer pour améliorer la classification. Jour. de Bot. 12:214–215.

Tieghem, P. van, 1899. Sur les genres *Actinidie* et *Saurauie* considérés comme types d'une famille nouvelle, les Actinidiacées. Jour. de Bot. 13:170.

Tieghem, P. van, 1900a. Sur la structure de l'ovule et de la graine et sur les affinités des Salicacées. Bull. Mus. hist. nat. Paris 6:131.

Tieghem, P. van, 1900b. Sur la fréquente inversion de l'ovule et la stérilité corrélative du pistil dans certains *Statices.* Jour. de Bot. 14.

Tieghem, P. van, 1901. L'hypostase, sa structure et son rôle constantes, sa position et sa forme variables. Bull. Mus. hist. nat. Paris 7:412–418.

Tieghem, P. van, 1902. L'hypostase dans le fruit et dans la graine. Bull. Mus. hist. nat. Paris 8.

Tieghem, P. van, 1903a. Structure de l'ovule des Caricacées. Ann. Sci. nat. Bot. (8) 17:373–381.

Tieghem, P. van, 1903b. Structure de l'ovule des Dichapétalacées et la place de cette famille dans la classification. Jour. de Bot. 17:229–233.

Tieghem, P. van, 1906. Sur les Heliotropiacées. Ann. Sci. nat. Bot. (9). 4.

Tieghem, P. van, 1907a. Remarques sur l'organisation florale et la structure de l'ovule des Aracées. Ann. Sci. nat. Bot. (9) 5.

Tieghem, P. van, 1907b. Sur les Inovulées. Ann. sci. nat. Bot. (9). 6:125–260.

Tieghem, P. van, 1908a. Structure de l'ovule et direction de l'ovule dans la graine de l'Acanthacées. Jour. de Bot. (2) 1:5–11.

Tieghem, P. van, 1908b. Remarque sur l'orientation de l'embryon des Caprifoliacées. Ann. Sci. nat. Bot. (9) 7.

Tillman, O. J., 1906. The embryo sac and embryo of *Cucumis sativus.* Ohio Nat. 6:423–430.

Timm, H., 1928. Untersuchungen über die Sterilitätsursachen von *Hemerocallis fulva* und *H. citrina.* Planta 5:784–810.

Tinney, F. W., 1940. Cytology of parthenogenesis in *Poa pratensis.* J. Agr. Res. 60:351–360.

Tischler, G., 1899. Über die Verwandlung der Plasmastränge in Cellulose im Embryosack bei *Pedicularis.* Schrift. physik-ökon. Ges. Königsberg 40:1–18. Diss. Bonn.

Tischler, G., 1900. Untersuchungen über die Entwicklung des Endosperms und der Samenschale von *Corydalis cava.* Verh. Nat.-Med. Ver. Heidelberg 6:351–380.

Tischler, G., 1903a. Über eine merkwürdige Wachstumserscheinung in den Samenanlagen von *Cytisus adami*. Ber. dtsch. bot. Ges. 21:82–89.

Tischler, G., 1903b. Über Embryosack-Obliteration bei Bastard-Pflanzen. Beih. bot. Ztbl. 15:408–420.

Tischler, G., 1906. Über die Entwicklung des Pollens und der Tapetenzellen bei *Ribes*-Hybriden. Jahrb. f. wiss. Bot. 42:545–578.

Tischler, G., 1908. Zellstudien an sterilen Bastard-Pflanzen. Arch. f. Zellf. 1:33–151.

Tischler, G., 1910a. Untersuchungen über den Stärkegehalt des Pollens tropischer Gewächse. Jahrb. f. wiss. Bot. 47:219–242.

Tischler, G., 1910b. Untersuchungen über die Entwicklung des Bananen-Pollens 1. Arch. f. Zellf. 5:622–670.

Tischler, G., 1912. Über die Entwicklung der Samenanlagen in parthenokarpen Angiospermen-Früchten. Jahrb. f. wiss. Bot. 52:1–84.

Tischler, G., 1913. Über die Entwicklung der Samenanlagen in parthenokarpen Angiospermenfrüchten. Jahrb. f. wiss. Bot. 52:1–84.

Tischler, G., 1915. Die Periplasmodiumbildung in den Antheren der Commelinaceen und Ausblicke auf das Verhalten der Tapetenzellen bei den übrigen Monokotylen. Jahrb. f. wiss. Bot. 55:52–90.

Tischler, G., 1917. Über die Entwicklung und phylogenetische Bedeutung des Embryosacks von *Lythrum salicaria*. Ber. dtsch. bot. Ges. 35:233–246.

Tischler, G., 1918. Pollenbiologische Studien. Zeit. f. Bot. 9:417–488.

Tison, A., 1919. Sur le suspenseur du *Trapa natans*. Rev. gén. Bot. 31:219–228.

Tiwary, N. K., 1925. A preliminary note on the structure of the embryo sac and the origin of embryos in *Eugenia jambolana*. Proc. 13th. Indian Sci. Congr.

Tiwary, N. K., 1926a. On the occurrence of polyembryony in the genus *Eugenia*. J. Indian bot. Soc. 5:124–136.

Tiwary, N. K., 1926b. Development of the embryo sac of *Eugenia jambolana* Proc. 14th. Indian Sci. Congr.

Tiwary, N. K., 1934. Fruit and seed development of *Tinospora cordifolia*. Current Sci. 3:262–264.

Tiwary, N. K., 1936. Megasporogenesis and embryo development in *Cleome viscosa*. Sci. and Cult. 1:476–477.

Tiwary, N. K. and V. S. Rao, 1934. A preliminary note on the embryo sac development of *Callistemon linearis*. Current Sci. 2:399.

Tiwary, N. K. and V. S. Rao, 1936. A contribution to the life history of *Evolvulus nummularis*. Proc. 23rd. Indian Sci. Congr.

Tjutajuk, V. C., 1939. (Pollenbildung in gefüllten Blüten von *Matthiola incana*.) Dokl. Akad. Nauk SSSR 25:679–680.

Tkachenko, G. V., 1958. (Modifications in elements of the grape embryo sac after various methods of pollination.) Nauch. Dokl. Vysshei Shkoly. Biol. Nauk 4:129–133.

Tognini, F., 1900. Sull'embriologia di alcune Solanaceae di appunti lasciati. Atti Inst. Bot. Pavia (2) 6:109–122.

Tohda, H., 1960. Über die abnormen Samenanlagen bei den sterilen hermaphroditischen Pflanzen von *Moehringia lateriflora*. 1. Morphologische Untersuchungen. Sci. Rpts. Tôhoku Univ. (4) Biol. 26:37–44.

Tomita, K., 1931. Über die Entwicklung des nackten Embryos von *Crinum latifolium*. Sci. Rpts. Tôhoku Imp. Univ. (4) Biol. 6:163–169.

480   BIBLIOGRAPHY

Tomo, N., Y. Fuchinoue, and H. Fuchinoue, 1958. Embryological study on seeds
of a fruit of tea plant. Japanese J. Breed. 8:48.

Tong, K., 1930. Studien über die Familie der Hamamelidaceae, mit besonderer
Berücksichtigung der Systematik und Entwicklungsgeschichte von *Corylopsis*.
Bull. Dept. Biol., Coll. Sci., Sun Yat Sen Univ. Canton 2:1–72.

Tongiorgi, E., 1935. Il tips della monocotyledoni nella formazioni del uni periplasmodio nella familia delle Lauraceae. N. G. bot. Ital. 42:387–397.

Tongiorgi, E., 1936. Il gametofito di alcune Inuleae. N. G. bot. Ital. 43.

Tongiorgi, E., 1942. Il gametofito tetramegasporiale di *Helichrysum bracteatum*.
N. G. bot. Ital. 49:205–220.

Tören, J., 1950. Les caractères morphologiques, anatomiques et cytologiques
de *Bongardia chrysogonum*. Rev. Fac. Sci. Univ. Istanbul B. 15:239–263.

Tören, J., 1954. Recherches sur des écotypes de *Bongardia chrysogonum*. Rev.
Fac. Sci. Univ. Istanbul. B. 19:83–123.

Torres, J. P., 1963. Polyembryony in *Citrus* and study of hybrid seedlings.
Philipp. J. Agric. 7:37–58.

Tournois, J., 1911. Formations d'embryons chez le Houblon par l'action du
pollen du Chanvre. C. R. Acad. Sci. Paris 153:1160–1162.

Tournois, J., 1914. Etudes sur la sexualité de houblon. Ann. Sci. nat. Bot. (9)
19.

Trankowsky, D. A., 1930. Zytologische Beobachtungen über die Entwicklung
der Pollenschläuche einiger Angiospermen. Planta 12:1–18.

Transkowsky, D. A., 1938. (La spermogenèse et la fécondation chez la Drosère,
Drosera.) Bjul. Moskov Obsc. Ispyt. Prir. Biol. 47:104–112.

Traub, H. P., 1939. Polyembryony in *Myricaria cauliflora*. Bot. Gaz. 101:233–234.

Traub, H. P. and C. J. O'Rork, 1936. Papaya pollen germination and storage.
Proc. Amer. Soc. hort. Sci. 34:18.

Traub, H. P. and C. J. O'Rork, 1939. Course of pollen tube in *Carica papaya*
and *Cucurbita*. Nature 143:562.

Trécul, A., 1845. Recherches sur la structure et la développement du *Nuphar
lutea*. Ann. Sci. nat. Bot. (3) 4.

Tretjakow, S., 1895. Die Beteilung der Antipoden in Fällen der Polyembryonie
bei *Allium odorum*. Ber. dtsch. bot. Ges. 13:13–17.

Treub, M., 1879. Notes sur l'embryogénie de quelques Orchidées. Nat. Verh.
Akad. Amsterdam 19:1–50.

Treub, M., 1880. Sur les noyaux des cellules végétales. Arch. de Biol. 1:396–410.

Treub, M., 1881. Observations sur les Loranthacées. 1. Développement des sac
embryonnaires dans le *Loranthus sphaerocarpus*. 2. Embryogénie du *L.
sphaerocarpus*. Ann. Jard. bot. Buitenz. 2:54–76.

Treub, M., 1882. Observations sur les Loranthacées. Ann. Sci. nat. Bot. (6)
13:250–282.

Treub, M., 1883a. Observations sur les Loranthacées. 3. *Viscum articulatum*.
Ann. Jard. bot. Buitenz. 3:1–12.

Treub, M., 1883b. Notes sur l'embryon, le sac embryonnaire et l'ovule. 1. *Peri-
stylus grandis*. 2. *Avicennia officinalis*. Ann. Jard. bot. Buitenz. 3:77–87.

Treub, M., 1883c. Notes sur l'embryon, le sac embryonnaire et l'ovule. 3.
Gonyanthes candida, Burmannia javanica. 4. L'action des tubes polliniques
sur le développement des ovules chez les Orchidées. Ann. Jard. bot. Buitenz.
3:120–127.

Treub, M., 1883d. Observations sur les Loranthacées. 4. *Loranthus pentandrus* Ann. Jard. bot. Buitenz. 3:184–190.

Treub, M., 1883e. L'action des tubes polliniques sur le développement des ovules chez les Orchidées. Ann. Jard. bot. Buitenz. 3.

Treub, M., 1884. Notes sur l'embryon, le sac embryonnaire et l'ovule. 5. L'embryon du *Barringtonia vriesei*. Ann. Jard. bot. Buitenz. 4:101–106.

Treub, M., 1891. Sur les Casuarinées et leur place dans le système naturel Ann. Jard. bot. Buitenz. 10:145–231.

Treub, M., 1898. L'organe femelle et l'apogamie du *Balanophora elongata*. Ann. Jard. bot. Buitenz. 15:1–22.

Treub, M., 1902. L'organe femelle et l'embryogénèse dans le *Ficus hirta*. Ann. Jard. bot. Buitenz. 18:124–154.

Treub, M., 1906. L'apogamie de l'*Elatostemma acuminatum*. Ann. Jard. bot. Buitenz. (2) 5:141–152.

Treub, M., 1911a. Le sac embryonnaire et l'embryon dans les Angiospermes. Nouv. série des recherches. Ann. Jard. bot. Buitenz. 24:1–27.

Treub, M., 1911b. Le sac embryonnaire et l'embryon dans les Angiospermes. Ann. Sci. nat. Bot. (2) 9:1–17.

Treub, M. and J. Mellink, 1880. Notice sur la développement du sac embryonnaire dans quelques angiospermes. Arch. Néerl. des Sci. 15:452–457.

Treviranus, L. C., 1839. Hat *Pinguicula vulgaris* zwei Kotyledonen? Flora 22:289.

Trochain, J., 1932. Sur la biologie de deux Commélinacées: *Commelina forskalaei* et *C. benghalensis*. C. R. Acad. Sci. Paris 194:443–445.

Troll, W., 1928. Über Antherenbau, Pollen und Pollination von *Galanthus nivalis*. Flora 23:321–343.

Troll, W., 1931. Botanische Mitteilungen aus den Tropen. 2. Zur Morphologie und Biologie von *Enalus acoroides*. Flora 25:427–456.

Troll, W., 1943. Vergleichende Morphologie der Pflanzen. Berlin.

True, R. H., 1893. On the development of the caryopsis. Bot. Gaz. 18:212–226.

Tschermak-Seysenegg, E., 1949. Reizfruchtung: Samenbildung ohne Befruchtung, Biol. Gen. 19:3–50.

Tschermak-Woess, E., 1947. Cytologische und embryologische Untersuchungen an *Rhoeo discolor*. Österr. bot. Zeit. 94:128–135.

Tschermak-Woess, E., 1956. Notizen über die Riesenkerne und Riesenchromosomen in den Antipoden von *Aconitum*. Chromosoma 8:114–134.

Tschistiakoff, J., 1876. Über die Entwicklungsgeschichte des Pollens bei *Epilobium angustifolium*. Jahrb. f. wiss. Bot. 10:7–48.

Tucker, S. C., 1959. Ontogeny of the inflorescence and the flower in *Drimys winteri* var. *chilensis*. Univ. of Calif. Publ. Bot. 30:257–336.

Tukey, H. B., 1933. Embryo abortion in early ripening varieties of *Prunus avium*. Bot. Gaz. 94:433–468.

Tukey, H. B., 1934. Anomalous embryos of cultivated varieties of *Prunus*, with particular reference to fruit breeding. Bot. Gaz. 95:493–497.

Tukey, H. B., 1936. Development of cherry and peach fruits as affected by destruction of the embryo. Bot. Gaz. 98:1–24.

Tukey, H. B. and F. A. Lee, 1937. Embryo abortion in the peach in relation to chemical composition and season of fruit ripening. Bot. Gaz. 98:586–597.

Tulasne, L. R., 1849. Etudes d'embryogénie végétale. Ann. Sci. nat. Bot. (3) 12:21–137.

Tulasne, L. R., 1855. Nouvelles études d'embryogénie végétale. Ann. Sci. nat. Bot. (4) 3:65–74.

Tupitsyn, D. I., 1957. (The dormancy period and microsporogenesis in plums.) Bot. Zhur. 42:457–461.

Turesson, G. and B. Turesson, 1960. Experimental studies in *Hieracium pilosella*. 1. Reproduction, chromosome number and distribution. Hereditas 46:717–736.

Turpin, P. J., 1837. Esquisse d'organographie végétale, pour servir à prouver la métamorphose des plantes de Goethe. Paris.

Tuschnajakowa, M., 1929a. Embryologische und zytologische Beobachtungen über *Listera ovata*. Planta 7:29–44.

Tuschnajakowa, M., 1929b. Untersuchungen über die Kernbeschaffenheit einiger diözischer Pflanzen. Planta 7:427–443.

Ubisch, G. V., 1927. Zur Entwicklungsgeschichte der Antheren. Planta 3:490–495.

Umiker, O., 1920. Entwicklungsgeschichtlich-zytologische Untersuchungen an *Helosis guayannensis*. Diss. Zürich.

Unger, D. F., 1849. Die Entwicklung des Embryos von *Hippuris vulgaris*. Bot. Zeit. 7:329–339.

Upcott, M., 1936. The mechanism of mitosis in the pollen tube of *Tulipa*. Proc. Roy. Soc. London B. 121:207–220.

Upcott, M., 1939. The external mechanics of the chromosomes. 7. Abnormal mitosis in the pollen grain. Chromosoma 1:178–190.

Uphof, J. C., 1934. Vergleichende blütenmorphologische und blütenbiologische Studien an *Commelina virginica*. Ber. dtsch. bot. Ges. 52:173–180.

Urbańska, K., 1956. (Studies in the biology of reproduction and embryology of *Homogyne alpina*.) Acta Soc. bot. Polon. 25:733–751.

Urbańska-Worytkiewicz, K., 1961. (Embryological investigations in *Antennaria*. 1. Development of the ovules of *A. carpatica*.) Acta biol. Cracov. Bot. 4:49–64.

Urbańska-Worytkiewicz, K., 1962. (Embryological investigations in *Antennaria*. 2. Development of the pollen of *A. carpatica*.) Acta Biol. Cracov. Bot. 5: 97–102.

Usteri, A., 1907. Studien über *Carica papaya*. Ber. dtsch. bot. Ges. 25:485–495.

Ustinova, E. I., 1944. (A comparative embryological study of normal and viviparous species of *Allium*.) Bot. Zhur. 29:232–239.

Ustinova, E. I., 1960a. (Specific structural characteristics of the female gametophyte and the phenomenon of polyembryony in Corn, *Zea mays*.) Bot. Zhur. 45:764–767.

Ustinova, E. I., 1960b. (Embryological study of female flowers from corn under various conditions of the life cycle). Nauch. Dokl. Vysshei Shkoly. Biol. Nauk 1:94–98.

Ustinova, E. I., 1960c. (Cyto-embryological investigation of the embryo sac and the process of fertilization in maize.) Zhur. Obshchei Biol. 21:261–269.

Ustinova, E. I., 1964. (Changes of female gametophyte of sunflower, *Helianthus annuus*.) Bjul. Moskov Obsc. Ispyt. Prir. Biol. 69:111–117.

Vaidya, P. B., 1961a. Occurrence of twin embryo sacs in *Capparis aphylla*. Current Sci. 30:187–188.

Vaidya, P. B., 1961b. Male and female gametophytes of *Acanthospermum hispidum*. J. Biol. Sci. Bombay 4:11–15.

Valle, O., 1959. Pollination and seed setting in tetraploid red clover in Finland. Acta Agral. Fennica 95:1–35.

Valle, O., M. Salminen, and E. Huokuna, 1960. Pollination and seed setting in tetraploid red clover in Finland. 2. Acta Agral. Fennica 97:3–62.

Vandendries, R., 1909. Contribution à l'étude du développement des Crucifères. 1. Cellule 25:412–459.

Vandendries, R., 1912. Contribution à l'étude du développement de l'ovule dans les Crucifères. 2. L'archésporium dans le genre *Cardamine*. Cellule 28:215–225.

Vandevelde, A. J. J., 1896–1905. De Kieming der Zaadplanten. Ghent.

Varghese, T. M., 1963. Studies in the family Scrophulariaceae. 1. A contribution to the embryology of *Veronica agrestis*. Proc. Indian Acad. Sci. B. 58:333–347.

Varitchak, B., 1940. La développement du sac embryonnaire et le nombre de chromosomes chez la plante *Narthecium scardicum*. Bull. Acad. Sci. B. (Beograd) 6:97–105.

Vasil, I. K., 1955. Morphology and embryology of *Ehretia laevis*. Proc. 42nd. Indian Sci. Congr. 3:239.

Vasil, I. K., 1960. Studies on pollen germination of certain Cucurbitaceae. Amer. J. Bot. 47:239–247.

Vasil, I. K., 1962. Formation of male gametes in the pollen tubes of some crop plants. *In* Plant Embryology: A Symposium. CSIR., New Delhi: 254:260.

Vasil, I. K. and M. M. Johri, 1964. The style, stigma and pollen tube. 1. Phytomorphology 14:352–369.

Vazart, B., 1955. Contribution à l'étude caryologique des éléments reproducteurs et de la fécondation chez les végétaux angiospermes. Rev. Cytol. biol. Végét. 16:211–390.

Vazart, B., 1958. Différenciation des cellules sexuelles et fécondation chez les Phanérogames. Protoplasmatologia (7) 3 A:1–158.

Veh, R. von, 1942. Blüten- und Fruchtbildung, Geschlechtsbestimmung und Polarität. Biol. Gen. 15:358–393.

Veillet-Bartoszewska, M., 1956a. Recherches embryologiques sur le *Dolichos lablab*. Bull. Soc. bot. France 103:235–240.

Veillet-Bartoszewska, M., 1956b. Recherches embryogéniques sur le *Glycyrrhiza foetida*. Bull. Soc. bot. France 103:439–443.

Veillet-Bartoszewska, M., 1957a. La polyembryonie chez le *Primula auricula*. Bull. Soc. bot. France 104:473–475.

Veillet-Bartoszewska, M., 1957b. Ericacées. Développement de l'embryon chez le *Rhododendron ferrugineum*. C. R. Acad. Sci. Paris 244:1952–1954.

Veillet-Bartoszewska, M., 1957c. Primulacées. Développement d l'embryon chez le *Primula auricula*. C. R. Acad. Sci. Paris 245:2363–2366.

Veillet-Bartoszewska, M., 1958a. Ericacées. Développement de l'embryon chez le *Vaccinium myrtillus*. C. R. Acad. Sci. Paris 246:824–826.

Veillet-Bartoszewska, M., 1958b. Embryogénie des Plumbagacées. Développement de l'embryon chez le *Plumbago europaea*. C. R. Acad. Sci. Paris 247:2178–2181.

Veillet-Bartoszewska, M., 1959a. Développement de l'albumen chez le *Rhododendron ferrugineum*. Bull. Soc. bot. France 106:17–20.

Veillet-Bartoszewska, M., 1959b. Embryogénie des Ericacées. Développement de l'embryon chez le *Gaultheria shallon*. C. R. Acad. Sci. Paris 248:720–722.

Veillet-Bartoszewska, M., 1959c. Embryogénie des Empétracées. Développement du proembryon chez le *Corema album*. C. R. Acad. Sci. Paris 249:857–859.

Veillet-Bartoszewska, M., 1960a. Embryogénie des Styracacées. Développement de l'embryon chez le *Styrax officinalis*. C. R. Acad. Sci. Paris 250:905–907.

Veillet-Bartoszewska, M., 1960b. Embryogénie des Ericacées. Développement de l'embryon chez l'*Erica tetralix*. C. R. Acad. Sci. Paris 250:1711–1714.

Veillet-Bartoszewska, M., 1960c. Embryogénie des Ericacées. Développement de l'embryon chez le *Ledum palustre*. C. R. Acad. Sci. Paris 251:777–779.

Veillet-Bartoszewska, M., 1960d. Embryogénie des Cléthracées. Développement de l'embryon chez le *Clethra alnifolia*. C. R. Acad. Sci. 251:2572–2574.

Veillet-Bartoszewska, M., 1961a. Embryogénie des Ericacées. Développement de l'embryon chez le *Calluna vulgaris*. C. R. Acad. Sci. Paris 252:1192–1194.

Veillet-Bartoszewska, M., 1961b. Embryogénie des Epacridacées. Développement de l'embryon chez le *Dracophyllum secundum*. C. R. Acad. Sci. Paris 253:1000–1002.

Veillet-Bartoszewska, M., 1963. Recherches embryogéniques sur les Ericales. Comparaison avec les Primulales. Thèse. Paris.

Velser, J., 1913. Zur Entwicklungsgeschichte von *Akebia quinata*. Diss. Bonn.

Venkata Rao, C., 1948. Development of the embryo sac in some Sterculiaceae. Current Sci. 17:304–305.

Venkata Rao, C., 1949. Contributions to the embryology of Sterculiaceae. 1. J. Indian bot. Soc. 28:180–197.

Venkata Rao, C., 1950. Contributions to the embryology of Sterculiaceae. 2. *Waltheria indica*. J. Indian bot. Soc. 29:163–176.

Venkata Rao, C., 1951a. Life history of *Muntingia calabura*. Current Sci. 20:47–48.

Venkata Rao, C., 1951b. Contributions to the embryology of Sterculiaceae. 3. *Melochia corchorifolia*. J. Indian bot. Soc. 30:122–131.

Venkata Rao, C., 1952a. Occurrence of persistent pollen tubes in Malvaceae. Current Sci. 21:49–50.

Venkata Rao, C., 1952b. The embryology of *Muntingia calabura*. J. Indian bot. Soc. 31:87–101.

Venkata Rao, C., 1952c. Contributions to the embryology of Sterculiaceae. 4. *Pterospermum suberifolium*. J. Indian bot. Soc. 31:250–260.

Venkata Rao, C., 1953a. Floral anatomy and embryology of two species of *Elaeocarpus*. J. Indian bot. Soc. 32:21–33.

Venkata Rao, C., 1953b. Contributions to the embryology of Sterculiaceae. 5. J. Indian bot. Soc. 32:208–238.

Venkata Rao, C., 1954a. A contribution to the embryology of Bombacaceae. Proc. Indian Acad. Sci. B. 39:51–75.

Venkata Rao, C., 1954b. Embryological studies in Malvaceae. 1. Development of gametophytes. Proc. Nat. Inst. Sci. India B. 20:127–150.

Venkata Rao, C., 1955a. Embryological studies in Malvaceae. 2. Proc. Nat. Inst. Sci. India B. 21:53–67.

Venkata Rao, C., 1955b. Endosperm and seed development in *Chrysalidocarpus lutescens*. Current Sci. 24:381–382.

Venkata Rao, C., 1955c. Embryological studies in Palmae. 1–3. Proc. 42nd. Indian Sci. Congr. 3:230–232.

Venkata Rao, C., 1956. Embryological studies in Palmae. 4–6. Proc. 43rd. Indian Sci. Congr. 3:225–227.

Venkata Rao, C., 1958. Contributions to the embryology of the Palmae. 2. Ceroxylinae. J. Indian bot. Soc. 38:46–75.

Venkata Rao, C., 1960. Studies in the Proteaceae. 1. Tribe Persooneae. Proc. Nat. Inst. Sci. India B. 26:300–336.

Venkata Rao, C., 1961. Studies in the Proteaceae. 2. Tribes Placospermeae and Conospermeae. Proc. Nat. Inst. Sci. India 27:126–151.

Venkata Rao, C., 1962. Morphology and embryology of *Lomatia*, with a discussion on its probable origin. *In* Plant Embryology: A Symposium CSIR, New Delhi: 261–273.

Venkata Rao, C., 1963. Studies in the Proteaceae. 3. Tribe Oriteae. Proc. Nat. Inst. Sci. India 29:489–510.

Venkata Rao, C., 1964. Pollen grains of *Grevillea vestita*. Current Sci. 33:722–724.

Venkata Rao, C. and K. V. S. Rao, 1952. A contribution to the embryology of *Triumfetta rhomboidea* and *Corchorus acutangulus*. J. Indian bot. Soc. 31:56–68.

Venkata Rao, C. and S. R. Rao, 1954. Embryology of *Cryptostegia grandiflora* and *Caralluma attenuata*. J. Indian bot. Soc. 33:453–472.

Venkataramani, K. S., 1950. An instance of polyembryony in tea. Plant Chron. 45:180–181.

Venkatasubban, K. R., 1945. Cytological studies in Bignoniaceae. 4. The cytology of *Dolichandrone rheedii* and allied genera. Proc. Indian Acad. Sci. B. 21:77–92.

Venkatasubban, K. R., 1950a. Studies in the Droseraceae. 1. The cytology of *D. indica, D. burmanni* and *D. peltata*, with special reference to pollen mitoses. Proc. Indian Acad. Sci. B. 31:308–330.

Venkatasubban, K. R., 1950b. Studies in the Droseraceae. 2. A contribution to the embryology of three species of *Drosera*. Proc. Indian Acad. Sci. B. 32:23–38.

Venkataswaralu, V., 1937. A note on the development of the embryo sac in *Phrynium capitatum*. J. Indian bot. Soc. 16:95–98.

Venkatesh, C. S., 1951. The inflorescence and flowers of *Dichrostachys cinerea*. Proc. Indian Acad. Sci. B. 34:183–187.

Venkatesh, C. S., 1952. The anther and pollen grains of *Zannichellia palustris*. Current Sci. 21:225–226.

Venkatesh, C. S., 1955. The structure and dehiscence of the anther in *Memecylon* and *Mouriria*. Phytomorphology 5:435–440.

Venkatesh, C. S., 1956a. The special mode of dehiscence of anthers of *Polygala* and its significance in autogamy. Bull. Torrey bot. Cl. 83:19–26.

Venkatesh, C. S., 1956b. Structure and dehiscence of the anther in *Najas*. Bot. Notiser 1956:75–82.

Venkatesh, C. S., 1956c. The form, structure and special modes of dehiscence in anthers of *Cassia*. 1. Subgenus *Fistula*. Phytomorphology 6:168–176.

Venkatesh, C. S., 1956d. The form, structure and special ways of dehiscence of anthers of *Cassia*. 2. Subgenus *Lasiorhegma*. Phytomorphology 6:272–277.

Venkatesh, C. S., 1956e. The curious anther of *Bixa*: its structure and dehiscence. Amer. Midl. Nat. 55:473–476.

Venkatesh, C. S., 1957. The form, structure and special ways of dehiscence of anthers of *Cassia*. 3. Subgenus *Senna*. Phytomorphology 7:253–273.

Venkateswarlu, J., 1936a. A preliminary note on the embryology of *Duabanga sonneratioides*. Current Sci. 4:742–743.

Venkateswarlu, J., 1936b. Some observations on the ovule and embryo sac of *Sonneratia apetala*. Current Sci. 5:201.

Venkateswarlu, J., 1937a. Structure and development of the embryo sac of *Pemphis acidula*. J. Indian bot. Soc. 16:259–262.

Venkateswarlu, J., 1937b. A contribution to the embryology of the Sonneratiaceae. Proc. Indian Acad. Sci. B. 5:206–223.

Venkateswarlu, J., 1941a. Vascular supply in the ovules of some Compositae. Current Sci. 10:367–368.

Venkateswarlu, J., 1941b. Vascular supply in the ovules of some Compositae. 1. *Launaea pinnatifida*. Proc. Indian Acad. Sci. B. 51:38–46.

Venkateswarlu, J., 1945. Embryological studies in the Thymelaeaceae. 1. *Thymelaea arvensis*. J. Indian bot. Soc. 24:45–66.

Venkateswarlu, J., 1946. A case of polyembryony in *Daphne cannabina*. Current Sci. 15:169.

Venkateswarlu, J., 1947a. Embryological studies in the Thymelaeaceae. 2. *Daphne cannabina* and *Wikstroemia canescens*. J. Indian bot. Soc. 26:13–39.

Venkateswarlu, J., 1947b. A contribution to the embryology of *Pisonia aculeata*. J. Indian bot. Soc. 26:182–194.

Venkateswarlu, J., 1947c. Development of the embryo of *Thymelaea arvensis*. Bot. Gaz. 108:581–586.

Venkateswarlu, J., 1952a. Contributions to the embryology of Combretaceae. 1. *Poivrea coccinea*. Phytomorphology 2:231–240.

Venkateswarlu, J., 1952b. Embryological studies in Lecythidaceae. 1. J. Indian bot. Soc. 31:103–116.

Venkateswarlu, J., 1959. A note on the structure and development of the ovule and the embryo sac in two species of *Launaea*. Current Sci. 8:556–557.

Venkateswarlu, J. and B. Atchutaramamurti, 1955a. Contribution to the embryology of two Boraginaceae. Proc. 42nd. Indian Sci. Cong. 3:237–238.

Venkateswarlu, J. and B. Atchutaramamurti, 1955b. Life history of *Coldenia procumbens*. Current Sci. 24:26–27.

Venkateswarlu, J. and B. Atchutaramamurti, 1955c. Embryological studies in the Boraginaceae. 1. *Coldenia procumbens*. J. Indian bot. Soc. 34:235–247.

Venkateswarlu, J. and P. I. Devi, 1964. Embryology of some Indian grasses. Current Sci. 33:104–106.

Venkateswarlu, J. and H. Maheswari Devi, 1955a. Embryological studies in Compositae. 1. *Launea pinnatifida*. Proc. Indian Acad. Sci. B. 41:38–46.

Venkateswarlu, J. and H. Maheswari Devi, 1955b. Embryological studies in Compositae. 2. Helenieae. Proc. Nat. Inst. Sci. India B. 21:149–161.

Venkateswarlu, J. and L. L. Narayana, 1955. Life history of *Hydrocera triflora*. Current Sci. 24:52–53.

Venkateswarlu, J. and L. L. Narayana, 1957. A contribution to the embryology of *Hydrocera triflora*. Phytomorphology 7:194–203.

Venkateswarlu, J. and G. R. Rao, 1954. Contribution to the embryology of *Rubia cordifolia* and *Hamelia patens*. Proc. 41st. Indian Sci. Congr. 3:144.

Venkateswarlu, J. and G. R. Rao, 1958. A contribution to the life history of *Rubia cordifolia*. J. Indian bot. Soc. 37:442–454.

Venkateswarlu, J. and P. N. Rao, 1963. Endosperm in Euphorbiaceae and occurrence of endosperm haustoria in two species of *Croton*. Current Sci. 32:514–516.

Venkateswarlu, J. and V. Seshavatarum, 1964. Germination of pollen grains in *Nelumbium speciosum*. Current Sci. 33:117.

Ventura, M., 1930a. Contributo allo studio embriologico di una forma anomala di *Nicotiana silvestris*. Ann. di Bot. 18:169–178.

Ventura, M., 1930b. Osservazioni sulla embriologia di *Daphniphyllum macropodum*. Ann. di Bot. 18:395–401.

Ventura, M., 1933. Sviluppo del gametofito femminile di *Euphorbia mauretanica*. Ann. di Bot. (Roma) 20:267–273.

Ventura, M., 1934. Sulla poliembryonia di *Mallotus japonicus*. Ann. di Bot. (Roma) 20:568–578.

Ventura, M., 1937. Osservazioni embryologiche su *Arechavaletia uruguayensis*. Ann. di Bot. (Roma) 21:527–533.

Ventura, M., 1940. Nuovo contributo alla embriologia delle Euforbiacee. Ann. di Bot. (Roma) 22:42–52.

Venugopalan, S., 1949. Cytological study of the Indian Aristolochiaceae. 1. Proc. 36th. Indian Sci. Cong. 3:137.

Vermoesen, C., 1911. Contribution à l'étude de l'ovule, du sac embryonnaire et de la fécondation dans les angiospermes. Cellule 27:113–162.

Vernin, J., 1952a. Etat de la question sur le développement du sac embryonnaire, de l'albumen et de l'embryon chez les Composées. Thèse. Paris.

Vernin, J., 1952b. Contribution à l'étude du développement de l'albumen et de l'embryon chez les Composées. Thèse. Paris.

Vesque, J., 1859. Développpment du sac embryonnaire des Phanérogames. Abh. Kön. Sächs. Ges. Wiss. 6:533–672.

Vesque, J., 1878. Développement du sac embryonnaire des phanérogames angiospermes. Ann. Sci. nat. Bot. (6) 6:237–285.

Vesque, J., 1879a. Neue Untersuchungen über die Entwicklung des Embryosackes der Angiospermen. Bot. Zeit. 37:505–509. C. R. Akad. Sci. Paris 88:1359–1361.

Vesque, J., 1879b. Nouvelles recherches sur le développement du sac embryonnaire des Phanérogames Angiospermes. Ann. Sci. nat. Bot. (6) 8:261–390.

Vesque, J., 1885. Charactères des principales familles gamopétales tirés de l'anatomie de la feuille. Ann. Sci. nat. Bot. (7) 1:183–360.

Vignoli, L, 1936. Cariologia del genre *Agave*. 1. Lav. R. 1st. Bot. Palermo (5) 7.

Vignoli, L., 1937a. Fenomeni riproduttivi di *Oxalis cernua*. Lav. R. 1st. Bot. Palermo (5) 8:5–30.

Vignoli, L., 1937b. Cariologia del genre *Agave*. 2. Lav. R. 1st. Bot. Palermo (5) 8.

Vijayaraghavan, C. and V. P. Rao, 1936. False polyembryony in *Setaria italica*. Current Sci. 4:820.

Vijayaraghavan, M. R., 1962. Studies in the family Ranunculaceae. 2. The female gametophyte of *Clematis gauriana*. Phytomorphology 12:45–49.

Vijayaraghavan, M. R., 1964. Morphology and embryology of a vessexless dicotyledon—*Sarcandra irvingbaileyi*, and systematic position of the Chloranthaceae. Phytomorphology 14:429–441.

Vilcins, M. and K. Abele, 1927. On the development of pollen and embryo sac of *Papaver rhoeas*. Acta Hort. Bot. Univ. Latviensis 2:125–130.

Virkki, N., 1962. Meiosis and development of the embryo sac in *Gunnera insignis*. J. Agr. Univ. Puerto Rico 46:254–268.

Voigt, A., 1888. Untersuchungen über Bau und Entwicklung von Samen mit ruminiertem Endosperm aus den Familien der Palmen, Myristicaceen und Anonaceen. Ann. Jard. bot. Buitenz. 7:150–190.

Voroshilova, G. I., 1964. (Structure of the embryo and seedling of wild and cultivated soybean, Glycine, in the Far East.) Vest. Leningr. No. 9. Ser. Biol. 2:45–51.

Vos, M. P. de, 1945. Die Ontwikkeling van die Saadknop by die Selagineae. Tyd. Wetensk. kuns. (5) Tweedie Aft.:134–142.

Vos, M. P. de, 1947. Die Ontwikkeling van die Saadknop en saad by die Myoporaceae en die Systematiese Posisie van Oftia. Sth. Afr. J. Sci. 43:171–187.

Vos, M. P. de, 1948. The development of the ovule and seed in the Hypericaceae. 1. Ianthe. J. Sth. Afr. Bot. 14:159–169.

Vos, M. P. de, 1949. The development of the ovule and the seed in the Hypoxideae. 2. The genera Pauridia and Forbesia. J. Sth. Afr. Bot. 15:13–22.

Vos, M. P. de, 1950. Die Ontwikkeling van die Saadknop en Saad by Cyanella capensis: 'n Gefal von Polyembryonie. Sth. Afr. J. Sci. 46:220–226.

Vos, M. P. de, 1956. Studies on the embryology and relationships of South African genera of the Haemodoraceae: Dilatris and Wachendorfia. J. Sth. Afr. Bot. 22:41–63.

Vos, M. P. de, 1961. On the embryology and relationships of the South African genera of the Haemodoraceae. In Recent Advances in Botany, Toronto.: 694–698.

Vos, M. P. de, 1963. Studies on the embryology and relationships of the South African genera of the Haemodoraceae: Lanaria. J. Sth. Afr. Bot. 29:79–90.

Vukolov, V. A., 1929. Polyembryony in blue grass, Poa spp. Sbor. českosl. akad. Zemědělské Prag. 4:193–218.

Wager, A. V., 1928. The structure and life history of the South African Lagarosiphon. Trans. Roy. Soc. Sth. Afr. 16:191–204.

Wagner, S., 1914. Contribution à l'étude anatomique du fruit des Labiées. Thèse. Paris.

Wakakuwa, S., 1934. Embryological studies of the different seed development in reciprocal interspecific crosses of wheat. Jap. J. Bot. 7:151–186.

Walker, R. I., 1938a. Macrosporogenesis and embryo development in Ulmus fulva. Bot. Gaz. 99:592–598.

Walker, R. I., 1938b. The effect of colchicine on the developing embryo sac of Tradescantia paludosa. J. Arnold Arbor. 19:442–445.

Walker, R. I., 1944. Chromosome number, megasporogenesis and development of embryo sac of Clintonia. Bull. Torrey bot. Cl. 71:529–535.

Walker, R. I., 1947. Megasporogenesis and embryo development in Tropaeolum majus. Bull. Torrey bot. Cl. 74:240–249.

Walker, R. I., 1950. Megasporogenesis and development of megagametophyte in Ulmus. Amer. J. Bot. 37:47–52.

Walker, R. I., 1955. Cytological and embryological studies in Solanum section tuberarium. Bull. Torrey bot. Cl. 82:87–101.

Walters, J. L., 1962. Megasporogenesis and gametophyte selection in Paeonia californica. Amer. J. Bot. 49:787–792.

Wangenheim, K. H. von, 1957. Untersuchungen über den Zusammenhang zwischen Chromosomenzahl und Kreuzbarkeit bei Solanum-Arten. Z. indukt. Abst. u. Vererb. 88:21–37.

Wanscher, J. H., 1939. Contribution to the cytology and life history of apple and pear. Roy. Vet. Agr. Coll. Copenhagen Yearbook: 21-70.

Want, G., 1963. Sporogenesis, gametogenesis and embryogeny of *Wahlenbergia bicolor*. Amer. J. Bot. 11:152-167.

Ward, H. M., 1880a. On the embryo sac and development of *Gymnadenia conopsea*. Quart. J. Micr. Sci. 20:1-18.

Ward, H. M., 1880b. A contribution to our knowledge of the embryo sac in Angiosperms. J. Linn. Soc. London (Bot.). 17:519-546.

Wardlaw, C. W., 1955. Embryogenesis in Plants. London.

Wardlaw, C. W., 1963. Plant embryos as reaction systems. *In* P. Maheshwari (*ed.*), Recent Advances in the Embryology of Angiosperms: 355-360.

Warming, E., 1873. Untersuchungen über pollenbildende Phyllome und Kaulome. Hanstein's Bot. Abhandl. 2:1-90.

Warming, E., 1878. De l'ovule. Ann. Sci. nat. Bot. (6) 5:177-266.

Warming, E., 1912. The structure and biology of Arctic flowering plants. 1. Ericineae. Morphology and biology. Medd. om Grönland 36.

Warming, E., 1913. Observations sur la valeur systématique de l'ovule. Mind. Jap. Steen. 24:1-45.

Warmke, H. E., 1943. Macrosporogenesis, fertilization and early embryogeny of *Taraxacum kok-saghyz*. Bull. Torrey bot. Cl. 70:164-173.

Warmke, H. E., 1954. Apomixis in *Panicum maximum*. Amer. J. Bot. 41:5-11.

Warth, G., 1923. Über Fuchsien mit verschieden gestaltetem Pollen und verschiedener Chromosomenzahl. Ber. dtsch. bot. Ges. 41:282-285.

Warth, G., 1925. Zytologische, histologische und starmesgeschichtliche Fragen aus der Gattung *Fuchsia*. Zeit. f. ind. Abst.-u. Vererb. 38:201-257.

Watanabe, K., 1933. (Biology of *Mitrastemon yamamotoi*. 1. Fruit and seed.) Bot. Mag. Tokyo 47:798-805.

Watanabe, K., 1936. Morphologisch-biologische Studien über die Gattung *Mitrastemon*. 4. J. Japanese Bot. 12:848-858.

Watkins, A. E., 1925. Genetic and cytological studies in wheat. 2. J. Genetics 15.

Watkins, G. M., 1937. Embryo sac development in *Yucca rupicola*. Amer. J. Bot. 24:481-484.

Wcislo, H., 1951. (Cytological and embryological studies in *Doronicum*.) Bull. Int. Acad. Sci. Polon. B. 1:147-166.

Weatherwax, P., 1916. Morphology of the flowers of *Zea mays*. Bull. Torrey bot. Cl. 43:127-144.

Weatherwax, P., 1917. The development of the spikelets of *Zea mays*. Bull. Torrey bot. Cl. 44:483-496.

Weatherwax, P., 1919. Gametogenesis and fecundation in *Zea mays* as the basis of Xenia and heredity in the endosperm. Bull. Torrey bot. Cl. 46:73-90.

Weatherwax, P., 1926. Persistance of the antipodal tissue in the development of the seeds of maize. Bull. Torrey bot. Cl. 53:381-384.

Weatherwax, P., 1930. The endosperm of *Zea* and *Coix*. Amer. J. Bot. 17:371-380.

Weatherwax, P., 1934. Flowering and seed production in *Amphicarpon floridanum*. Bull. Torrey bot. Cl. 61:211-215.

Weatherwax, P., 1955. Structure and development of reproductive organs. *In* Corn and Corn Improvement. New York.

Weaver, J. B., 1957. Embryological studies following interspecific crosses in *Gossypium*. 1. *G. hirsutum* x *G. arboreum*. Amer. J. Bot. 44:209-214.

490 BIBLIOGRAPHY

Weaver, J. B., 1958. Embryological studies following interspecific crosses in *Gossypium*. 2. *G. arboreum* x *G. hirsutum*. Amer. J. Bot. 45:10–16.

Weaver, N., 1943. The origin and development of the embryo sac in *Cooperia pedunculata*. Texas A. and M. College.

Webb, J. E., 1902. A morphological study of the flower and embryo of *Spiraea*. Bot. Gaz. 33:451–460.

Webber, E., 1929. Entwicklungsgeschichtliche Untersuchungen über die Gattung *Allium*. Bot. Archiv. 25:1–44.

Webber, H. J., 1931. The economic importance of apogamy in *Citrus* and *Mangifera*. Proc. Amer. Soc. hort. Sci. 28:57–61.

Webber, H. J. and L. D. Batchelor, 1946. The Citrus Industry: History, Botany and Breeding. Unif. Calif.

Webber, J. M., 1938. Cytology of twin cotton plants. J. Agric. Res. 57:155–160.

Webber, J. M., 1940. Polyembryony. Bot. Rev. 6:575–598.

Webber, J. M., 1953. The Yuccas of the south-west. U.S. Dept. Agr. Monogr. 17.

Wefelscheid, G., 1911. Über die Entwicklung der generativen Zelle im Pollenkorn der dikotylen Angiospermen. Diss. Bonn.

Weidner-Rauh, E., 1939. Untersuchungen über die partielle Sterilität der Oenotheren: das Pulver bei Eu-Oenotheren. Zeit. ind. Abst. Vererb. 76:422–486.

Weiling, F., 1958. Über das Auftreten und die Bedeutung diploider Pflanzen mit Gigaspollen. Flora 146:340–353.

Weiling, F. and P. Schagen, 1955. Über die Präparation und Gestalt des Endospermhaustoriums bei den gross-Samigen Kürbitsarten. Ber. dtsch. bot. Ges. 68:1–10.

Weinedel-Lieban, F., 1928. Zytologische Untersuchungen an *Artemisia*-Arten. Jahrb. f. wiss. Bot. 69:636–686.

Weinstein, A. J., 1926. Cytological studies on *Phaseolus vulgaris*. Amer. J. Bot. 13:248–263.

Weinzieher, S., 1914. Beiträge zur Entwicklungsgeschichte von *Xyris indica*. Flora 106:393–432.

Weir, C. E. and H. M. Dale, 1960. A developmental study of wild rice, *Zizania aquatica*. Canad. J. Bot. 38:719–739.

Weiss, G., 1932. Weitere Beiträge zur Kenntnis der Endospermhaustorien in der Gattung *Veronica*. Flora 126:418–464.

Welch, J. E. and E. L. Grimball, 1947. Male sterility in the carrot. Science 106:954.

Wellington, R., 1913. Natural and artificial parthenogenesis in the genus *Nicotiana*. Amer. Nat. 47:279–306.

Welsford, E. J., 1914. The genesis of the male nuclei in *Lilium*. Ann. Bot. 28:265–270.

Weniger, W., 1917. Development of embryo sac and embryo in *Euphorbia preslii* and *E. splendens*. Bot. Gaz. 63:266–281.

Weniger, W., 1918. Fertilization in *Lilium*. Bot. Gaz. 66:259–268.

Went, F. A. F. C., 1887a. Etude sur la forme du sac embryonnaire des Rosacées. Ann. Sci. nat. Bot. (7) 6:331–341.

Went, F. A. F. C., 1887b. Beobachtungen über Kern- und Zellteilungen. Ber. dtsch. bot. Ges. 5:247–258.

Went, F. A. F. C., 1909. The development of the ovule, embryo sac and egg in Podostomaceae. Rec. Trav. bot. Néerl. 5:1–16.

Went, F. A. F. C., 1910. Untersuchungen über Podostemaceen. 1. Verh. Kon. Akad. Wetensch. (2) 16:1–88.

Went, F. A. F. C., 1912. Untersuchungen über Podostemaceen. 2. Verh. Kon. Akad. Wetensch. (2) 17:5–18.

Went, F. A. F. C., 1962. Untersuchungen über Podostemonaceen. 3. Verh. Kong. Akad. Wetensch. (2) 25:3–58.

Went, F. A. F. C., 1929. Morphological and histological peculiarities of the Podostemonaceae. Proc. Internatl. Congr. Plt. Sci. Ithaca 1:351–358.

Went, F. A. F. C. and A. H. Blaauw, 1906. A case of apogamy with *Dasylirion acrostichum*. Rec. Trav. Bot. Néerl. 2:223–234.

Werner, E., 1915. Zur Oekologie atypischer Samenanlagen. Beih. bot. Ztbl. 33:1–11.

Werth, E. and E. Drygalski, (eds.). 1911. Die Vegetation der subantarktischen Inseln Kerguelen-, Possession- und Heard-Eiland. Dtsch. Südpol. Exped. 8:221–371.

West, G., 1930. Cleistogamy in *Viola riviniana*, with special reference to the cytological aspects. Ann. Bot. 44:87–109.

Westergård, M., 1936. A cytological study of *Gagea spathacea*, with a note on the chromosome number and embryo sac formation in *Gagea minima*. C. R. Trav. Lab. Carlsb. Sér. Phys. 21:437–451.

Westermaier, M., 1876. Die ersten Zellteilungen im Embryo von *Capsella bursa-pastoris*. Flora 59:483–491, 499–507, 515–520.

Westermaier, M., 1890. Zur Embryologie der Phanerogamen, insbesondere über die sogenannten Antipoden. Nov. Acta Ksl. Leop.-Carol dtsch. Akat. Nat. 17.

Westermaier, M., 1897a. Zur Physiologie und Morphologie der Angiospermen-Samenknospen. Beitr. wiss. Bot. 1:255–280.

Westermaier, M., 1897b. Berichtigung zu meiner Arbeit: "Zur Physiologie und Morphologie der Angiospermen-Samenknospe". Ber. dtsch. bot. Ges. 14:33–35.

Westermaier, M., 1898. Historische Bemerkungen zur Lehre von der Bedeutung der Antipoden-Zellen. Ber. dtsch. bot. Ges. 16:215–216.

Wet. J. M. J. de and D. S. Borgaonkar, 1963. Aneuploidy and apomixis in *Bothriochloa* and *Dichanthium*. Bot. Gaz. 124:437–440.

Wettstein, R. von, 1908. Über Parthenokarpie bei *Diospyros kali*. Österr. bot. Zeit. 58:457–462.

Wettstein, R. von, 1924. Handbuch der systematischen Botanik. Leipzig. Wien.

Wettstein, R. von, 1925. Facultative parthenogenesis bei Hopfen, *Humulus lupulus*. Flora 118–119. Goebel Festschr.:600–604.

Wettstein, R. von, 1932. Blütenpflanzen. Handw. Nat. wiss. 2:1–33.

White, N. H., 1950. The significance of endosperm. Aust. J. Sci. 13:7–8.

White, P. R., 1928. Studies on the banana: an investigation of the floral morphology and cytology of certain types of the genus *Musa*. Zeit. f. Zellf. mikr. Anat. 7:673–733.

Whitehead, M. R. and C. A. Brown, 1940. The seed of the spider lily, *Hymenocallis occidentalis*. Amer. J. Bot. 27:199–203.

Whyte, R. O., 1929. Studies in *Ranunculus*. 2. The cytological basis in *R. acris*. J. Genetics 21:183–191.

Wiegand, K. M., 1898. Notes on the embryology of *Potamogeton*. Bot. Gaz. 25:116–117.

Wiegand, K. M., 1899. The development of the microsporangium and microspores in *Convallaria* and *Potamogeton*. Bot. Gaz. 28:328–359.

Wiegand, K. M., 1900. The development of the embryo sac in some monocotyledonous plants. Bot. Gaz. 30:25–47.

Wiger, J., 1930. Ein neuer Fall von autonomer Nuzellarembryonie. Bot. Notiser 1930:368–370.

Wiger, J., 1935. Embryological studies on the families Buxaceae, Meliaceae, Simarubaceae and Burseraceae. Diss. Lund.

Wiger, J., 1936. Reply to remarks on my paper on Buxaceae, Meliaceae etc. Bot. Notiser 1936:585–589.

Wiggins, I. L., 1959. Development of the ovule and megagametophyte in *Saxifraga hieracifolia*. Amer. J. Bot. 46:692–697.

Wilcke, J., 1930. Karyologische Untersuchungen an drei Saisonformen des *Alectorolophus hirsutus*. Österr. bot. Zeit. 79:78–94.

Wilczek, E., 1892. Beiträge zur Kenntnis des Baues der Frucht und des Samens der Frucht der Cyperaceen. Bot. Ztbl. 51:129–138, 193–201, 225–233, 257–265.

Wille, N., 1882a. Om Pollenkornenes udtvidkling hos Juncaceer og Cyperaceer. Forh. Vidensk-Selsk. Krist. 16:1–4.

Wille, N., 1882b. Om kimens udtvidklingshistorie hos *Ruppia rostellata* og *Zannichellia palustris*. Vidensk. Medd. Nat. Foren. Kjøbenhavn 1882–86:1-4

Wille, N., 1886. Über die Entwicklungsgeschichte der Pollenkörner der Angiospermen und das Wachsthum der Membranen durch Intussusception. Forh. Vidensk.-Selsk. Krist. 5:1–71.

Williams, E. J., 1955. Seed failure in the chippewa variety of *Solanum tuberosum*. Bot. Gaz. 117:10–15.

Williams, M. E., 1932. The development of the embryo of *Kochia scoparia*. Bull. Torrey bot. Cl. 59:391–400.

Wilson, H., 1843. Embryo of *Tropaeolum majus*. London J. Bot. 2:623–629.

Wimmel, T., 1850. Zur Entwicklungsgeschichte des Pollens. Bot. Zeit. 8:225–235, 241–248, 289–294, 313–320.

Winge, Ö., 1914a. Oogenesis hos *Senecio*. Bot. Tidssk. 33.

Winge, Ö., 1914b. The pollination and fertilization processes in *Humulus lupulus* and *H. japonicus*. C. R. trav. Lab. Carlsberg 11.

Winge, Ö., 1917. Studier over Planterigets chromosomtal og chromosomernes Betydnig. C. R. trav. Lab. Carlsberg 13:127.

Winkler, A., 1874. Über die Keimblätter der deutschen Dikotylen. Verh. Bot. Ver. Prov. Brandenb. 16:6–21.

Winkler, A., 1882. Über das Vorkommen verwachsener Embryonen. Verh. Bot. Ver. Prov. Brandenb. 24:94–96.

Winkler, H., 1904. Die Parthenogenesis bei *Wikstroemia indica*. Ber. dtsch. bot. Ges. 22:573–580.

Winkler, H., 1906. Botanische Untersuchungen aus Buitenz. 2. Über Parthenogenesis bei *Wikstroemia indica*. Ann. Jard. bot. Buitenz. (2) 5:208–276.

Winkler, H., 1908. Über Parthenogenesis und Apogamie in Pflanzenreich. Prog. Rei. bot. Jena. 2:293–454.

Winkler, H., 1913. Fortpflanzung der Gewächse. 6. Apogamie und Parthenogenesis. Handw. d. Nat. 4:265–276.

Winkler, H., 1927. Über eine *Rafflesia* aus Zentralborneo. Planta 4:1–97.

Winkler, H., 1934. Fortpflanzung der Gewächse. 7. Apomixis. Handw. d. Nat. 4:451–461.

Winter, D. M., 1960. The development of the seed of *Abutilon theophrasti.* 1. Ovule and embryo. Amer. J. Bot. 47:8–14.

Wirth, M. and C. L. Withner, 1959. Embryology and development on the Orchidaceae. *In* L. C. Withner, The Orchids: a Scientific Survey. New York.

Wirz, H., 1910 Beiträge zur Entwicklungsgeschichte von *Sciaphila* spec. und von *Epirrhizanthes elongata.*

Wiśniewska, E., 1931. Die Entwicklung der Pollenkörner bei *Potamogeton perfoliatus.* Acta Soc. bot. Polon. 8:157–174.

Witkus, E. R., 1945. Endomitotic tapetal cell divisions in *Spinacia.* Amer. J. Bot. 32:326–330.

Witmer, S. W., 1937. Morphology and cytology of *Vallisneria spiralis.* Amer. Midl. Nat. 18:309–333.

Wodehouse, R. P., 1935. Evolution of pollen grains. Bot. Rev. 2:53–84.

Wolf, F. T., 1940. Macrosporogenesis and the development of the embryo sac in *Yucca aloifolia.* Bull. Torrey bot. Cl. 67:755–761.

Wolf, P., 1929. Zytologische Untersuchungen über verschiedene Formen der *Mentha piperita.* Beitr. Pflanz. 17:351–392.

Wolpert, G., 1910. Vergleichende Anatomie und Entwicklungsgeschichte von *Alnus alnobetula* und *Betula.* Flora 100:37–67.

Wolter, H., 1933. Bausteine zu einer Monographie von *Ficaria.* 8. Über Bestäubung, Fruchtbildung und Keimung bei *Ficaria verna.* Beitr. Biol. Pflanz. 21:219–255.

Woodburn, W. L., 1911. Development of the embryo sac and endosperm in some seedless persimmons. Bull. Torrey bot. Cl. 38:379–384.

Woodcock, E. F., 1914. Observations on the development and germination of the seed in certain Polygonaceae. Amer. J. Bot. 1:454–476.

Woodcock, E. F., 1918. Structure of the mature seed of *Eriogonum microthecum.* Ann. Rep. Mich. Acad. Sci. 20:233–235.

Woodcock, E. F., 1925. Observations on the morphology of the seed in *Phytolacca.* Papers Mich. Acad. Sci., Arts and Letters 4:413–417.

Woodcock, E. F., 1926a. Morphology of the seed in *Claytonia virginica.* Papers Mich. Acad. Sci., Arts and Letters 5:195–199.

Woodcock, E. F., 1926b. Morphological studies of the seed of *Alsine media.* Papers Mich. Acad. Sci., Arts and Letters 6:397–402.

Woodcock, E. F., 1928. Observations on the morphology of the seed of *Cerastium vulgatum.* Papers Mich. Acad. Sci., Arts and Letters 8:233–238.

Woodcock, E. F., 1929a. Seed studies in Nyctaginaceae. Papers Mich. Acad. Sci., Arts and Letters 9:495–502.

Woodcock, E. F., 1929b. Seed development in *Thelygonum cynocrambe.* Papers Mich. Acad. Sci., Arts and Letters 11:341–347.

Woodcock, E. F., 1930. Morphological studies on the seed of *Mesembryanthemum crystallinum.* Papers Mich. Acad. Sci., Arts and Letters 13:221–226.

Woodcock, E. F., 1931. Seed development in *Amarantus caudatus.* Papers Mich. Acad. Sci., Arts and Letters 15:173–178.

Woodcock, E. F., 1943. Seed development in morning glory, *Ipomoea rubrocoerulea.* Papers Mich. Acad. Sci., Arts and Letters 28:209–212.

Woodroof, J. G., 1926. The fruit-bud, the flower and then the pecan nut. Proc. Nat. Pecan Growers' Assoc.: 81–88.

Woodroof, J. G., 1930. Studies of the staminate inflorescence and pollen of *Hicoria pecan.* J. Agr. Res. 40:1059–1104.

Woodroof, J. G. and N. C. Woodroof, 1926. Fruit-bud differentiation and subsequent development of the flowers of *Hicoria pecan.* J. Agr. Res. 33:677–685.

Woodroof, J. G. and N. C. Woodroof, 1927. The development of the pecan nut, *Hicoria pecan.* J. Agric. Res. 34:1049–1063.

Woodroof, N. C., 1928. Development of the embryo sac and young embryo in *Hicoria pecan.* Amer. J. Bot. 15:416–421.

Woodworth, R. H., 1928. Cytological studies in the Betulaceae. 1. *Betula.* Bot. Gaz. 87:331–363.

Woodworth, R. H., 1929a. Cytological studies in the Betulaceae. 2. *Corylus* and *Alnus.* Bot. Gaz. 88:383–399.

Woodworth, R. H., 1929b. Parthenogenesis and polyembryony in *Alnus rugosa.* Science 70:192–193.

Woodworth, R. H., 1930a. Cytological studies in the Betulaceae. 3. Parthenogenesis and polyembryony in *Alnus rugosa.* Bot. Gaz. 89:402–409.

Woodworth, R. H., 1930b. Cytological studies in the Betulaceae. 4. *Betula. Carpinus, Ostrya, Ostryopsis.* Bot. Gaz. 90:108–115.

Wordsell, W. C., 1897. On the development of the ovule of *Christisonia,* a genus of the Orobanchaceae. J. Linn. Soc. London (Bot.). 31:576–584.

Wordsell, W. C., 1904. The structure and morphology of the ovule. An historical sketch. Ann. Bot. 18:57–86.

Wordsell, W. C., 1916. The morphology of the monocotyledonous embryo and that of the grass in particular. Ann. Bot. 30:509–524.

Wormer, T. M., 1963. An abnormality in the growth of the endosperm of *Coffea arabica.* Turrialba 13:237–238.

Wóycicki, Z., 1907a. Die Kerne in den Zellen der Suspensorfortsatzes bei *Tropaeolum majus.* Bull. Acad. Sci. Cracov 550–557.

Wóycicki, Z., 1907b. Über den Bau des Embryosackes bei *Tropaeolum majus.* Bull. Acad. Sci. Cracov 557–570.

Wóycicki, Z., 1911a. (Late phases in pollen development in *Yucca recurva.*) C. R. Soc. Sci. Varsovie 4:17–23.

Wóycicki, Z., 1911b. Zur Frage der Entstehung der Pollenhaut bei *Malva silvestris.* Ber. dtsch. bot. Ges. 29:636–646. Sitz. Ges. Wiss. Warschau 401–411.

Wóycicki, Z., 1917. Recherches sur les Malvacées. La formation du pollen chez les *Malva silvestris, Malva rotundifolia* et *Althaea officinalis.* C. R. Soc. Sci. Varsovie 26:1–64.

Wóycicki, Z., 1922. Quelques détails sur la structure du sac embryonnaire et le développement de l'embryon chez *Malva silvestris* et *M. rotundifolia.* Sep.-Abdr. Kosmos Lwôw.

Wóycicki, Z., 1923. Quelques remarques à propos de mes recherches sur la formation du pollen des Malvacées. Acta Soc. bot. Polon. 1:149–164.

Wóycicki, Z., 1924. Recherches sur la déhiscence des anthères et le rôle du stomium. Rev. gén. Bot. 36:196.

Wóycicki, Z., 1926. Grains de pollen, tubes polliniques et spermatogenèse chez *Haemanthus katharinae.* Bull. intern. Acad. Polon. Sci. B. 1926:177–188, 535–557.

Wóycicki, Z., 1929. Die Entwicklung des Embryosackes bei *Haemanthus katharinae.* Acta Soc. bot. Polon. 6:195–202.

Wóycicki, Z., 1931. Über den Keimungsprozess der Samen und den Degenerationscharakter der Samenanlagen bei *Haemanthus katharinae.* Acta Soc. bot. Polon. 8:85–108.

Wóycicki, Z., 1932. Über die simultane Tetradenteilung. Acta Soc. bot. Polon. 9:457–472.

Wright, H., 1907. *Theobroma cacao* or cocoa: its Botany, Cultivation, Chemistry and Diseases. Colombo.

Wu, H. K., 1960. Embryogenesis in tea plant. Bot. Bull. Acad. Sinica 1:165–168.

Wulff, H. D., 1933. Zur Zytologie des männlichen Gametophyten der Angiospermen. Planta 19:651–652.

Wulff, H. D., 1934a. Beiträge zur Kenntnis männlichen Gametophyten der Angiospermen. Planta 21:12–50.

Wulff, H. D., 1934b. Untersuchungen an Pollenkörnern und Pollenschläuchen von *Impatiens parviflora*. Ber. dtsch bot. Ges. 53:43–47.

Wulff, H. D., 1939a. Die Pollenentwicklung der Juncaceen. Jahrb. f. wiss. Bot. 87:533–556.

Wulff, H. D., 1939b. Die Entwicklung der Pollenkörner von *Triglochin palustris* und die verschiedenen Typen der Pollenkornentwicklung des Angiospermen. Jahrb. f. wiss. Bot. 88:141–168.

Wulff, H. D. and P. Maheshwari, 1938. The male gametophyte of angiosperms—a critical review. J. Indian bot. Soc. 17:117–140.

Wulff, H. D. and T. S. Raghavan, 1937. Beobachtungen an Pollenschlauchkulturen von der Hydrophyllaceae *Nemophila insignis*. Planta 27:466–473.

Wunderlich, R., 1936. Vergleichende Untersuchungen von Pollenkörnern einiger Liliaceen und Amaryllidaceen. Österr. bot. Zeit. 85:32–55.

Wunderlich, R., 1937. Zur vergleichenden Embryologie der Liliaceae-Scilloideae. Flora 132:48–90.

Wunderlich, R., 1938. Ein künstlich bestäubter Fruchtknoten von *Yucca filamentosa*. Österr. bot. Zeit. 87:109–113.

Wunderlich, R., 1950. Die Agavaceae Hutchinson's im Lichte ihrer Embryologie, ihres Gynözeum-, Staubblatt- und Blattbaues. Österr. bot. Zeit. 97:437–502.

Wunderlich, R., 1954. Über das Antherentapetum mit besonderer Berücksichtigung seiner Kernzahl. Österr. bot. Zeit. 101:1–63.

Wunderlich, R., 1959. Zur Frage der Phylogenie der Endospermtypen bei den Angiospermen. Österr. bot. Zeit. 106:203–293.

Wurdinger, M., 1910. Bau und Entwicklungsgeschichte des Embryosackes von *Euphrasia rostkoviana*. Denkschr. Akad. wiss. Wien. 85:511–530.

Wyatt, R. L., 1955. An embryological study of four species of *Asarum*. J. Elisha Mitchell Sci. Soc. 71:64–82.

Wylie, R. B., 1904. The morphology of *Elodea canadensis*. Bot. Gaz. 37:1–22.

Wylie, R. B., 1917. Cleistogamy in *Heteranthera dubia*. Bull. Lab. nat. Hist. Univ. Iowa 7:48–58.

Wylie, R. B., 1923. Sperms of *Vallisneria spiralis*. Bot. Gaz. 75:191–202.

Wylie, R. B., 1941. Some aspects of fertilization in *Vallisneria*. Amer. J. Bot. 28:169–172.

Wylie, R. B., and A. E. Yoccom, 1923. The endosperm of *Utricularia*. Univ. Iowa Studies nat. Hist. 10:3–18.

Ya-E, M., 1941. Development of the embryo sac in *Statice japonica*. Sci. Rpts. Tôhoku Imp. Univ. Biol. 16:279–303.

Yakovlev, M. S., 1946. La monocotylédonie à la lumière des données embryologiques. Sovetsk. bot. 14:351–363.

Yakovlev, M. S., 1950. (The structure of endosperm and embryo in cereals as a systematic feature.) Izv. Akad. Nauk. Arm. SSR. Bot. 1:121–218.

Yakovlev, M. S., 1959. The main groups of polyembryony in higher plants. Congr. Internatl. Bot. 9th. 2:437.

Yakovlev, M. S. and M. D. Yoffe, 1957. On some peculiar features in the embryogeny of *Paeonia*. Phytomorphology 7:74–82.

Yakovlev, M. S. and M. D. Yoffe, 1959. On a new type of embryogenesis in *Paeonia*. Congr. Internatl. Bot. 9th. 2:437–438.

Yamaha, G., 1926. Über die Zytokinese bei der Pollentetradenbildung, zugleich weitere Beiträge zur Kenntnis über die Zytokinese im Pflanzenreich. Japanese J. Bot. 3:139–162.

Yamaura, A., 1933. Karyologische und embryologische Studien über einige *Bambusa*-Arten. Bot. Mag. Tokyo 47:551–555.

Yamazaki, T., 1953. On the floral structure, seed development and affinities of *Deinostema*, a new genus of Scrophulariaceae. J. Japanese Bot. 28:129–133; Bot. Mag. Tokyo 66:141–149.

Yamazaki, T., 1954. Notes on *Lindernia, Vandellia, Torenia* and their allied genera in eastern Asia. J. Japanese Bot. 29:299–306; Bot. Mag. Tokyo 68:14–24.

Yamazaki, T., 1957a. Taxonomical and phylogenetic studies of Scrophulariaceae-Veronicae, with special reference to *Veronica* and *Veronicastrum* in eastern Asia. J. Fac. Sci. Univ. Tokyo (3) 7:91–162.

Yamazaki, T., 1957b. Seed formation of *Ellisiophyllum pinnatum* var. *reptans*. Bot. Mag. Tokyo 70:162–168.

Yamazaki, T., 1963. Embryology of *Mitrasacme alsinoides* var. *indica*. Sci. Rpts. Tôhoku Univ. (4) Biol. 29:201–205.

Yasuda, S., T. Inaba, and Y. Takakashi, 1935. Parthenocarpy caused by the stimulation of pollination in some plants of the Cucurbitaceae. Agr. and Hort. 10:1385–1390.

Yasui, K., 1915. Studies of *Diospyros kaki*. 1. Bot. Gaz. 60:362–373.

Yasui, K., 1935. Cytological studies in diploid and triploid *Hosta*. Cytologia 6:484–491.

Yasui, K., 1936. The anatomy of the embryo and the seedling of *Oryza sativa*, with special reference to the structure of cotyledon and mesocotyl in Gramineae. Bot. Mag. Tokyo 50:632–640.

Yasui, K., 1937. Karyological studies in *Magnolia*, with special reference to the cytokinesis in pollen mother cells. Bot. Mag. Tokyo 51:539–546.

Yasui, K. and N. Sawada, 1940. (On the spore and embryo sac formation with special reference to the sterility of *Iris japonica*.). Bot. Mag. Tokyo 54:96–102.

Yasui, K. and N. Suita, 1939. A note on the refractive granules in the microspore mother cell and the microspores of *Tradescantia*. Bot. Mag. Tokyo 53:521–524.

Yen, T.-K., 1936. Floral development and vascular anatomy of the fruit of *Ribes aureum*. Bot. Gaz. 98:105–120.

Yen, T.-K., 1950. Structure and development of the flower and the fruit of *Myrica rubra*. Peking nat. hist. Bull. 19:2–20.

York, H. H., 1904. The embryo sac of *Nelumbo*. Ohio Nat. 4:167–176.

York, H. H., 1913. The origin and development of the embryo sac and embryo of *Dendrophthora opuntioides* and *D. gracile*. 1.2. Bot. Gaz. 56:89–111, 200–216.

Yoshida, O., 1957. Embryologische Studien über die Ordnung Piperales. 1. Embryologie von *Chloranthus japonicus*. J. Coll. Arts and Sci., Chiba Univ. (Nat. Sci.) 2:172–178.

Yoshida, O., 1959a. Embryologische Studien über die Ordnung Piperales. 2. Embryologie von *Chloranthus serratus*. J. Coll. Arts and Sci., Chiba Univ. (Nat. Sci.) 2:295–303.

Yoshida, O., 1959b. Embryologische Studien über die Ordnung Piperales. 3. Embryologie von *Sarcandra glabra*. J. Coll. Arts and Sci., Chiba Univ. (Nat. Sci.) 3:55–60.

Yoshida, O., 1960. Embryologische Studien über die Ordnung Piperales. 4. Embryologie von *Piper futokazura*. J. Coll. Arts and Sci. Chiba Univ. (Nat. Sci.) 3:155–162.

Yoshida, O., 1962. Embryologische Studien über *Schisandra chinensis*. J. Coll. Arts, Sci., Univ. Chiba 4:459–462.

Young, W. J., 1905. The embryology of *Melilotus albus*. Proc. Indiana Acad. Sci. 15:133–141.

Young, W. J., 1922. Potato ovules with two embryo sacs. Amer. J. Bot. 9:213–214.

Young, W. J., 1923. The formation and degeneration of germ cells in the potato. Amer. J. Bot. 10:325–335.

Youngman, W., 1927. Studies in the cytology of the Hibisceae. Ann. Bot. 41:755–778.

Zabban, B., 1936. Osservazioni sulla embriologia di *Myricaria germanica*. Ann. di Bot. (Roma) 21:1–15.

Zahur, M. S., 1962. Early ontogeny of the ovule in *Coccinia indica*. Biologia 8:179–197.

Zaman, B., 1950. The embryology of *Juncus prismatocarpus* und *J. effusus*. Proc. Indian Acad. Sci. B. 31:223–234.

Zamotailov, S. S., 1955. (Embryology of figs under variable conditions of pollination.) Izv. Akad. Nauk SSSR Biol. 2:103–120.

Zamotailov, S. S., 1960. (The resting stage of the embryo in *Arachis hypogaea*.) Bot. Zhur. 45:1435–1445.

Zenkteler, M., 1962. Microsporogenesis and tapetal development in normal and male sterile carrots, *Daucus carota*. Amer. J. Bot. 49:341–348.

Zhebrak, E. A., 1961. (Embryological and histochemical studies of the fertilization process in diploid and tetraploid *Polygonum*.) Byull. Glaonogo Bot. Sada Akad. Nauk SSSR 41:73–79.

Ziegler, A., 1925. Beiträge zur Kenntnis des Androeciums und der Samenentwicklung einiger Melastomaceen. Bot. Arch. Mez. 9:398–467.

Zimmermann, W., 1911. Hermaphroditismus und Sexualmutation. Abnormes sexuelles Verhalten von Weizen. Allg. Bot. Zeti. 17:49–56.

Zinger, N., 1898. Beiträge zur Kenntnis der weiblichen Blüten and Inflorescenzen bei Cannabineen. Flora 85:189–292.

Zweifel, R., 1939. Cytologisch-embryologische Untersuchungen *Balanophora abbreviata* und *B. indica*. Vjschr. naturf. Ges. Zürich 84:245–306 Diss. Zürich.

APPENDIX

The following literature has been published or has come to my attention since completion of the manuscript.

ACERACEAE

Kushalani, I., 1963. Floral morphology and embryology of *Acer oblongum*. Phyton 10:275–284.

Mestre, J.-C., 1965. Embryogénie des Acéracées: Développement de l'embryon chez l'*Acer pseudoplatanus*. C. R. Acad. Sci. Paris 261:5602–5604.

ACTINIDIACEAE

Vijayaraghavan, M. R., 1965. Morphology and embryology of *Actinidia polygama* and systematic position of the family Actinidiaceae. Phytomorphology 15:224–235.

ALISMATACEAE

Pogan, E., 1965. Embryological studies in a triploid hybrid of *Alisma*. Acta Biol. Cracov. Bot. 8:11–19.

AMARYLLIDACEAE

Berg, R. Y., and J. R. Maze, 1966. Contribution to the embryology of *Muilla*, with a remark on the taxonomic position of the genus. Madroño 18:143–151.

Mendoza, D. R., 1954. Megasporogenesis and the development of the megagametophyte in *Atamosco rosea*. Philippine J. Sci. 83:219–238.

ARACEAE

Panicker, T. K. B., 1965. Female gametophyte and endosperm in *Lagenandra ovata*. Current Sci. 34:614–615.

ASCLEPIADACEAE

Mulay, B. N., B. D. Deshpande, and U. Tolani, 1965. Studies in Asclepiadaceae. 2. Floral morphology and gametogenesis in certain members of the Asclepiadaceae. J. Indian bot. Soc. 44:95–104.

BERBERIDACEAE

Budell, B., 1964. Untersuchungen der Antherentwicklung einiger Blutenpflanzen. Bot. Zeit. 52:1–28.

CABOMBACEAE

Khanna, P., 1965. Morphological and embryological studies in Nymphaeaceae. 2. *Brasenia schreberei* and *Nelumbo nucifera*. Aust. J. Bot. 13:379–387.

Ramji, M. V., and D. Padmanabhan, 1965. Developmental studies on *Cabomba caroliniana*. 1. Ovule and carpel. Proc. Indian Acad. Sci. B. 62:215–223.

CARYOPHYLLACEAE

Tohda, H., 1965. Morphological investigations on the staminodia of the female plants in *Moehringia lateriflora*. 1. On the development of tapetal cells and pollen mother cells. Sci. Rpts. Tôhoku Univ., Sendai (4) Biol. 31:83–92.

CELASTRACEAE

Mestre, J.-C., 1965. Embryogénie des Célastracées. Développement de l'embryon chez l'*Evonymus europaeus*. C. R. Acad. Sci. Paris 260:3453–3456.

COMPOSITAE

Bauer, Z., 1964. Cytological and embryological studies in the genus *Inula*. Acta Biol. Cracov. Bot. 7:117–130.

Budell, B., 1964. Untersuchungen der Antherentwicklung einiger Blutenpflanzen. Bot. Zeit. 52:1–28.

Czapik, R., 1954. (Cytological and embryological studies in *Centaurea scabiosa*.) Acta Soc. bot. Polon. 23:175–194.

Małecka, J., 1961. Studies in the mode of reproduction of the diploid endemic species *Taraxacum pieninicum*. Acta Biol. Cracov. Bot. 4:25–42.

Małecka, J., 1964. Multinucleate pollen grains in *Taraxacum serotinum*. Acta Biol. Cracov. Bot. 7:107–116.

Sokołowska-Kulczycka, A., 1959. Apomixis in *Leontopodium alpinum*. Acta Biol. Cracov. Bot. 2:51–63.

Szwabowicz, A., 1954. (Embryological studies in *Hypochoeris uniflora*.) Acta Soc. bot. Polon. 23:243–257.

Urbańska-Worytkiewicz, K., 1962. Embryological investigations in *Antennaria*. 3. Experimental hybrids between *A. carpatica* and *A. dioica*. Acta Biol. Cracov. Bot. 5:103–115.

Zinger, N. V., V. A. Poddubnaja-Arnoldi, T. P. Petrovskaya, and N. N. Polunina, 1965. (The question of the causes of apomixis. Histochemical investigation of the female generative organs in apomictic representatives of *Taraxacum* and *Citrus*.) Bjul. Moskov Obsc. Ispyt. Prir. Biol. 13:201–237.

CORNACEAE

Chopra, R. N., and H. Kaur, 1965. Some aspects of the embryology of *Cornus*. Phytomorphology 15:353–359.

CRUCIFERAE

Černohorský, Z., 1947. Graines des Crucifères de Bohême. Etude anatomique et morphologique. Opera Botanica Čechica 5:1–92.

Pollock, E. G., and W. A. Jensen, 1964. Cell development during early embryogenesis in *Capsella* and *Gossypium*. Amer. J. Bot. 51:915–921.

CUCURBITACEAE

Chopra, R. N., and B. Basu, 1965. Female gametophyte and endosperm of some members of the Cucurbitaceae. Phytomorphology 15:217–223.

Singh, D., 1965. Ovule and seed of *Sechium edule:* a reinvestigation. Current Sci. 34:696–697.

Turała, K., 1958. Endomitosis in the tapetal cells of *Cucurbita pepo.* Acta Biol. Cracov. Bot. 1:25–34.

Turała, K., 1963. Studies in endomitotical processes during the differentiation of the tapetal layer of the Cucurbitaceae. Acta Biol. Cracov. Bot. 6:87–102.

CUSCUTACEAE

Tiagi, B., 1965. Development of the embryo sac and embryogeny in *Cuscuta lupuliformis.* Current Sci. 34:671–672.

CYPERACEAE

Gręzicka, W., 1964. Megasporogenesis, ovule and embryo sac development in *Carex aristata* var. *cujavica.* Acta Soc. bot. Polon. 33:307–322.

EHRETIACEAE

Fathima, T., 1966. Sporogenesis and the development of gametophytes in *Cordia alba.* Current Sci. 35:73–74.

ERICACEAE

Budell, B., 1964. Untersuchungen der Antherentwicklung einiger Blutenpflanzen. Bot. Zeit. 52:1–28.

EUPHORBIACEAE

Singh, R. P., 1965. Structure and development of seeds in *Codiaeum variegatum.* J. Indian bot. Soc. 44:205–210.

Singh, R. P., and J. L. Jain, 1965. Development of female gametophyte in *Euphorbia pilosa.* Current Sci. 34:611–612.

FRANKENIACEAE

Walia, K., and R. N. Kapil, 1965. Embryology of *Frankenia*, with some comments on the systematic position of the Frankeniaceae. Bot. Notiser 1965:412–429.

GRAMINEAE

Klyuchareva, M. V., 1963. (Embryological studies on unripe *Triticum* seeds.) Tr. Inst. Genet. Akad. Nauk SSSR 30:283–290.

Tateoka, T., 1964. Notes on some grasses. 16. Embryo structure of the genus *Oryza* in relation to systematics. Amer. J. Bot. 51:539–543.

Yakovlev, M. S., and M. P. Solntzeva, 1965. (Some problems of flower morphology and embryology of feather grasses.) *In* M. S. Yakovlev, (ed.) (Flower Morphology and Reproductive Processes of Angiosperms), Leningrad, 61–73.

GROSSULARIACEAE

Komar, G. A., 1965. (On the arillus structure of certain Grossulariaceae.) *In* M. S. Yakovlev, (ed.) (Flower Morphology and Reproductive Processes in Angiosperms), Leningrad, 114–130.

HELLEBORACEAE

Bhandari, N. N. and R. N. Kapil, 1964. Studies in the family Ranunculaceae. 7. Two types of embryo sac in *Trollius*. Beitr. Biol. Pflanz. 40:113–120.

Trela, Z., 1958. Cyto-histological processes during the differentiation of the tapetal cells of *Aconitum variegatum*. Acta Biol. Cracov. Bot. 1:35–43.

LABIATAE

Budell, B., 1964. Untersuchungen der Antherentwicklung einiger Blutenpflanzen. Bot. Zeit. 52:1–28.

LAURACEAE

Budell, B., 1964. Untersuchungen der Antherentwicklung einiger Blutenpflanzen. Bot. Zeit. 52:1–28.

LENTIBULARIACEAE

Farooq, M., 1964. Studies in the Lentibulariaceae. 1. The embryology of *Utricularia stellaris* var. *inflexa*. Pt. 1. Flower, organogeny, ovary, megasporogenesis and female gametophyte. Proc. Nat. Inst. Sci. India 30:263–279.

Farooq, M., 1964. Studies in the Lentibulariaceae. 1. The embryology of *Utricularia stellaris* var. *inflexa*. Pt. 2. Microsporangium, male gametophyte, fertilization, endosperm, embryo and seed. Proc. Nat. Inst. Sci. India 30:280–299.

Farooq, M., and S. A. Siddiqui, 1964. Haustorial antipodals in *Utricularia stellaris* var. *inflexa*. Naturwiss. 18:1–2.

Farooq, M., and S. A. Siddiqui, 1965. Abnormal ovules and embryo sacs in *Utricularia vulgaris* var. *americana*. Zeit. die Naturw. 4:1–3.

Maqbool Begum, 1965. Studies on the embryology of *Utricularia graminifolia*. Current Sci. 34:355–356.

Siddiqui, S. A., and M. Farooq, 1965. Degeneration in the ovules of *Utricularia coerulea* var. *filicaulis*. Bull. Torrey bot. Cl. 92:245–249.

LILIACEAE

Ogura, H., 1964. On the embryo sac of two species of *Tricyrtis*. Sci. Rpts. Tôhoku Univ., Sendai, 4. Biol. 30:219–222.

Pechenitsyn, V. P., 1963. (Embryogenesis in *Tulipa vvedenskyi*.) *In* (Problems of biology and regional medicine), 4:239–243.

Sokołowska-Kulczycka, A., 1965. Experimental studies in seed development of *Lilium bulbiferum*. Acta Biol. Cracov. Bot. 8:63–81.

LINACEAE

Kantor, T. V., 1964. (The characteristics of *Linum usitatissimum* embryogenesis and the influence of external conditions.) *In* (Problems of Modern Embryology), Moscow, 131–136.

Rao, D., and L. L. Narayana, 1965. The embryology of Linaceae. Current Sci. 34:92–93.

MAGNOLIACEAE

Kapil, R. N., and N. N. Bhandari, 1964. Morphology and embryology of *Magnolia*. Proc. Nat. Inst. Sci. India 30:245–262.

MALVACEAE

Pollock, E. G., and W. A. Jensen, 1964. Cell development during early embryogenesis in *Capsella* and *Gossypium*. Amer. J. Bot. 51:915–921.

MYRTACEAE

Polunina, N. N., 1957. (Comparative studies of embryology and flowering in some varieties of *Eucalyptus*.) Dokl. Akad. Nauk SSSR 115:819–821.

Polunina, N. N., 1959. (The embryology of *Eucalyptus*.) Trud. glav. Bot. Gdn., Leningrad 6:191–210.

Polunina, N. N., 1964. (A comparative study on the embryology, the biology of blooming and fruit bearing in *Feijoa selloviana* under various conditions of growth.) *In* (Problems of Modern Embryology), Moscow, 153–158.

NYCTAGINACEAE

Hjelmqvist, H. and F. Grazi, 1965. Studies on variation in embryo sac development. 2. Bot. Notiser 1965:329–360.

NYMPHAEACEAE

Khanna, P., 1965. Morphological and embryological studies in Nymphaeaceae. 2. *Brasenia schreberei* and *Nelumbo nucifera*. Aust. J. Bot. 13:379–387.

Valtzova, O. B., and E. Savich, 1965. (Development of embryo in *Nymphaea candida* and *N. tetragona*.) Bot. Zhur. URSS 50:1323–1326.

PAEONIACEAE

Yakovlev, M. S., and M. D. Yoffe, 1965. (The embryology of the genus *Paeonia*.) *In* M. S. Yakovlev, (*ed*.) (Flower Morphology and Reproductive Processes of Angiosperms), Leningrad 140–176.

PAPILIONACEAE

Trankovsky, D. A., 1964. The pollen grain development in two *Lathyrus* hybrids. Bjul. Moskov Obsc. Ispyt. Prir. Biol. 69:91–97.

PHILYDRACEAE

Kapil, R. N., and K. Walia, 1965. The embryology of *Philydrum lanuginosum* and the systematic position of the Philydraceae. Beitr. Biol. Pflanzen 41:381–404.

PITTOSPORACEAE

Sheela, R., and L. L. Narayana, 1966. Embryology of Pittosporaceae. Current Sci. 35:74–75.

PLANTAGINACEAE

Misra, R. C., 1964. Development and structure of the Angiosperm seed. 3. *Plantago*. Bull. Nat. Bot. Gdn., Lucknow 105:1–14.

PORTULACACEAE

Guignard, J.-L., 1965. Embryogénie des Portulacacées. Développement de l'embryon chez le *Talinum patens*. C. R. Acad. Sci. Paris 261:5599–5601.

RANUNCULACEAE

Bhandari, N. N., 1965. Studies in the family Ranunculaceae. 8. Variations in the development of the embryo sac of *Anemone vitifolia*. Phytomorphology 15:285–291.

Trela, Z., 1963. Embryological studies in *Anemone nemorosa*. Acta Biol. Cracov. Bot. 6:1–14.

Trela, Z., 1963. Cytological studies in the differentiation of the endosperm in *Anemone nemorosa*. Acta Biol. Cracov. Bot. 6:177–183.

ROSACEAE

Czapik, R., 1961. Binucleate pollen mother cells in *Potentilla alba*. Acta Biol. Cracov. Bot. 4:43–47.

Czapik, R., 1961. Embryological studies in the genus *Potentilla*. 1. *P. crantzii*. Acta Biol. Cracov. Bot. 4:97–119.

Czapik, R., 1962. Embryological studies in the genus *Potentilla*. 2. *P. arenaria*. Acta Biol. Cracov. Bot. 5:29–42.

Czapik, R., 1962. Embryological studies in *Potentilla*. 3. Hybrids between *P. crantzii* and *P. arenaria*. Acta Biol. Cracov. Bot. 5:43–61.

Solntzeva, M. P., 1965. (On the development of the multicellular archesporium in strawberry.) *In* M. S. Yakovlev, (ed.) (Flower Morphology and Reproductive Processes of Angiosperms): 177–188.

RUTACEAE

Zinger, N. V., V. A. Poddubnaja-Arnoldi, T. P. Petrovskaya, and N. N. Polunina, 1965. (The question of the causes of apomixis. Histochemical investigation of the female generative organs in apomict representatives of *Taraxacum* and *Citrus*.) Bjul. Moskov. Obsc. Ispyt. Prir. Biol. 13:201–237.

SANTALACEAE

Johri, B. M., and S. Agarwal, 1965. Morphological and embryological studies in the family Santalaceae. 8. *Quinchamalium chilense*. Phytomorphology 15:360–372.

SAXIFRAGACEAE

Korobova-Sementchenko, L., 1965. (Embryological findings in the family Saxifragaceae. Megasporogenesis and development of the female gametophyte in *Bergenia crassifolia* and *Chrysosplenium alternifolium*.) Sci. Rpts. High School Biol. Sci. USSR 4:101–107.

SOLANACEAE

Turała, K., and K. Urbańska-Worytkiewicz, 1964. Cytological processes during the differentiation of the tapetal layer in *Solanum dulcamara* and *S. nigrium*. Acta Biol. Cracov. Bot. 7:171–183.

TROCHODENDRACEAE

Yoffe, M. D., 1965. (On the embryology of *Trochodendron aralioides*. Embryo and endosperm development.) *In* M. S. Yakovlev, (ed.) (Flower Morphology and Reproductive Processes of Angiosperms), Leningrad: 177–188.

ULMACEAE

Hjelmqvist, H., and F. Grazi, 1965. Studies on variation in embryo sac development. 2. Bot. Notiser 1965:329–360.

UMBELLIFERAE

Gupta, S. G., and M. Gupta, 1964. Embryological investigations on *Bupleurum tenue*. Beitr. Biol. Pflanz. 40:301–323.

VALERIANACEAE

Skalińska, M., 1958. Studies in the karyological differentiation of the tapetum in *Valeriana officinalis*. Acta Biol. Cracov. Bot. 1:45–54.

GENERAL

Savchenko, M. I., G. A. Komar, 1965. (Morphology of the monocotyledonous ovules.) *In* M. S. Yakovlev, (*ed.*) (Flower Morphology and Reproductive Processes of Angiosperms), Leningrad: 74–113.

Yakovlev, M. S. (*ed.*), 1965. (Flower Morphology and Reproductive Processes of Angiosperms.) Leningrad.

AUTHOR INDEX

FAMILY AND PLANT

INDEX

511

45202